SPOTLiGHT on

LITERATURE

BRONZE LEVEL

AUTHORS

CANDY DAWSON BOYD
JOYCE BUCKNER
JAMES FLOOD
JAMES V. HOFFMAN
ROBERT J. KEALEY

DIANE LAPP
ROY SINGLETON
CHARLES TEMPLE
ARNOLD W. WEBB
KAREN D. WOOD

Macmillan McGraw-Hill

NEW YORK   FARMINGTON

Macmillan/McGraw-Hill

A Division of The McGraw·Hill Companies

Cover Art:

Vasily Kandinsky, **Autumn in Bavaria,** *1908. Musée National d'Art Moderne, Centre George Pompidou, Paris.*

Macmillan/McGraw-Hill
1221 Avenue of the Americas
New York, New York 10020

Printed in the United States of America
ISBN 0-02-181011-7/6, L.12
1 2 3 4 5 6 7 8 9 VHJ 02 01 00 99 98 97

AUTHORS, CONSULTANTS, AND REVIEWERS

Authors

Candy Dawson Boyd
St. Mary's College, California

Joyce Buckner
Omaha Public School System, Nebraska

James Flood
San Diego State University, California

James V. Hoffman
University of Texas, Austin

Robert J. Kealey
Department of Elementary Schools,
National Catholic Association

Diane Lapp
San Diego State University, California

Roy Singleton
University of North Florida, Gainesville

Charles Temple
Hobart and William Smith Colleges, New York

Arnold W. Webb
Research for Better Schools, Inc.
Philadelphia, Pennsylvania

Karen D. Wood
University of North Carolina, Charlotte

Multicultural and Educational Consultants

Alma Flor Ada, Yvonne Beamer, Joyce Buckner, Helen Gillotte, Cheryl Hudson, Narcita Medina, Lorraine Monroe, James R. Murphy, Sylvia Pena, Joseph B. Rubin, Ramon Santiago, Cliff Trafzer, Hai Tran, Esther Lee Yao

Literature Consultants

Ashley Bryan, Joan I. Glazer, Paul Janeczko, Margaret H. Lippert

International Consultants

Edward B. Adams, Barbara Johnson, Raymond L. Marshall

Music and Audio Consultants

John Farrell, Marilyn C. Davidson, Vincent Lawrence, Sarah Pirtle, Susan R. Snyder, Rick and Deborah Witkowski, Eastern Sky Media Services

Teacher Reviewers

Terry Baker, Jane Bauer, James Bedi, Nora Bickel, Vernell Bowen, Donald Cason, Jean Chaney, Carolyn Clark, Alan Cox, Kathryn DesCarpentrie, Carol L. Ellis, Roberta Gale, Brenda Huffman, Erma Inscore, Sharon Kidwell, Elizabeth Love, Isabel Marcus, Elaine McCraney, Michelle Moraros, Earlene Parr, Dr. Richard Potts, Jeanette Pulliam, Michael Rubin, Henrietta Sakamaki, Kathleen Cultron Sanders, Belinda Snow, Dr. Jayne Steubing, Margaret Mary Sulentic, Barbara Tate, Seretta Vincent, Willard Waite, Barbara Wilson, Veronica York

CONTENTS

Living and Learning

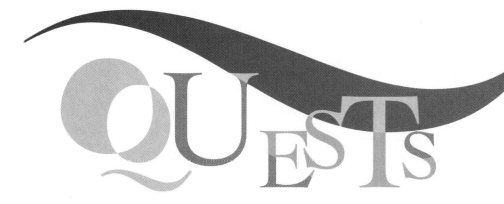

QUESTS

GENRE FOCUS

DETERMINATION

UNIT

4

TIME

· ·

UNIT 5

Belonging

GENRE FOCUS

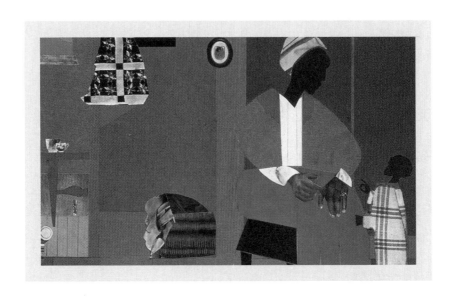

Challenges

GENRE FOCUS

STUDENT RESOURCES

Living

Jungle Tales   1895   James J. Shannon   Metropolitan Museum of Art

and Learning

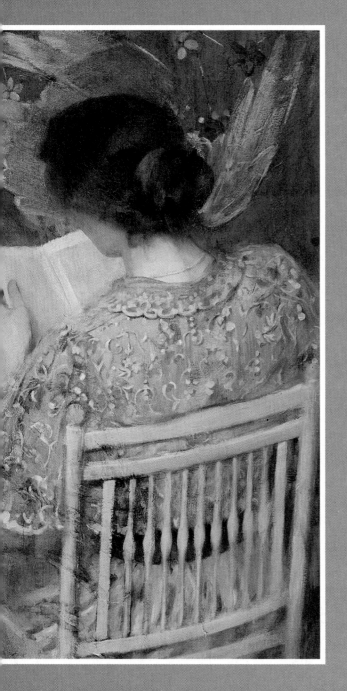

TO YOU

To sit and dream, to sit and read,
To sit and learn about the world
Outside our world of here and now—
    Our problem world—
To dream of vast horizons of the soul
Through dreams made whole,
Unfettered, free—help me!
All you who are dreamers too,
    Help me to make
    Our world anew.
I reach out my dreams to you.

—Langston Hughes

Living and Learning

BEFORE READING

....

S.O.R. LOSERS

CONNECT TO LITERATURE

How do you feel about competition in sports? Is it more important to win or to enjoy playing the game? In your journal, explain what you like about competing. Then explain what you dislike about it. As you read the selection, compare your ideas with those of the narrator.

THINKING ABOUT TONE

Depending on the way it is told, the same story can seem happy or sad. The author's *tone,* or attitude toward the subject or events, usually makes the difference. When a selection—like this one—is narrated by one of the characters, that narrator sets the tone. Much of the humor in "S.O.R. Losers" comes from the unusual way the narrator, Ed Sitrow, sees things. Ed's attitude is *ironic*—the opposite of what is expected. Everyone else assumes that losing every game must make Ed and his teammates unhappy. As you will discover, they don't seem to mind at all.

HAVE YOU EVER?

Have you ever laughed at a joke that nobody else thought was funny? Have you ever cried about something other people considered unimportant? Being true to your feelings sometimes means standing up to peer pressure. In this excerpt from the novel by Avi, the members of the special seventh-grade soccer team at South Orange River Middle School face exactly that situation.

This excerpt occurs near the end of the novel. In previous chapters, Ed explained that he and his teammates are playing soccer against their wishes. They are nonathletic boys in a sports-crazed school. Having lost every game they have played, the boys are now facing great pressure to win their final game of the season.

S.O.R.
LOSERS

BY AVI

Each student at South Orange River Middle School is required to play one sport a year. After all, the school is famous for its winning teams. But Ed Sitrow and his friends have managed to slip through sixth grade without playing a sport, so a special seventh grade soccer team is created just for them. Despite encouragement from everyone, including the coach, Mr. Lester, and the school counselor, Mr. Tillman, the team has lost every game so far. The pressure is on for them to win their last game!

The Tension Builds...

I should have guessed what was going to happen next when this kid from the school newspaper interviewed me. It went this way.

Newspaper: How does it feel to lose every game?

Me: I never played on a team that won, so I can't compare. But it's . . . interesting.

Newspaper: How many teams have you been on?

Me: Just this one.

Newspaper: Do you want to win?

Me: Wouldn't mind knowing what it feels like. For the novelty.

Newspaper: Have you figured out why you lose all the time?

Me: They score more goals.

Newspaper: Have you seen any improvement?

Me: I've been too busy.

Newspaper: Busy with what?

Me: Trying to stop their goals. Ha-ha.

Newspaper: From the scores, it doesn't seem like you've been too successful with that.

Me: You can imagine what the scores would have been if I wasn't there. Actually, I'm the tallest.

Newspaper: What's that have to do with it?

Me: Ask Mr. Lester.

Newspaper: No S.O.R. team has ever lost all its games in one season. How do you feel about that record?

Me: I read somewhere that records are made to be broken.

Newspaper: But how will you feel?

Me: Same as I do now.

Newspaper: How's that?

Me: Fine.

Newspaper: Give us a prediction. Will you win or lose your
  last game?

Me: As captain, I can promise only one thing.

Newspaper: What's that?

Me: I don't want to be there to see what happens.

Naturally, they printed all that. Next thing I knew some kids
decided to hold a pep rally.

"What for?" asked Radosh.

"To fill us full of pep, I suppose."

"What's pep?"

Hays looked it up. "Dash," he read.

Saltz shook his head.

"What's dash?" asked Porter.

"Sounds like a deodorant soap," said Eliscue.

And then Ms. Appleton called me aside. "Ed," she said, sort of
whispering (I guess she was embarrassed to be seen talking to any
of us), "people are asking, 'Do they *want* to lose?'"

"Who's asking?"

"It came up at the last teachers' meeting. Mr. Tillman thinks you
might be encouraging a <u>defeatist</u> attitude in the school. And Mr.
Lester . . ."

"What about him?"

"He doesn't know."

It figured. "Ms. Appleton," I said, "why do people care so much
if we win or lose?"

"It's your . . . attitude," she said. "It's so unusual. We're not used
to . . . well . . . not winning sometimes. Or . . . or not caring if you lose."

"Think there's something the matter with us?" I wanted to know.

"No," she said, but when you say "no" the way she did, slowly,
there's lots of time to sneak in a good hint of "yes." "I don't think
you *mean* to lose."

---

defeatist (di fē′tist) *adj.* expecting defeat, or accepting it too readily.

"That's not what I asked."

"It's important to win," she said.

"Why? We're good at other things. Why can't we stick with that?"

But all she said was, "Try harder."

I went back to my seat. "I'm getting nervous," I mumbled.

"About time," said Saltz.

"Maybe we should defect."

"Where to?"

"There must be some country that doesn't have sports."

Then, of course, when my family sat down for dinner that night it went on.

"In two days you'll have your last game, won't you," my ma said. It was false cheerful, as if I had a terminal illness and she wanted to pretend it was only a head cold.

"Yeah," I said.

"You're going to win," my father announced.

"How do you know?" I snapped.

"I sense it."

"Didn't know you could tell the future."

"Don't be so smart," he returned. "I'm trying to be supportive."

"I'm sick of support!" I yelled and left the room.

Twenty minutes later I got a call. Saltz.

"Guess what?" he said.

"I give up."

"Two things. My father offered me a bribe."

"To lose the game?"

"No, to win it. A new bike."

"Wow. What did you say?"

"I told him I was too honest to win a game."

"What was the second thing?"

"I found out that at lunch tomorrow they are doing that pep rally, and worse. They're going to call up the whole team."

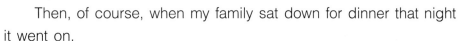

defect (di fekt´) *v.i.* desert a group, country, or cause, especially to go to another that is opposed to it.

supportive (sə pôr´tiv) *adj.* providing approval, aid, or encouragement.

I sighed. "Why are they doing all this?" I asked.

"Nobody loves a loser," said Saltz.

"Why?" I asked him, just as I had asked everybody else.

"Beats me. Like everybody else does." He hung up.

I went into my room and flung myself on my bed and stared up at the ceiling. A short time later my father came into the room. "Come on, kid," he said. "I was just trying to be a pal."

"Why can't people let us lose in peace?"

"People think you feel bad."

"We feel *fine!*"

"Come on. We won't talk about it any more. Eat your dinner."

I went.

Full of Pep...

Next day, when I walked into the school eating area for lunch there was the usual madhouse. But there was also a big banner across the front part of the room:

Make the Losers Winners
Keep Up the Good Name of
S.O.R.

I wanted to start a food fight right then and there.

I'm not going through the whole bit. But halfway through the lunch period, the president of the School Council, of all people, went to a microphone and called for attention. Then she made a speech.

"We just want to say to the Special Seventh-Grade Soccer Team that we're all behind you."

"It's in front of us where we need people," whispered Saltz. "Blocking."

The president went on. "Would you come up and take a bow." One by one she called our names. Each time one of us went up, looking like <u>cringing</u> but grinning worms, there was some general craziness, hooting, foot stomping, and an occasional milk carton shooting through the air.

---

cringing (krin′jing) *v.i.* shrinking, flinching, or crouching, as in fear, pain, or horror.

The president said: "I'd like the team captain, Ed Sitrow, to say a few words."

What could I do? Trapped, I cleared my throat. Four times. "Ah, well . . . we . . . ah . . . sure . . . hope to get there . . . and . . . you know . . . I suppose . . . play and . . . you know!"

The whole room stood up to cheer. They even began the school chant.

"Give me an S! Give me an O . . ."

After that we went back to our seats. I was madder than ever. And as I sat there, maybe two hundred and fifty kids filed by, thumping me hard on the back, shoulder, neck and head, yelling, "Good luck! Good luck!" They couldn't fool me. I knew what they were doing: beating me.

"Saltz," I said when they were gone and I was merely numb, "I'm calling an emergency meeting of the team."

Secret Meeting...

Like thieves, we met behind the school, out of sight. I looked around. I could see everybody was feeling rotten.

"I'm sick and tired of people telling me we have to win," said Root.

"I think my folks are getting ready to <u>disown</u> me," said Hays. "My brother and sister too."

"Why can't they just let us lose?" asked Macht.

"Yeah," said Barish, "because we're not going to win."

"We might," Lifsom offered. "Parkville is supposed to be the pits too."

"Yeah," said Radosh, "but we're beneath the pits."

"Right," agreed Porter.

For a moment it looked like everyone was going to start to cry.

"I'd just like to do my math," said Macht. "I like that."

There it was. Something clicked. "Hays," I said, "you're good at music, right."

"Yeah, well, sure—rock 'n' roll."

---

disown (dis ōn') *v.t.* refuse to recognize as one's own; deny responsibility for or connection with.

"Okay. And Macht, what's the lowest score you've pulled in math so far?"

"A-plus."

"Last year?"

"Same."

"Lifsom," I went on, getting excited, "how's your painting coming?"

"I just finished something real neat and . . ."

"That's it," I cut in, because that kid can go on forever about his painting. "Every one of us is good at something. Right? Maybe more than one thing. The point is, *other* things."

"Sure," said Barish.

"Except," put in Saltz, "sports."

We were quiet for a moment. Then I saw what had been coming to me: "That's *their* problem. I mean, we are good, good at *lots* of things. Why can't we just plain stink in some places? That's got to be normal."

"Let's hear it for normal," chanted Dorman.

"Doesn't bother me to lose at sports," I said. "At least, it didn't bother me until I let other people make me bothered."

"What about the school record?" asked Porter. "You know, no team ever losing for a whole season. Want to be famous for that?"

"Listen," I said, "did we want to be on this team?"

"No!" they all shouted.

"I can see some of it," I said. "You know, doing something different. But I don't like sports. I'm not good at it. I don't enjoy it. So I say, so what? I mean if Saltz here writes a stinko poem—and he does all the time—do they yell at him? When was the last time Mr. Tillman came around and said, 'Saltz, I *believe* in your being a poet!'"

"Never," said Saltz.

"Yeah," said Radosh. "How come sports is so important?"

"You know," said Dorman, "maybe a loser makes people think of things *they* lost. Like Mr. Tillman not getting into pro football. Us losing makes him remember that."

"Us winning, he forgets," cut in Eliscue.

"Right," I agreed. "He needs us to win for *him,* not for us. Maybe it's the same for others."

"Yeah, but how are you going to convince them of that?" said Barish.

"By not caring if we lose," I said.

"Only one thing," put in Saltz. "They say this Parkville team is pretty bad too. What happens if we, you know, by mistake, win?"

That set us back for a moment.

"I think," suggested Hays after a moment, "that if we just go on out there, relax, and do our best, and not worry so much, we'll lose."

There was general agreement on that point.

"Do you know what I heard?" said Eliscue.

"What?"

"I didn't want to say it before, but since the game's a home game, they're talking about letting the whole school out to cheer us on to a win."

"You're kidding."

He shook his head.

There was a long, deep silence.

"Probably think," said Saltz, "that we'd be ashamed to lose in front of everybody."

I took a quick count. "You afraid to lose?" I asked Saltz.

"No way."

"Hays?"

"No."

"Porter?"

"Nope."

And so on. I felt encouraged. It was a complete vote of no confidence.

"Well," I said, "they just might see us lose again. With Parkville so bad I'm not saying it's automatic. But I'm not going to care if we do."

"Right," said Radosh. "It's not like we're committing <u>treason</u> or something. People have a right to be losers."

We considered that for a moment. It was then I had my most brilliant idea. "Who has money?"

"What for?"

"I'm your tall captain, right? Trust me. And bring your soccer T-shirts to me in the morning, early."

I collected about four bucks and we split up. I held Saltz back.

"What's the money all about?" he wanted to know. "And the T-shirts."

"Come on," I told him. "Maybe we can show them we really mean it."

Back Words...

When I woke the next morning, I have to admit, I was excited. It wasn't going to be an ordinary day. I looked outside and saw the sun was shining. I thought, "Good."

For the first time I *wanted* a game to happen.

I got to breakfast a little early, actually feeling happy.

"Today's the day," Dad announced.

---

treason (trē′zən) *n.* betrayal of one's country, especially by giving aid to the enemy in wartime.

"Right."

"Today you'll really win," chipped in my ma.

"Could be."

My father leaned across the table and gave me a tap. "Winning the last game is what matters. Go out with your head high, Ed."

"And my backside up if I lose?" I wanted to know.

"Ed," said my ma, "don't be so hard on yourself. Your father and I are coming to watch."

"Suit yourselves," I said, and beat it to the bus.

As soon as I got to class Saltz and I collected the T-shirts. "What are you going to do with them?" the others kept asking.

"You picked me as captain, didn't you?"

"Mr. Lester did."

"Well, this time, trust *me*."

When we got all the shirts, Saltz and I sneaked into the home ec room and did what needed to be done. Putting them into a bag so no one would see, we went back to class.

"Just about over," I said.

"I'm almost sorry," confessed Saltz.

"Me too," I said. "And I can't figure out why."

"Maybe it's—the team that loses together, really stays together."

"Right. Not one fathead on the whole team. Do you think we should have gotten a farewell present for Mr. Lester?"

"Like what?"

"A begging cup."

It was hard getting through the day. And it's impossible to know how many people wished me luck. From all I got it was clear they considered me the unluckiest guy in the whole world. I kept wishing I could have banked it for something important.

But the day got done.

It was down in the locker room, when we got ready, that I passed out the T-shirts.

Barish held his up. It was the regular shirt with "S.O.R." on the back. But under it Saltz and I had ironed on press letters. Now they all read:

S.O.R.
LOSERS

13

Barish's reaction was just to stare. That was my only nervous moment. Then he cracked up, laughing like crazy. And the rest, once they saw, joined in. When Mr. Lester came down he brought Mr. Tillman. We all stood up and turned our backs to them.

"Oh, my goodness," moaned Mr. Lester.

"That's sick," said Mr. Tillman. "Sick!" His happy beads shook furiously.

"It's honest," I said.

"It's defeatist," he yelled.

"Mr. Tillman," I asked, "is that true, about your trying out for pro football?"

He started to say something, then stopped, his mouth open. "Yeah. I tried to make it with the pros, but couldn't."

"So you lost too, right?"

"Yeah," chimed in Radosh, "everyone loses sometime."

"Listen here, you guys," said Mr. Tillman, "it's no fun being rejected."

"Can't it be okay to lose sometimes? You did. Lots do. You're still alive. And we don't dislike you because of that."

"Right. We got other reasons," I heard a voice say. I think it was Saltz.

Mr. Tillman started to say something, but turned and fled.

Mr. Lester tried to give us a few final pointers, like don't touch the ball with our hands, only use feet, things that we didn't always remember to do.

"Well," he said finally, "I enjoyed this."

"You did?" said Porter, surprised.

"Well, not much," he admitted. "I never coached anything before. To tell the truth, I don't know anything about soccer."

"Now you tell us," said Eliscue. But he was kidding. We sort of guessed that before.

Just as we started out onto the field, Saltz whispered to me, "What if we win?"

"With our luck, we will," I said.

And on we went.

---

rejected (ri jek'tid) *adj.* not accepted; turned down or cast aside.

MEET Avi

Avi (born 1937) and the characters he created for *S.O.R. Losers* know something about failure and losing, and they share the experience of turning defeat into victory.

It may come as quite a surprise to learn that this successful author once had problems with writing and needed a summer tutor to keep from failing high school English. That summer, as he learned how to write, Avi also learned something else—that he really wanted to write. He recalls, "It was the one thing everybody said I could not do."

It was not until Avi had his own children that he thought about writing books for a young audience. He quickly discovered just how much he enjoyed trying to communicate with young people.

Avi gets reactions about early manuscript drafts from some very tough critics—his children, his wife, and local high school students. He reworks his stories, over and over, until they are just right, for he believes in giving his readers his very best.

The care he takes in his writing shows. His novels *The True Confessions of Charlotte Doyle* and *Nothing But the Truth* were Newbery Honor Books in 1991 and 1992, respectively. Other award winners include *The Fighting Ground, Encounter at Easton,* and *Man from the Sky.*

RESPONDING TO *Literature*

THINK • TALK • WRITE

1 Would you recommend this selection to a friend? In your journal, tell why or why not.

2 Why do the other students give the soccer team members a pep rally? Why is or isn't this a good idea?

3 Why does Ed call the secret team meeting? Why does Radosh say they "have a right to be losers"?

4 Which do you think would make a better ending to the S.O.R. Losers' season—a win or a loss? Explain.

5 Ed jokes about moving to "some country that doesn't have sports." Do you think the United States places too much emphasis on athletic success? Why or why not?

ACTIVITIES

- **Write with Tone** Write an editorial for your school newspaper about the importance of winning in sports. Choose a tone that shows whether you agree with Ed that people overemphasize winning or you may feel disgusted at his team's lack of competitive spirit.

- **Create a Cheer** Ed and his friends use humor and word play to show how they feel about sports. Work with a small group to make up a cheer, song, or rap that would be appropriate for the S.O.R. Losers.

VOCABULARY PRACTICE

On a separate piece of paper, write the letter of the word or phrase that best completes each sentence below.

1 In order to **defect,** Eve would need to
  a. stick up for her teammates
  b. desert her native country
  c. excel at sports
  d. make a mistake on her math homework

2 **Supportive** teachers always try to be
  a. athletic   **b.** critical
  c. stressful   **d.** encouraging

3 Every time the ball came near him, the new goalie was **cringing,** o r
  a. hovering   **b.** boasting
  c. hustling   **d.** flinching

4 If Carter's parents **disown** him, it means that they
  a. no longer accept him as part of the family
  b. give him extra clothes to wear
  c. take away part of his allowance
  d. admire him for doing what he feels is right

5 Being **rejected** made Mr. Miller feel like he had
  a. been given an unfair advantage
  b. been thrown away
  c. just climbed Mount Everest
  d. won a million dollars

BEFORE READING

LAST SUMMER WITH MAIZON

CONNECT TO LITERATURE

What happens when best friends separate? In your journal, write some ideas on how you might cope if your best friend moved away. As you read "Last Summer with Maizon," notice how Margaret handles the changes in her friendship with Maizon.

THINKING ABOUT CHARACTER

Like all good writers, author Jacqueline Woodson does not simply explain what the people in her story are like. She lets her characters' words and actions reveal their personalities. Readers learn what kind of person the main character, Margaret, is by observing what she says and does.

Characters in novels often change a lot from the beginning to the end. This selection focuses on a girl who gains insights that help her cope with some painful losses. Look for the ways Margaret grows more mature in the course of the selection.

DID YOU KNOW?

Did you know that New York City is divided into five major sections called *boroughs?* The characters in this selection live in one borough, Brooklyn, and travel by train to another, Manhattan. Each borough has important landmarks, but Manhattan is the city's hub. Wall Street, the United Nations, the Broadway theater district, and Central Park are in Manhattan.

This selection occurs midway through the novel *Last Summer with Maizon.* Earlier in the book, Margaret's father died; she, her mother, and her brother, Li'l Jay, are still recovering from the loss. Now Margaret's best friend, Maizon, is leaving for private school in Connecticut, and they must say good-bye.

LAST SUMMER WITH MAIZON

BY JACQUELINE WOODSON
ILLUSTRATED BY CORNELIUS VAN WRIGHT

IT WAS THE SUMMER MARGARET TORY'S FATHER DIED. WHILE TRYING TO COME TO TERMS WITH THIS LOSS, MARGARET ALSO HAS TO FACE BEING SEPARATED FROM HER BEST FRIEND, MAIZON, WHO IS GOING AWAY TO BOARDING SCHOOL. AS MARGARET AND HER MOTHER ACCOMPANY MAIZON AND HER GRANDMOTHER TO THE TRAIN STATION IN NEW YORK CITY, BOTH GIRLS WONDER HOW THEY WILL GET ALONG WITHOUT EACH OTHER.

"Sure wish you weren't going away," Margaret said, choking back tears for what seemed like the millionth time. They were sitting on the M train, crossing the Williamsburg Bridge, and Margaret shivered as the train passed over the water. The L train would have made the trip easier but the L didn't go over the bridge and Maizon had wanted to ride over it once more before she left.

Maizon sat nervously drumming her fingers against the windowpane. "Me too," she said absently.

Margaret looked over at Mama and Grandma. Grandma stared out of her window. She looked old and out of place on the train.

"Maizon?" Margaret said, turning back toward her.

"Hmm?" Maizon frowned. She seemed to be concentrating on something in the water. It rippled and danced below them.

"Even though I wrote you those two letters, you only have to write me one back if you don't have a lot of time or something." Margaret looked down at her fingers. She had begun biting the cuticles, and now the skin surrounding her nails was red and ragged.

■——————————————————

choking (chōk'ing) *v.t.* holding back or repressing; stifling.

"I'll write you back," Maizon promised.

"Maizon . . ."

"What, Margaret!"

Margaret jumped and looked at Maizon. There was an <u>uneasiness</u> in her eyes she had never seen before.

"Forget it," she said.

Ms. Tory leaned over. "We'll be getting off in a few stops."

They rode the rest of the way in silence. At Delancey Street they changed for another train and a half hour later they were at Penn Station.

"I guess now we'll have to call each other to plan the same outfits," Maizon said as they waited for her train. Her voice sounded forced and fake, Margaret thought, like a grown-up trying to make a kid smile.

"I guess," Margaret said. The conductor called Maizon's train.

"I guess I gotta go," Maizon said softly, and Margaret felt a lump rise in her throat.

"I'll write you back, Margaret. Promise. Thanks for letting me keep the double-dutch trophy even if it is only second place." They hugged for a long time. Maizon sniffed loudly. "I'm scared, Margaret," she whispered.

Margaret didn't know what to say. "Don't be."

"Bye, Ms. Tory."

■————————————————

uneasiness (un ē′zē nis) *n.* anxiety; restlessness; tension.

Margaret's mother bent down and hugged Maizon. "Be good," she said as Maizon and her grandmother made their way toward the train.

"Mama," Margaret said as they watched Maizon and her grandmother disappear into the tunnel.

"What, dear?"

"What's the difference between a best friend and an old friend?"

"I guess . . ." Her mother thought for a moment. "I guess an old friend is a friend you once had and a best friend is a friend you'll always have."

"Then maybe me and Maizon aren't best friends anymore."

"Don't be silly, Margaret. What else would you two be? Some people can barely tell you apart. I feel like I've lost a daughter."

"Maybe . . . I don't know . . . Maybe we're old friends now. Maybe this was our last summer as best friends. I feel like something's going to change now and I'm not going to be able to change it back."

Ms. Tory's heels made a clicking sound through the terminal. She stopped to buy tokens and turned to Margaret.

"Like when Daddy died?" she asked, looking worried.

Margaret swallowed. "No. I just feel empty instead of sad, Mama," she said.

Her mother squeezed her hand as they waited for the train. When it came, they took seats by the window.

Ms. Tory held on to Margaret's hand. "Sometimes it just takes a while for the pain of loss to set in."

"I feel like sometimes Maizon kept me from doing things, but now she's not here. Now I don't have any"—Margaret thought for a moment, but couldn't find the right words— "now I don't have any excuse not to do things."

When the train emerged from its tunnel, the late afternoon sun had turned a bright orange. Margaret watched it

---

terminal (tûr'mə nəl) *n.* station at either end of a railroad, bus, air, or other transportation line.

for a moment. She looked at her hands again and discovered a cuticle she had missed.

Margaret pressed her pencil to her lips and stared out the classroom window. The school yard was <u>desolate</u> and gray. But everything seemed that way since Maizon left. Especially since a whole week had passed now without even a letter from her. Margaret sighed and chewed her eraser.

"Margaret, are you working on this assignment?"

Margaret jumped and turned toward Ms. Peazle. Maizon had been right—Ms. Peazle was the crabbiest teacher in the school. Margaret wondered why she had been picked to teach the smartest class. If students were so smart, she thought, the least the school could do was reward them with a nice teacher.

"I'm trying to think about what to write, Ms. Peazle."

"Well, you won't find an essay on your summer vacation outside that window, I'm sure. Or is that where you spent it?"

The class snickered and Margaret looked down, embarrassed. "No, ma'am."

"I'm glad to hear that," Ms. Peazle continued, looking at Margaret over granny glasses. "And I'm sure in the next ten minutes you'll be able to read your essay to the class and prove to us all that you weren't just daydreaming. Am I right?"

"I hope so, ma'am," Margaret mumbled. She looked around the room. It seemed everyone in 6-1 knew each other from the previous year. On the first day, a lot of kids asked her about Maizon, but after that no one said much to her. Things had changed since Maizon left. Without her, a lot of the fun had gone out of sitting on the stoop with Ms. Dell, Hattie, and Li'l Jay. Maybe she could write about that. No, Margaret thought, looking down at the blank piece of paper in front of her. It was too much to tell. She'd never get finished and Ms. Peazle would scold her—making her feel too dumb to be in 6-1. Margaret chewed her eraser and stared out the window again. There had to be something she could write about quickly.

---

desolate (des′ə lit) *adj.* without people; deserted; cheerless.

"Margaret Tory!" Ms. Peazle warned. "Am I going to have to change your seat?"

"Ma'am? I was just . . ."

"I think I'm going to have to move you away from that window unless you can prove to me that you can sit there without being distracted."

"I can, Ms. Peazle. It helps me write," she lied.

"Then I take it you should be ready to read your essay in"—Ms. Peazle looked at her watch—"the next seven minutes."

Margaret started writing frantically. When Ms. Peazle called her to the front of the room, her sheet of notebook paper shook in her hand. She pulled nervously at the hem of the maroon dress she and Maizon had picked out for school and tried not to look out at the twenty-six pairs of eyes she knew were on her.

"Last summer was the worst summer of my life. First my father died and then my best friend went away to a private boarding school. I didn't go anywhere except Manhattan. But that wasn't any fun because I was taking Maizon to the train. I hope next summer is a lot better."

She finished reading and walked silently back to her desk and tried to concentrate on not looking out the window. Instead, she rested her eyes on the half-written page. Margaret knew she could write better than that, but Ms. Peazle had rushed her. Anyway, she thought, that is what happened last summer.

"I'd like to see you after class, Margaret."

"Yes, ma'am," Margaret said softly. *This is the end,* she thought. One week in the smartest class and it's over. Maizon was smart enough to go to a better *school* and I can't even keep up in this class. Margaret sighed and tried not to stare out the window for the rest of the day.

When the three o'clock bell rang, she waited uneasily in her seat while Ms. Peazle led the rest of the class out to the school yard. Margaret heard the excited screams and laughter as everyone poured outside.

---

distracted (di strak′tid) *adj.* having the mind or attention turned away; diverted.

frantically (fran′tə klē′) *adv.* with wild excitement from worried grief; in great haste.

The empty classroom was quiet. She looked around at the desks. Many had words carved into them. They reminded her of the names she and Maizon had carved into the tar last summer. They were faded and illegible now.

Ms. Peazle came in and sat at the desk next to Margaret's. "Margaret," she said slowly, pausing for a moment to remove her glasses and rub her eyes tiredly. "I'm sorry to hear about your father . . ."

"That's okay." Margaret fidgeted.

"No, Margaret, it's not okay," Ms. Peazle continued, "not if it's going to affect your schoolwork."

"I can do better, Ms. Peazle, I really can!" Margaret looked up pleadingly. She was surprised at herself for wanting so badly to stay in Ms. Peazle's class.

"I know you can, Margaret. That's why I'm going to ask you to do this. For homework tonight . . ."

Margaret started to say that none of the other students had been assigned homework. She decided not to, though.

"I want you to write about your summer," Ms. Peazle continued. "I want it to express all of your feelings about your friend Maizon going away. Or it could be about your father's death and how you felt then. It doesn't matter what you write, a poem, an essay, a short story. Just so long as it expresses how you felt this summer. Is that understood?"

"Yes, ma'am." Margaret looked up at Ms. Peazle. "It's understood."

Ms. Peazle smiled. Without her glasses, Margaret thought, she wasn't that mean-looking.

"Good, then I'll see you bright and early tomorrow with something wonderful to read to the class."

Margaret slid out of the chair and walked toward the door.

"That's a very pretty dress, Margaret," Ms. Peazle said.

Margaret turned and started to tell her that Maizon was wearing the same one in Connecticut, but changed her mind. What did Ms. Peazle know about best friends who were almost cousins, anyway?

---

fidgeted (fij′i tid) *v.i.* made restless movements; was nervous or uneasy.

pleadingly (plē′ding lē′) *adv.* in a begging way.

"Thanks, ma'am," she said instead, and ducked out of the classroom. All of a sudden, she had a wonderful idea!

The next morning Ms. Peazle tapped her ruler against the desk to quiet the class. "Margaret," she asked when the room was silent. "Do you have something you want to share with us today?"

Margaret nodded and Ms. Peazle beckoned her to the front of the room.

"This," Margaret said, handing Ms. Peazle the sheet of looseleaf paper. It had taken her most of the evening to finish the assignment.

Ms. Peazle looked it over and handed it back to her.

"We're ready to listen," she said, smiling.

Margaret looked out over the class and felt her stomach slide up to her throat. She swallowed and counted to ten. Though the day was cool, she found herself sweating. Margaret couldn't remember when she had been this afraid.

"My pen doesn't write anymore," she began reading.

"I can't hear," someone called out.

"My pen doesn't write anymore," Margaret repeated. In the back of the room, someone exaggerated a sigh. The class chuckled. Margaret ignored them and continued to read.

"It stumbles and trembles in my hand.
If my dad were here—he would understand.
Best of all—It'd be last summer again.

But they've turned off the fire hydrants
Locked green leaves away.
Sprinkled ashes on you
and sent you on your way.

I wouldn't mind the early autumn
if you came home today
I'd tell you how much I miss you
and know I'd be okay.

Mama isn't laughing now
She works hard and she cries
she wonders when true laughter
will relieve her of her sighs
And even when she's smiling
Her eyes don't smile along
her face is growing older
She doesn't seem as strong.
I worry cause I love her
Ms. Dell says, 'where there is love,
there is a way.'

It's funny how we never know
exactly how our life will go
It's funny how a dream can fade
With the break of day.

I'm not sure where you are now
though I see you in my dreams
Ms. Dell says the things we see
are not always as they seem.

So often I'm uncertain
if you have found a new home
and when I am uncertain
I usually write a poem.

Time can't erase the memory
and time can't bring you home
Last summer was a part of me
and now a part is gone."

The class stared at her blankly, silent. Margaret lowered her head and made her way back to her seat.

"Could you leave that assignment on my desk, Margaret?" Ms. Peazle asked. There was a small smile playing at the corners of her mouth.

"Yes, ma'am," Margaret said. Why didn't anyone say anything?

"Now, if everyone will open their history books to page two seventy-five, we'll continue with our lesson on the Civil War."

Margaret wondered what she had expected the class to do. Applaud? She missed Maizon more than she had in a long time. *She would know what I'm feeling,* Margaret thought. And if she didn't, she'd make believe she did.

Margaret snuck a look out the window. The day looked cold and still. *She'd tell me it's only a feeling poets get and that Nikki Giovanni feels this way all of the time.* When she turned back, there was a small piece of paper on her desk.

"I liked your poem, Margaret," the note read. There was no name.

Margaret looked around but no one looked as though they had slipped a note on her desk. She smiled to herself and tucked the piece of paper into her notebook.

The final bell rang. As the class rushed out, Margaret was bumped against Ms. Peazle's desk.

"Did you get my note?" Ms. Peazle whispered. Margaret nodded and floated home.

Ms. Dell, Hattie, and Li'l Jay were sitting on the stoop when she got home.

"If it weren't so cold," she said, squeezing in beside Hattie's spreading hips, "it would be like old times."

"Except for Maizon," Hattie said, cutting her eyes toward her mother.

"Hush, Hattie," Ms. Dell said. She shivered and pulled Li'l Jay closer to her. For a moment, Margaret thought she looked old.

"It's just this cold spell we're having," Ms. Dell said. "Ages a person. Makes them look older than they are."

Margaret smiled. "Reading minds is worse than eaves-dropping, Ms. Dell."

"Try being her daughter for nineteen years," Hattie said.

"Hattie," Margaret said, moving closer to her for warmth. "How come you never liked Maizon?"

"No one said I never liked her."

"No one had to," Ms. Dell butted in.

"She was just too much ahead of everyone. At least she thought she was."

"But she was, Hattie. She was the smartest person at P.S. 102. Imagine being the smartest person."

"But she didn't have any common sense, Margaret. And when God gives a person that much brain, he's bound to leave out something else."

"Like what?"

Ms. Dell leaned over Li'l Jay's head and whispered loudly, "Like the truth."

She and Hattie laughed but Margaret couldn't see the hu-mor. It wasn't like either of them to say something wrong about a person.

"She told the truth . . ." Margaret said weakly.

Ms. Dell and Hattie exchanged looks.

"How was school?" Hattie asked too brightly.

"Boring," Margaret said. She would tuck what they said away until she could figure it out.

"That's the only word you know since Maizon left. Seems there's gotta be somethin' else going on that's not so *boring* all the time," Ms. Dell said.

"Well, it's sure not school. I read a poem to that stupid class and no one but Ms. Peazle liked it." She sighed and rested her chin on her hand.

"That's the chance you gotta take with poetry," Ms. Dell said. "Either everybody likes it or everybody hates it, but you hardly ever know 'cause nobody says a word. Too afraid to

eavesdropping (ēvz'drop'ing) *n.* listening to the private conversation of others without their knowing it.

offend you or, worse yet, make you feel good."

Margaret looked from Ms. Dell to Hattie then back to Ms. Dell again.

"How come you know so much about poetry?"

"You're not the first li'l black girl who wanted to be a poet."

"And you can bet your dress you won't be the last," Hattie concluded.

"You wanted to be a poet, Hattie??!!"

"Still do. Still make up poems in my head. Never write them down, though. The paper just yellows and clutters useful places. So this is where I keep it all now," she said, pointing to her head.

"A poem can't exist inside your head. You forget it," Margaret said doubtfully.

"Poems don't exist, Miss Know-It-All. Poems live! In your head is where a poem is born, isn't it?"

Margaret nodded and Hattie continued. "Well, my poetry chooses to live there!"

"Then recite one for me, please." Margaret folded her arms across her chest the way she had seen Ms. Dell do so many times.

"Some poems aren't meant to be heard, smarty-pants."

"Aw, Hattie," Ms. Dell interrupted, "let Margaret be the judge of that."

"All right. All right." Hattie's voice

dropped to a whisper. "Brooklyn-bound robin redbreast followed me from down home / Brooklyn-bound robin, you're
a long way from your own / So fly among the pigeons and
circle the sky with your song."

They were quiet. Ms. Dell rocked Li'l Jay to sleep in
her arms. Hattie looked <u>somberly</u> over the block in silence
and Margaret thought of how much Hattie's poem made
her think of Maizon. What was she doing now that the sun
was almost down? she wondered. Had she found a new
best friend?

"Maybe," she said after a long time. "Maybe it wasn't that
the class didn't like my poem. Maybe it was like your poem,
Hattie. You just have to sit quietly and think about all the
things it makes you think about after you hear it. You have to
let . . . let it sink in!"

"You have to feel it, Margaret," Hattie said softly, draping
her arm over Margaret's shoulder.

"Yeah. Just like I felt when I wrote my poem, or you felt
when you found a place for that one in your head!"

"Margaret," Ms. Dell said, "you gettin' too smart for us
ol' ladies."

Margaret leaned against Hattie and listened to the fading
sounds of construction. Soon the building on Palmetto Street
would be finished. She closed her eyes and visions of last
summer came into her head. She saw herself running down
Madison Street arm in arm with Maizon. They were laughing.
Then the picture faded into a new one. She and Maizon were
sitting by the tree watching Li'l Jay take his first steps. He
stumbled and fell into Maizon's arms. Now it all seemed like
such a long time ago.

When she opened her eyes again, the moon was inching
out from behind a cloud. It was barely visible in the late
afternoon. The sky had turned a wintry blue and the street-
lights flickered on. Margaret yawned, her head heavy all of a
sudden from the long day.

---

somberly (som'bər lē') *adv.* with darkness and gloom.

"Looks like your mother's workin' late again. Bless that woman's heart. Seems she's workin' nonstop since your daddy passed."

"She's taking drawing classes. She wants to be an architect. Maybe she'll make a lot of money."

"Architects don't make a lot of money," Hattie said. "And anyway, you shouldn't be worrying your head over money."

"She has a gift," Ms. Dell said. "All of you Torys have gifts. You with your writing, your mama with her drawings, and remember the things your daddy did with wood. Oh, that man was something else!"

"What's Li'l Jay's going to be?"

Ms. Dell stood up and pressed Li'l Jay's face to her cheek.

"Time's gonna tell us, Margaret. Now, come inside and do your homework while I fix you something to eat. No use sitting out in the cold."

Margaret rose and followed them inside.

"You hear anything from Maizon yet?" Hattie asked.

Margaret shook her head. If only Maizon were running up the block!

"I wrote her two letters and she hasn't written me one. Maybe she knows we're not really best friends anymore." Margaret sighed. She had been right in thinking she and Maizon were only old friends now, not the friends they used to be. "Still, I wish I knew how she was doing," she said, turning away so Hattie wouldn't see the tears in her eyes.

"We all do, honey," Hattie said, taking Margaret's hand. "We all do."

MEET JACQUELINE WOODSON

A seven-year-old Jacqueline Woodson refused to give up her dream of becoming a writer—not even when her older sister told her that no one would publish her book of poems.

Years later, Woodson's determination to be a writer finally paid off. Her first published novel, *Last Summer with Maizon,* a book about friends and change, takes place on the Brooklyn street where Woodson once lived. It is based partly on her childhood friendship with a girl named Maria. "I wanted to write a book about friendship so that people could remember how important friends are." She explains further, "You can't write a book without putting a little bit of yourself into it. You mix that bit of yourself up with your imagination. That's how you create fiction. Well, that's how *I* create fiction."

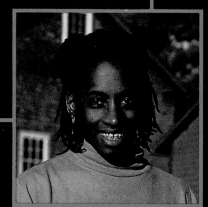

RESPONDING TO *Literature*

THINK • TALK • WRITE

1 Did any of Margaret's experiences remind you of experiences you have had yourself? Write an entry in your journal.

2 Why is Margaret so upset that Maizon is leaving? Do you think she understands how Maizon may be feeling as she goes away?

3 Why does Margaret find it so hard to write about her summer when she is in school? Why is it easier for her to express herself at home?

4 Who left the note on Margaret's desk after she read her poem? Why do you think this character did that?

5 How does Margaret feel about poetry? Why does it help her to learn that she's "not the first li'l black girl who wanted to be a poet," as Ms. Dell says?

ACTIVITIES

- **Write About Character** Write a scene in which Margaret and a new classmate talk after school. Through their dialog, express the character of Margaret and reveal what her new friend is like.

- **Make a Collage** Think about what you did over the summer. Draw pictures or cut out photographs from magazines to make a collage reflecting your own summer vacation.

VOCABULARY PRACTICE

Choose the vocabulary word that best fits in each blank. Write the word on a separate piece of paper.

choking	frantically
uneasiness	fidgeted
terminal	pleadingly
desolate	eavesdropping
distracted	somberly

Amanda's bus pulled into the ____**1**____ shortly before midnight. There were only a few other people around; to Amanda it seemed like the most ____**2**____ place in the world. Her stomach churned with ____**3**____. She sat down and took out her book, but she was too ____**4**____ to concentrate. Restless, she ____**5**____ in her seat.

Just before boarding the bus, she had talked ____**6**____ with her brother on the phone. Amanda had practically begged him to come on time. Now he was late again, and she was barely succeeding in ____**7**____ back tears.

Without meaning to, Amanda started ____**8**____ on a conversation between the bus driver and a man at the counter. The driver looked very serious and was ____**9**____ explaining that the station would be closing in 15 minutes. Growing almost desperate, Amanda began ____**10**____ searching through her wallet for her brother's phone number.

Suddenly, in walked her brother!

Unfolding Bud

Succulent Study   1994   Betsy Bauer

One is amazed
By a water-lily bud
Unfolding
With each passing day,
Taking on a richer color
And new dimensions.

One is not amazed,
At a first glance,
By a poem,
Which is as tight-closed
As a tiny bud.

Yet one is surprised
To see the poem
Gradually unfolding,
Revealing its rich inner self
As one reads it
Again
And over again.

—Naoshi Koriyama

The World Is Not a Pleasant Place to Be

Untitled   c.1983   Keith Haring

the world is not a pleasant place
to be without
someone to hold and be held by

a river would stop
its flow if only
a stream were there

an ocean would never laugh
if clouds weren't there
to kiss her tears

the world is not
a pleasant place to be without
someone

Before Reading

SEVENTH GRADE

CONNECT TO LITERATURE

How did you feel on the first day of school this year? Describe some of your emotions in your journal. What was it like to see old friends, meet new people, and start new classes? What hopes did you have for the year ahead? Have you fulfilled any of those hopes so far? As you read "Seventh Grade," compare your feelings with the feelings of Victor, the main character.

THINKING ABOUT THIRD-PERSON POINT OF VIEW

The story "Seventh Grade" is told by an invisible narrator who does not take part in the action. This kind of point of view is called *third-person* because the narrator refers to all the characters using third-person pronouns, such as *she, he,* and *they.*

The narrator of "Seventh Grade" not only tells what Victor does but also what Victor thinks and feels. At times, the narrator reveals what other characters are thinking and feeling as well. This helps readers understand both how Victor sees himself and how other people see him. Readers get to glimpse important story events through more than one person's eyes.

HAVE YOU EVER?

Have you ever felt both terrible and wonderful—embarrassed and triumphant—within a few hours? Victor experiences a wide range of emotions on his first day of seventh grade. Some of his feelings come from seeing his friends; some come from what happens in his classes. Events that become normal in the course of the year often seem special at the beginning.

Meet Gary Soto

Gary Soto's success as a writer may have surprised some people—perhaps even himself. Recalling his childhood in a poor Mexican-American family, Soto says, "I don't think I had any literary aspirations when I was a kid. . . . We didn't have books, and no one encouraged us to read."

Later, as a college student, Soto discovered a collection of poems and thought, "This is terrific; I'd like to do something like this." He felt that writing would be a way to communicate the problems and emotions of people like the Chicanos he knew.

"Seventh Grade" is from Soto's book of short stories *Baseball in April.* His other works include *Living up the Street,* a collection of autobiographical essays, and *A Fire in My Hands,* a book of poems.

Seventh grade

by Gary Soto

illustrated by John Ceballos

On the first day of school, Victor stood in line half an hour before he came to a wobbly card table. He was handed a packet of papers and a computer card on which he listed his one elective, French. He already spoke Spanish and English, but he thought some day he might travel to France, where it was cool; not like Fresno, where summer days reached 110 degrees in the shade. There were rivers in France, and huge churches, and fair-skinned people everywhere, the way there were brown people all around Victor.

Besides, Teresa, a girl he had liked since they were in catechism classes at Saint Theresa's, was taking French too. With any luck they would be in the same class. Teresa is going to be my girl this year, he promised himself as he left the gym full of students in their new fall clothes. She was cute. And good at math, too, Victor thought as he walked down the hall to his homeroom. He ran into his friend, Michael Torres, by the water fountain that never turned off.

They shook hands, _raza_-style, and jerked their heads at one another in a _saludo de vato_. "How come you're making a face?" asked Victor.

"I ain't making a face, _ese_. This _is_ my face." Michael said his face had changed during the summer. He had read a _GQ_ magazine that his older brother borrowed from the Book Mobile and noticed that the male models all had the same look on their faces. They would stand, one arm around a beautiful woman, and _scowl_. They would sit at a pool, their rippled stomachs dark with shadow, and _scowl_. They would sit at dinner tables, cool drinks in their hands, and _scowl_.

"I think it works," Michael said. He scowled and let his upper lip quiver. His teeth showed along with the ferocity of his soul. "Belinda Reyes walked by a while ago and looked at me," he said.

Victor didn't say anything, though he thought his friend looked pretty strange. They talked about recent movies, baseball, their parents, and the horrors of picking grapes in order

---

raza (rä′sä) _Spanish._ Latino people.

saludo de vato (sä lü′dō dā vä′to) _Spanish._ special handshake.

ese (ās′ä) _Spanish. Slang._ man.

ferocity (fə ros′i tē) _n._ fierceness.

to buy their fall clothes. Picking grapes was like living in Siberia, except hot and more boring.

"What classes are you taking?" Michael said, scowling.

"French. How 'bout you?"

"Spanish. I ain't so good at it, even if I'm Mexican."

"I'm not either, but I'm better at it than math, that's for sure."

A tinny, three-beat bell propelled students to their homerooms. The two friends socked each other in the arm and went their ways, Victor thinking, man, that's weird. Michael thinks making a face makes him handsome.

On the way to his homeroom, Victor tried a scowl. He felt foolish, until out of the corner of his eye he saw a girl looking at him. Umm, he thought, maybe it does work. He scowled with greater <u>conviction</u>.

In homeroom, roll was taken, emergency cards were passed out, and they were given a bulletin to take home to their parents. The principal, Mr. Belton, spoke over the crackling loudspeaker, welcoming the students to a new year, new experiences, and new friendships. The students squirmed in their chairs and ignored him. They were anxious to go to first period. Victor sat calmly, thinking of Teresa, who sat two rows away, reading a paperback novel. This would be his lucky year. She was in his homeroom, and would probably be in his English and math classes. And, of course, French.

The bell rang for first period, and the students herded noisily through the door. Only Teresa lingered, talking with the homeroom teacher.

"So you think I should talk to Mrs. Gaines?" she asked the teacher. "She would know about ballet?"

"She would be a good bet," the teacher said. Then added, "Or the gym teacher, Mrs. Garza."

Victor lingered, keeping his head down and staring at his desk. He wanted to leave

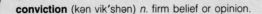

conviction (kən vik′shən) *n.* firm belief or opinion.

when she did so he could bump into her and say something clever.

He watched her on the sly. As she turned to leave, he stood up and hurried to the door, where he managed to catch her eye. She smiled and said, "Hi, Victor."

He smiled back and said, "Yeah, that's me." His brown face blushed. Why hadn't he said, "Hi, Teresa," or "How was your summer?" or something nice?

As Teresa walked down the hall, Victor walked the other way, looking back, admiring how gracefully she walked, one foot in front of the other. So much for being in the same class, he thought. As he trudged to English, he practiced scowling.

In English they reviewed the parts of speech. Mr. Lucas, a portly man, waddled down the aisle, asking, "What is a noun?"

"A person, place, or thing," said the class in <u>unison</u>.

"Yes, now somebody give me an example of a person— you, Victor Rodriguez."

"Teresa," Victor said <u>automatically</u>. Some of the girls giggled. They knew he had a crush on Teresa. He felt himself blushing again.

"Correct," Mr. Lucas said. "Now provide me with a place."

Mr. Lucas called on a freckled kid who answered, "Teresa's house with a kitchen full of big brothers."

After English, Victor had math, his weakest subject. He sat in the back by the window, hoping that he would not be called on. Victor understood most of the problems, but some of the stuff looked like the teacher made it up as she went along. It was confusing, like the inside of a watch.

After math he had a fifteen-minute break, then social studies, and, finally, lunch. He bought a tuna casserole with buttered rolls, some fruit cocktail, and milk. He sat with Michael, who practiced scowling between bites.

---

unison (ū′nə sen) *n.* union, as when two or more voices speak as one.
automatically (ô′tə mat′ik lē) *adv.* as if acting, moving or operating by itself; as if done without a person's control.

Girls walked by and looked at him.

"See what I mean, Vic?" Michael scowled. "They love it."

"Yeah, I guess so."

They ate slowly, Victor scanning the horizon for a glimpse of Teresa. He didn't see her. She must have brought lunch, he thought, and is eating outside. Victor scraped his plate and left Michael, who was busy scowling at a girl two tables away.

The small, triangle-shaped campus bustled with students talking about their new classes. Everyone was in a sunny mood. Victor hurried to the bag lunch area, where he sat down and opened his math book. He moved his lips as if he were reading, but his mind was somewhere else. He raised his eyes slowly and looked around. No Teresa.

He lowered his eyes, pretending to study, then looked slowly to the left. No Teresa. He turned a page in the book and stared at some math problems that scared him because he knew he would have to do them eventually. He looked to the right. Still no sign of her. He stretched out lazily in an attempt to disguise his snooping.

Then he saw her. She was sitting with a girlfriend under a plum tree. Victor moved to a table near her and daydreamed about taking her to a movie. When the bell sounded, Teresa looked up, and their eyes met. She smiled sweetly and gathered her books. Her next class was French, same as Victor's.

They were among the last students to arrive in class, so all the good desks in the back had already been taken. Victor was forced to sit near the front, a few desks away from Teresa, while Mr. Bueller wrote French words on the chalkboard. The bell rang, and Mr. Bueller wiped his hands, turned to the class, and said, *"Bonjour."*

"Bonjour," braved a few students.

"Bonjour," Victor whispered. He wondered if Teresa heard him.

Mr. Bueller said that if the students studied hard, at the end of the year they could go to France and be understood by the populace.

One kid raised his hand and asked, "What's 'populace'?"

"The people, the people of France."

Mr. Bueller asked if anyone knew French. Victor raised his hand, wanting to impress Teresa. The teacher beamed and said, *"Très bien. Parlez-vous français?"*

Victor didn't know what to say. The teacher wet his lips and asked something else in French. The room grew silent. Victor felt all eyes staring at him. He tried to bluff his way out by making noises that sounded French.

"La me vava me con le grandma," he said uncertainly.

Mr. Bueller, wrinkling his face in curiosity, asked him to speak up.

Great rosebushes of red bloomed on Victor's cheeks. A river of nervous sweat ran down his palms. He felt awful. Teresa sat a few desks away, no doubt thinking he was a fool. Without looking at Mr. Bueller, Victor mumbled, "Frenchie oh wewe gee in September."

Mr. Bueller asked Victor to repeat what he had said.

"Frenchie oh wewe gee in September," Victor repeated.

Mr. Bueller understood that the boy didn't know French and turned away. He walked to the blackboard and pointed to the words on the board with his steel-edged ruler.

Bonjour (bôn zhür') *French.* good morning; good day.
Très bien. Parlez-vous français? (trā bi a' pär'lā vü fron sā') *French.* Very good. Do you speak French?

"Le bateau," he sang.

"Le bateau," the students repeated.

"Le bateau est sur l'eau," he sang.

"Le bateau est sur l'eau."

Victor was too weak from failure to join the class. He stared at the board and wished he had taken Spanish, not French. Better yet, he wished he could start his life over. He had never been so embarrassed. He bit his thumb until he tore off a sliver of skin.

The bell sounded for fifth period, and Victor shot out of the room, avoiding the stares of the other kids, but had to return for his math book. He looked sheepishly at the teacher, who was erasing the board, then widened his eyes in terror at Teresa who stood in front of him. "I didn't know you knew French," she said. "That was good."

Mr. Bueller looked at Victor, and Victor looked back. Oh please, don't say anything, Victor pleaded with his eyes. I'll wash your car, mow your lawn, walk your dog—anything! I'll be your best student, and I'll clean your erasers after school.

Mr. Bueller shuffled through the papers on his desk. He smiled and hummed as he sat down to work. He remembered his college years when he dated a girlfriend in borrowed cars. She thought he was rich because each time he picked her up he had a different car. It was fun until he had spent all his money on her and had to write home to his parents because he was broke.

Victor couldn't stand to look at Teresa. He was sweaty with shame. "Yeah, well, I picked up a few things from movies and books and stuff like that." They left the class together. Teresa asked him if he would help her with her French.

"Sure, anytime," Victor said.

"I won't be bothering you, will I?"

"Oh no, I like being bothered."

Le bateau est sur l'eau. (lù ba tō′ ā sür lō) *French.* The boat is on the water.

"*Bonjour,*" Teresa said, leaving him outside her next class. She smiled and pushed wisps of hair from her face.

"Yeah, right, *bonjour,*" Victor said. He turned and headed to his class. The rosebushes of shame on his face became bouquets of love. Teresa is a great girl, he thought. And Mr. Bueller is a good guy.

He raced to metal shop. After metal shop there was biology, and after biology a long sprint to the public library, where he checked out three French textbooks.

He was going to like seventh grade.

---

bouquets (bō kāz′, bü kāz′) *n. pl.* bunches of picked flowers.

RESPONDING TO *Literature*

THINK • TALK • WRITE

1 Did you enjoy this story? Did the characters seem realistic? Write your reactions in your journal.

2 Why is French class particularly important to Victor? Do you think he will work hard to learn the language? Why or why not?

3 What does Victor do that leaves him feeling very embarrassed? What leads him to decide that Mr. Bueller is a "good guy"?

4 How would "Seventh Grade" have been different if Victor himself had told the story? What might this story have been like if Teresa had told it instead?

5 Imagine rewriting this story so that it takes place in another part of the world—in France, for example. Which parts of the story might remain the same? Which might be different?

ACTIVITIES

- **Write About Narrative Point of View** Choose a day later in the school year, and describe what Victor is doing between classes, at lunch, and/or after school. To whom is he talking, and about what are they talking? Use the third-person narrative point of view.

- **Make a Travel Poster** Victor imagines France as a place with rivers, huge churches, and fair-skinned people everywhere. Choose a country you have never visited. Research in an encyclopedia, other books, or magazines to learn more about this country. Make a travel poster showing three interesting features, such as its natural beauty, historical landmarks, and art works.

VOCABULARY PRACTICE

Read each book title below. Choose the vocabulary word that best suggests the subject of each book. On a separate piece of paper, write the word you chose for each title.

ferocity   automatically
conviction   bouquets
unison

1 *All Together Now: An Introduction to Line Dancing*

2 *Robots: The New Factory Workers*

3 *Flower Arrangements for Your Wedding*

4 *Lions on the African Plains*

5 *Take a Stand: How to Believe in Yourself*

BEFORE READING

TO LIVE IN TWO WORLDS

CONNECT TO LITERATURE

Have you ever had to move? Even if you have not, you can probably imagine how hard it can be to leave behind favorite places and friends. What are some things that you would miss if you moved away from where you live? List these things in your journal. As you read "To Live in Two Worlds," note how Lynn (the girl profiled) feels about the home she must temporarily leave behind.

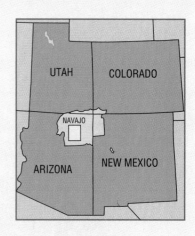

THINKING ABOUT SETTING

Setting—the time and place of the action—is particularly important in this excerpt from the nonfiction book *To Live in Two Worlds*. Lynn loves living on the Navajo reservation, but she can get better schooling elsewhere. Lynn must balance her love of home with her desire to get the best education she can.

DID YOU KNOW?

- With 200,000 people, the Navajos are the largest Native American tribe in the United States. The Navajo nation has its own government, police force, and educational system.

- The Navajos traditionally lived in an area bounded by four mountains they considered sacred. Many believed that anyone who left these lands would meet misfortune. In 1864, the U. S. Army forced the Navajos off their traditional lands and onto a reservation. Hundreds died of cold and starvation on the 350-mile journey, known as the Long Walk.

- Today the Navajo reservation, located in parts of Arizona, New Mexico, Colorado, and Utah, covers over 24,000 square miles (62,000 sq km). See the map above.

LYNN WAS BORN ON THE NAVAJO
RESERVATION IN ARIZONA. HER
RELATIVES HELPED HER FAMILY BY
PROVIDING THEM WITH PLACES TO
STAY. AS A RESULT, LYNN MOVED
AROUND THE RESERVATION
FREQUENTLY AS SHE GREW UP.

TO LIVE IN TWO WORLDS

By Brent Ashabranner
Photographs by Paul Conklin
Illustrated by Shonto Begay

Lynn was happiest when they stayed with her grandparents. They lived in a hogan, the traditional one-room Navajo dwelling made of logs and packed earth. It never seemed crowded despite extra people, and it was from her grandmother and grandfather that Lynn learned most about Navajo ways and beliefs.

She learned that the Navajo hogan is a home but also a holy place that must be built in the right way, just as the Holy People built the first hogans as examples for the Earth People. Before the hogan can be lived in, it must be blessed with songs from the blessing ceremony, and the door to every hogan must face east to catch the first light of the morning sun. In that way Changing Woman, the greatest of the Holy People, is honored. The sun was the father of Changing Woman's two sons, Monster Slayer and Born for the Water, and it was they who helped the Earth People in many ways.

On summer nights everyone slept outside the hogan, so that they could enjoy the soft breezes and the clean fresh air. Lynn would lie on her sheepskin and look up at the blanket of bright stars. Often as she drifted into sleep, she could hear the yipping bark of a coyote somewhere far off in the darkness, but she was not afraid.

Lynn went to school at four different places on the reservation, but moving around did not cause a learning problem for her. She had grown up speaking both Navajo and English, and her English improved quickly in school. She made top grades everyplace, and when she finished elementary school, she received a scholarship to go to a mission school in a large town off the reservation.

That was the beginning of a new life in a new world for Lynn. It was a world that kept opening up, expanding, showing her new things. The school had a library with more books than she could imagine. Even though she was only in the ninth grade, her teachers made it clear to her that she was at the mission school because they knew she could be a good student, and they expected her to be one.

The town was by far the biggest place she had ever been in. There were supermarkets, department stores, restaurants, motels, theaters,

---

mission school (mish'ən skül) school founded by church people sent to spread their religion.

THE NAVAJO COMMUNITY COLLEGE
IN TSAILE, ARIZONA, HAS USED
TRADITIONAL TRIBAL MOTIFS IN ITS
ARCHITECTURE. IN THE FOREGROUND
IS A HOGAN, TRADITIONAL HOME OF
THE SOUTHWESTERN DESERT. IN
THE BACKGROUND IS A MODERN NEW
ADMINISTRATION BUILDING IN WHICH
THE HOGAN SHAPE APPEARS IN GLASS.

NAVAJO WEAVER SPINNING HER WOOL

and even bookstores. Sometimes on Saturday afternoons she would walk down the main street, just looking in the shop windows and wandering through the supermarkets. She had no money to buy things, but that did not matter.

At first she was very homesick for her family and friends on the reservation. Before going to the mission school she had never spent a single night away from her family. But all of the students at the school were Navajos from the reservation and that helped a great deal.

TO HERSELF SHE SAID, "I KNOW I WON'T BE SELECTED, SO THERE IS NOTHING TO WORRY ABOUT."

Lynn thought that she would be at the mission school until she graduated from high school, and it was a complete surprise when, about midway in the second term of her sophomore year, a group of her teachers asked her to come in for a conference. They told her about a new government program for finding minority high school students—blacks, Hispanics, American Indians—who showed unusual academic ability and sending them to some of the best college preparatory schools in America.

"We want you to try to win a place in the program," Lynn's teachers told her. "The competition will be very great, but we think you have a chance."

Lynn felt a small stab of fear. "If I am selected, where will I go?" she asked.

"We don't know," one of the teachers told her, "but most of the schools are in California and on the East Coast."

"That would be so far from the reservation," Lynn said.

Her teachers continued to talk to her over the following days, and they seemed so sure she should apply for the program that Lynn finally agreed to fill out the application papers and take the entrance examination. To herself she said, "I know I won't be selected, so there is nothing to worry about."

A short time later she took the entrance examination in which she had to compete with all of the other minority students across the country who wanted to get into the program. She had never taken a test like that before, and she was sure that she had done miserably on it. She put it out of her mind and returned to her classwork and school life. The term

---

academic (ak'ə dem'ik) *adj.* of or relating to liberal or general education, especially to studies that prepare a student for college.
preparatory (prep'pər ə tôr'ē) *adj.* serving to prepare, especially for college.

was nearly over, and the thought of going back to the reservation made her happy.

And then one day she was called to the principal's office. He smiled when she walked in and he held up a piece of paper. "Congratulations, Lynn," he said. "You've been chosen! You're going to Brandermill School in Vermont." (At Lynn's request, the name of the school has been changed.)

Lynn would never forget the numb feeling in the pit of her stomach. "But it's so far away," she said.

"Well," the principal said, "Brandermill is one of the best college preparatory schools in the country. You're very lucky to be going there."

Yes, Lynn thought, she was lucky. She knew that. And she did want a good education. But why did she have to go so far away to get it? "Will I go in September?" she asked.

"That is one thing you may not like so well," the principal replied. "There's a special summer program at the University of Texas. You'll get courses in speed reading, English, and math, so that you will be better prepared for the fall term at Brandermill."

The numb feeling grew in Lynn's stomach. "Do I have to go?" she asked. "To the summer school, I mean?"

The principal smiled again. "I'm afraid you do," he said. "And you really need that work to get ready for the fall."

Lynn could feel the hurting at the back of her eyes, but she fought back the tears. "But I need to go home," she said.

"You can go home," the principal told her, "but not for a long visit. The summer program starts in June."

And that was the way it was. Instead of three months at home she would have two weeks. Two weeks to be with her family! On the bus ride from the school back to the reservation she sat in a window seat, and when they crossed into the reservation, she stared out at the red earth, at the huge bare rocks sculpted over thousands of centuries by wind and water into fantastic shapes. She stared at the <u>awesome</u> bulk of Black Mesa in the background and at the little patches of spring desert wild flowers along the roadside, tiny spots of purple, red, yellow, and white.

Lynn went to her grandparents' hogan, and her mother and brother came there so that they were all together. The two weeks passed like the flashing of pictures on a screen, and yet like pictures, some scenes stood still, and Lynn knew that she could carry them with her anywhere.

---

awesome (ô′səm) *adj.* inspiring great wonder combined with fear or reverence.

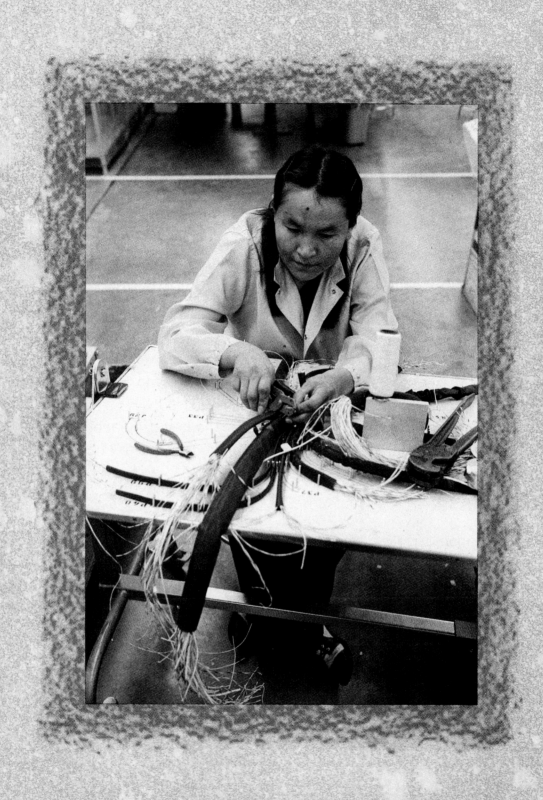

HERE A NAVAJO LEARNS THE INTRICACIES
OF ELECTRONIC ASSEMBLY AT A PLANT ON
THE ARIZONA RESERVATION.

There were the times she would go with her grandfather for water. The hogan had no running water, and every few days he would drive his old pickup truck to a windmill down the road and fill two wooden barrels. Upon their return to the hogan, Lynn would help transfer the water from the barrels to containers inside and outside the house.

THE DAY CAME TOO QUICKLY WHEN LYNN TOOK A BUS TO PHOENIX AND BOARDED AN AIRPLANE FOR THE FLIGHT TO TEXAS.

Some mornings Lynn would sit with her grandmother and help her grind corn for bread or mush. One morning as they worked, her grandmother explained again why grinding stones are so important. They were first brought to Navajos by the Holy People, she said, and women who learn to use them properly will be happy and healthy and even live longer. And the greasewood stirring sticks, if they are kept clean, will mean that a family will never be hungry. Hunger, which is really an evil spirit, thinks that the sticks are arrows which will kill it, so it stays away.

These were not the kinds of things that a person learned in school, Lynn thought, but she was glad that she knew about them. They were the teachings that her grandmother and her Navajo ancestors had lived by, and Lynn felt truth and meaning in them. Perhaps hunger was not an evil spirit, but it was bad, and it had less chance of getting into homes where women were happy and busy and knew how to prepare clean and nutritious food.

The day came too quickly when Lynn took a bus to Phoenix and boarded an airplane for the flight to Texas. She had never flown before and she was excited. She had thought she would be frightened, but she was so nervous thinking about the summer program that first-time flying fears couldn't crowd their way into her mind.

I'll bet I won't even get through the summer program, she thought, as she stared out of the plane window at the blur of ground below. I'll never make it to Vermont.

But it was not that way at all. When she reached the university, she was plunged into such a whirlwind of activity that she had no time to be frightened, uncertain, or even homesick. The program instructors pushed her and the other students into all-day classroom and laboratory sessions in mathematics, reading improvement, and English.

The teaching staff used methods and equipment that Lynn had never heard of, but after only a week she knew that she was reading faster and understanding more of what she read than she ever had before. She was pleased and excited by what was happening to her, and she was sure that she was doing well in the math program. English was the only problem. All her life she had spoken both English and Navajo, but sometimes, especially when she was under stress, she thought in Navajo. It was a problem she would just have to work out, Lynn knew, and she was determined not to lose her Navajo language in solving it.

The other students in the program were a happy surprise for her. They were there because of their high test scores but also because they were from minority groups and poor families. They all wanted a good education.

These <u>similarities</u> made it easier for them to talk, to get to know each other, to relax together. After a hard day of classes, it was fun to get to-gether in someone's room and talk about how they got to this place and what was happening to them here. On weekends when a group of them would go out for pizza or to a movie, it seemed to Lynn that she had known them for a long time.

Almost before she knew it, the summer program was over. She said her good-byes, some of them sad ones. She packed her suitcase and caught the plane for the East Coast.

She would never forget her first impressions of Brandermill: the huge old ivy-covered buildings, the beautifully landscaped campus still green at summer's end, the hundreds of cool, confident white-skinned girls walking in pairs, sitting on building steps in small groups, laughing and talking. It seemed to Lynn that they all had long blonde hair.

She learned some things about Brandermill before arriving. She knew that it was a prep school for the children of rich people. The tuition for one year was several thousand dollars, which was more money than Lynn could imagine. The school could afford to hire the very best teachers and it did. Brandermill's academic standards were the highest. Everyone had told Lynn how lucky she was to get to go to such a school.

---

similarities (sim′ə lar′i tēz) *n., pl.* instances or points of likeness.

NAVAJO ON HORSEBACK HERDING
SHEEP DOWN SAND DUNES AT
MONUMENT VALLEY

NAVAJO HOLDING
HIS SAND PAINTING

NAVAJO WEAVERS
NEAR HOGAN

But two weeks into the school term she was miserable. She was desperately lonely and homesick for her family and Navajo friends. She longed to see the red earth of the reservation, the great rocks, the sheltering bulk of Black Mesa. In the muggy New England September, she could almost feel the crisp, clean Arizona air. The ache inside her was a physical thing.

And for the first time in her life Lynn knew what it meant to feel depressed. She sat silently in all her classes, afraid to speak up, feeling that she could not compete with her well-educated classmates. In literature class they talked about books and writers that she had never heard of but that everyone else seemed to know. Math had seemed easy; here at Brandermill it was suddenly hard. She was having problems with her written English. As the fall term wore on, Lynn was sure that she was failing.

And she made no friends. A few of the girls in her <u>dorm</u> talked briefly with her sometimes, usually about a class assignment, but no one made an effort to really get to know her. She did not make an effort either because she did not know how. She would have liked to know more about them, about how they lived, but they did not seem curious about her. Most of them had known each other from past years at Brandermill, and they were turned in on their friendships and little social groups. Lynn did not think that they were being deliberately unfriendly.

I'm not a part of their lives, so they just don't see me, Lynn thought. It's like I wasn't here.

By mid-October Lynn was sure that she should leave Brandermill and return to the reservation. She went to her counselor to tell him of her decision. He listened quietly as she explained that she was not making it in her classes and that she was unhappy with her life at the school.

"I'm a Navajo," she said, "and I should be back where I belong."

"You are a Navajo," her counselor replied, "and right now this is where you belong."

"But I'm failing," Lynn repeated.

"Only in your mind," the counselor said, "and we've got to change that. Have any of your teachers told you you're failing?"

"No," Lynn said. "I just know it."

The <u>counselor</u> smiled. "You just think you know it," he said. "I've been following your work. I've talked with all your teachers within the last week. You're doing okay in everything. You're

---

dorm (**dormitory**) (dôr′mi tôr′ē) *n.* building designed for group housing, as for students at a college to live and sleep in.

counselor (koun′sə lər) *n.* person who gives counsel or advice; adviser.

doing well in history, in fact. Your written English needs work, but you're certainly not failing in English."

"But I'm not happy here," Lynn said.

"YOU CAN DO IT," HE SAID. "WHEN YOU FIRST CAME HERE, I WASN'T SURE THAT YOU COULD, BUT NOW I AM."

"That's a different thing," the counselor said, "and that's why you think you're failing. What you are doing is about as hard to do as it can be. You have come out of a very special way of life into one that is entirely different. The people are different. The country is different. The school is different. There are very few people who could do what you're doing and succeed at it. That's why the selection board picked you. They believed you could do it."

"But I can't," Lynn said.

The counselor looked at her. "You can do it," he said. "When you first came here, I wasn't sure that you could, but now I am. If you leave school now and go back to the reservation, you won't feel good about yourself. You'll feel that you let down your tribe, your family, and your

friends. You'll be sorry you left here. I don't want to put more pressure on you than you can handle, but I have to tell you what I think is the truth."

Lynn nodded but did not say anything.

"Look," her counselor said, "you hang on until Christmas break. You'll get to go home then. Dig in now. Mark off the days on a calendar. Do anything you have to do to stick it out. When you get home, back to the reservation, you can decide whether you want to come back to Brandermill or whether you can come back. That's the place to make the decision."

Somehow it became a little easier after her talk with the counselor. Lynn did not mark off days on the calendar. What she did was throw herself into her studies with fierce energy. She spent more time at the library, more time going over her assignments a second and even a third time. The hard work made the days slide by more quickly.

She forced herself to speak up in her classes, even literature class, and it pleased and excited her that more than once the teachers praised her answers. She began to talk a little more to the other girls in the dorm, and now and then someone stopped by her room just to chat.

But on the last day before the Christmas break her excitement at the thought of going home was almost more than she could bear, and the feeling continued throughout the long flight to Phoenix. Just as in the summer, she again would have two weeks with her family in Navajoland. Then in so short a time she would have to go back to Vermont. But suppose she decided not to return. She could spend the rest of her life on the reservation. Was that what she wanted? The thought left Lynn confused and curbed some of the excitement inside her.

That night Lynn sat with her mother and grandparents in their hogan and ate mutton stew, corn, and fry bread for the first time in months. A cold winter wind howled around the hogan, but it was warm inside. They sat by the fire, and Lynn told them about Brandermill, her courses, her teachers, the big beautiful buildings, her fine dormitory room.

"I never thought I would be in a school as grand as that," Lynn said, "but I would rather be here, right where I am now."

"This is your home," her grandfather said.

During her visit Lynn talked to her mother and grandmother about something that was troubling her greatly. "What if I turn into a white person?" she asked. "If I learn white ways and how they think, if I learn their language and read their books, if I spend most of my time with them—won't I become a white person?"

Her grandmother answered in Navajo and used the Navajo word for their tribe, *Dine,* which means "The People." "You should learn the ways of the white people," she said. "But the ways of The People are deep inside you. I do not think you will forget who you are."

And her mother said, "Nothing can make you a white person unless you want to be one."

In that moment Lynn's decision was made. She would return to Brandermill. On the day she left the reservation and flew east to begin her second term, Lynn said her good-byes sadly, but she felt a confidence she had not known before.

When she arrived at Brandermill, the great campus, the fine buildings, the blonde students did not frighten her. She knew what was ahead for her, and she knew now that she could do the work. Most important, she was sure she could do it and still be what she was and wanted to be, a Navajo.

---

campus (kam′pəs) *n.* grounds, including buildings, of a school, college, or university.

MEET
BRENT ASHABRANNER

When Brent Ashabranner was young, he roamed the world by reading about it. Books gave him a way to be in two places at once — the small Oklahoma town where he lived with his family and the far-away places he visited in stories.

Years later, an assignment with a foreign aid program took Ashabranner and his wife and children to Africa. After that, jobs took him to India, the Philippines, and Central America, among other places. Everywhere he traveled, Ashabranner listened to people. He began weaving what he heard into tales of his own. "No matter where I was or what I was doing," he says, "I have always had another life as a writer."

Ashabranner especially wants to help young readers understand people and cultures different from their own. Much of his writing is about cultural and ethnic groups in the United States. He feels that the years he spent abroad have helped him "understand better their hopes, desires, frustrations, and fears." In his award-winning book *To Live in Two Worlds*, Ashabranner explores the difficult choices Native Americans must make to find a place between two cultures: their own and that of white America. Two of his other award-winning books, *Morning Star, Black Sun* and *Children of the Maya*, also focus on issues of importance to Native Americans.

RESPONDING TO *Literature*

THINK • TALK • WRITE

1 What do you like best about Lynn? Explain in your journal.

2 Who teaches Lynn the Navajo ways and beliefs? How does this knowledge help Lynn when she leaves home to go to school?

3 What helps Lynn feel less homesick at the mission school? What does she have in common with the other students at the summer program in Texas?

4 What are some of the difficulties that Lynn faces at the school in Vermont? How does she make the decision to stay?

5 Why does Lynn feel it is important not to "turn into a white person"? How do you think people can keep their heritage while living in the broader American culture?

ACTIVITIES

- **Write About Setting** Imagine that Lynn writes a postcard to her counselor over Christmas vacation. Describe her grandparents' home. What is the hogan made of? Where is the door? Why is the door in that place? What is it like there during the winter?

- **Hold a Folk Tale Festival** Lynn learns traditional Navajo stories from her grandmother. Research tales from other Native American peoples. Choose a favorite, and retell the story at a class folk tale festival. You may wish to use props and costumes.

VOCABULARY PRACTICE

On a separate piece of paper, write the word from the vocabulary list that best completes each sentence.

academic   similarities
preparatory   counselor
awesome

1 Rebecca wants to become a paleontologist because she thinks fossils are _____.

2 She read about a scientist who discovered close _____ between ancient ferns and modern-day plants.

3 Rebecca did so well in all her classes that she won a medal for _____ excellence.

4 She wanted to make sure that she took courses that would be _____ for studying paleontology in college.

5 She asked her school's guidance _____ for advice.

The Mission

San Francisco

good morning
colors
life of mine

good afternoon
laughter
fragrant bread

what's new
people
the latest gossip

sad doors
music
from windows

young faces
riches
of the very poor

one day
I may leave
this place

but el barrio
will never
leave me

La Misión

San Francisco

buenos días
colores
vida mía

buenas tardes
risas
pan de olor

cómo están
gente
mitorera

puertas tristes
música
de ventanas

caras jóvenes
riqueza
de los más pobres

un día
yo puedo dejar
el barrio

pero éste
nunca saldrá
de mí

—Francisco X. Alarcón
translated by Francisco Aragón

SPOT on

AUTOBIOGRAPHY

"I find that I have painted my life—things happening in my life—without knowing," the artist Georgia O'Keeffe once said. As you look at the painting below, think about what it suggests about important people, places, and events in the artist's life.

School's Out *1936 Allan Rohan Crite National Museum of American Art, Washington, D.C.*

Do you think this painting portrays something fictional or something that actually happened? What makes you think so?

Why do you think the artist chose to capture and preserve this scene? What clues might the title of the piece provide?

What sense of time and place does the painting convey? Which details in the setting—if any—leap out at you?

Do you feel as if you have gotten to know the artist at all through this painting? In what ways is this painting like and unlike a scene from an autobiography?

LiGHT

ELEMENTS OF AN AUTOBIOGRAPHY

An autobiography is the true story of a person's life written by that same person. Writers reveal the effects of certain events on their lives. Here are some important elements of autobiographies.

CHARACTERS are well developed in detail and are true-to-life.

SETTING is described vividly.

DETAILS are interesting. Writers of autobiographies use objective and subjective details and anecdotes to tell their life stories.

- *Objective details* can be proved.
- *Subjective details* are based on personal feelings and opinions and cannot be proved.
- *Anecdotes* are short, often humorous, stories that enliven writing and illustrate a point.

CHRONOLOGICAL ORDER is the order in which real-life events occur and the order in which most writers of autobiographies tell their stories. Often events are arranged from childhood to adulthood.

POINT OF VIEW is the perspective from which an autobiography is written. Since autobiographies are written by their subjects, they are told from the *first-person point of view* and use the pronouns *I, me,* and *mine.* Readers experience events through the writers' eyes— knowing only what they think and feel about any given experience.

AUTHOR'S PURPOSE is the author's reason for writing. Authors of autobiographies often want to make sense of events in their lives and to communicate an important personal statement about life. They may also want to give credit to people who influenced them. Controversial individuals often write autobiographies to explain or justify their actions.

In the selections that follow, you will explore autobiographies. Your discoveries will help you to understand and enjoy this important type of literature and to write an autobiographical incident yourself.

AUTOBIOGRAPHY

....

MISS HARRIET'S ROOM

CONNECT TO LITERATURE

What do you remember about your first day of school? Were you frightened by your new surroundings? Were you excited to receive school supplies, such as pencils and scissors? Record your memories in your journal. As you read "Miss Harriet's Room," compare your feelings with those Betsy Byars describes.

INTRODUCTION TO THE MODEL AUTOBIOGRAPHY

In an autobiography, an author writes about real events in his or her life. When you read the autobiographies in this unit, you will find that they are made up of similar elements. For example, each selection includes characterization and the author's purpose, and each is written from a specific point of view.

As you read "Miss Harriet's Room," use the notes in the margin. The notes will help you see the structure of the selection and show you how the basic elements of autobiography are connected to one another. As you read the selection, you might wish to jot down your own thoughts and impressions in your journal.

HAVE YOU EVER?

Have you ever done something that made the world stop turning? In first grade, on the very first day of school, Betsy Byars challenged the principal and the rules of her school. As you read her account of that day, you will see what a big difference a little determination can make.

"Miss Harriet's Room" is one chapter from Byars's autobiography, *The Moon and I.* In this book, the Newbery-winning author combines descriptions of how she writes books with stories of her childhood.

Miss Harriet's Room

BY BETSY BYARS

When I was four, my mother took my sister downtown, and this is what my mother and Nancy came home with:

- A plaid book <u>satchel</u>
- A box of brand-new crayons
- Assorted dark plaid dresses, new brown shoes, new socks, new sweater
- A pencil box with little drawers that opened, and in the drawers were a ruler and a two-sided eraser and pencils and a pencil sharpener and a compass and a lot of other things I didn't know the names of.

My sister was going to school.

---

satchel (sach′əl) *n.* bag or small suitcase for carrying clothing, instruments, books, or other articles.

ILLUSTRATIONS BY MARY NEWELL DEPALMA

Up until this moment I had never had the faintest desire to go to school. I was perfectly content to run wild. Back then there were no preschools or kindergartens, so children generally ran wild until the age of six.

Notice how Byars recreates her thoughts and feelings as a child here and throughout the selection. This is called **point of view.** The point of view in an autobiography is always the author's.

I would have been perfectly content to run wild for the rest of my life if I had not seen the pencil box. I wanted that pencil box. I <u>coveted</u> that pencil box. That pencil box was a symbol of everything that I wanted and was going to have to wait three years to get! Back then, three years was an <u>eternity</u>.

My sister went to school and her teacher's name was Miss Harriet, and my envy of the pencil box was nothing compared to my envy of what went on in Miss Harriet's room.

These details about Miss Harriet's class show what kind of teacher she is. Autobiographies share many elements with fiction, including **characterization,** the author's development of characters.

The kids painted in Miss Harriet's room—and not just pictures. They painted orange crates and furniture, and they had to have one of their father's old shirts to do this painting in. No one in my family had ever been allowed to have one of my father's old shirts—they were sacred—but my sister got one for Miss Harriet's room.

The kids made a store in Miss Harriet's room, and they had to bring little empty boxes to stock the store and purses so that they could go shopping at the store. No one in my family had been allowed to have one of my mother's old purses—they, too, were sacred—but my sister got one for Miss Harriet's room.

Miss Harriet read the kids a book called *The Adventures of Mabel,* and it was the best book in the world—my sister described it to me, chapter

---

coveted (kuv′i tid) *v.t.* eagerly desired (someone else's possession).
eternity (i tûr′ni tē) *n.* seemingly endless length of time.

by chapter, and I looked forward to hearing Miss Harriet read it the way other kids looked forward to the circus.

Well, the three years finally passed, and I was ready for first grade. At last I would have Miss Harriet and make the store and the terrarium—yes, they made one of those, too—and hear *The Adventures of Mabel*. Now I would begin to *live!*

I was herded into the auditorium with the other new students and the principal introduced the teachers, who stood and smiled. We were cautioned to listen very carefully for our names so we could follow our teachers to our rooms.

You could have heard a pin drop.

Mrs. Clark's class was called. Mrs. Clark's class filed out of the auditorium.

Then came Miss Harriet. There was a flurry of anticipation because everyone, it turned out, had heard of and wanted to be in Miss Harriet's room.

The list of her students was called. I waited and waited and waited, but I didn't hear my name.

Miss Harriet's students lined up behind her, and I made a quick decision and lined up along with them. I didn't care what list I was on. I had been waiting three years to be in Miss Harriet's room and I was going to be in Miss Harriet's room. Period.

I took an empty desk in Miss Harriet's room, and in about a half hour the principal and my sister appeared in the doorway.

It had been discovered that I was missing from my assigned room, and it was feared that I had become lost en route. Since my sister was the

The first-person pronoun *I* tells you that author Betsy Byars is relating something that happened to her. The type of writing in which authors tell about events in their own lives is called **autobiography.**

Notice how Byars is revealing something about her own personality in writing about her first teacher. Do you think Byars would be an interesting person to know?

---

terrarium (tə râr′ē əm) *n.* small enclosure or container, often of glass, used for growing plants or raising small land animals, such as snakes, turtles, or lizards.

flurry (flûr′ē) *n.* sudden commotion; stir.

en route (än rüt′) *adv.* on the way.

only one who could identify me, she had to make the search with Miss Blankenship.

"There she is," my sister said.

She pointed. Everyone in the room turned to look at me.

I looked at my desk.

Miss Blankenship came over. She explained in a kind way how much I had worried everyone. This time she herself would accompany me to my room so I wouldn't get lost a second time.

I shook my head regretfully. "I want to be in Miss Harriet's room," I told my desk.

There was a silence.

I corrected my original statement. "I have to be in Miss Harriet's room."

The world stopped turning for a moment. It actually ground to a halt.

Then in this awesome silence, Miss Harriet said, "Oh, let her stay."

"If you're sure . . ." the principal said. She sounded uncertain.

But Miss Harriet was not uncertain at all. "Yes, let her stay."

And with an <u>audible</u> click the world started up again.

That happened more than fifty years ago. Since that time, there have been lots of things in my life that I have looked forward to, only to have them turn out to be disappointments, things that never quite lived up to what I thought they would be, books that didn't turn out as I'd hoped, stories that ended up in the trash can.

But being in Miss Harriet's room was not one of life's disappointments. It was all I had dreamed.

---

audible (ô'də bəl) *adj.* loud enough to be heard.

And when I at last got to hear Miss Harriet read *The Adventures of Mabel,* it was better than anybody had ever read a book before or since.

Miss Harriet loved that book, and when she read it, every kid in the room—even the boys—became Mabel. *We* whistled the Lizard's Call. *We* communicated with wild animals. The frogs lined up on the bridge were there to warn *us* the bridge was about to collapse.

I didn't learn in first grade that I wanted to write books myself, but I did learn something that would prove true my whole life long—a good book, like *The Adventures of Mabel,* is well worth a three-year wait.

Was Byars trying to entertain, inform, or convince her readers of something? The reason for writing is called the **author's purpose.**

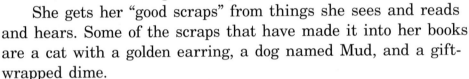

Betsy Byars

After her year in Miss Harriet's room, Betsy Byars (born 1928) grew up to be an award-winning author who has written more than 30 books.

Her formula for a good book is
- a plot with possibilities
- characters to make the plot happen
- a believable setting
- lots and lots of good scraps

She gets her "good scraps" from things she sees and reads and hears. Some of the scraps that have made it into her books are a cat with a golden earring, a dog named Mud, and a gift-wrapped dime.

Byars's readers seem to like her writing formula: She receives about 200 letters a week from children. Her book *The Summer of the Swans* won the Newbery Medal.

More Autobiographies by Writers

- *Homesick: My Own Story* by Jean Fritz (Dell, 1982). Although she was born in China and spent her first twelve years there, Jean Fritz always felt homesick for America, the land she knew only through her grandmother's letters.

- *On the Way Home: The Diary of a Trip from South Dakota to Mansfield, Missouri in 1894* by Laura Ingalls Wilder (Harper Trophy, 1962). Here is a glimpse into the real-life adventures of the author of the "Little House" series as she and her family undertake the arduous journey by wagon to their new farm in the Ozarks.

- *Anonymously Yours* by Richard Peck (Julian Messner, 1991). Richard Peck writes novels about teenagers and their problems. Discover what Peck himself was like growing up as you read his life story.

RESPONDING TO *Literature*

THINK • TALK • WRITE

1 Could you have done what Betsy did on her first day of school? In your journal, tell why or why not.

2 What is the first thing that changes Betsy's attitude about school? Why do you think this appeals to her?

3 What does Nancy do that makes Betsy want to go to school even more? How does Betsy feel about her sister?

4 Why does Betsy decide to go with Miss Harriet's class even though her name wasn't called? Why do you think Miss Harriet lets her stay?

5 Do you agree with Byars that "A good book . . . is well worth a three-year wait"? Why or why not?

ACTIVITY

● **Write About Autobiography** Make two copies of this character-traits web. Complete one for Betsy Byars and one for Miss Harriet.

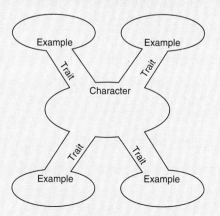

VOCABULARY PRACTICE

On a separate piece of paper, write the letter of the description that best suggests the meaning of the word in color.

1 **satchel**
 a. an item used to hold golf clubs
 b. a bag a teenager might use for textbooks and school supplies
 c. a group of boys on a hiking trip

2 **coveted**
 a. a boy looking jealously at his brother's baseball card collection
 b. a mother proudly watching her daughter take her first steps
 c. a teacher listening attentively to her students' presentations

3 **flurry**
 a. a horse refusing to wade across a stream
 b. a cat sleeping beside a sunny window
 c. a large flock of geese suddenly flying off

4 **audible**
 a. the snoring of an old dog
 b. the opening of a flower
 c. a cloud floating across the sky

5 **eternity**
 a. a girl anxiously awaiting her birthday
 b. a girl racing down a track
 c. a police officer winding her watch

AUTOBIOGRAPHY

TOUCH SYSTEM

CONNECT TO LITERATURE

What are some ways you could save time in your daily routine? For example, some people set out their clothes for school the night before. In your journal, write ideas for saving time and tell what you could do with your extra time. As you read "Touch System," note how the father tries to make the most of time and how the rest of the family reacts.

THINKING ABOUT HUMOR

The authors use humor in telling about their family life. Humor makes the reader or listener laugh. Because the authors' purpose is to show the comic side of a large family, they recount outrageous and funny episodes from their childhood.

Many humorous situations in the selection are ironic, or the opposite of what is expected. Look for the irony in the father's teaching methods as you read each Gilbreth family anecdote.

DID YOU KNOW?

The parents in "Touch System" were efficiency experts—industrial engineers who helped factories speed up production. Mrs. Gilbreth was a psychologist. Mr. Gilbreth specialized in motion study. They often applied these skills in raising their twelve children. One idea was the Family Council, modeled on owner-worker boards at factories. Dad was the chairman. The children, as members, assigned and received chores.

"Touch System" is a chapter from the book *Cheaper by the Dozen*. Written by two of the Gilbreth children, the book chronicles many of the family's true adventures.

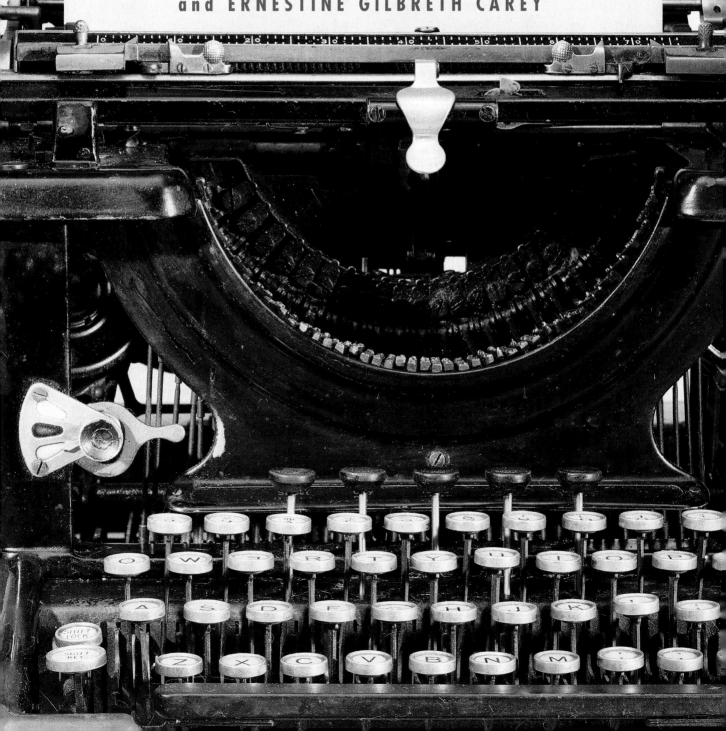

Touch System

by FRANK B. GILBRETH, JR., and ERNESTINE GILBRETH CAREY

Like most of Dad's and Mother's ideas, the Family Council was basically sound and, although it verged sometimes on the hysterical, brought results. Family purchasing committees, duly elected, bought the food, clothes, furniture, and athletic equipment. A utilities committee levied one-cent fines on wasters of water and electricity. A projects committee saw that work was completed as scheduled. Allowances were decided by the Council, which also meted out rewards and punishment. Despite Dad's forebodings, there were no ponies or roadsters.

One purchasing committee found a large department store which gave us wholesale rates on everything from underwear to baseball gloves. Another bought canned goods directly from a manufacturer, in truckload lots.

It was the Council, too, which worked out the system of submitting bids for unusual jobs to be done.

When Lill was eight, she submitted a bid of forty-seven cents to paint a long, high fence in the backyard. Of course it was the lowest bid, and she got the job.

"She's too young to try to paint that fence all by herself," Mother told Dad. "Don't let her do it."

"Nonsense," said Dad. "She's got to learn the value of money and to keep agreements. Let her alone."

Lill, who was saving for a pair of roller skates and wanted the money, kept insisting she could do it.

"If you start it, you'll have to finish it," Dad said.

"I'll finish it, Daddy. I know I can."

"You've got yourself a contract, then."

It took Lill ten days to finish the job, working every day after school and all day weekends. Her hands blistered, and some nights she was so tired she couldn't sleep. It worried Dad so that some nights he didn't sleep very well either. But he made her live up to her contract.

"You've got to let her stop," Mother kept telling him. "She'll have a breakdown or something—or else you will."

"No," said Dad. "She's learning the value of money and she's learning that when you start something it's necessary to finish it if you want to collect. She's got to finish. It's in her contract."

---

levied (lev′ēd) v.t. imposed or collected.
meted (mēt′id) v.t. distributed by or as if by measuring.
forebodings (fôr bō′dingz) n., pl. feelings that something bad is going to happen.
roadsters (rōd′stərz) n., pl. open automobiles with a single seat for two or more people, often with a rumble seat or luggage compartment in the rear.

Roller skate, c. 1920

"You sound like Shylock," Mother said.

But Dad stood firm.

When Lill finally completed the job, she came to Dad in tears.

"It's done," she said. "I hope you're satisfied. Now can I have my forty-seven cents?"

Dad counted out the change.

"Don't cry, honey," he said. "No matter what you think of your old Daddy, he did it for your own good. If you go look under your pillow you'll find that Daddy really loved you all the time."

The present was a pair of roller skates.

Fred headed the utilities committee and collected the fines. Once, just before he went to bed, he found that someone had left a faucet dripping and that there was a bathtub full of hot water. Jack had been asleep for more than an hour, but Fred woke him up.

"Get in there and take a bath," he said.

"But I had a bath just before I went to bed."

"I know you did, and you left the faucet dripping," Fred told him. "Do you want to waste that perfectly good water?"

"Why don't you take a bath?" Jack asked.

"I take my baths in the morning. You know that. That's the schedule."

Jack had two baths that night.

One day Dad came home with two victrolas and two stacks of records. He whistled assembly as he hit the front steps, and we helped him unload.

"Kids," he said, "I have a wonderful surprise. Two victrolas and all these lovely records."

"But we have a victrola, Daddy."

"I know that, but the victrola we have is the downstairs victrola. Now we are going to have two upstairs victrolas. Won't that be fun?"

"Why?"

"Well from now on," said Dad, "we are going to try to do away with unavoidable delay. The victrolas will go in the bathrooms—one in the

---

Shylock (shī′lok′) demanding moneylender in Shakespeare's play *The Merchant of Venice*.

victrolas (vik trō′ləz) *n., pl. Trademark.* early types of record players.

boys' bathroom and the other in the girls' bathroom. I'll bet we'll be the only family in town with a victrola in every bath. And when you are taking a bath, or brushing your teeth, or otherwise occupied, you will play the victrolas."

"Why?"

"Why, why, why," mimicked Dad. "Why this and why that. Does there have to be a why for everything?"

"There doesn't have to be, Daddy," Ernestine explained patiently. "But with you there usually is. When you start talking about unavoidable delay and victrolas, dance music is not the first thing that pops into our minds."

"No," Dad admitted. "It's not dance music. But you're going to find this is just as good in a way, and more educational."

"What kind of records are they?" Anne asked.

"Well," Dad said, "they are very entertaining. They are French and German language lesson records. You don't have to listen to them consciously. Just play them. And they'll finally make an impression."

"Oh, no!"

Dad soon tired of diplomacy and psychology.

"Shut up and listen to me," he roared. "I have spent one hundred and sixty dollars for this equip-

ment. Did I get it for myself? I most emphatically by jingo well did not. I happen already to be able to speak German and French with such fluency that I frequently am mistaken for a native of both of those countries."

This was at best a terribly gross exaggeration, for while Dad had studied languages for most of his adult life, he never had become very familiar with French, although he could stumble along fairly well in German. Usually he insisted that Mother accompany him as an interpreter on his business trips to Europe. Languages came naturally to Mother.

"No," Dad continued, "I did not buy this expensive equipment for myself, although I must say I would like nothing better than to have my own private victrola and my own private language records. I bought it for you, as a present. And you are going to use it. If those two victrolas aren't going every morning from the minute you get up until you come down to breakfast, I'm going to know the reason why."

"One reason," said Bill, "might be that it is impossible to change records while you are in the bathtub."

"A person who applies motion study can be in and out of the tub in the time it takes one record to play."

That was perfectly true. Dad would sit in the tub and put the soap in his right hand. Then he'd place his right hand on his left shoulder and run it down the top of his left arm, back up the bottom of his left arm to his armpit, down his side, down the outside of his left leg, and then up the inside of his left leg. Then he'd change the soap to his left hand and do the same thing to his right side. After a couple of circular strokes on his midsection and his back, and some special attention to his feet and face, he'd duck under for a rinse and get out. He had all the boys in the bathroom several times to demonstrate just how he did it, and he sat in the middle of the living room rug one day, with all his clothes on, to teach the girls.

So there was no more unavoidable delay in the bathroom, and it wasn't long before we were all speaking at least a <u>pidgin</u> variety of French and German. For ten years, the victrolas ground out their lessons on the second floor of our Montclair house. As we became fairly fluent, we often would speak the languages at the dinner table. Dad was left out of the conversation when the talk was in French.

"Your German accents are not so bad," he said. "I can understand most of what you say when you talk German. But your French accents are so atrocious that no one but yourselves could possibly understand you. I believe you've developed some exotic language all your own, which has no more relation to French than it does to Pig Latin."

We giggled, and he turned furiously to Mother.

"Don't you think so, Lillie?"

"Well, dear," she said. "I don't think anyone would mistake them for natives of France, but I can usually make out what they're getting at."

"That," said Dad, with some dignity, "is because you learned your French in this country, where everybody talks with an accent, whereas my knowledge of the language came straight from the streets of Paris."

"Maybe so, dear," said Mother. "Maybe so."

That night, Dad moved the boys' bathroom victrola into his bedroom, and we heard him playing French records, far into the night.

At about the time that he brought home the victrolas, Dad became a consultant to the Remington typewriter company and, through motion study methods,

---

pidgin (pij'ən) *adj.* mixing two or more languages by simplifying grammar and vocabulary, used for communication between people who speak different languages.

helped Remington develop the world's fastest typist.

He told us about it one night at dinner—how he had put little flashing lights on the fingers of the typist and taken moving pictures and <u>time exposures</u> to see just what motions she employed and how those motions could be reduced.

"Anyone can learn to type fast," Dad concluded. "Why I've got a system that will teach touch typing in two weeks. Absolutely guaranteed."

You could see the Great Experiment hatching in his mind.

"In two weeks," he repeated. "Why I could even teach a child to type touch system in two weeks."

"Can you type touch system, Daddy?" Bill asked.

"In two weeks," said Dad. "I could teach a child. Anybody can do it if he will do just exactly what I tell him to do."

The next day he brought home a new, perfectly white typewriter, a gold knife, and an Ingersoll watch. He unwrapped them and put them on the dining room table.

"Can I try the typewriter, Daddy?" asked Mart.

"Why is the typewriter white?" Anne wanted to know.

---

time exposures photographs made by exposing the film for a relatively long period of time, often for several seconds or more.

Victor Victrola, c.1920

"All typewriters I've ever seen were black. It's beautiful, all right, but why is it white?"

"It's white so that it will photograph better," Dad explained. "Also, for some reason, anyone who sees a white typewriter wants to type on it. Don't ask me why. It's psychology."

All of us wanted to use it, but Dad wouldn't let anyone touch it but himself.

"This is an optional experiment," he said. "I believe I can teach the touch system in two weeks. Anyone who wants to learn will be able to practice on the white machine. The one who can type the fastest at the end of two weeks will receive the typewriter as a present. The knife and watch will be prizes awarded on a handicap basis, taking age into consideration."

Except for the two youngest, who still weren't talking, we all said we wanted to learn.

"Can I practice first, Daddy?" Lill asked.

"No one practices until I say 'practice.' Now first I will show you how the typewriter works." Dad got a sheet of paper. "The paper goes in here. You turn this—so-oo. And you push the carriage over to the end of the line—like this."

And Dad, using two fingers, hesitatingly pecked out the first thing that came to his mind—his name.

"Is that the touch system, Daddy?" Bill asked.

"No," said Dad. "I'll show you the touch system in a little while."

"Do you know the touch system, Daddy?"

"Let's say I know how to teach it, Billy boy."

"But do you know it yourself, Daddy?"

"I know how to teach it," Dad shouted. "In two weeks, I can teach it to a child. Do you hear me? I have just finished helping to develop the fastest typist in the world. Do you hear that? They tell me Caruso's voice teacher can't sing a by jingoed note. Does that answer your question?"

"I guess so," said Bill.

"Any other questions?"

There weren't. Dad then brought out some paper diagrams of a typewriter keyboard, and passed one to each of us.

"The first thing you have to do is to memorize that keyboard. QWERTYUIOP. Those are the letters in the top line. Memorize them. Get to know them forward and backwards. Get to know them so you can say them with your eyes closed. Like this."

Caruso's (kə rü′sōz) of Enrico Caruso (1873–1921), celebrated Italian opera singer.

Dad closed his right eye, but kept his left open just a slit so that he could still read the chart.

"QWERTYUIOP. See what I mean? Get to know them in your sleep. That's the first step."

We looked crestfallen.

"I know. You want to try out that white typewriter. Pretty, isn't it?"

He clicked a few keys.

"Runs as smoothly as a watch, doesn't it?"

We said it did.

"Well, tomorrow or the next day you'll be using it. First you have to memorize the keyboard. Then you've got to learn what fingers to use. Then you'll graduate to Moby Dick here. And one of you will win him."

Once we had memorized the keyboard, our fingers were colored with chalk. The little fingers were colored blue, the index fingers red and so forth. Corresponding colors were placed on the key zones of the diagrams. For instance, the Q, A and Z, all of which are hit with the little finger of the left hand, were colored blue to match the blue little finger.

"All you have to do now is practice until each finger has learned the right color habit," Dad said. "And once you've got that, we'll be ready to start."

In two days we were fairly adept at matching the colors on our fingers with the colors on the keyboard diagrams. Ernestine was the fastest, and got the first chance to sit down at the white typewriter. She hitched her chair up to it confidently, while we all gathered around.

"Hey, no fair, Daddy," she wailed. "You've put blank caps on all the keys. I can't see what I'm typing."

Blank caps are fairly common now, but Dad had thought up the idea and had had them made specially by the Remington company.

"You don't have to see," Dad said. "Just imagine that those keys are colored, and type just like you were typing on the diagram."

Ern started slowly, and then picked up speed, as her fingers jumped instinctively from key to key. Dad stood in back of her, with a pencil in one hand and a diagram in the other. Every time she made a mistake, he brought the pencil down on the top of her head.

"Stop it, Daddy. That hurts. I can't concentrate knowing that that pencil's about to descend on my head."

"It's meant to hurt. Your head has to teach your fingers not to make mistakes."

---

crestfallen (krest′fô′lən) *adj.* having had one's feelings or pride hurt.

adept (ə dept′) *adj.* highly skilled; expert.

Ern typed along. About every fifth word, she'd make a mistake and the pencil would descend with a bong. But the bongs became less and less frequent and finally Dad put away the pencil.

"That's fine, Ernie," he said. "I believe I'll keep you."

By the end of the two weeks, all children over six years old and Mother knew the touch system reasonably well. Dad said he knew it, too. We were a long way from being fast—because nothing but practice gives speed—but we were reasonably accurate.

Dad entered Ernestine's name in a national speed contest, as a sort of child prodigy, but Mother talked him out of it and Ern never actually competed.

"It's not that I want to show her off," he told Mother. "It's just that I want to do the people a favor—to show them what can be done with proper instructional methods and motion study."

"I don't think it would be too good an idea, dear," Mother said. "Ernestine is high strung, and the children are conceited enough as it is."

Dad compromised by taking moving pictures of each of us, first with colored fingers practicing on the paper diagrams and then actually

Mr. Gilbreth's stopwatch

working on the typewriter. He said the pictures were "for my files," but about a month later they were released in a newsreel, which showed everything except the pencil descending on our heads. And some of us today recoil every time we touch the backspace key.

Since Dad thought eating was a form of unavoidable delay, he utilized the dinner hour as an instruction period. His primary rule was that no one could talk unless the subject was of general interest.

Dad was the one who decided what subjects were of general interest. Since he was convinced that everything he uttered was interesting, the rest of the family had trouble getting a word in edgewise.

prodigy (prod'i jē) *n.* extremely gifted or talented person, especially a child.

recoil (ri koil') *v.i.* draw or shrink back, as in fear, horror, or surprise.

"Honestly, we have the stupidest boy in our history class," Anne would begin.

"Is he cute?" Ernestine asked.

"Not of general interest," Dad roared.

"I'm interested," Mart said.

"But I," Dad announced, "am bored stiff. Now if Anne had seen a two-headed boy in history class, that would have been of general interest."

Usually at the start of a meal, while Mother served up the plates at one end of the table, Dad served up the day's topic of conversation at the other end.

"I met an engineer today who had just returned from India," he said. "What do you think he told me? He believes India has fewer industries for its size than has any other country in the world."

We knew, then, that for the duration of that particular meal even the dullest facts about India would be <u>deemed</u> of exceptional general interest; whereas neighboring Siam, Persia, China, and Mongolia would, for some reason, be considered of but slight general interest, and events which had transpired in Montclair, New Jersey, would be deemed of no interest whatsoever. Once India had been selected as the destination, Dad would head toward it as relentlessly as if Garcia were waiting there, and we had the message.

Sometimes, the topic of conversation was a motion study project, such as clearing off the dishes from the table. Motion study was always of great general interest.

"Is it better to stack the dishes on the table, so that you can carry out a big pile?" Dad asked. "Or is it better to take a few of them at a time into the butler's pantry, where you can rinse them while you stack? After dinner we'll divide the table into two parts, and try one method on one part and the other method on the other. I'll time you."

Also of exceptional general interest was a series of tricks whereby Dad could multiply large numbers in his head, without using pencil and paper. The explanation of how the tricks are worked is too complicated to explain in detail here, and two fairly elementary examples should suffice.

1. To multiply forty-six times forty-six, you figure how much greater forty-six is than twenty-five. The answer is twenty-one. Then you figure how much less forty-six is than fifty. The answer is four. You can square the four and get sixteen. You put the twenty-one and the sixteen together, and the answer is twenty-one sixteen, or 2,116.

---

deemed (dēmd) *v.t.* thought; believed; judged.

2. To multiply forty-four times forty-four, you figure how much greater forty-four is than twenty-five. The answer is nineteen. Then you figure how much less forty-four is than fifty. The answer is six. You square the six and get thirty-six. You put the nineteen and the thirty-six together, and the answer is nineteen thirty-six, or 1,936.

"I want to teach all of you how to multiply two-digit numbers in your head," Dad announced at dinner.

"Not of general interest," said Anne.

"Now if you had learned to multiply a two-digit number by a two-headed calf," Ern suggested.

"Those who do not think it is of general interest may leave the table and go to their rooms," Dad said coldly, "and I understand there is apple pie for dessert."

Nobody left.

"Since everyone now appears to be interested," said Dad, "I will explain how it's done."

It was a complicated thing for children to understand, and it involved memorizing the squares of all numbers up to twenty-five. But Dad took it slowly, and within a couple of months the older children had learned all the tricks involved.

While Mother carved and served the plates—Dad sometimes carved wood for a hobby, but he never touched a carving knife at the table—Dad would shout out problems in mental arithmetic for us.

"Nineteen times seventeen."

"Three twenty-three."

"Right. Good boy, Bill."

"Fifty-two times fifty-two."

"Twenty-seven zero four."

"Right. Good girl, Martha."

Dan was five when this was going on, and Jack was three. One night at supper, Dad was firing questions at Dan on the squares of numbers up to twenty-five. This involved straight memory, and no mental arithmetic.

"Fifteen times fifteen," said Dad.

"Two twenty-five," said Dan.

"Sixteen times sixteen," said Dad.

Jack, sitting in his high chair next to Mother, gave the answer. "Two fifty-six."

At first Dad was irritated, because he thought one of the older children was butting in.

"I'm asking Dan," he said, "you older children stop showing off and . . ." Then he registered a double take.

"What did you say, Jackie boy?" Dad cooed.

"Two fifty-six."

Dad drew a nickel out of his pocket and grew very serious.

"Have you been memorizing the squares as I asked the questions to the older children, Jackie?"

Jack didn't know whether that was good or bad, but he nodded.

"If you can tell me what seventeen times seventeen is, Jackie boy, this nickel is yours."

"Sure, Daddy," said Jack. "Two eighty-nine."

Dad passed him the nickel and turned beaming to Mother.

"Lillie," he said, "we'd better keep that boy, too."

Martha, at eleven, became the fastest in the family at mental mathematics. Still feeling frustrated because he hadn't been able to take Ernestine to the speed typing contest, Dad insisted on taking Martha to an adding machine exhibition in New York.

"No, Lillie," he told Mother. "This one is not high strung. I was willing to compromise on moving pictures of the typing, but you can't take movies of this. She goes to New York with me."

Martha stood up on a platform at the adding machine show, and answered the problems quicker than the calculators could operate. Dad, of course, stood alongside her. After the final applause, he told the assemblage modestly:

"There's really nothing to it. I've got a boy named Jack at home who's almost as good as she is. I would have brought him here with me, but Mrs. Gilbreth said he's still too young. Maybe next year, when he's four . . ."

By this time, all of us had begun to suspect that Dad had his points as a teacher, and that he knew what he was talking about. There was one time, though, when he failed.

"Tomorrow," he told us at dinner, "I'm going to make a cement bird bath. All those who want to watch me should come home right after school, and we'll make it in the late afternoon."

Dad had long since given up general contracting, to devote all of his time to scientific management and motion study, but we knew he had been an expert bricklayer and had written a book on reinforced concrete.

The next afternoon he built a mold, mixed his concrete confidently, and poured his bird bath.

"We'll let it set for awhile, and then take the mold off," he said.

Dad had to go out of town for a few weeks. When he returned, he changed into old clothes,

---

assemblage (ə sem'blij) *n.* gathering of persons.

whistled assembly, and led us out into the yard.

"I've had this bird bath on my mind all the time I was away," he said. "It should be good and hard now."

"Will the birds come and take a bath in it, Daddy?" Fred asked.

"I would say, Freddy, that birds will come for miles to take a bath in it. Indeed, on Saturday nights I would say the birds will be standing in line to use our lovely bathtub."

He leaned over the mold. "Stand back, everybody," he said. "We will now unveil the masterpiece. Get your towels ready, little birdies, it's almost bathing time."

We stood hushed and waiting. But as he lifted the bird bath out of the mold, there was an unbelievable grating sound, and a pile of dust and rubble lay at our feet. Dad stood deflated and silent. He took it so seriously that we felt sorry for him.

"Never mind, Daddy," Lill said. "We know you tried, anyway."

"Bill," Dad said sternly. "Did you?"

"Did I what, Daddy?"

"Did you touch my bird bath?"

"No, Daddy, honest."

Dad reached down and picked up some of the concrete. It crumbled into dust between his fingers.

"Too much sand," he muttered. And then to Bill. "No, it's my fault. Too much sand. I know you didn't touch it, and I'm sorry I <u>implied</u> that you did."

But you couldn't keep Dad down for long.

"Well," he said, "that didn't work out so very well. But I've built some of the finest and tallest buildings in the whole world. And some bridges and roads and canals that stretch for miles and miles."

"Is a bird bath harder to build than a tall building, Daddy?" asked Dan.

Dad, deflated all over again, kicked the rubble with his toe and started toward the house.

"Too much sand," he muttered.

---

implied (im plīd′) *v.t.* suggested or expressed indirectly.

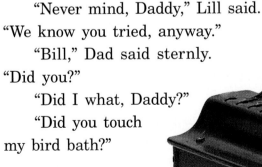

Comptometer adding machine, c.1920

Frank B. Gilbreth, Jr., and Ernestine Gilbreth Carey

With the publication of *Cheaper by the Dozen,* the Gilbreth family became an American legend. The book portrays life with "Dad" Gilbreth, an efficiency expert who used his 12 children as guinea pigs to test his "motion study" theories. Life with a dozen children was always interesting and often hilarious. More than once, the family was mistaken for an orphanage on an outing.

Gilbreth family, 1923. Frank, Jr., is third from top left; Ernestine is third from top right.

Over three million copies of the book have been sold, and in 1950 it was made into a movie. The authors, Frank B. Gilbreth, Jr. (born 1911), and Ernestine Gilbreth Carey (born 1908), also wrote a best-selling sequel, *Belles on Their Toes.* When not writing, Ernestine Carey was a buyer for a department store, and Frank Gilbreth, Jr., worked as a newspaper reporter and publisher.

More Autobiographies About Living and Learning

- *Belles on Their Toes* by Frank B. Gilbreth, Jr., and Ernestine Gilbreth Carey (Bantam Books, 1984). Take another peek at the antics of the Gilbreth family in this hilarious sequel.

- *Bill Peet: An Autobiography* by Bill Peet (Houghton Mifflin, 1989). Bill Peet grew up with a pencil in his hand. Here he tells how he became the top writer-illustrator on many of Disney's best-loved films and a popular author of picture books.

- *My Life with the Chimpanzees* by Jane Goodall (Pocket Books, 1988). Through fierce determination, Jane Goodall achieved her dream—to become a naturalist. This is the story of her adventures in Africa studying chimpanzees.

RESPONDING TO *Literature*

1 Would you like to read the rest of *Cheaper By The Dozen*? Explain in your journal.

2 Why does Dad insist that Lill finish painting the fence? What would you have done in his situation?

3 Why does Dad want to teach the children the touch system? What is ironic about his role as teacher?

4 What would you like about being in a family of twelve children? What would you not like?

5 Mr. Gilbreth went to very unusual lengths to make sure his children learned French and German. Do you agree it is important to learn other languages? Why or why not?

ACTIVITIES

- **Write About Humor** The authors of "Touch System" write brief stories, or anecdotes, describing their father's actions. Think of a relative or friend you love and admire. Write about something funny this person did that reveals his or her personality.

- **Role-playing** With a group of classmates, act out an imaginary dinner table discussion at the Gilbreths'. Choose parts to play, such as Dad, Mother, Ernestine, Lill, Fred, or Martha.

VOCABULARY PRACTICE

On a separate piece of paper, write the vocabulary word that best substitutes for the italicized word or phrase.

levied	prodigy
adept	deemed
meted	recoil
forebodings	implied
crestfallen	assemblage

1 Isabel is *highly skilled* at writing.

2 Michael is such a *gifted child* that he helps the teacher with problems.

3 Bianca *measured* out baking powder to other students in the lab.

4 The bang that ended the experiment made Jon *jump back.*

5 The librarian *collected* fines for overdue books.

6 In the auditorium, Nilda recited her poem to the *group of people.*

7 She also read a work by Pablo Neruda, who is *thought* to be one of the greatest poets of this century.

8 The group's silence *suggested* they were paying close attention.

9 The crackling loudspeaker gave Joseph strong *feelings that something bad might happen.*

10 Danielle was *dejected* when she only got a 70 on the math test.

AUTOBIOGRAPHY

STARS COME OUT WITHIN

CONNECT TO LITERATURE

What are some ways you can help people around you? In your journal, list some things young people can do to help others, such as carrying packages for an elderly neighbor or teaching a child to shoot baskets. As you read "Stars Come Out Within," note the different ways the children and teacher help each other.

THINKING ABOUT DESCRIPTIVE DETAILS

Descriptive details are pieces of information that help the reader imagine people, places, and events. These details often appeal to a variety of senses. In this selection, Jean Little provides very specific information about her students. Little's descriptions help readers feel as if they are actually in the classroom where much of the action occurs. Since the selection is part of an autobiography, the author also describes her own thoughts and feelings in detail.

HAVE YOU EVER?

Have you ever wanted to learn about jobs where you can help people? You will read about several jobs like that in this selection. A physiotherapist, or physical therapist, treats injured or disabled people by giving them massages and helping them do exercises. This treatment can increase a person's ability to move around as well as lessen pain. An occupational therapist helps a disabled person learn skills for daily living, such as getting around in a wheelchair. In this excerpt, the opening chapter of her autobiography *Stars Come Out Within,* Jean Little discusses another career that can make other people's lives better: being an author!

STARS
COME OUT
WITHIN
■ ■ ■ ■ ■ ■

by JEAN LITTLE

"Jeanie," Rose Vanderweit, the nursing assistant at the Crippled Children's Centre, shrieked. "Look at your shoes! You've got on one blue and one brown."

"Stop teasing," I said and looked down at my feet. Even I could not have come to school on my very first teaching day wearing mismatched shoes.

She was right. I had dressed in the dark, hoping to fool myself into believing that I need not go through this first day of being a schoolteacher. Groping for my shoes, I had forgotten that my brown Brevitts had been so comfortable, I had recently bought a twin pair in blue.

If only I had begun teaching in September like everyone else! Then the sun would have been up before me. But it had taken me all fall to find my students, explain the program to their families and transform the great empty space at the Guelph Crippled Children's Centre into a well-equipped and welcoming classroom.

"In winter, I get up at night," Robert Louis Stevenson had written in *A Child's Garden of Verses*. He was not the only one. But why hadn't Mother checked me over? I raced to the phone.

"I'll be right there," said my <u>repentant</u> parent.

I hung up, praying that the children would be late. God was not listening. Before Mother could possibly have had time to drive across town, I heard the first carload pulling up. Rose laughed as I tucked one foot behind the other and swivelled to face the door, feeling far more crippled than any of the five boys I was about to welcome.

In they came—Clifford, Billy and Max on crutches, Barry walking with the painful slowness of a child with muscular dystrophy and, last in line, five-year-old Alec with his wild ataxic stagger. Automatically stepping forward to catch hold of him, I forgot my odd shoes. Like Bill and Clifford, he had cerebral palsy but could not balance well enough to walk without help. As I grabbed his flailing arms and supported him, he looked up at me.

He was a funny-looking little boy. Except for one rebellious <u>cowlick</u>, his sandy hair flopped down over his forehead. His ears stuck straight out like cup handles. He was skinny, all sharp elbows and

---

repentant (ri pen'tənt) *adj.* feeling, showing, or marked by sorrow or regret.

cowlick (kou'lik') *n.* tuft of hair that grows in a different direction from the rest of the hair and will not lie flat.

spindly, spidery legs. His eyes, raised to meet mine, looked serious.

Then he smiled. It was like the sun coming up over the edge of the world and flooding the land with light.

"Good morning, Miss Little," he said.

Miss Little! The respect he put into that simple title changed me. His words struck exactly the ceremonious note I needed. This five-year-old with a smile like sunrise knew who I was. I was not a scared twenty-six-year-old who was certain she was going to forget "God Save the Queen." I was his teacher.

I unwound his long scarf and helped him out of his coat. As I got him settled in his desk, Mother arrived with my other brown shoe. I jammed it on my foot with all the children watching.

"I can't see well," I heard myself telling them, "and this morning I didn't turn on the light when I was getting dressed . . ."

Mother left. The boys sized me up. Then they laughed. But their laughter was kind. They, too, often had difficulty dressing.

Clifford cleared his throat. Blushing scarlet, he said, "If you don't mind my asking, Miss Little, what happened to your eyes?"

Soft-hearted Billy tried to shush him, but the rest waited for my reaction. It was right that they should be told. After all, I knew all about them, didn't I?

"I don't mind," I patted Bill's shoulder. He beamed up at me. Alec's smile had been like sunrise; Billy's was like high noon.

"I was born blind," I said.

They gasped. Blind!

"But I don't remember being blind," I continued.

"Did you have an operation?" they asked. They knew about operations. Each of them had spent time in doctors' offices and hospitals. All knew kids who had been helped by surgery.

"No operation," I said. "My eyes were scarred somehow before I was born. Nobody knows exactly how. But after I was born, the scars shrank a bit and my eyes grew so that before I turned two, my parents realized I was starting to see after all."

"They must have been happy," Max commented. He sounded interested but a little impatient. He wanted to start learning.

"Why . . . well, what I mean is . . . your eyes . . . ?" Cliff struggled to ask why I was cross-eyed, but could not find polite words.

"My eyes cross because I only use one at a time," I explained. "I can't look through both at once. One of my pupils, the little black holes you see through, is higher than the other so the pictures they make are too different to fuse into one."

They looked puzzled, so I drew a diagram of the human eye on the board. Part of my mind was telling me that we had not yet sung "God Save the Queen." But the teacher I was becoming dismissed the rigidity of schedules. Everyone in my class was learning plenty, even Max. We'd get around to the Queen.

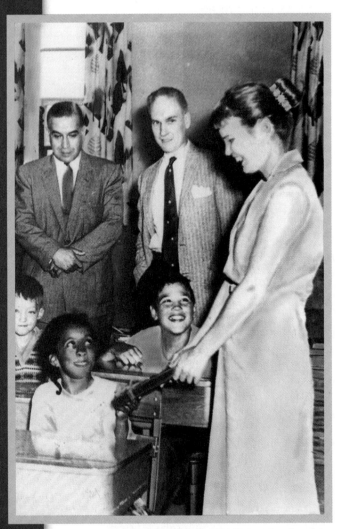

Jean receiving a good-bye gift from her first class

"So," I finished, "when I use my right eye, it sees you, but my left one, which I'm not using, slides over by my nose and waits till I need it. I can switch back and forth. Watch."

As I looked through one eye and then the other, they first stared and then giggled. Barry spoke up for the first time.

"Your eyes sort of . . . jiggle," he observed. "I mean, even when you are looking at us, the one eye kind of . . . keeps wobbling."

A positive shriek of laughter greeted this perfectly accurate observation. I nodded at Barry.

"That's called nystagmus," I told him. "The proper word for 'crossed eyes' is strabismus."

---

rigidity (ri jid´i tē) *n.* state of being fixed, not changing.

I remembered being a disabled child. It had helped me a lot to learn the clinical terms that described my condition. Did these boys know how to tell others about their diagnoses? I asked them.

Max did. He had not had Legg Perthes for long. The others had heard the words "cerebral palsy" and "muscular dystrophy" but could not pronounce them correctly or use them with confidence. I taught each child an impressive string of diagnostic terms to use when he needed them. They were enchanted with this accomplishment.

Billy, for instance, was soon able to rhyme off, "I have cerebral palsy. I'm a spastic quadriplegic."

Later I myself heard Barry silence a couple of insensitive student nurses who were speculating in loud whispers about what ailed him. "I have childhood muscular dystrophy," he informed them. "There's no cure for it yet but they are doing research."

"Miss Little, how far can you see?" Alec asked.

"I can see as far as the sun," I said solemnly. Then I told him what he really wanted to know. "I can see the same things you can—the walls, the windows, you, Rose, the easel. But I can't tell what colour your eyes are. I can see trees out that window, but I can't see separate leaves. I can read, but only if I hold the book up close. When I was a little girl, my mum was always sending me to wash the printer's ink off my nose—especially if I'd been reading comic books."

At last I began trying to follow my carefully prepared lesson plans. But before we embarked on the curriculum, my five students had learned dignified adult words with which to talk about themselves, and they had discovered that they were not the only people with disabilities. And I had found that some of the best teaching is done when you are following your instinct rather than the lessons you spent so much time preparing. I had also seen a boy whom I had been informed had "only a 40 I.Q." memorize the medical terminology for his disability without effort.

The boys now felt free to share with me the embarrassing moments they had experienced. They also began watching for opportunities to help me. It soon became clear that while they needed me to help them move about the room or use their hands, I needed them to find what I lost and see what I missed.

Children came and went at the Centre. Max recovered from his crippling condition and departed. Others went to hospital for surgery and then returned. Finally a girl joined the class. Some of the kids progressed slowly towards greater independence. Barry, and later his younger brother, Randy, had to live with a progressive disease that made them steadily weaker.

"It must be so depressing teaching those poor kids," people who did not know them often said. "I don't see how you bear it."

But I was not teaching "those poor kids"; I was working with Billy, Ellen, Cliff, Barry and Alec. I lost my temper at them. I laughed with them. I taught them songs and stories. I tripped over their crutches. I helped them earn enough money to buy two guinea pigs and took them to the pet store to choose them. We flew kites and went to the circus, the zoo, a hockey game and a fall fair. We took bus and train rides. I invented a dangerous but exciting game called Crutch Ball. I worked hard at teaching them to read. They corrected my arithmetic. We were too busy to get depressed.

Since Alec was ataxic, his sense of balance was faulty. He would pull himself to his feet, aim his body at a chair or bookcase and launch himself through space. He would go <u>careening</u> across to it, waving his arms wildly and, just in time, clutch at its support. When he did not quite make it he went sprawling, but he was prac- tised at falling and never did himself lasting damage.

Every day Rose would take each of the kids out of class to physio- and occupational therapy. There they would do a succession of exercises to help them gain <u>mobility</u> and some daily living skills. In Alec's case they worked on his sense of balance. One afternoon he asked the <u>physiotherapist</u> when he could begin to use crutches. She said he could start to practise balancing that very day, found him crutches that fitted him and stood him correctly with one under each armpit.

"Now just stand and get used to them for a bit," she said, turning to another task. "You'll need lots of practise."

---

careening (kə rēn′ing) *v.i.* swaying from side to side while moving quickly; lurching.
mobility (mō bil′i tē) *n.* quality of being able to move.
physiotherapist (fiz′ē ō ther′ə pist) *n.* person who treats disease or injury by physical methods, such as heat, massage, or exercise.

When she next turned around, Alec was walking away, moving his left foot and his right crutch together and then, the next moment, swinging his right crutch and his left foot forward. He had not studied Clifford and Billy for nothing. She gawked at him and then rushed to call the rest of us.

In seconds, all of us who could get there were in the hall watching the miracle. It was not a cure, but it seemed every bit as dramatic and splendid to us. It was Alec's first experience of being in control of his own mobility. Never again would he have to depend on convenient pieces of furniture and outstretched hands. Alec, before our eyes, was taking his first true steps. From now on, if he could complete this journey, he would be choosing his own path. Slowly and steadily, with immense concentration, he came swinging down the long hall towards the classroom.

"See the beads of sweat on his forehead," somebody whispered.

When he reached the door, the children still in their desks cheered. Even Barry, who had been walking when he came to the Centre but was now in a wheelchair, was beaming.

"Hey, Alec," he called, "that's showing them, boy!"

Alec did not turn his head or even smile. He was concentrating every muscle, every nerve, every thought on this immense undertaking. When he finally reached his own desk, he swivelled his body, carefully lowered himself onto the seat and took his two crutches and stowed them out of harm's way on the floor. He gave a tired sigh and, finally, looked at our exultant faces. Self-conscious though it was, his grin left me dazzled.

"You're shaking, Alec," said Margaret Bryant, Rose's replacement.

"So would you be if you'd done what he's just done," the therapist told her. She blew her nose like a trumpet.

She was not the only one whose eyes were wet.

After school we all crammed into the therapist's car and went home with Alec. Before she honked the horn to let his mother know we had arrived, we stood him up with a crutch under each arm. As his mother came out onto the doorstep, she saw her son come walking up the sidewalk, on his own two feet for the first time in his life.

---

gawked (gôkt) *v.i. Informal.* stared stupidly; gaped.

Mrs. Arnett took one look at him, gave a strangled sob and sat down hard on the step. Then, not caring if all the world saw her, she buried her face in her hands and burst into tears. Once again the kids were cheering. Once again we adults were fishing in our pockets for Kleenexes.

I had begun to teach with very little training. After nearly three years of teaching, I took some time off to become fully qualified. Before returning to the Centre I wrote the first draft of a children's book called *Mine for Keeps.* It was the story of ten-year-old Sally Copeland who happened to have cerebral palsy.

I wanted to try writing a novel. My students loved Anne Shirley of Green Gables, Pooh and Piglet, Henry Huggins of Klickitat Street, Heidi, and Dorothy and Toto of Oz. Yet I felt strongly that somewhere among this throng of beloved heroes and heroines there should be at least one thoroughly real child who had to use crutches or was in a wheelchair like my kids. I had found a few disabled fictional children: Jimmy Bean in *Pollyanna,* Clara in *Heidi,* Prince Dolor in *The Little Lame Prince,* invalidish Carol Bird in *The Birds' Christmas Carol.* But my class and I had discovered that in almost every case, boys and girls who started out crippled invariably ended up either dying like Beth in *Little Women* or being cured miraculously like Colin Craven in *The Secret Garden.* The kids were puzzled by these outcomes. I thought them insulting. Why couldn't any of these authors imagine a happy ending that was honest? Did they, deep down, believe that you could not remain disabled and have a full, joyful life? If that was it, they were crazy. *Mine for Keeps,* with Sally still on crutches at the finish, was my answer to their lack of imagination.

I returned to teach at the Centre, but I continued working on my book when I could. Once it was done, I entered it in the Little, Brown Canadian Children's Book Competition.

Then, while I waited for results, I worked both at teaching and at preparing myself for the inevitable rejection letter. Every writer I had read about had insisted that no first book gets accepted on its initial trip to a publisher's office. Even Dr. Seuss, a great favourite with my students, was said to have had his first book turned down more than twenty times.

Yet no matter how I tried not to hope, an <u>intrepid</u> little voice inside me kept saying, "It's good. Even if they don't give it the prize, they might take it if you agree to do more work."

In May the letter came. They not only wanted to publish it; they were actually giving me the money!

The morning after this bombshell struck, I had a hard time keeping my mind on teaching. As I assigned pages of arithmetic and heard my scholars read, I kept staring into space and smiling goofily. The children, who had heard the story in manuscript and who had seen the incredible letter now in my pocket, exchanged amused glances as I overlooked blatant errors.

"Four nines are twenty-seven," Janice said.

"Very good, Janice," I replied dreamily.

When the older children exploded into peals of laughter, I was taken completely by surprise. As the little ones joined in, I replayed the exchange and felt my cheeks grow pink.

Should I claim I had done it on purpose, just to see whether they were alert? One look at their <u>gleeful</u> faces told me that, this time, they could not be hoodwinked.

Jean with her mother

"Put your work away," I said with dignity. "It's lunchtime."

After lunch, Margaret helped me unstack the canvas cots and get the kids onto them. Then the children quieted, waiting for me to start reading a new book.

---

intrepid (in trep′id) *adj.* having or showing no fear; courageous; fearless.
gleeful (glē′fəl) *adj.* merry; joyous.

Even though they ranged in age from six to thirteen, I read aloud to the whole group every day at this hour. This was supposed to take about thirty minutes but had been known to stretch to an hour on days when a good story had us in its grip.

The day before we had finished the last Mary Poppins story.

Even knowing how much the kids enjoyed all kinds of books, I had been astonished by their devotion to P. L. Travers' redoubtable magic nanny. When I had finished reading the first book about this personage, they had insisted on going on to its sequels. And the day before, when I had closed *Mary Poppins Opens the Door* and had had to tell them that there were no more books about her, Alec had flabbergasted everyone by beginning to cry.

Janice had saved the day. "Miss Little, Mary Poppins bought a Return Ticket," she had said. "You only do that if you're coming back."

"That's true," I had said gratefully.

"The lady is probably working on another book right this minute," Laurie had put in.

Nobody mentioned Mary Poppins now; nobody looked at Alec. Yet I could feel their <u>wistfulness</u>. They wanted that faraway, adventure-filled, yet totally safe world.

I myself could hardly wait to begin sharing *Warrior Scarlet* by Rosemary Sutcliff with them. The week before, I had stayed up half the night reading it. She, too, had written about a disabled kid who remained handicapped to the end. I was certain that my class, as they listened, would share my sense of affirmation. The Bronze Age hero, Drem, has one useless arm. My kids had far more in common with him than they did with Mary Poppins.

The language was not easy for them to grasp at first. Even when Drem's grandfather barked, "Think you the young one will ever win his way into the Men's Side, with a spear arm that he cannot use?" most of the kids missed the meaning of his speech. I did not stop to explain. They would catch on before long.

They remained dreamy, drowsy, until we came to these words:

> . . . *he looked at his right arm as though he had never*
> *seen it before: his spear arm that he could not use,*

---

wistfulness (wist′fəl nes) *n.* quality of sad longing or yearning.

the Grandfather had said. It was thinner than his left, and somehow brittle-looking, as though it might snap like a dry stick. He felt it exploringly with his left hand. It was queer, like something that did not quite belong to him. He had always known, of course—when he thought about it at all—that he couldn't use that arm, but it hadn't seemed important. He held things in his teeth and he held things between his knees, and he managed well enough without it. . . .

"It's like Paddy's," someone whispered. I paused <u>momentarily</u> and looked at the children. Six-year-old Paddy, who did indeed have just such an arm, was sitting up straight by the time I finished. Brian was feeling his crippled hand, checking to see if it felt like Drem's. Nobody interrupted but not one of them was sleepy any longer. My class had taken on Drem's fight for <u>acceptance</u>, recognizing it as their own. When Drem failed his wolf-slaying, the entire class was sniffling. When, later, he did win his Warrior Scarlet, every child in the room triumphed with him.

Walking home that night, I thought about Janice's faith in Mary Poppins' Return Ticket. Would children ever hope I was writing a sequel? Would they want another book about the Copelands?

That mattered far more to me than the one-thousand-dollar prize. I hoped some day to give up teaching to become a writer. Some people managed to combine the jobs, but I knew that I could not. Each needed my full attention, my whole heart, all my skill.

But how would the children I so loved get along without me?

I had it backwards. My students, like Drem, were tough as well as <u>vulnerable</u>. They would survive and, even, triumph.

The real question was how would I get along without them. Just the thought of leaving them made my heart ache.

I did not yet know that they would never desert me, that one or more of them would sneak into every book I would some day write, that every one of my students was mine for keeps.

---

momentarily (mō′mən ter′ə lē) *adv.* briefly; for a short time.
acceptance (ak sep′təns) *n.* approval; favorable reception.
vulnerable (vul′nər ə bəl) *adj.* sensitive; easily hurt.

JEAN LITTLE

Jean (bottom right) with her family in Taiwan

When Jean Little (born 1932) was teaching disabled children, she thought about her own childhood as a person with limited vision. "Remembering how I had never found a cross-eyed heroine in a book, I decided to search for books about children with motor handicaps," she wrote in her memoir *Little by Little.* Not finding any appropriate novels, she wrote *Mine for Keeps,* an unsentimental portrait of a girl with cerebral palsy. The book launched her writing career. Little has written eighteen books and won many awards, including the Canadian Children's Book Award and the Vicky Metcalf Award.

Jean Little was born in Taiwan but grew up in Canada in a large and supportive family.

More Autobiographies About Overcoming Difficulties

- *Zlata's Diary: A Child's Life in Sarajevo* by Zlata Filipović (Viking Penguin, 1994). When Zlata begins her diary, she is an average eleven-year-old schoolgirl. Then war breaks out in Bosnia, and, for the next two years (until she and her parents flee to Paris), Zlata describes the unsettling effects of the war on her life.

- *Rosa Parks: My Story* by Rosa Parks with Jim Haskins (Dial Books, 1992). When she refused to give up her seat on an Alabama bus, Rosa Parks sparked the civil rights movement. But there is more to her story than this one incident, and Parks relates it in a straightforward and dramatic manner.

- *Voices from the Fields: Children of Migrant Farmworkers Tell Their Stories,* interviews and photographs by S. Beth Atkin (Little, Brown, 1993). In their own words, Mexican-American children of migrant farmworkers describe the hardships and the happy times their families experience as they follow the harvests across the land.

RESPONDING TO Literature

THINK • TALK • WRITE

1 Which character in the selection do you like the most? Why?

2 Why is the teacher nervous at the beginning of the selection? How do her students help put her at ease?

3 What do Jean and her class talk about on the first morning? Why is this conversation important to them?

4 Why does learning to use crutches improve Alec's life? Which details help bring this scene to life?

5 What does Jean Little object to in the literature she reads that includes disabled characters? Why does she write *Mine for Keeps*?

ACTIVITIES

- **Write with Descriptive Details** Write a letter to a friend in which you describe a classmate—what the person looks like and what his or her interests are. Tell something the person said or did that shows what he or she is like. Use details that appeal to all five senses.

- **Make a Diagram** On her first day of teaching, Jean Little drew a diagram to show how the human eye works. Research how something you are interested in works. Then make a diagram. For example, you might show how magnets attract, or teach the five positions in ballet.

VOCABULARY PRACTICE

On a separate piece of paper, write the letter of the word that is most similar in meaning to the colored word.

1 repentant
  a. apparent **b.** sorry **c.** forgiving

2 rigidity
  a. force **b.** sweetness **c.** firmness

3 careening
  a. swimming **b.** flying **c.** lurching

4 mobility
  a. society **b.** moveability
  c. moderation

5 gawked
  a. tripped **b.** gaped **c.** walked

6 intrepid
  a. afraid **b.** fearless **c.** unfriendly

7 momentarily
  a. certainly **b.** briefly **c.** mistakenly

8 wistfulness
  a. lightness **b.** mysterious
  c. longing

9 acceptance
  a. reject **b.** approval **c.** accusation

10 vulnerable
  a. sensitive **b.** vivid **c.** angry

WRITING

You can learn even from bad experiences! Choose one memorable experience as the subject of an autobiographical incident.

PREWRITE

How will you approach your incident? Think of an unforgettable incident in your life. Was it funny? Frightening? What tone will you use to describe it? Jot down some notes in your writer's journal.

Once you have your incident, you might want to map it out on a storyboard like this one:

Now it's time to pull together your prewriting notes. Try to organize them into a storyboard.

Beginning

baseball finals and my birthday

Problem

thunderstorm

Events

baseball finals canceled

Complication

Mom got wrong present sent by mistake

Ending

surprise visit from my cousin Rick, who is a professional baseball player

DRAFT

Read the beginning of the draft of this writer's incident. Does it make you want to find out what will happen next? Discuss your reactions with your friends.

Beginning your incident with a question for your readers will grab their attention immediately. ----------▶

Rainy-Day Birthday

How would you feel if your birth day and your favorite sports event got rained out? When I climbed out of bed on my birthday disappointment was the last thing that I'd bargained for.

Begin *your* incident now. Don't be afraid to change your writing plans as other thoughts occur to you.

110

AUTOBIOGRAPHY

REVISE

Look closely at your draft. How can you improve its tone or make it more vivid? The writer of our sample wanted readers to share the character's emotions right away.

The writer adds the first phrase to make the question more precise. Does adding the second phrase give an idea of the writer's emotions? - - - - - - - - →

> How would you feel if your birth day
>
> and your favorite sports event got
>   *at the same time   scrambled joyously*
> rained out? When I ~~climbed~~ out of bed
>
> on my birthday disappointment was
>
> the last thing that I'd bargained for.

It's time to revise your own draft. Does each event lead to the next? Are feelings and events clearly expressed?

PROOFREAD

Study the writer's proofreading corrections. Did you notice the mistakes before the corrections were made?

A computer's spell checker won't - - - - - - - - → catch this error, but it is a handy writer's tool. Use this computer function if you like. But reread your piece carefully, looking for errors the computer has missed.

> How would you feel if your birth day
>
> and your favorite sports event got
>   *at the same time   scrambled joyously*
> rained out? When I ~~climbed~~ out of bed
>
> on my birthday disappointment was
>
> the last thing that I'd bargained for.

Proofread your incident twice. Check once for spelling and punctuation, then again for incorrect grammar or usage.

PUBLISH

The writer of the sample pasted down a photo taken on the day she described. How can you present your incident? Would photos help? Put your ideas in a journal for use with this or another project.

WRITING

EFFECTIVE LEADS AND ENDINGS

ENRICH YOUR WRITING OF **AUTOBIOGRAPHICAL INCIDENTS.**

Effective leads help capture the reader's interest. Endings that make sense help readers understand the writer's intentions.

Read these opening and closing passages from a memoir. How do they make you react?

Lead: I was born in Parksville. When I was nine years old, something unusual happened.
Ending: Now I knew his secret. I guess the story ends here.

Lead: Parksville seemed like a sleepy place without much happening. Then, a week after my ninth birthday, the entire town woke up.
Ending: When I finally learned his secret, my life was changed forever. I promised myself that one day I would tell what had happened.

PRACTICE 1 Respond on a separate piece of paper.

1. Which details in the second lead grab your attention? Which information in the second ending brings the story to a satisfying close?

2. Add different details to the second versions of leads and endings. How do they read now?

COMBINING SENTENCES

REMEMBER THESE RULES ABOUT COMBINING SENTENCES WHEN YOU ARE WRITING **AUTOBIOGRAPHICAL INCIDENTS.**

- You can combine two sentences by using two subjects or two predicates in the same sentence.

- Use the conjunctions *and, or,* or *but* to combine subjects or predicates. Or combine information without using a conjunction.

PRACTICE 2 On a separate piece of paper, combine each pair of sentences.

1 He asked me to step outside. He whispered in my ear.

2 There was a gleam in his eyes. His eyes were large and green.

3 Albert walked into the shop. Maria went in with him.

4 The shop window was broken. So was the cash register.

EXPANDING SENTENCES

USE THESE RULES ABOUT EXPANDING SENTENCES WHEN YOU ARE WRITING **AUTOBIOGRAPHICAL INCIDENTS.**

- An expanded sentence is one with greater descriptive detail. You can expand sentences by adding prepositional phrases.

- You can also expand them by adding adjectives or adverbs.

PRACTICE 3 On a separate piece of paper, expand these sentences by adding prepositional phrases, adjectives, or adverbs.

1 I listened to his story.

2 The sound of the parade filled the town.

3 The shuttle traveled through space.

4 Katie danced onstage.

THEME WRITING

WRITING AN EDITORIAL

When you have a strong opinion, you usually want to speak up about it. You may even want to convince other people to agree with you. Writing an editorial can be a powerful way to persuade them.

PREWRITE

List issues that you care about in your journal. Choose one issue and jot down your position statement. See whether your reasons lead to a strong conclusion. Try using a graphic organizer like the one at right.

DRAFT Your classmates probably have strong opinions about your topic. Talk to them, and take notes. Remember, your editorial's goal is to persuade your classmates to agree with you. Check your notes and organizer. Then start writing.

REVISE Do you need to use more persuasive words? Think about words that might capture attention. Revise your draft to include these words.

PROOFREAD Find a quiet place. Read your editorial to yourself, aloud and very slowly. Reading aloud to yourself can help you spot errors.

PUBLISH Try submitting your editorial to your school or local newspaper. See whether your school or community radio station would allow you to read it on air.

POSITION STATEMENT
SCHOOL HAS TO
BUY NEW COMPUTERS

Reason Old ones do not work

EXPLANATION
OUT-OF-DATE AND BREAK

Reason School has money in budget now

EXPLANATION
MONEY FOR NEW
SPORTS GEAR

Reason Money could be used for computers

EXPLANATION
SPORTS GEAR
BOUGHT LAST YEAR

CONCLUSION
BUY NEW COMPUTERS,
NOT SPORTS GEAR

▶ *Proofreading Alert!*

Use commas to separate parts of a sentence. Check page 204 in *Spotlight on Success: Writing and Language Handbook.*

PROJECTS

WRITE A SKIT ABOUT LIVING AND LEARNING

REMEMBER TO: • PREWRITE • DRAFT • REVISE • PROOFREAD • PUBLISH

Dramatize how you "lived and learned" something. Work with a few friends to act out an experience that changed one of your opinions.

Use the "5 W's and H" focus questions to help plan your skit. What exactly happened? Who was involved? When did it happen? Where did it happen? Why did it happen? How did it change your opinion? Now work with classmates to write or improvise a skit. Perform it for the class.

"5 W'S AND H" QUESTIONS

Why?
Who?
Where?
How?
What?
When?

PROJECT 3

MAKE A BULLETIN BOARD DISPLAY

REMEMBER TO: • PREWRITE • DRAFT • REVISE • PROOFREAD • PUBLISH

Create a "Living and Learning" bulletin board display about growing older. What do we learn as we grow older? How do we change? Use drawings, photos, and posters.

Work with a small group to plan the display. You'll need to settle on some specific ideas once your group has brainstormed. A cluster like the one below might help tie your ideas together. Make your display colorful and eyecatching.

Community Activities — LIVING AND LEARNING — Family Picnics
Clubs in School — LIVING AND LEARNING — Playing Sports with Friends

TELEVISION IN THE CLASSROOM

Watching television at home can be relaxing and fun. But does television belong in our classrooms, too? Today many programs are intended to help us learn about a subject or event. Seeing history dramatized by professional actors can be exciting, but seeing an event isn't necessarily the same as studying it. As more educational programs are produced, we have to question how or if they should be used as teaching tools in our schools.

CONSIDER THIS ISSUE: Your class is studying the American Revolution. The social studies department decides to show a series of television programs about the war to all sixth-grade students. Do you think the series should be used as a learning tool in the classroom? Think about both sides of the issue.

- Will the programs excite students' interest in the Revolutionary War?
- Will students pay attention, or will they consider the programs an opportunity to slack off?
- Will the programs provide some students with another way of learning about United States history?

Read the following viewpoints about using television as a teaching tool in the classroom. Decide which opinion is closest to your own. Think of more arguments to support your position.

VIEWPOINT 1

I think television should be used in the classroom because it will make students more interested in learning about a subject.

- Television programs can make the subject come alive for students in a way that books can't.
- Watching a program will encourage students to find out more about the topic by doing independent reading.

VIEWPOINT 2

I think television should be used as a classroom teaching tool because it helps some students to learn more effectively.

- Watching the program with classmates and then talking about it makes students feel more involved in the learning process.
- Educational television can help teach students who have problems with reading or writing.
- Since students like to watch television, they'll be more interested in seeing the program and will pay more attention.

VIEWPOINT 3

Using television as a teaching tool in the classroom isn't a good idea because many students won't take it seriously enough.

- Students will treat the television program as a "show" and will not try to learn from it.
- Students won't work as hard as they do when they read their textbooks or do their own research.

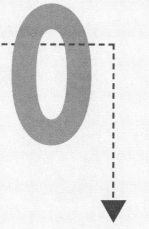

WHAT DO YOU THINK?

Spend a few minutes thinking about this issue. Do you share one of the viewpoints above, or do you have another? Discuss your views with a small group.

real life
CONNECT

LIVING AND LEARNING: Our school experiences can help us better understand ourselves and our world.

Learning goes beyond tests and textbooks. In "To Live in Two Worlds," a girl learns the importance of her Navajo heritage when she goes away to boarding school. In the same way, what we learn in school can make a difference in our everyday lives. Think about how often you follow directions in your school day. Then look at the directions for treating heat exhaustion below.

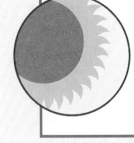

Heat Exhaustion

Heat exhaustion typically occurs among people who are not used to hot weather. It is more common among people who perspire a lot.

Symptoms: heavy sweating; fatigue; clammy, pale skin; and (sometimes) headache; nausea and vomiting; muscle cramps; fainting

What to do:
- Help the victim move to a cool, shaded area and lie down.
- Loosen or remove his or her clothing.
- Place cool, wet cloths on the victim's forehead and wrists.
- If the victim has fainted and doesn't respond promptly, hold aromatic spirits of ammonia under his or her nose.
- If the victim is conscious, give him or her juice, a soft drink, or a flavored beverage.
- Make sure the victim continues to rest until fully recovered. Iced coffee or a sweet drink at this point should help hasten recovery.
- If the measures given above don't work or if the symptoms last longer than one hour, seek medical help.

Directions are step-by-step instructions that can explain how to do or to make something. Directions are written in a simple style and in a particular sequence, or order. The order is important so that readers will be able to follow the directions easily.

IONS

Here are three activities in which you follow or provide directions. Think of situations in which following directions is important. Then choose an activity below or one of your own and talk or write about it.

PROJECT 1

WRITE DIRECTIONS Select two places of interest in your community. Then write directions for getting from one place to the other. Imagine you are writing the directions for a friend who's visiting your community for the first time. Cover up the name of the final destination and then exchange papers with a partner. Try to guess the final destination in each other's directions.

PROJECT 2

FIRST-AID POSTER Eye-catching, easy-to-read posters are used to explain important first-aid techniques. Research a simple first-aid method, such as applying a bandage to a cut or sprain. Then list on a colorfully illustrated poster the steps to perform this first-aid technique. Display your poster in your classroom.

PROJECT 3

WELL-WRITTEN DIRECTIONS Directions should be written clearly so that they're easy to follow. Work with a small group to find at least five examples of written directions in real-life use, such as recipes or contest forms. Discuss which directions are easiest to follow and why.

La Montagna Sainte-Victoire   1896–1898 Paul Cézanne
The Hermitage Museum, St Petersburg

Travellers

Come, let us go a-roaming!
    The world is all our own,
And half its paths are still untrod,
    And half its joys unknown.

The way that leads to winter
    Will lead to summer too,
For all roads end in other roads
    Where we may start anew.

—Arthur St. John Adcock

121

QUESTS

BEFORE READING

PRESIDENT CLEVELAND, WHERE ARE YOU?

CONNECT TO LITERATURE

Have you ever felt a conflict between your family responsibilities and the things you wanted to do with your friends? Jot down some ideas about this conflict in your journal. As you read "President Cleveland, Where Are You?" compare your ideas and experiences with the narrator's.

THINKING ABOUT PLOT

Plot is the organization of events in a story. Analyzing the plot means recognizing that each event in a story happens for a reason and looking for a pattern or structure underlying the action. It also means identifying the central problem or conflict that the main character faces. Analyzing plot helps readers understand characters' actions and predict how the story will progress.

The plot of "President Cleveland, Where Are You?" hinges on several key moments of decision for the main character, Jerry. Analyzing how Jerry acts at those times will help you understand what he values most. You will gain insight into his strengths and weaknesses and will sharpen your ability to predict his choices.

HAVE YOU EVER?

Have you ever collected trading cards? Do any of your friends collect them now? This story takes place in the 1930s. In it, the narrator and his friends collect cards of cowboy actors and then of United States presidents. At that time, trading cards cost five cents a package. How much does a package of cards cost now? What types of cards are popular in your class? In what ways do people trade cards today?

President Cleveland,
WHERE ARE YOU?

GROVER CLEVELAND

AMERICAN HEROES CARAMEL

by Robert Cormier

That was the autumn of the cowboy cards—Buck Jones and Tom Tyler and Hoot Gibson and especially Ken Maynard. The cards were available in those five-cent packages of gum: pink sticks, three together, covered with a sweet white powder. You couldn't blow bubbles with that particular gum, but it couldn't have mattered less. The cowboy cards were important—the pictures of those rock-faced men with eyes of blue steel.

On those wind-swept, leaf-tumbling afternoons we gathered after school on the sidewalk in front of Lemire's Drugstore, across from St. Jude's Parochial School, and we swapped and bargained and matched for the cards. Because a Ken Maynard serial was playing at the Globe every Saturday afternoon, he was the most popular cowboy of all, and one of his cards was worth at least ten of any other kind. Rollie Tremaine had a treasure of thirty or so, and he guarded them jealously. He'd match you for the other cards, but he risked his Ken Maynards only when the other kids threatened to leave him out of the competition altogether.

You could almost hate Rollie Tremaine. In the first place, he was the only son of Auguste Tremaine, who operated the Uptown Dry Goods Store, and he did not live in a <u>tenement</u> but in a big white birthday cake of a house on Laurel Street. He was too fat to be effective in the football games between the Frenchtown Tigers and the North Side Knights, and he made us constantly aware of the jingle of coins in his pockets. He was able to stroll into Lemire's and casually select a quarter's worth of cowboy cards while the rest of us watched, aching with envy.

TOM TYLER
appearing in Universal pictures

Once in a while I earned a nickel or dime by running errands or washing windows for blind old Mrs. Belander, or by finding pieces of copper, brass, and other valuable metals at the dump and selling them to the junkman. The coins clutched in my hand, I would race to Lemire's to buy a cowboy card or two, hoping that Ken Maynard would stare boldly out at me as I opened the pack. At one time, before a disastrous matching session with Roger Lussier (my best

---

tenement (ten′ə mənt) *n.* apartment building or rooming house that is poorly built or maintained and often overcrowded.

friend, except where the cards were involved), I owned five Ken Maynards and considered myself a millionaire, of sorts.

One week I was particularly lucky; I had spent two afternoons washing floors for Mrs. Belander and received a quarter. Because my father had worked a full week at the shop, where a rush order for fancy combs had been received, he <u>allotted</u> my brothers and sisters and me an extra dime along with the usual ten cents for the Saturday-afternoon movie. Setting aside the movie fare, I found myself with a bonus of thirty-five cents, and I then planned to put Rollie Tremaine to shame the following Monday afternoon.

Monday was the best day to buy the cards because the candy man stopped at Lemire's every Monday morning to deliver the new assortments. There was nothing more exciting in the world than a fresh batch of card boxes. I rushed home from school that day and hurriedly changed my clothes, eager to set off for the store. As I burst through the doorway, letting the screen door slam behind me, my brother Armand blocked my way.

He was fourteen, three years older than I, and a freshman at Monument High School. He had recently become a stranger to me in many ways—indifferent to such matters as cowboy cards and the Frenchtown Tigers—and he carried himself with a mysterious dignity that was <u>fractured</u> now and then when his voice began shooting off in all directions like some kind of vocal fireworks.

"Wait a minute, Jerry," he said. "I want to talk to you." He motioned me out of earshot of my mother, who was busy supervising the usual afterschool <u>skirmish</u> in the kitchen.

I sighed with impatience. In recent months Armand had become a figure of authority, siding with my father and mother occasionally. As the oldest son he sometimes took advantage of his age and experience to issue rules and regulations.

"How much money have you got?" he whispered.

KEN MAYNARD

---

allotted (ə lo′tid) *v.t.* gave out or assigned as a share.

fractured (frak′chərd) *adj.* cracked, split, or broken.

skirmish (skûr′mish) *n.* brief fight between small groups of persons; any brief or minor conflict.

"You in some kind of trouble?" I asked, excitement rising in me as I remembered the <u>blackmail</u> plot of a movie at the Globe a month before.

He shook his head in annoyance. "Look," he said, "it's Pa's birthday tomorrow. I think we ought to chip in and buy him something . . ."

I reached into my pocket and caressed the coins. "Here," I said carefully, pulling out a nickel. "If we all give a nickel we should have enough to buy him something pretty nice."

He regarded me with contempt. "Rita already gave me fifteen cents, and I'm throwing in a quarter. Albert handed over a dime—all that's left of his birthday money. Is that all you can do—a nickel?"

"Aw, come on," I protested. "I haven't got a single Ken Maynard left, and I was going to buy some cards this afternoon."

"Ken Maynard!" he snorted. "Who's more important—him or your father?"

His question was unfair because he knew that there was no possible choice—"my father" had to be the only answer. My father was a huge man who believed in the things of the spirit, although my mother often maintained that the spirits he believed in came in bottles. He had worked at the Monument Comb Shop since the age of fourteen; his booming laugh—or grumble—greeted us each night when he returned from the factory. A steady worker when the shop had enough work, he quickened with <u>gaiety</u> on Friday nights and weekends, a bottle of beer at his elbow, and he was fond of making long speeches about the good things in life. In the middle of the Depression, for instance, he paid cash for a piano, of all things, and insisted that my twin sisters, Yolande and Yvette, take lessons once a week.

I took a dime from my pocket and handed it to Armand.

"Thanks, Jerry," he said. "I hate to take your last cent."

"That's all right," I replied, turning away and consoling myself with the thought that twenty cents was better than nothing at all.

---

blackmail (blak′māl′) *n.* attempt to gain money by threatening to reveal damaging information.
gaiety (gā′i tē) *n.* cheerfulness; merrymaking; festivity.

When I arrived at Lemire's I sensed disaster in the air. Roger Lussier was kicking <u>disconsolately</u> at a tin can in the gutter, and Rollie Tremaine sat sullenly on the steps in front of the store.

"Save your money," Roger said. He had known about my plans to splurge on the cards.

"What's the matter?" I asked.

"There's no more cowboy cards," Rollie Tremaine said. "The company's not making any more."

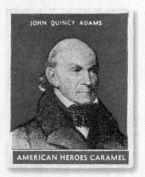

"They're going to have President cards," Roger said, his face twisting with disgust. He pointed to the store window. "Look!"

A placard in the window announced: "Attention, Boys. Watch for the New Series. Presidents of the United States. Free in Each 5-Cent Package of Caramel Chew."

"President cards?" I asked, dismayed.

I read on: "Collect a Complete Set and Receive an Official Imitation Major League Baseball Glove, Embossed with Lefty Grove's Autograph."

Glove or no glove, who could become excited about Presidents, of all things?

Rollie Tremaine stared at the sign. "Benjamin Harrison, for crying out loud," he said. "Why would I want Benjamin Harrison when I've got twenty-two Ken Maynards?"

I felt the warmth of guilt creep over me. I jingled the coins in my pocket, but the sound was hollow. No more Ken Maynards to buy.

"I'm going to buy a Mr. Goodbar," Rollie Tremaine decided.

I was without appetite, indifferent even to a Baby Ruth, which was my favorite. I thought of how I had betrayed Armand and, worst of all, my father.

"I'll see you after supper," I called over my shoulder to Roger as I hurried away toward home. I took the shortcut behind the church, although it involved leaping over a tall wooden fence, and I zigzagged recklessly through Mr. Thibodeau's garden, trying to outrace my guilt. I pounded up the steps and into the house, only to learn that Armand

---

disconsolately (dis kon′sə lit lē) *adv.* with such sadness as to be without cheer, hope, or comfort.

had already taken Yolande and Yvette uptown to shop for the birthday present.

I pedaled my bike furiously through the streets, ignoring the indignant horns of automobiles as I sliced through the traffic. Finally I saw Armand and my sisters emerge from the Monument Men's Shop. My heart sank when I spied the long, slim package that Armand was holding.

"Did you buy the present yet?" I asked, although I knew it was too late.

"Just now. A blue tie," Armand said. "What's the matter?"

"Nothing," I replied, my chest hurting.

He looked at me for a long moment. At first his eyes were hard, but then they softened. He smiled at me, almost sadly, and touched my arm. I turned away from him because I felt naked and exposed.

"It's all right," he said gently. "Maybe you've learned something." The words were gentle, but they held a curious dignity, the dignity remaining even when his voice suddenly cracked on the last syllable.

I wondered what was happening to me, because I did not know whether to laugh or cry.

Sister Angela was amazed when, a week before Christmas vacation, everybody in the class submitted a history essay worthy of a high mark—in some cases as high as A-minus. (Sister Angela did not believe that anyone in the world ever deserved an A.) She never learned—or at least she never let on that she knew—we all had become experts on the Presidents because of the cards we purchased at Lemire's. Each card contained a picture of a President, and on the reverse side, a summary of his career. We looked at those cards so often that the biographies imprinted themselves on our minds without effort. Even our street-corner conversations were filled with such information as the fact that James Madison was called "The Father of the Constitution," or that John Adams had intended to become a minister.

---

imprinted (im prin′tid) *v.t.* fixed firmly in the memory.

The President cards were a roaring success and the cowboy cards were quickly forgotten. In the first place we did not receive gum with the cards, but a kind of chewy caramel. The caramel could be tucked into a corner of your mouth, bulging your cheek in much the same manner as wads of tobacco bulged the mouths of baseball stars. In the second place the competition for collecting the cards was fierce and frustrating—fierce because everyone was intent on being the first to send away for a baseball glove and frustrating because although there were only thirty-two Presidents, including Franklin Delano Roosevelt, the variety at Lemire's was at a minimum. When the deliveryman left the boxes of cards at the store each Monday, we often discovered that one entire box was devoted to a single President—two weeks in a row the boxes contained nothing but Abraham Lincolns. One week Roger Lussier and I were the heroes of Frenchtown. We journeyed on our bicycles to the North Side, engaged three boys in a matching bout and returned with five new Presidents, including Chester Alan Arthur, who up to that time had been missing.

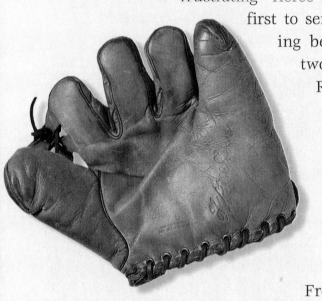

Lefty Grove model baseball glove, c. 1935

Perhaps to sharpen our desire, the card company sent a sample glove to Mr. Lemire, and it dangled, orange and sleek, in the window. I was half sick with longing, thinking of my old glove at home, which I had inherited from Armand. But Rollie Tremaine's desire for the glove outdistanced my own. He even got Mr. Lemire to agree to give the glove in the window to the first person to get a complete set of cards, so that precious time wouldn't be wasted waiting for the postman.

We were delighted at Rollie Tremaine's frustration, especially since he was only a substitute player for the Tigers. Once after spending fifty cents on cards—all of which turned out to be Calvin Coolidge—he threw them to the ground, pulled some dollar bills out of his pocket and said, "The heck with it. I'm going to buy a glove!"

"Not that glove," Roger Lussier said. "Not a glove with Lefty Grove's autograph. Look what it says at the bottom of the sign."

We all looked, although we knew the words by heart: "This Glove Is Not For Sale Anywhere."

Rollie Tremaine scrambled to pick up the cards from the sidewalk, pouting more than ever. After that he was quietly obsessed with the Presidents, hugging the cards close to his chest and refusing to tell us how many more he needed to complete his set.

I too was obsessed with the cards, because they had become things of comfort in a world that had suddenly grown dismal. After Christmas a layoff at the shop had thrown my father out of work. He received no paycheck for four weeks, and the only income we had was from Armand's afterschool job at the Blue and White Grocery Store—a job he lost finally when business <u>dwindled</u> as the layoff continued.

Although we had enough food and clothing—my father's credit had always been good, a matter of pride with him—the inactivity made my father restless and irritable. He did not drink any beer at all, and laughed loudly, but convincingly, after gulping down a glass of water and saying, "<u>Lent</u> came early this year." The twins fell sick and went to the hospital to have their tonsils removed. My father was confident that he would return to work eventually and pay off his debts, but he seemed to age before our eyes.

When orders again were received at the comb shop and he returned to work, another disaster occurred, although I was the only one aware of it. Armand fell in love.

I discovered his situation by accident, when I happened to pick up a piece of paper that had fallen to the floor in the bedroom he and I shared. I frowned at the paper, puzzled.

"Dear Sally, When I look into your eyes the world stands still . . ."

---

dwindled (dwin´dəld) *v.i.* became gradually smaller or less; diminished.
Lent *n.* period of penitence and prayer observed in Christian churches before Easter.

The letter was snatched from my hands before I finished reading it.

"What's the big idea, snooping around?" Armand asked, his face crimson. "Can't a guy have any privacy?"

He had never mentioned privacy before. "It was on the floor," I said. "I didn't know it was a letter. Who's Sally?"

He flung himself across the bed. "You tell anybody and I'll muckalize you," he threatened. "Sally Knowlton."

Nobody in Frenchtown had a name like Knowlton.

"A girl from the North Side?" I asked, incredulous.

He rolled over and faced me, anger in his eyes, and a kind of despair too.

"What's the matter with that? Think she's too good for me?" he asked. "I'm warning you, Jerry, if you tell anybody . . ."

"Don't worry," I said. Love had no particular place in my life; it seemed an unnecessary waste of time. And a girl from the North Side was so remote that for all practical purposes she did not exist. But I was curious. "What are you writing her a letter for? Did she leave town, or something?"

"She hasn't left town," he answered. "I wasn't going to send it. I just felt like writing to her."

I was glad that I had never become involved with love—love that brought <u>desperation</u> to your eyes, that caused you to write letters you did not plan to send. Shrugging with indifference, I began to search in the closet for the old baseball glove. I found it on the shelf, under some old sneakers. The webbing was torn and the padding gone. I thought of the sting I would feel when a sharp grounder slapped into the glove, and I winced.

"You tell anybody about me and Sally and I'll—"

"I know. You'll muckalize me."

I did not divulge his secret and often shared his agony, particularly when he sat at the supper table and left my mother's special butterscotch pie untouched. I had never

---

desperation (des′pə rā′shən) *n.* recklessness arising from loss of hope.

GROVER CLEVELAND

AMERICAN HEROES CARAMEL

realized before how terrible love could be. But my compassion was short-lived because I had other things to worry about: report cards due at Eastertime; the loss of income from old Mrs. Belander, who had gone to live with a daughter in Boston; and, of course, the Presidents.

Because a stalemate had been reached, the President cards were the <u>dominant</u> force in our lives—mine, Roger Lussier's and Rollie Tremaine's. For three weeks, as the baseball season approached, each of us had a complete set—complete except for one President, Grover Cleveland. Each time a box of cards arrived at the store we hurriedly bought them (as hurriedly as our funds allowed) and tore off the

dominant (dom'ə nənt) adj. most important; having the main influence, authority, or control.

wrappers, only to be confronted by James Monroe or Martin Van Buren or someone else. But never Grover Cleveland, never the man who had been the twenty-second *and* the twenty-fourth President of the United States. We argued about Grover Cleveland. Should he be placed between Chester Alan Arthur and Benjamin Harrison as the twenty-second President or did he belong between Benjamin Harrison and William McKinley as the twenty-fourth President? Was the card company playing fair? Roger Lussier brought up a <u>horrifying</u> possibility—did we need *two* Grover Clevelands to complete the set?

Indignant, we stormed Lemire's and protested to the harassed storeowner, who had long since vowed never to stock a new series. Muttering angrily, he searched his bills and receipts for a list of rules.

"All right," he announced. "Says here you only need one Grover Cleveland to finish the set. Now get out, all of you, unless you've got money to spend."

Outside the store, Rollie Tremaine picked up an empty tobacco tin and scaled it across the street. "Boy," he said. "I'd give five dollars for a Grover Cleveland."

When I returned home I found Armand sitting on the <u>piazza</u> steps, his chin in his hands. His mood of dejection mirrored my own, and I sat down beside him. We did not say anything for a while.

"Want to throw the ball around?" I asked.

He sighed, not bothering to answer.

"You sick?" I asked.

He stood up and hitched up his trousers, pulled at his ear and finally told me what the matter was—there was a big dance next week at the high school, the Spring Promenade, and Sally had asked him to be her escort.

I shook my head at the folly of love. "Well, what's so bad about that?"

"How can I take Sally to a fancy dance?" he asked desperately. "I'd have to buy her a corsage . . . And my shoes are practically falling apart. Pa's got too many worries now to

---

horrifying (hôr′ə fī′ing) *adj.* very dreadful; terrible.

piazza (pē az′ə) *n.* veranda; porch.

buy me new shoes or give me money for flowers for a girl."

I nodded in sympathy. "Yeah," I said. "Look at me. Baseball time is almost here, and all I've got is that old glove. And no Grover Cleveland card yet . . ."

"Grover Cleveland?" he asked. "They've got some of those up on the North Side. Some kid was telling me there's a store that's got them. He says they're looking for Warren G. Harding."

"Holy Smoke!" I said. "I've got an extra Warren G. Harding!" Pure joy sang in my veins. I ran to my bicycle, swung into the seat—and found that the front tire was flat.

"I'll help you fix it," Armand said.

Within half an hour I was at the North Side Drugstore, where several boys were matching cards on the sidewalk. Silently but blissfully I shouted: President Grover Cleveland, here I come!

After Armand had left for the dance, all dressed up as if it were Sunday, the small green box containing the corsage under his arm, I sat on the railing of the piazza, letting my feet dangle. The neighborhood was quiet because the Frenchtown Tigers were at Daggett's Field, practicing for the first baseball game of the season.

I thought of Armand and the ridiculous expression on his face when he'd stood before the mirror in the bedroom. I'd avoided looking at his new black shoes. "Love," I muttered.

Spring had arrived in a sudden stampede of apple blossoms and fragrant breezes. Windows had been thrown open and dust mops had banged on the sills all day long as the women busied themselves with housecleaning. I was puzzled by my <u>lethargy</u>. Wasn't spring supposed to make everything bright and gay?

I turned at the sound of footsteps on the stairs. Roger Lussier greeted me with a sour face.

"I thought you were practicing with the Tigers," I said.

"Rollie Tremaine," he said. "I just couldn't stand him." He slammed his fist against the railing. "Jeez, why did *he*

---

lethargy (leth′ər jē) *n.* state or quality of being without strength, energy, or alertness.

137

have to be the one to get a Grover Cleveland? You should see him showing off. He won't let anybody even touch that glove. . . ."

I felt like Benedict Arnold and knew that I had to confess what I had done.

"Roger," I said, "I got a Grover Cleveland card up on the North Side. I sold it to Rollie Tremaine for five dollars."

"Are you crazy?" he asked.

"I needed that five dollars. It was an—an emergency."

"Boy!" he said, looking down at the ground and shaking his head. "What did you have to do a thing like that for?"

I watched him as he turned away and began walking down the stairs.

"Hey, Roger!" I called.

He squinted up at me as if I were a stranger, someone he'd never seen before.

"What?" he asked, his voice flat.

"I had to do it," I said. "Honest."

He didn't answer. He headed toward the fence, searching for the board we had loosened to give us a secret passage.

I thought of my father and Armand and Rollie Tremaine and Grover Cleveland and wished that I could go away someplace far away. But there was no place to go.

Roger found the loose slat in the fence and slipped through. I felt betrayed: weren't you supposed to feel good when you did something fine and noble?

A moment later two hands gripped the top of the fence and Roger's face appeared. "Was it a real emergency?" he yelled.

"A real one!" I called. "Something important!"

His face dropped from sight and his voice reached me across the yard: "All right."

"See you tomorrow!" I yelled.

I swung my legs over the railing again. The gathering dusk began to soften the sharp edges of the fence, the rooftops, the distant church steeple. I sat there a long time, waiting for the good feeling to come.

MEET *Robert Cormier*

"Teenagers do not live in a peppermint world of fun and frolic," says Robert Cormier (born 1925). "Their world is vividly real, perhaps harsher and more tragedy-prone than the world their mothers and fathers inhabit." Cormier likes to write about "the vibrant songs of youth—tender, hectic, tragic, and ecstatic," which can sometimes have unhappy endings.

At least two of Cormier's novels rank as young-adult classics: *The Chocolate War* and *I Am the Cheese.* For "President Cleveland, Where Are You?" he drew on both his memories of growing up during the Great Depression and his experience as a father of teenagers.

Though he tackles difficult subjects, Cormier thinks of himself as "an optimist, and yet entirely a realist, if that can be." He strives for emotions that ring true. "If they do," he says, "then I have done my work properly."

✳ Pictured throughout this selection are actual cowboy and President trading cards from the 1930s. The photographs on pages 124, 127, 131, and 135 come from the same era.

RESPONDING TO
Literature

THINK • TALK • WRITE

1 If you had been in Jerry's situation, would you have made the same sacrifice he made at the end of the story? Explain in your journal.

2 Why did Jerry *not* want to contribute all his money toward his dad's birthday present? How did he feel later when he wanted to give more but it was too late?

3 Why did Jerry and his classmates do so well on their history essays? Why do you think the owner of Lemire's vowed never to order a new line of trading cards?

4 Why did Armand need five dollars? How do you learn what Jerry did to earn the money for his brother?

5 To Jerry, there is a real division between Frenchtown and the North Side. What kinds of differences might Jerry have perceived? Do you think the people in each neighborhood were actually as different as he believed? Explain.

ACTIVITIES

• **Write About Plot** Imagine Jerry had won two Grover Cleveland cards, not one, when he went trading on the North Side. How would the ending of the story be different? Write a paragraph describing how you think the plot would have turned out.

• **Hold a Collectors' Fair** Help organize a class collectors' fair. Have students ask for permission to bring in different objects they collect. Encourage each collector to set up a display in your classroom and to make a brief presentation to the class.

VOCABULARY PRACTICE

On a separate piece of paper, write whether the following pairs of words are *synonyms* (words that have the same meaning) or *antonyms* (words that have opposite meanings).

1 allotted—collected

2 fractured—cracked

3 gaiety—gloominess

4 dwindled—grew

5 horrifying—awful

6 disconsolately—happily

Match each phrase with the word that has the same meaning. Write the number and letter on a separate piece of paper.

7 skirmish   **a** fixed firmly

8 desperation   **b** most important

9 imprinted   **c** brief fight in a war

10 dominant   **d** recklessness caused by loss of hope

BEFORE READING

EXPLORING THE *TITANIC*

CONNECT TO LITERATURE

Can you imagine what it would be like to be on a sinking ship? Put yourself in the place of a passenger or crew member of the *Titanic,* a famous ship that sank in 1912. In your journal, write what you might have seen and heard on the day of the disaster. As you read "Exploring the *Titanic,*" note the details about the ship and its passengers that the author provides.

THINKING ABOUT FIGURATIVE LANGUAGE

To describe the exploration of the *Titanic,* author Robert Ballard relies on *figurative language* to provide vivid, colorful images. He makes use of both similes and metaphors. A *simile* is a figure of speech in which a comparison is made using the word *like* or *as.* For example, Ballard writes, "In places the rust formations over the portholes looked like eyelashes with tears." A *metaphor* is a comparison stated without using *like* or *as.* A metaphor talks about one thing as though it were another, as when Ballard calls the robot *JJ,* "our remote-controlled swimming eyeball."

DID YOU KNOW?

- The *Titanic* was 882 feet (269 m)—almost four city blocks—long. Her nine decks towered as high as an 11-story building.

- It took 20 horses to pull one of the ship's 15½ ton anchors.

- The *Titanic* was the first ocean liner to have a swimming pool.

- The ship's captain, Edward J. Smith, had served the White Star Line of passenger ships for 38 years. He planned to retire after this last trip, a tribute to his long and successful career.

EXPLORING THE
TITANIC

By Robert D. Ballard

The ocean liner R.M.S. Titanic was built in 1911 and deemed "virtually unsinkable." However, on its maiden voyage in 1912, the ship struck an iceberg in the North Atlantic and sank, killing 1,500 of the 2,200 passengers aboard. In 1985, Robert D. Ballard and his team discovered the remains of the Titanic on the ocean floor. A year later, the team returned to explore the ship in their submarine Alvin, with the help of Jason Jr., or JJ, their robot.

Rusticles hang from two large bollards.

As *Alvin*'s lights glow from above, *Jason Junior* explores the *Titanic*'s starboard anchor.

Our second view of the *Titanic* was breathtaking. As we glided soundlessly across the ocean bottom, the razor's edge of the bow loomed out of the darkness. The great ship towered above us. Suddenly it seemed to be coming right at us, about to run us over. My first reaction was that we had to get out of the way. But the *Titanic* wasn't going anywhere. As we gently brought our sub closer, we could see the bow more clearly. Both of her huge anchors were still in place. But the bow was buried more than sixty feet in mud, far too deep for anyone to pull her out of the ooze.

It looked as though the metal hull was slowly melting away. What seemed like frozen rivers of rust covered the ship's side and spread out over the ocean bottom. It was almost as if the blood of the great ship lay in pools on the ocean floor.

As *Alvin* rose in slow motion up the ghostly side of the ship, I could see our lights reflecting off the still-unbroken glass of the *Titanic's* portholes. They made me think of cats' eyes gleaming in the dark. In places the rust formations over the portholes looked like eyelashes with tears, as though

This scale drawing shows the enormous distance between Ballard's search ship *Knorr* and the *Titanic* wreck.

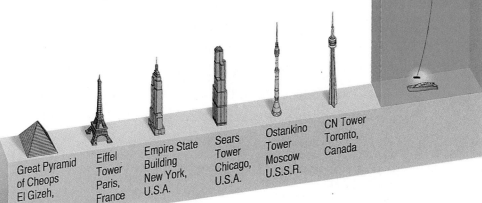

Great Pyramid of Cheops El Gizeh, Egypt

Eiffel Tower Paris, France

Empire State Building New York, U.S.A.

Sears Tower Chicago, U.S.A.

Ostankino Tower Moscow U.S.S.R.

CN Tower Toronto, Canada

437 ft/133 m
This is the deepest a scuba diver has ever gone.

1,500 ft/465 m
Naval submarines dive no deeper than this. There is no light below this level.

3,028 ft/940 m
Pioneer underwater explorers William Beebe and Otis Barton reached this depth in a ball-shaped bathysphere in 1930.

1 mile/1,609 m
Many sea creatures here are transparent or can glow in the dark.

2 miles/3,218 m
The water temperature at this depth stays a few degrees above the freezing point.

12,460 ft/3,965 m
The water pressure where the Titanic lies is approximately 6,000 lbs. per square inch.

the *Titanic* were crying. I could also see a lot of reddish-brown <u>stalactites</u> of rust over the wreck, like long icicles. I decided to call them "rusticles." This rust turned out to be very fragile. If touched by our sub, it disappeared like a cloud of smoke.

As we rose further and began to move across the mighty forward deck, I was amazed at the sheer size of everything: giant bollards and shiny bronze capstans that were used for winding ropes and cables; the huge links of the anchor chains. When you were there on the spot, the ship was truly <u>titanic</u>.

 strained to get a good look at the deck's wood planking, just four feet below us. Then my heart dropped to my stomach. "It's gone!" I muttered. Most of the *Titanic*'s wooden deck had been eaten away. Millions of little wood-eating worms had done more damage than the iceberg and the salt water. I began to wonder whether the metal deck below the destroyed wood planking would support our weight when *Alvin* landed.

We would soon find out. Slowly we moved into position to make our first landing test on the forward deck just next to the fallen mast. As we made our approach, our hearts beat quickly. We knew there was a real risk of crashing through the deck. The sub settled down, making a muffled crunching noise. If the deck gave way, we'd be trapped in collapsing wreckage. But it held, and we settled firmly. That meant there was a good chance that the *Titanic*'s decks would support us at other landing sites.

We carefully lifted off and turned toward the stern. The dim outline of the ship's superstructure came into view: first B Deck, then A, finally the Boat Deck—the top deck where the bridge was located. It was here that

The *Titanic*'s bridge in 1912

The *Titanic*'s bridge in 1986

---

stalactites (stə lak′tīts) *n., pl.* mineral formations resembling icicles, which hang from a cave ceiling.
titanic (tī tan′ik) *adj.* huge.

The bow section of the *Titanic*

the captain and his officers had guided the ship across the Atlantic. The wooden wheelhouse was gone, probably knocked away in the sinking. But the bronze telemotor control to which the ship's wheel had once been attached stood <u>intact</u>, polished to a shine by the current. We then safely tested this second landing site.

I had an eerie feeling as we glided along exploring the wreck. As I peered through my porthole, I could easily imagine people walking along the deck and looking out the windows of the ship that I was looking into. Here I was at the bottom of the ocean looking at a kind of time capsule from history.

Suddenly, as we rose up the port side of the ship, the sub shuddered and made a clanging noise. A waterfall of rust covered our portholes. "We've hit something!" I exclaimed. "What is it?"

---

intact (in takt') *adj.* whole; not damaged.

"I don't know," our pilot replied. "I'm backing off." Unseen overhangs are the nightmare of the deep-sub pilot. Carefully, the pilot backed away from the hull and brought us slowly upward. Then, directly in front of our forward porthole, a big lifeboat davit slid by. We had hit one of the metal arms that held the lifeboats as they were lowered. This davit was one of the two that had held boat No. 8, the boat Mrs. Straus had refused to enter that night. She was the wife of the owner of Macy's department store in New York. When she had been offered a chance to save herself in one of the lifeboats, she had turned to her husband and said, "We have been living together for many years. Where you go, I go." Calmly, the two of them had sat down on a pile of deck chairs to wait for the end.

Now, as we peered out our portholes, it seemed as if the Boat Deck were crowded with passengers. I could almost hear the cry, "Women and children first!"

We knew from the previous year's pictures that the stern had broken off the ship, so we continued back to

The Grand Staircase in 1912

search for the severed end of the intact bow section. Just beyond the gaping hole where the second funnel had been, the deck began to plunge down at a dangerous angle. The graceful lines of the ship disappeared in a twisted mess of torn steel plating, upturned portholes, and jumbled wreckage. We saw enough to know that the decks of the ship had collapsed in on one another like a giant accordion. With an unexpectedly strong current pushing us toward this twisted wreckage, we veered away and headed for the surface.

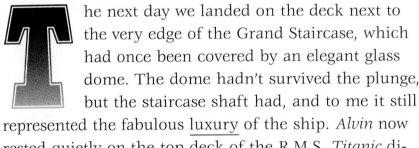

The next day we landed on the deck next to the very edge of the Grand Staircase, which had once been covered by an elegant glass dome. The dome hadn't survived the plunge, but the staircase shaft had, and to me it still represented the fabulous <u>luxury</u> of the ship. *Alvin* now rested quietly on the top deck of the R.M.S. *Titanic* directly above the place where three elevators had carried first-class passengers who did not wish to use the splendid Grand Staircase.

We, however, would take the stairs with *JJ* the robot, our R2D2 of the deep. This would be the first deep-water test for our remote-controlled swimming eyeball, and we were very nervous about it. No one knew whether *JJ*'s motors could stand up to the enormous ocean pressure of more than 6,000 pounds per square inch.

---

luxury (luk′shə rē) *n.* comfort or pleasure that goes beyond what is really necessary.

Using a control box with a joystick that operated like a video game, the operator cautiously steered *JJ* out of his garage attached to the front of *Alvin*. Slowly *JJ* went inching down into the <u>yawning</u> blackness of the Grand Staircase. More and more cable was let out as he dropped deeper and deeper.

We could see what *JJ* was seeing on our video in the sub. But at first *JJ* could see nothing. Then, as he dropped deeper, a room appeared off the portside foyer on A Deck. *JJ* swung around and our co-pilot saw something in the distance. "Look at that," he said softly. "Look at that chandelier."

Now I could see it, too. "No, it can't be a chandelier," I said. "It couldn't possibly have survived."

I couldn't believe my eyes. The ship had fallen two and a half miles, hitting the bottom with the force of a train running into a mountain, and here was an almost perfectly preserved light fixture! *JJ* left the stairwell and

Jason Junior **illuminates a pillar still standing in the foyer of the Grand Staircase. *Alvin* has landed on the Boat Deck beside the collapsed roof that once held the glass dome over the staircase. From inside the submarine we guide *JJ* down the staircase shaft as far as B Deck. The illustration (*inset*) shows a cross-section of *JJ*'s descent with an outline of the original staircase.**

---

yawning (yôn′ing) *adj.* wide open.

started to enter the room, managing to get within a foot of the fixture. To our astonishment, we saw a feathery piece of coral sprouting from it. We could even see the sockets where the light bulbs had been fitted! "This is fantastic," I exulted.

"Bob, we're running short of time. We have to return to the surface." Our pilot's words cut like a knife through my excitement. Here we were deep inside the *Titanic,* actually going down the Grand Staircase, but we had used up all the time that we had to stay safely on the bottom. I knew our pilot was just following orders, but I still wanted to shout in protest.

Our little robot soldier emerged from the black hole and shone his lights toward us, bathing the interior of the sub in an unearthly glow. For a moment it felt as if an alien spaceship were hovering nearby. But that feeling quickly gave way to one of victory, thanks to our little friend. *JJ* had been a complete success.

On our next day's dive, we crossed over what had once been Captain Smith's cabin. Its outer wall now lay collapsed on the deck, as though a giant had brought his fist down on it. We passed within inches of one of the cabin's windows. Was this, I wondered, a window that Captain Smith had cranked open to let a little fresh air into his cabin before going to bed?

Captain Edward J. Smith

Suddenly a large piece of broken railing loomed out of the darkness. It seemed to be heading right for my viewport. I immediately warned the pilot who quickly turned *Alvin*'s stern around, rotating us free of the obstacle.

Now we began to drop onto the starboard Boat Deck. As we glided along, I felt as though I were visiting a ghost town where suddenly one day everyone had closed up shop and left.

An empty lifeboat davit stood nearby. Ahead I could see where the *Titanic*'s lifeboats had rested. It was on this very deck that the crowds of passengers had stood waiting to get into the boats. They had not known until the last moments that there were not

Wives saying goodbye to their husbands as lifeboats are loaded on the Boat Deck

enough lifeboats for everyone. It was also from this deck that you could have heard the *Titanic*'s brave band playing cheerful music to boost the crowd's spirits as the slope of the deck grew steeper and steeper.

Jason Jr. now went for a stroll along the Boat Deck. As he slowly made his way along, he looked in the windows of several first-class cabins as well as into some passageways, including one that still bore the words, "First-Class Entrance." As JJ passed by the gymnasium windows, I could see bits and pieces of equipment amid the <u>rubble</u>, including some metal grillwork that had been part of the electric camel, an old-fashioned exercise machine. We could also see various wheel shapes and a control lever. Much of the gym's

---

rubble (rub'əl) *n.* rough, broken pieces of solid material, as stone or rock.

Stern Section

- A painted metal footboard from a bed (*top left*)
- This sink from a second-class stateroom could be tipped to allow the water to drain out (*top middle*)
- The white porcelain of this bathtub is almost hidden by rust in contrast (*top right inset*) to the way it appeared when new (*top right*).
- The cast-iron frame of one of the benches from the *Titanic's* decks (*bottom right*).

ceiling was covered with rust. This was where the gym instructor, dressed in white flannel trousers, had urged passengers to try the gym machines. And, on the last night, passengers had gathered here for warmth as the lifeboats were being lowered.

I could see *JJ* far off down the deck, turning this way and that to get a better view inside doorways and various windows. It was almost as though our little robot had a mind of his own.

But now we had to bring him home. We had been on the *Titanic* for hours. Once again it was time to head back to the surface.

The morning of July 18 was lovely and warm, but I felt edgy about the day's mission. We had decided to visit the *Titanic's* debris field. Along the 1,970 feet that separated the broken-off bow and stern pieces of the wreck, there was a large scattering of all kinds of objects from

---

debris (də brē′) *n.* remains of something broken or destroyed; rubbish.

The Debris Field

Between the separated sections of the *Titanic* lie thousands of objects that spilled out of the ship when she sank.

Bow Section

the ship. Everything from lumps of coal to wrought-iron deck benches had fallen to the bottom as she broke in two and sank. But I was anxious about what we might find down there among the rubble. I had often been asked about the possibility of finding human bodies. It was a chilling thought. We had not seen any signs of human remains so far, but I knew that if we were to find any, it would most likely be during this dive.

As the first fragments of wreckage began to appear on the bottom, I felt like we were entering a bombed-out museum. Thousands upon thousands of objects littered the rolling fields of ocean bottom, many of them perfectly preserved. The guts of the *Titanic* lay spilled out across the ocean floor. Cups and saucers, silver serving trays, pots and pans, wine bottles, boots, chamber pots, space heaters, bathtubs, suitcases, and more.

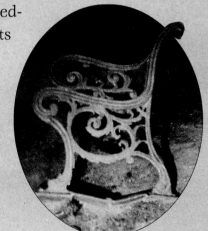

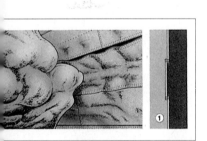

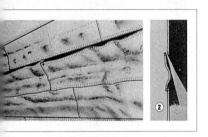

The iceberg scraping against the hull plates of the *Titanic* (*top*) popped many of the steel rivets that held them in place (*top right*). This allowed water to pour in through the seams (*above right*).

Then, without warning, I found myself looking into the ghostly eyes of a small, white smiling face. For a split second I thought it was a skull—and it really scared me. Then I realized I was looking at a doll's head, its hair and clothes gone.

My shock turned to sadness as I began to wonder who had owned this toy. Had the girl survived in one of the lifeboats? Or had she clutched the doll tightly as she sank in the icy waters?

We moved on through this amazing scenery. There were so many things scattered about that it became difficult to keep track of them. We came across one of the ship's boilers, and there on top of it sat an upright rusty metal cup like the ones the crew had used. It looked as though it had been placed there by a stoker moments before water had burst into the boiler room. It was astonishing to think that in fact this cup had just fluttered down that night to land right on top of a boiler.

Then in the light of *Alvin*'s headlights, we spotted a safe ahead of us. I had heard about the story of fabulous treasure, including a leather-bound book covered with jewels, being locked in the ship's safes when she sank. Here was the chance of a lifetime, and I wanted to get a good look at it.

The safe sat there with its door face up. The handle looked as though it was made of gold, although I knew it had to be brass. Next to it, I could see a small circular gold dial, and above both a nice shiny gold crest.

Why not try to open it? I watched as *Alvin*'s sample-gathering arm locked its metal fingers onto the handle. Its metal wrist began to rotate clockwise. To my surprise, the handle turned easily. Then it stopped. The door just wouldn't budge. It was rusted shut. I felt as if I'd been caught with my hand in the cookie jar.

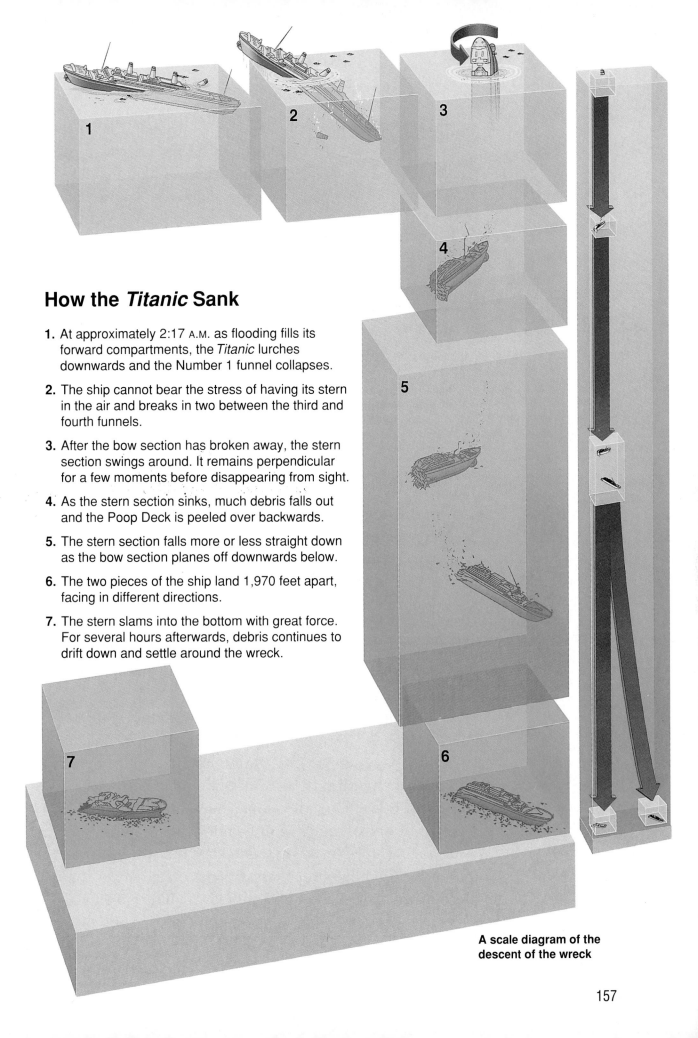

How the *Titanic* Sank

1. At approximately 2:17 A.M. as flooding fills its forward compartments, the *Titanic* lurches downwards and the Number 1 funnel collapses.

2. The ship cannot bear the stress of having its stern in the air and breaks in two between the third and fourth funnels.

3. After the bow section has broken away, the stern section swings around. It remains perpendicular for a few moments before disappearing from sight.

4. As the stern section sinks, much debris falls out and the Poop Deck is peeled over backwards.

5. The stern section falls more or less straight down as the bow section planes off downwards below.

6. The two pieces of the ship land 1,970 feet apart, facing in different directions.

7. The stern slams into the bottom with great force. For several hours afterwards, debris continues to drift down and settle around the wreck.

A scale diagram of the descent of the wreck

157

The dial and brass crest of this safe are still shiny. We turned the handle with _Alvin_'s mechanical arm.

Oh, well, I thought, it was probably empty, anyway. In fact, when we later looked at the video footage we had taken, we could see that the bottom of the safe had rusted out. Any treasure should have been spread around nearby, but there was none to be seen. Fortunately, my promise to myself not to bring back anything from the _Titanic_ was not put to the test.

Two days passed before I went down to the _Titanic_ again. After the rest, I was <u>raring</u> to go at it once more. This time we were going to explore the torn-off stern section that lay 1,970 feet away from the bow. It had been very badly damaged during the plunge to the bottom. Now it lay almost unrecognizable amidst badly twisted pieces of wreckage. We planned to land _Alvin_ on the bottom directly behind the stern section and then send _JJ_ in under the overhanging hull. Unless the _Titanic_'s three huge propellers had fallen off when she sank, I figured they still ought to be there, along with her enormous 101-ton rudder.

We made a soft landing on the bottom and discovered that one of _JJ_'s motors wouldn't work. Our dive looked like a washout. I sat glumly staring out of my viewport at the muddy bottom. Suddenly the mud started to move! Our pilot was slowly inching _Alvin_ forward on its single ski right under the dangerous overhanging stern area. He was taking the sub itself to search for the huge propellers. Was he crazy? What if a piece of wreckage came crashing down? But our pilot

---

raring (râr′ing) _adj._ very eager.

was a professional, so I figured he must know exactly what he was doing.

I could see an area ahead covered with rusticles that had fallen from the rim of the stern above. Until now we had had ocean above us. Crossing this point was like taking a dangerous dare. Once on the other side, there was no sure way of escaping if disaster struck. None of us spoke. The only sound in the sub was our breathing.

Slowly a massive black surface of steel plating seemed to inch down toward us overhead. The hull seemed to be coming at us from all sides. As we looked closely, we could see that like the bow, the stern section was buried deep in the mud—forty-five feet or so. Both the middle and the starboard propellers were under the mud. Only about sixteen feet of the massive rudder could be seen rising out of the ooze.

In *Alvin* we explore under the over-hanging deck of the *Titanic*'s sev-ered stern section and photograph the buried rudder.

"Let's get out of here," I said. Ever so gently, *Alvin* retraced the path left by its ski. As we crossed over from the area covered with rusticles into the clear, we sighed with relief. We were out of danger. All of us were glad that this adventure was over.

Before we left the bottom this time, however, there was one mission that I wanted to complete. I wanted to place a memorial plaque on the twisted and tangled wreckage of the stern, in memory of all those lost on the *Titanic*. Those who had died had gathered on the stern as the ship had tilted bow first. This had been their final <u>haven</u>. So we rose up the wall of steel to the top of the stern. With great care, *Alvin*'s mechanical arm plucked the plaque from where it had been strapped outside the sub, and gently released it. We watched as it sank quietly to the deck of the stern.

As we lifted off and began our climb to the surface, our camera kept the plaque in view as long as possible. As we rose, it grew smaller and smaller, until finally it was swallowed in the gloom.

---

haven (hā′vən) *n.* place of safety or shelter.

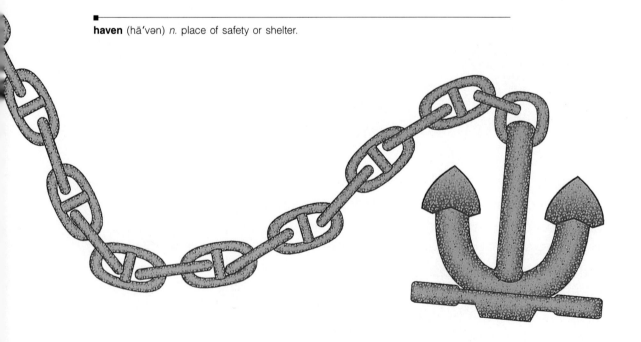

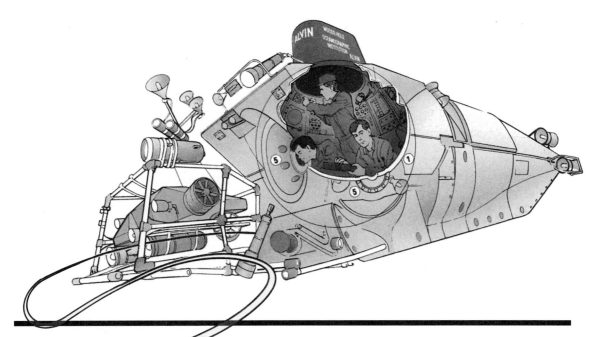

MEET ROBERT D. BALLARD

A doll's head and a man's patent leather shoe are usually not objects of wonder. But they were truly haunting images to explorer and oceanographer Robert Ballard, because of where they were found—among the wreckage of the *Titanic*. Ballard saw these objects through the eyes of a small robot operated from a three-man submarine, both of which he developed. Searching a 150-square-mile area of the ocean floor for the *Titanic* "makes finding a needle in a haystack seem trivial," he says.

Ballard continues to be intrigued by technology and by what lies in the depths of the ocean. His book *The Lost Wreck of the Isis* describes his discovery of a sunken Roman ship.

RESPONDING TO *Literature*

THINK • TALK • WRITE

1 How do you think it would feel to be the first person to see the *Titanic* after more than 70 years? Write your thoughts down in your journal.

2 What are some of the things Ballard discovered? What do you think was his single most important discovery? Why?

3 On page 157, both the description and the diagram explain how the *Titanic* sank. What do you as a reader learn from each? Why did the author include both a description and a diagram?

4 Why do you think Ballard promised himself not to bring back anything from the *Titanic?* Do you agree with this decision? Explain.

5 Different people and cultures have various ways of honoring the dead. Ballard placed a memorial plaque on the ship's wreckage. What do you think of this idea? What other tributes do you think might have been appropriate?

ACTIVITIES

• **Write with Similes/Figurative Language** Write similes and metaphors that express strong emotions or moods such as "The cold finger of fear traced itself down my spine" or "I was so embarrassed that my face looked like a tomato." Then use at least two of them in a short paragraph or poem.

• **Rebuild the *Titanic*** Make a model or drawing of the *Titanic*. Use the illustrations and descriptions in the selection as a guide. You can depict her as she was in April 1912, or you can show her as Ballard found her.

VOCABULARY PRACTICE

On a separate piece of paper, write the vocabulary word that is the best substitute for each italicized word or phrase.

intact   debris

rubble   haven

luxury

1 The submarine served as a *safe place* for Ballard and his team as they explored the sunken ship.

2 Once-beautiful objects were shattered into small bits of *wreckage*.

3 Cups and saucers, bathtubs, suitcases, and other objects lay amidst the *broken steel and glass*.

4 Ballard found a safe that appeared to be *untouched*.

5 Passengers traveling first class were accustomed to *great abundance and comfort.*

Before Reading

MUMMIES, TOMBS, AND TREASURE

CONNECT TO LITERATURE

Imagine discovering a mummy thousands of years after it had been entombed. Would you be awestruck, afraid, curious? Would you want to tell the world, or would you leave it untouched? Write your thoughts in your journal. As you read the selection, notice how different people—Howard Carter, the grave robbers, and others—act after they have discovered mummies' tombs.

THINKING ABOUT CHRONOLOGICAL ORDER

In "Mummies, Tombs, and Treasure," much of the text is organized in *chronological order*—that is, time order, the order in which things happened. The events are basically presented in sequence from beginning to end. Keeping track of chronological order is important, though, because the events range over 3,000 years. Also, author Lila Perl occasionally pauses to tell about events that led to or caused something that happened years later.

DID YOU KNOW?

A mummy is simply a dead body that has been preserved—either accidentally by nature or on purpose by humans. Without preservation, animal and plant matter decays very quickly. Decay is caused by Earth's recyclers—bacteria, worms, and other decomposers. These organisms break down the tissues of once-living things and return them to nature to be reused in other forms.

Early Egyptians discovered by accident that hot, dry sand acts as a preservative. They farmed the fertile black soil along the Nile River. Rather than burying their dead in this precious farmland, they buried them in the desert. By rapidly absorbing the bodies' moisture, the hot sand killed bacteria and preserved the bodies. The first Egyptian mummies had been created.

Mummies, Tombs, and Treasure

SECRETS OF ANCIENT EGYPT

by Lila Perl

A night view of the pyramid of King Khafre with the Sphinx in the foreground, lit by floodlights. Insets, clockwise from top: the coffin of a royal official of Thebes, a pendant from King Tutankhamen's tomb, and a statue of King Ramses II

tombs ~~as~~ ~~the bodies of Egypt~~ *royalty and upper-class citizens. A tomb contained everything the spirit would need for a comfortable life after death—favorite possessions, games, food, and water.* Shabtis, *miniature figures of humans, were placed in the tomb to act as servants to the dead.* Containers called *canopic jars held the deceased's preserved internal organs, which would magically rejoin the body in the afterlife. After the funeral, the tomb was sealed, supposedly forever. But often, robbers opened tombs in search of the riches buried within.*

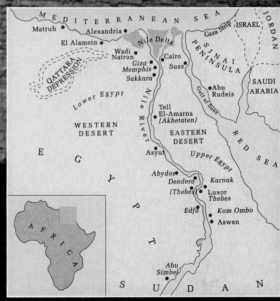

Map of Egypt today. Cities and sites of ancient Egypt are in italics.

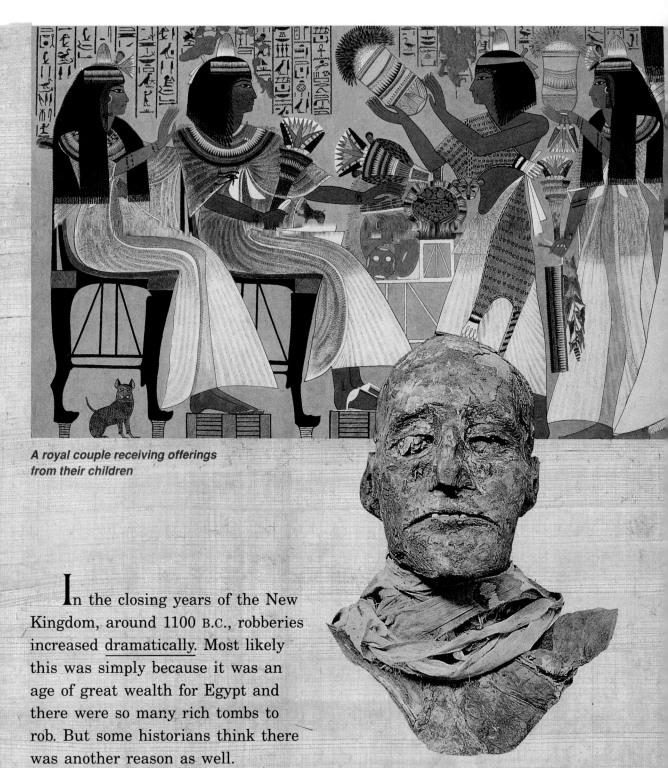

A royal couple receiving offerings from their children

In the closing years of the New Kingdom, around 1100 B.C., robberies increased <u>dramatically</u>. Most likely this was simply because it was an age of great wealth for Egypt and there were so many rich tombs to rob. But some historians think there was another reason as well.

In the part of Asia that was closest to Egypt, the Iron Age had arrived. People learned to mine and work iron into sturdy tools and weapons. Egypt, however, did not have

The mummy of Ramses III in its tattered wrappings after its discovery in 1881 in an abandoned tomb, where it had been placed for safekeeping. The hieroglyphs at the border of this page, and the following pages, are taken from a list of ancient Egyptian rulers found at Abydos, in the Temple of Seti I.

dramatically (drə mat′ik lē) *adv.* strikingly.

that many more people turned to thievery.

Whatever the reason, around 1000 B.C. a group of priests of the Twenty-first Dynasty took steps to rescue the tattered remains of some of the royal mummies whose graves had been looted. They found an abandoned tomb near the temple of Queen Hatshepsut and secretly transferred the mummies to the new hiding place. Many were re-bandaged and marked with their names taken from the old wrap-pings. Even the dates of rewrapping were inscribed on the cloth. Some of the mummies were given new coffins. Also reburied with them were those belongings the thieves had ignored as being of lesser value. Among them were papyrus scrolls, canopic jars, and *shabtis*.

For nearly three thousand years the mummies rested peace-fully in their new home. Then, in 1875, unusual objects began to ap-pear for sale in the shops, hotels, and bazaars of Luxor. This new city had sprung to life on the east bank of the Nile, on the site of tourists, souvenir seekers, art col-lectors, and archaeologists who were studying the monuments and digging for the remains of Egypt's ancient civilization.

The mysterious objects that were coming on the market turned out to be scrolls, *shabtis*, and other articles belonging to various rulers of the New Kingdom and of the Twenty-first Dynasty, which followed it. Finally, in 1881, the Egyptian government tracked down the source of the articles. Sure enough, one of the old tomb-robbing fami-lies had been at work again. A pair of brothers had discovered the hid-ing place of the mummies near the temple of Queen Hatshepsut.

Aside from the items they had stolen, the modern tomb robbers had done little further damage to the mummies. Among them were such famed rulers of the New Kingdom as Ahmose, Amenhotep I, Thutmose I, II, and III, Seti I, and Ramses I, II, and III. With great care, the mummies were trans-ported to Cairo where many can be

---

deposits (di poz′its) *n., pl.* natural layers, as of minerals.
bazaars (bə zärz′) *n., pl.* marketplaces or streets lined with shops or stalls.

The mummy labeled Thutmose I turned out to be that of an unknown youth of about eighteen. Thutmose I, who must have been about fifty when he died, has not so far been found.

In 1898, yet another tomb was found in the Valley of the Kings crammed with mummies hidden away for safekeeping by priests. In this group were found Amenhotep II, Thutmose IV, Amenhotep III, Ramses IV, and Ramses V, among others. They, too, were brought to the museum's Mummy Room to be displayed in glass cases.

Little by little the gaps in Egypt's royal history were being filled in. Mummies were being found, and so were the empty, echoing tombs of their onetime owners, magnificent with their painted walls and ceilings but bare of their contents. People wondered if anyone would ever uncover a royal tomb that looked just as it had on the day that the <u>mourners</u> departed and the entrance was sealed, presumably forever.

Two of the four seated sandstone colossi of the Great Temple of Ramses II, Abu Simbel, now located on the plateau above its original site

the Valley of the Kings. Digging in the Valley was a costly undertaking, however. So Carter was lucky in having met up with a wealthy British nobleman, Lord Carnarvon, who shared Carter's goal and funded his work.

Because of his health, Lord Carnarvon spent winters in Egypt's warm, dry climate. The months from November to March were also the only time when digging in the Valley was possible. The summers were far too hot.

By 1922, Carter had spent six unsuccessful seasons fine-combing a particular part of the Valley in search of the burial place of a little-known pharaoh named Tutankhamen. Years earlier another archaeologist had discovered some puzzling remains both near and under a large tilted rock in the vicinity. They included a bit of gold leaf and a blue cup marked with Tutankhamen's name. There were also some dried floral collars and some animal bones left behind by the guests of a funeral banquet of long, long ago. Could they have

mourners (môr′nərz) *n., pl.* people who feel sadness, especially those attending a funeral.

been the guests at the funeral banquet of Tutankhamen?

In the autumn of 1922 Carter arrived in the Valley for what was to be the very last season of the search for Tutankhamen. He brought with him a tiny companion, a canary, to keep him company in the small, domed house he had built for himself on the Valley road on the west bank of the Nile. The local Egyptians hired to work on the dig were amazed by the "golden bird." No songbirds had ever been seen or heard in the grim, treeless Valley.

Perhaps, as Carter's work team predicted, the little canary brought Carter luck. The site he had chosen for the last season's dig was directly under some ancient grave-workers' huts in front of the tomb of Ramses VI, a pharaoh who had lived about two hundred years later than Tutankhamen. In the past, Carter had hesitated to dig there because the empty tomb of Ramses VI was a heavily visited tourist attraction.

As it turned out, the innocent-appearing workers' huts stood atop none other than the long-forgotten tomb of Tutankhamen. On the very day that the foundations of the first hut were dug away, a step was discovered cut into the rock

beneath it. Another step and then another revealed sixteen steps in all. These led down to a sealed passageway filled with broken rocks and then to a second sealed doorway leading into the tomb itself.

Carter sent a historic telegram to Lord Carnarvon who was still in England. It read: "At last have made wonderful discovery in Valley; a magnificent tomb with seals intact; re-covered same for your arrival; congratulations."

On November 26, 1922, with Lord Carnarvon beside him, Carter made an eye-level opening

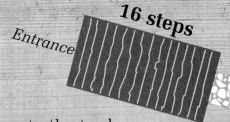

Entrance   16 steps

in the door to the tomb and put a candle through the hole. His own words record the thrill of that moment in which he glimpsed the inside of the tomb.

"At first I could see nothing, the hot air escaping from the chamber causing the candle to flicker, but presently, as my eyes grew accustomed to the light, details of the room within emerged slowly from the mist, strange animals, statues, and gold—everywhere the glint of gold. For the

ously, 'Can you see anything.' It was all I could do to get out the words, 'Yes, wonderful things.'"

Carter was looking into the first of four rooms of a surprisingly small royal tomb. The Antechamber, as the first and largest room was called, was only about twelve by twenty-six feet, the measurements of a fair-sized living room. It was heaped with chairs, footstools, and chests of alabaster,

made of clay.

Sealed doorways, one guarded by two gold-encrusted statues of Tutankhamen, led to the other three rooms of the tomb—an Annex that was even more jumbled than the Antechamber, the Burial Chamber in which the mummy lay, and a small room beyond that called the Treasury.

Carter was not surprised at the disarray that met his eyes, for he had already suspected that Tutankhamen's tomb had been broken into in ancient times. But the robbers had had to leave hastily, even dropping some gold rings and other small articles on their way out. Their lost loot had probably included the bit of gold leaf and the blue cup found outside the tomb in Carter's day. The cemetery officials of ancient times had apparently roughly tidied and resealed the tomb. Then, happily, its entrance had been completely covered over by the building of the Ramses VI workers' huts.

Sealed Doors

Corridor
Passage filled with broken rocks

Ante-chamber

Annex

Treasury

Burial Chamber

The floor plan of the tomb of Tutankhamen

---

disarray (dis′ə rā′) *n.* condition of disorder or confusion.

Three anxious and tension-filled years were to pass before the great moment when Carter opened the coffin containing the mummy of Tutankhamen. During that time, while he was carefully cataloging and clearing the contents of the Antechamber, a number of strange events took place.

First, Carter's canary was eaten by a poisonous desert snake. Those who were superstitious took it as a bad omen. Did the snake represent the pharaoh's anger at having had his tomb disturbed? On his death mask, it was later discovered, Tutankhamen wore the cobra and vulture, twin royal symbols of Lower and Upper Egypt.

Next, less than five months after the opening of the tomb, Lord

The jumbled treasure in the first room of Tutankhamen's tomb as first seen by Howard Carter

Carnarvon died of blood poisoning from a mysterious insect bite on his cheek that had become infected. He was never to see the great, carved stone coffin in the Burial Chamber that rested inside a series of four nested wooden cases covered with gold leaf. Nor was he ever to see the three richly gleaming mummy-shaped coffins nested inside the rectangular stone coffin or, of course, the mummy of Tutankhamen.

Lastly, soon after the discovery of the tomb, Carter himself ran up against numerous problems with the Egyptian government. One of the disputes had to do with which officials and their guests were to be permitted to visit the tomb while the delicate work of recording its contents was going on.

---

coffin (kô'fin) *n.* box or case into which a dead person is placed for burial.

For a time the tomb was sealed up, and Carter actually left Egypt in anger and despair.

Did all of these unpleasant happenings have a hidden meaning? Was there such a thing as a "mummy's curse"? Were Carter and Carnarvon being punished for unearthing the resting place of the pharaoh who had slept longer in his treasure-filled tomb than any other yet known?

Many people thought so. They went to great trouble to try to prove that death was stalking and striking all who had worked with Carter, from the humblest laborer to the most distinguished archaeologist. But Carter himself never believed the wild stories that sprang from his discovery. And, in fact, he went on to live for many more years, dying in 1939 at the age of sixty-five.

The first viewing of Tutankhamen's mummy took place at last in the autumn of 1925. Of the three mummy-shaped coffins, the two outer ones were of wood covered with sheets of gold, while the innermost was of solid gold!

Inside the gold innermost coffin lay the bandaged mummy of Tutankhamen, its head and shoulders covered with a solid-gold mask

174

inlaid with blue lapis lazuli, other semi-precious stones, and colored glass. The mask, serene, youthful, and noble, shows the king wearing the ceremonial false beard and a striped headcloth called a *nemes* (NEM-eez) with the royal cobra and vulture at the brow.

The hasty thieves of ancient times who had invaded Tutankhamen's tomb had been looking only for small objects they could carry away quickly. They had entered the Burial Chamber but had never broken into any of its nested coffins.

On unwrapping the mummy, Carter discovered that there were thirteen layers of linen bandages containing one hundred and forty-three precious gold and bejeweled objects. Among them

---

inlaid (in′lād′) *adj.* decorated with a material set into the surface.
serene (sə rēn′) *adj.* peaceful; calm.

The solid-gold mask found on the mummy of Tutankhamen (left)

The outermost gilded wood coffin in which the mummy of King Tutankhamen rests today in the Burial Chamber of his tomb (bottom)

were necklaces, collars, pendants, bracelets, rings, belts, gold-
sheathed daggers, gold sandals,
and slender golden tubes that
encased the mummy's fingernails
and toenails.

Beneath all this splendor,
however, the mummy itself was a
pitiful disappointment. Blackened
and shrunken by the careless
pouring on of oils and resins, it
was one of the poorer examples of
the New Kingdom art of mummi-
fication.

Who was Tutankhamen?
Why was he buried in such a
small tomb with such great
riches? Why was his mummy so
badly prepared?

To Carter's disappointment,
no papyrus scrolls telling anything
of Tutankhamen's reign or of his
family history were found in the
tomb. We know only that he is
believed to have been either the
brother or the illegitimate son of
the previous king, Amenhotep IV,
who had turned away from the
many gods of Thebes to worship
the sun as the one and only god.
In so doing, Amenhotep IV changed
his name to Akhenaten (Ahk-eh-
NAH-ten), meaning "pleasing to
Aten" (the sun). He also moved

his capital from Thebes to a new
site known as Akhetaten (Ahk-eh-
TAH-ten), or "horizon of the Aten."

As Akhenaten's successor,
Tutankhamen is thought to have
come to the throne as a child of
nine, to have reigned briefly, and
to have died as a youth of eighteen. He married a princess who
may have been his half-sister. He
left no heirs. In the richly stocked
Treasury, the room just off the
Burial Chamber, Carter found two
tiny coffins with the mummified
remains of girl infants who had
probably been dead at birth. Were
they the children of Tutankhamen
and his young wife?

As to Tutankhamen him-
self, we do not know how or why
he died. Was his death caused
by an accident, an illness, or
could he have been murdered?
There is a suspicious scar, possibly from an arrow tip, in front of
the mummy's ear. Did the priests
of Thebes who served the many
gods want Tutankhamen dead because of his relationship with
Akhenaten, who had turned his
back on their religion?

Whatever the reason, Tutankhamen's sudden death may account
for the small size of his tomb.

---

pendants (pen'dənts) *n., pl.* ornamental objects, such as jewels, that hang
from other things.
splendor (splen'dər) *n.* great display, as of riches; magnificence.

Perhaps it had been meant for someone else but was used for the young pharaoh because his own was not ready. On the other hand, Tutankhamen may simply have been an unimportant king who, through Howard Carter's discovery, became the most famous of all of Egypt's kings.

If Tutankhamen's treasure, however, was that of an "unimportant" king buried in a hastily prepared tomb, can we ever guess at the splendor of the contents of those much larger and grander tombs that the grave robbers of Egypt emptied thousands of years ago!

Gold collar from Tomb of Tutankhamen (left), c. 1342 B.C.; detail from Tomb of Amunherkhopshef, son of Ramses III (below), c. 1160 B.C.

Meet Lila Perl

Author Lila Perl says that when she was growing up, she "never thought of being a writer." But, as a child, she unknowingly laid the foundation for becoming one. As she says, "I read a lot. Every time I was told to 'go outside and play,' I went off somewhere with a book." She has written more than fifteen books, including cookbooks and fiction and nonfiction books for young adults.

Perl hopes that her joy in creating each story comes across to her readers. Letters from her readers are a source of great satisfaction to her, and she says that "every single letter is answered."

Perl's first book for young adults, *Red-Flannel Hash and Shoo-Fly Pie: American Regional Foods and Festivals*, was an ALA Notable Book.

RESPONDING TO *Literature*

THINK • TALK • WRITE

1 If you could ask Howard Carter one question, what would it be? Write your ideas in your journal.

2 How did the arrival of the Iron Age around 1100 B.C. affect Egypt? What happened to the mummies as a result?

3 Why did Carter choose to dig for Tutankhamen's tomb where he did? How did he feel when he first glimpsed the inside of the tomb? How do you think you would have felt?

4 What were some of the things Carter found in Tutankhamen's tomb? Why was the discovery of this tomb so exciting for those who studied ancient Egypt?

5 Why did some people believe Carter and Carnarvon were being punished by the "mummy's curse"? What do you think? Should Carter and Carnarvon have been allowed to enter the tomb to study the pharaoh's remains?

ACTIVITIES

- **Write with Chronological Order** The discovery of Tutankhamen's tomb was big news. Imagine that you are a reporter covering the story of Carter and Carnarvon's mummy quest. Write an article about their discoveries. Make sure the sequence of events is clear.

- **Build a Pyramid** A pyramid has three sides and a base. The three sides meet at the top in a point. See the photograph on page 179 for an example. Build a pyramid out of clay or modeling wax. Scrape lines in the sides so that they look like they were built from stone slabs or bricks.

VOCABULARY PRACTICE

On a separate piece of paper, write whether the following pairs of words are *synonyms* or *antonyms*.

1 dramatically—boringly

2 bazaars—markets

3 disarray—order

4 inlaid—undecorated

5 pendants—jewels

6 serene—excitable

7 splendor—grandness

8 deposits—layers

9 mourners—grievers

10 coffin—cradle

Ozymandias

BY PERCY BYSSHE SHELLEY

I met a traveler from an antique land

Who said: Two vast and trunkless legs of stone

Stand in the desert . . . Near them, on the sand,

Half sunk, a shattered visage lies, whose frown,

And wrinkled lip, and sneer of cold command,

Tell that its sculptor well those passions read

Which yet survive, stamped on these lifeless things,

The hand that mocked them, and the heart that fed:

And on the pedestal these words appear:

"My name is Ozymandias, king of kings:

Look on my works, ye Mighty, and despair!"

Nothing beside remains. Round the decay

Of that colossal wreck, boundless and bare

The lone and level sands stretch far away.

bicycle riding

My feet rise
off the planet,
pedal wheels of steel
that sparkle as
they spin me through
the open space I feel
winging out
to galaxies
far beyond the sun,
where bicycles
are satellites,
their orbits never done.

—Sandra Liatsos

BEFORE READING

....

URANUS, NEPTUNE, PLUTO

CONNECT TO LITERATURE

What do you know about Uranus, Neptune, and Pluto? What would you like to know? Jot at least two questions down in your journal. Then, as you read the selection, note facts that might answer your questions.

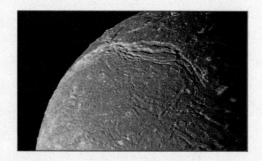

THINKING ABOUT EXPOSITION

Science articles, such as this one about space exploration, are examples of *exposition*. Exposition in nonfiction is the orderly presentation of facts. The purpose of an expository article or report is to provide information. The writer may use any of the following to develop and explain the main idea: facts, examples, definitions, and comparison and contrast.

DID YOU KNOW?

- Once every 176 years, the outer planets line up in such a way that a spacecraft from Earth can visit four in one trip. That time came in 1977. The National Aeronautics and Space Administration (NASA) took advantage by launching the two *Voyager* probes.

- The *Voyager* spacecraft did not carry astronauts. One reason is that it would be nearly impossible to supply human beings with the food, water, and air necessary for life for such a long trip. *Voyager 2,* for example, took nearly a decade to reach Uranus.

- If all goes well, the *Voyagers* will eventually leave the solar system. It is very unlikely that either *Voyager* will ever be found by space travelers from another world. Just in case, though, each carries a message from Earth. A special disk contains pictures, music, and greetings in over 60 languages.

Uranus
Neptune
Pluto

DARK WORLDS

by Patricia Lauber

It takes very sharp eyes to see the dim gleam of Uranus in our night sky. The planet is one of the giants, but it is so far from the sun—1¾ billion miles—that it reflects little light. Through a telescope Uranus appears only as a ghostly blue-green globe.

Even so, astronomers had learned a surprising amount about Uranus before *Voyager 2* reached the planet in January 1986. They knew that the atmosphere held clouds of methane, which gave the planet its color. They knew that Uranus was oddly tilted on its axis. In effect, the planet lies on its side. For part of the year, the north pole faces the sun, then the equator does, then the south pole, then the equator.

methane (meth′ăn) *n.* gas made of carbon and hydrogen.
axis (ak′sis) *n.* imaginary line around which a planet rotates.

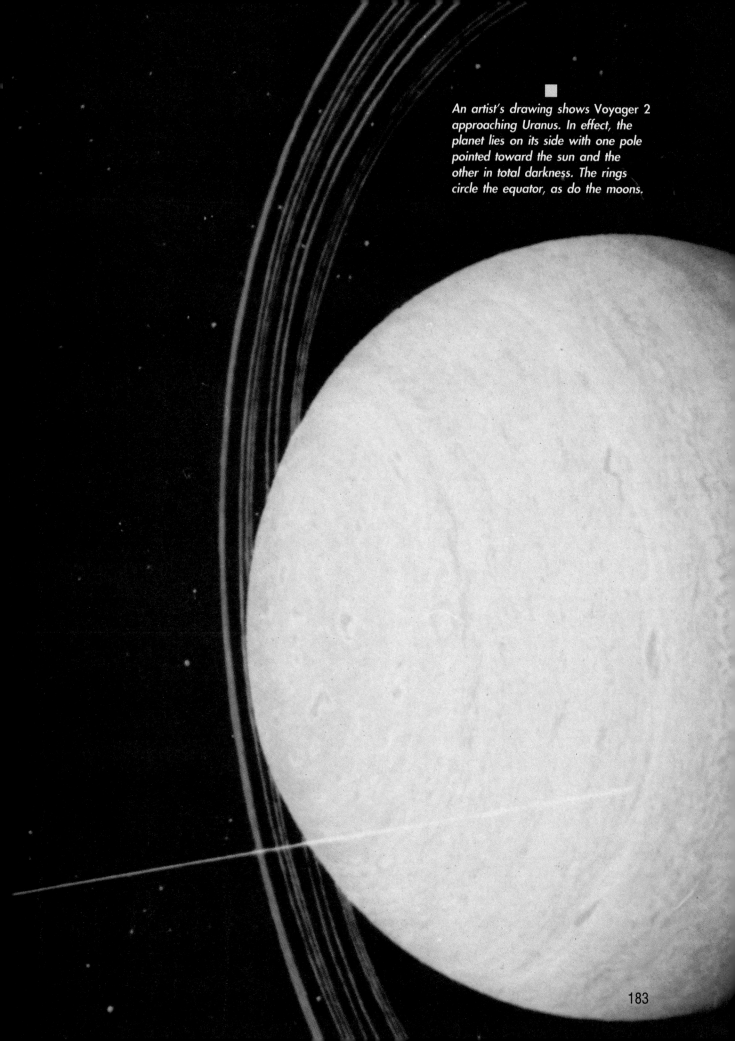

An artist's drawing shows Voyager 2 approaching Uranus. In effect, the planet lies on its side with one pole pointed toward the sun and the other in total darkness. The rings circle the equator, as do the moons.

Scientists think young Uranus may have collided with an Earth-sized object and been knocked onto its side. Uranus takes 84 years to complete one orbit of the sun.

Astronomers had also learned that Uranus had at least nine dark rings and five moons. *Voyager* gave them a good look at the rings and moons.

Unlike Saturn's broad rings of bright, icy particles, the Uranian ones are narrow bands made of chunks of black material that look like lumps of coal ranging in size from 3 to 3,000 feet across. They circle the planet at its equator and revolve around it once every eight hours. As well as the previously known rings, scientists saw two others. Among the rings they also discovered ten small moons. Two appear to be the kind of sheepdog moons found in the rings of Saturn.

The five known moons were surprising. Scientists had thought they might be balls of ice mixed with a little rock and pocked with craters. Instead, they found dingy surfaces, more rock than they had expected, and a number of strange features, perhaps caused by mammoth collisions with comets, perhaps by gravitational tugs from other moons and Uranus, perhaps

by the freezing of material inside the moons.

The two outermost moons, Oberon and Titania, are both about 1,000 miles in diameter and heavily cratered. Several craters on Oberon appear to have been flooded with some kind of dark material. The moon has a mountain that sticks up at least 12 miles above the horizon and a number of straight and curved cliffs. Titania has trenches and cliffs and a strange frostlike pattern that runs beside big cracks, suggesting that material sprayed out, froze, and fell to the surface.

The third moon is Umbriel. Its surface is dark, old, and covered

Titania (right) is marked by craters and fault valleys. What may be frost can be seen along the valley's right center. The icy face of Oberon (below), outermost of the moons, is scarred by impact craters with white rays. A crater with a peak can be seen at center. A mountain can be seen at the lower left edge of the moon.

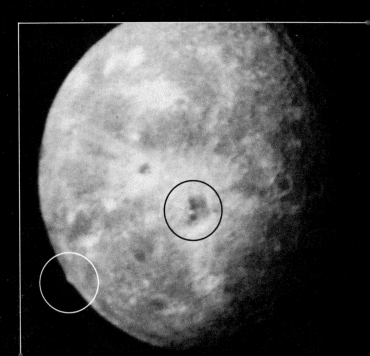

---

particles (pär'ti kəlz) *n., pl.* very small bits; specks.
mammoth (mam'əth) *adj.* huge; gigantic.

184

with big craters. No one knows why the surface is dark or why Umbriel does not show the signs of change that the other moons do.

Ariel, the next moon in, is about the same size as Umbriel—700 miles in diameter. It is crisscrossed with broad, curving valleys and has jagged canyons. Some of its features appear to have been smoothed over, perhaps by glaciers or flooding.

Strangest of all is Miranda, the innermost and smallest moon, only 300 miles in diameter. It looks like a patchwork of features from other moons and planets. Like Mars, Miranda has long, curving valleys. Like Jupiter's Ganymede, it has grooves; some come together in V-shaped patterns, while others form ovals within ovals, in a racetrack pattern. Miranda has cratered highlands that look like those of Earth's moon and cliffs that are ten times higher than the walls of the Grand Canyon. Why Miranda looks as it does is a puzzle. One idea is that the small moon has been blasted apart in giant collisions and that its gravity plastered the pieces back together again.

Uranus itself also offered a number of surprises and puzzles. One puzzle has to do with the

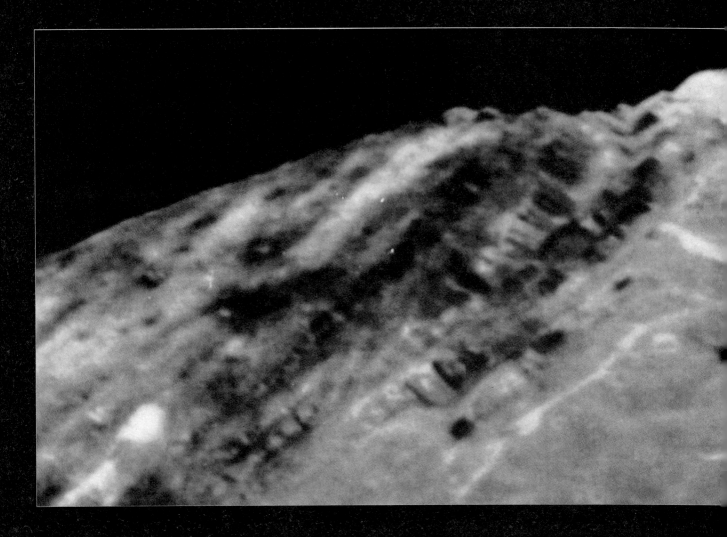

planet's magnetic poles. On other planets, such as Earth, the magnetic poles are close to the geographic poles. On Uranus they are not. If the earth's magnetic poles were like those of Uranus, one would be at Los Angeles and the other in the Indian Ocean. Another puzzle had to do with temperature, which was the same at the pole

Umbriel's cratered surface (left) is probably the oldest in the system of Uranian moons. Its strangest feature is the bright ring at top, which may be related to a crater.

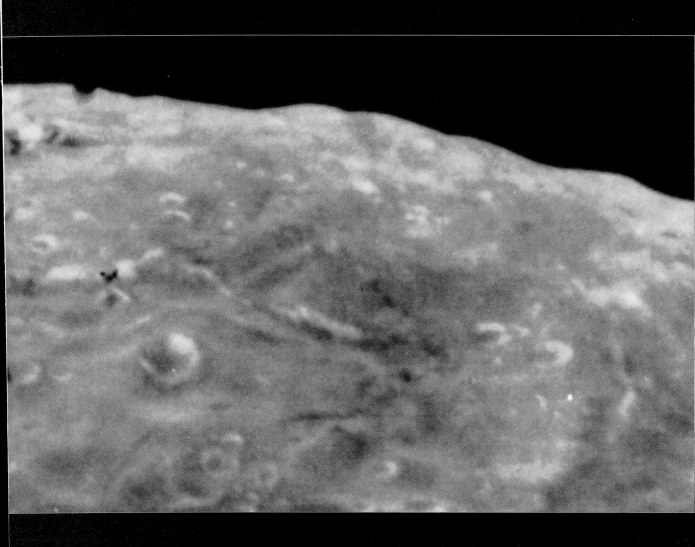

facing the sun as at the equator. The region between the two was colder. Scientists wondered whether these odd findings had to do with the fact that Uranus is tipped over on its side. Then, some three and a half years later, *Voyager* arrived at Neptune and made the same discoveries about tipped magnetic poles and temperatures. Because

■

Right, cliffs and winding valleys crisscross the crater-pocked face of Ariel. At the top left portion of the planet (above), stepped terraces jut up on Miranda. They mark the edge of one of the sets of ovals within ovals.

Neptune is not tipped over but sits upright, scientists knew they would have to start over in their search for an explanation.

At the time *Voyager* reached Neptune, in late summer of 1989, little was known about the planet. Outermost of the giants, it is so dim and distant that it cannot be seen from Earth without a telescope, and a telescope shows only a faint greenish planet with some markings in its atmosphere. Scientists knew that Neptune took 165 years to travel once around the sun, that it had at least two moons, a big one and a small one, and that it seemed to have pieces of rings. They expected to find a near-twin of Uranus. The two planets are about the same size. Each is a big ball of molten rock and water wrapped in an atmosphere of hydrogen, helium, and methane. They seem more closely related to comets than to Jupiter and Saturn—and may, indeed, have formed out of colliding comets.

But as *Voyager* neared Neptune, surprise followed surprise. Neptune turned out to be warmer than Uranus, even though it is a billion miles farther from the sun. The temperature in its upper atmosphere is 261 degrees below zero, as compared with −360 degrees on Uranus. Unlike Uranus, Neptune has its own heat, probably left over from the days of its formation. The heat disturbs the frigid gases of the atmosphere and sets them rolling, with winds of up to 1,500 miles an hour. And there is still more weather. Neptune has a giant storm system, the size of Earth, where winds blow at 700 miles an hour. Because it reminded them of Jupiter's Great Red Spot, scientists named it the Great Dark Spot. A smaller storm system lies farther south in the atmosphere.

Alone among the giant planets, Neptune has fleecy white clouds that look like cirrus clouds on Earth. Some stretch out for thousands of miles. The clouds may be pockets of frozen methane. Some seem attached to the Great Dark Spot and the smaller dark spot.

Before *Voyager* reached Neptune, the planet appeared to have pieces of rings—bright arcs— circling it. Pictures from the spacecraft show that Neptune's rings are complete and that there are at least five. One of them, however, has places where material clumps together and the ring thickens. From far, far away, these places looked like arcs.

---

frigid (frij′id) *adj.* very cold.

arcs (ärks) *n., pl.* curved lines between points on a circle.

The arcs turned out to be bright clumps of matter in Neptune's outer ring. This picture shows only the two brightest rings. Scientists cannot be sure exactly how many rings Neptune has.

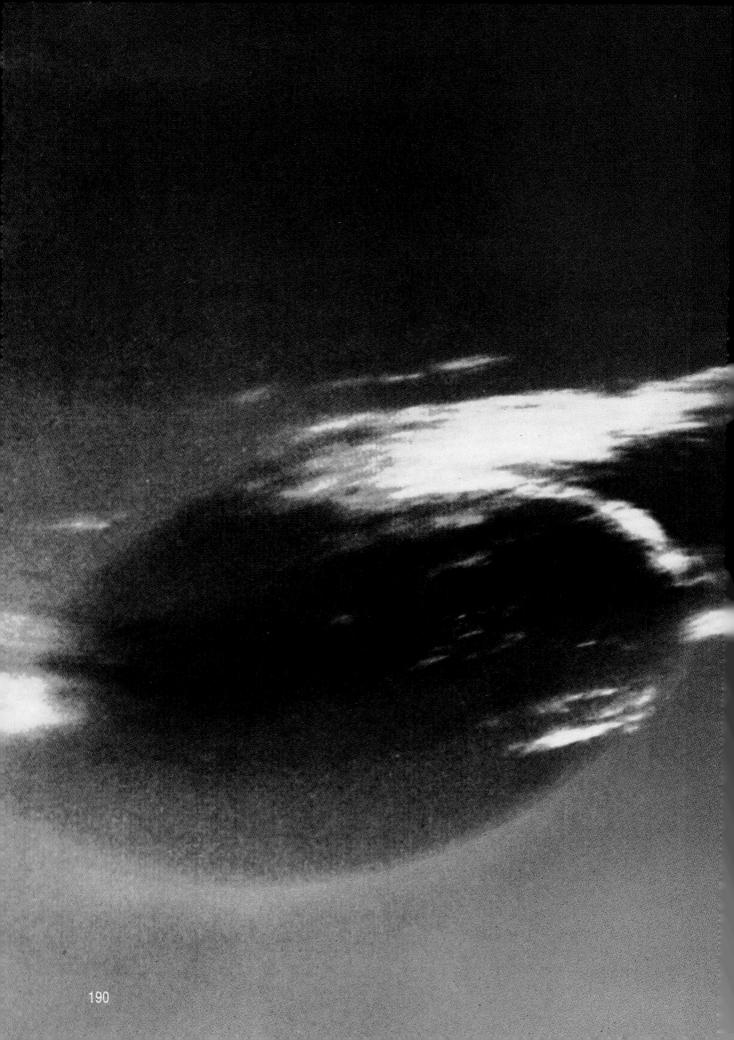

Scientists suspect that the clumping may be caused by the kind of sheepdog moons found in the rings of Saturn and Uranus, even though *Voyager* did not see any. But it did find six previously unknown moons, fewer than scientists had expected. All are dark and small—30 to 300 miles in diameter—with odd shapes and battered faces.

The two moons known earlier are Nereid and Triton. Nereid, which is the smaller, has an unusual orbit. It is both large and oval, unlike the circular orbits of most moons. Scientists think this moon may be an object, such as an <u>asteroid</u>, that was captured by Neptune's gravity.

Triton is "a world unlike any other," scientists say. Early pictures showed a ball glazed with methane and nitrogen ice blitzed pink by radiation. Closer up, the moon proved to have a large cap at its south pole, possibly made of nitrogen ice. The regions beyond the polar cap are crinkled landscapes of canyons and peaks that look like the skin of a cantaloupe. They are slashed by long cracks that meet in X's and Y's, like highway <u>intersections</u>. Surface temperatures are 400 degrees below zero, making Triton the coldest place known in the solar system.

Triton has a very thin atmosphere, made mostly of nitrogen. For reasons not yet understood, the top of the atmosphere is warmer than the surface of the moon.

Voyager discovered two huge storm systems on Neptune, the Great Dark Spot and the smaller dark spot, with a bright center, farther south (shown opposite, far left). The small dark spot rotated at the same speed as the planet: once every 16 hours and three minutes. The Great Dark Spot took about 18 hours. Between the two storm systems is a bright feature nicknamed Scooter, because of the speed at which it moves. The white clouds are the only ones ever seen in the atmospheres of the outer planets. Triton's large south polar ice cap (above left) is to the left of a region that looks like the skin of a cantaloupe, marked by canyons and peaks and giant cracks that intersect one another. In this picture the cap is at the height of its 41-year-long summer and has evaporated away in places along its edge.

---

asteroid (as'tə roid') *n.* any of thousands of small, rocky bodies that revolve around the sun.

intersections (in'tər sek'shənz) *n., pl.* places where two roads meet and cross.

As scientists studied the surface of Triton, they were struck by the fact that the big moon had few craters, although like the planets and other moons, it too must have been bombarded. They think this is a sign of internal heat, that the moon must have been stretched and compressed, like Jupiter's Europa and Io. Slush forced its way up through the big cracks and resurfaced the moon, hiding the craters.

There is every reason to think that Triton still holds heat. The clue to this heat was the most surprising discovery of all: volcanoes. Careful study of pictures from *Voyager* showed violent plumes of gas erupting from the face of the moon and reaching several miles into space. The discovery made Triton the second moon known to have volcanoes.

Scientists had long known that Triton was a big moon. Close up, it proved to be 1,700 miles in diameter, a little smaller than anyone had thought and about 400 miles smaller than Earth's moon. They had also known that Triton orbited Neptune backward. Some small moons, which are probably captured asteroids, orbit their planets backward, but no other big moon does. Except for Triton, big moons all move in the same direction that their planets spin. This led scientists to wonder if Triton was originally a small planet that was captured by Neptune and became a big moon.

The new findings from *Voyager* support this idea. As Triton began to orbit Neptune, it would have swept up smaller moons, leaving only the few that *Voyager* saw. It would have been pumped by Neptune and heated up inside. And Pluto, which probably formed at the same time as Triton, would

Pluto's tiny size and great distance make it look like a faint star, even when photographed through a telescope. But Pluto is orbiting the sun and moving against the fixed stars.

It can be identified in photographs taken only 24 hours apart, as these were. Pluto was discovered in 1930 by comparing such photographs.

have become the one small planet in the outer solar system, so far out that it takes 248 Earth years to orbit the sun.

Pluto's orbit is peculiar. It is more oval than that of any other planet, and it crosses Neptune's orbit. In 1979 Pluto's orbit brought the planet inside Neptune's, where it will stay until 1999. During that time Neptune will be the planet farthest from the sun.

Pluto is about the same size as Triton and probably also has a thin atmosphere. At least some of its surface is covered with ice. The small planet has a large moon named Charon, with a diameter nearly a third of its own. The moon orbits close to Pluto, and each always keeps the same face toward the other. They are more like a double planet than a planet and a moon.

Although *Voyager* could not visit Pluto, scientists feel, in a way, that they have already seen the planet—that when some spacecraft does reach Pluto, it will turn out to be much like Triton, but without volcanoes.

Meet Patricia Lauber

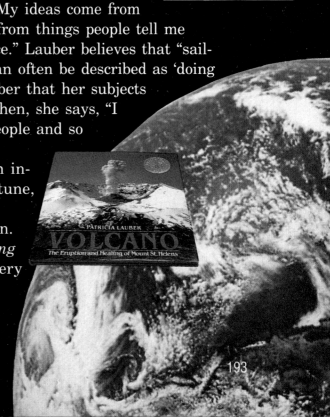

From the volcanoes of Earth to the farthest reaches of the solar system, Patricia Lauber's books span a wide variety of subjects. "My ideas come from everywhere—from things I read, from things people tell me about . . . from things I experience." Lauber believes that "sailing a boat or exploring a forest can often be described as 'doing research.'" It is important to Lauber that her subjects interest her very much, because then, she says, "I want to share them with other people and so I write about them."

Journey to the Planets, which includes the chapter "Uranus, Neptune, Pluto: Dark Worlds," received an American Book Award nomination. *Volcano: The Eruption and Healing of Mount St. Helens* was a Newbery Honor Book.

RESPONDING TO *Literature*

THINK • TALK • WRITE

1 What did you discover about the three outer planets in this selection? Jot down in your journal the facts you found most interesting.

2 What is the same about Uranus and Neptune? What is different? Why were scientists surprised by the information *Voyager 2* sent back regarding Neptune?

3 The subtitle of this selection is "Dark Worlds." Why is this subtitle appropriate? What other subtitle(s) would you suggest?

4 Almost everything that is known today of Uranus and Neptune comes from the *Voyager* expedition. Do you think it was worth the millions of dollars it took to launch the probes? Explain.

5 Planets are named after Greek and Roman gods due to the influence these cultures had on European and American astronomy. If you could rename Uranus and Neptune after prominent figures in your culture, whom would you pick? Why?

ACTIVITIES

• **Write with Exposition** Find out more about the *Voyager* missions. Find books or magazine articles at the library, or write to the headquarters of NASA in Washington, D. C. (A librarian can help you find the address.) Then write a report based on your research. Be sure you have a main idea and supporting details.

• **Make Model Planets** Use clay, papier-mâché, or another material to make models of Uranus, Neptune, and Pluto. Keep in mind that Uranus and Neptune are about the same size, with diameters of around 50,000 kilometers (30,000 mi.). Pluto is much smaller, with a diameter of 3,400 kilometers (2,000 mi.).

VOCABULARY PRACTICE

On a separate piece of paper, write the letter of the word that is least like the other words in the set.

particles   mammoth
frigid   arcs
intersections

1 **a.** particles   **b.** pieces
   c. fragments   **d.** whole

2 **a.** tiny   **b.** mammoth
   c. slight   **d.** miniature

3 **a.** icy   **b.** cold
   c. frigid   **d.** heat

4 **a.** arcs   **b.** curves
   c. circles   **d.** begins

5 **a.** crossings   **b.** interlinkings
   c. subtraction   **d.** intersections

I am

on my way

running

Jeanette Larzalere during
her coming-of-age
ceremony, Fort Apache
Reservation, Arizona, 1984

I am on my way running,
I am on my way running,
Looking toward me is the edge of the world,
I am trying to reach it,
The edge of the world does not look far away,
To that I am on my way running.

—Tohono O'odham Song for a Girl's Coming-of-Age Ceremony
   translated by Frances Densmore

195

SP O T

on

FOLKLORE

A philosopher once said that the best way to get to know a people is to look at its children's bedtime stories. These stories often treat basic issues of good and evil or of life and death. Many have survived for centuries without being written down.

The Giant 1923 N. C. Wyeth

Imagine that this painting is an illustration from a book. If you were going to tell a story based on this painting, how would you begin?

What do you notice about the children in this painting? What do you think their emotions are? How would you feel on that beach?

What fairy tales or stories have you read in which ordinary children meet giants? How is this giant like others you have read about?

196

LIGHT

TYPES OF FOLKLORE

The *folklore* of a culture includes the stories, songs, and poems that people pass along from generation to generation. Works that survive by word of mouth become part of a culture's *oral tradition.*

FOLK TALES entertain people. Many folk tales make fun of human weaknesses. Often the characters are farmers or laborers shown to have better values than their more wealthy, powerful neighbors.

FAIRY TALES are about fanciful characters with extraordinary abilities.

- *Characters* include giants, monsters, dragons, fairies, trolls, gnomes, evil beings, talking animals, and kindly godmothers.
- *Events* include transformations, granting of wishes, displays of superhuman strength or abilities, trickery, and magic.

TRICKSTER TALES tell how clever animals or people outsmart fools. Native American and African American folklore feature well-known trickster characters.

TALL TALES are humorous stories that exaggerate events and characters beyond belief.

FABLES are short stories that teach a lesson through a *moral*—a principle about right and wrong. Most fables have animal characters that behave like people.

MYTHS are set in ancient times and explain aspects of life and nature.

- *Creation myths* explain how the earth was formed.
- *Greek and Roman myths* tell of gods, goddesses, and mortal heroes and heroines.

LEGENDS are stories that usually describe real historical figures in fictional situations.

In the selections that follow, you will read different types of folklore. What you learn will add to your understanding and enjoyment of this type of literature. It will also help you in writing your own work of folklore.

FOLKLORE

BELLEROPHON AND THE FLYING HORSE

CONNECT TO LITERATURE

In your journal, write about one time when you were a hero—to others or just yourself. Then, as you read about the Greek hero Bellerophon (bə ler′ə fon′), notice what traits set him apart.

INTRODUCTION TO THE MODEL FOLK TALE

As you read the folklore in this unit, you will find that the tales share common elements. They all feature a hero or heroine with superhuman abilities. The hero or heroine sets off on a *quest,* or journey, and on the way must overcome major obstacles. He or she fulfills the quest and obtains special blessings.

As you read "Bellerophon and the Flying Horse," use the notes in the margin. The notes will help further your understanding of the basic elements of a myth. As you read, you might like to note your own thoughts and impressions in your journal.

DID YOU KNOW?

- In Greek mythology, Chimera (ki mîr′ə) is a fire-breathing monster composed of parts from a lion, a goat, and a snake. The word has come to mean any strange illusion or wild idea.

- Athena (ə thē′nə) was the Greek goddess of wisdom. According to myth, she hated war but enjoyed devising military strategy, as if it were a game. Athena had taught Bellerophon's mother until the woman was as wise as the gods.

- The ancient Greeks believed the winged horse Pegasus (peg′ə səs) was created when the hero Perseus killed a monster called the Gorgon.

BELLEROPHON
AND THE FLYING HORSE

Retold by PAMELA OLDFIELD

Bellerophon, riding Pegasus, fights the Chimera 6th century B.C.
Detail from red-figured cup from Rhodes, Greece   The Louvre, Paris

ONCE LONG AGO A YOUNG MAN NAMED BELLEROPHON
was staying with the King of Argos. The king's wife was impressed
by Bellerophon and said as much to her husband. She talked about
him so much that the king grew tired of listening to her.

"All you talk about is Bellerophon," he grumbled. "Try to think
about something different for a change. The boy is far too young
to be a hero."

His foolish wife took no notice. Day after day she told the king how handsome Bellerophon was, how clever and how brave. At last the king grew so jealous that he decided to get rid of Bellerophon, but without telling his wife. He handed Bellerophon a sealed letter and asked him to deliver it to the King of Lycia.

"This is a most important letter," he told Bellerophon. "Be sure you give it to him."

Bellerophon agreed to deliver the letter and set off at once. He soon reached Lycia and met the king. The two of them got on well right from the start. The king entertained him so lavishly that it was several days before Bellerophon remembered the letter.

"Forgive me, Your Majesty," he said. "I was asked to give you this." The king opened the letter. As he read it he turned quite pale.

"Whatever is the matter?" asked Bellerophon. "Is it bad news?" The king made no answer, but began to mutter to himself.

"This is treachery," he whispered. "I cannot believe it." Then he looked up at Bellerophon. "Never ask me about this letter," he commanded, and he threw it straight on the fire.

That night when Bellerophon went to bed he wondered about what was in the letter, but he was tired and soon fell asleep. The king, however, could not sleep. The letter had given him a terrible shock. It said that Bellerophon was a wicked young man and asked the king to have him killed.

"How could I do such a thing?" murmured the king. "Bellerophon seems such a pleasant young man, and he is a guest in my house. The King of Argos is known for his hot temper and he may soon regret this rash decision."

---

lavishly (lav′ish lē) *adv.* grandly; in great amounts.
treachery (trech′ə rē) *n.* betrayal of a trust.
rash (rash) *adj.* acting with or characterized by too much haste.

He paced up and down until at last he had an idea. "I shall send Bellerophon to slay the Chimera," he decided. "He may well die in the attempt, but if he succeeds even the King of Argos will have to admit that he is a true hero."

So the next day the king told Bellerophon about the ferocious monster that was causing distress to the people of his kingdom, and begged him to do something about it.

"The Chimera is ruining their lives," said the king. "I <u>implore</u> you to destroy it for me. You will find it over in the hills where the sun rises."

Bellerophon was rather puzzled by all this, but he agreed to go. He walked for many miles without seeing a sign of the monster and eventually stopped to ask an old farmer if he was going in the right direction. When Bellerophon mentioned what he was looking for, the old man's eyes widened in alarm.

"Stay away from the Chimera," he warned Bellerophon. "It's the <u>vilest</u> creature ever born. Plenty of young men have tried to kill it, but they have all died in the attempt."

"Perhaps I will have better luck," said Bellerophon hopefully. The old farmer shook his head.

"Young people today just will not listen to reason," he grumbled, "but if you are determined to get yourself killed, take that path through the woods. It will lead you to the Chimera."

Bellerophon thanked the farmer politely and went on his way, trying not to be alarmed by what he had been told. He was not looking forward to fighting the Chimera, but if he turned back without even trying he would be called a coward.

An hour later he sat down to rest, and to his astonishment a beautiful woman appeared before him.

The hero in a myth is often tested several times before he is proven worthy. Most heroes, like Bellerophon, face challenges that mean life or death.

Heroes in myths often receive warnings about future events. This device builds **suspense.**

---

implore (im plôr′) *v.t.* ask earnestly.
vilest (vīl′est) *adj.* most evil.

In Greek myths gods and goddesses often interfere in human life, as Athena does here.

"I am Athena, goddess of wisdom," she told him. "I know you plan to fight the Chimera and I will help you." She held out a <u>bridle</u>, and as Bellerophon took it from her she smiled at him and vanished.

"How odd," thought Bellerophon, staring at the bridle. "What possible use could a bridle be when I have no horse?" The bridle was of finest white leather studded with gold and decorated with precious jewels. "I shall take it with me," he said, and went on his way, puzzling over the strange gift. What Bellerophon did not notice was that far above him Pegasus, the winged horse of the gods, was wheeling and prancing among the clouds. Suddenly the snow-white horse flew down to earth to drink at a spring of pure water. Bellerophon was overjoyed when he saw the graceful creature before him. Now he knew why Athena had given him the bridle.

Myths often tell about **fantastic creatures,** both good and evil. What unusual qualities does Pegasus have?

He approached the horse slowly, speaking softly to reassure him. "I know you are Pegasus," he said. "You are always ridden by the gods. I am not a god, but Athena has given me this bridle and I must ride you when I go to fight the dreadful Chimera." Pegasus nodded his head as if he understood, but just as Bellerophon reached out to touch him, the horse sprang into the air and out of reach. For a

bridle (brī′dəl) *n.* part of a horse's harness, including the bit and reins, that fits over the head, used to guide or control the animal.

moment Bellerophon thought the horse would fly away, but then he came down again to drink. Eventually Bellerophon gave up his attempt to catch the horse. He put down the bridle and stood by, quietly observing. Pegasus was a fine animal with hoofs and wings of silver and a flowing mane and tail. Suddenly Bellerophon ran forward, jumped onto the horse's back, and clung to its mane. The horse tried every trick he knew to throw off his unwanted rider. He flew up into the air and swooped down again, but somehow Bellerophon managed to stay on its back. At last Pegasus flew down to land beside the spring once more.

Bellerophon guessed that now Pegasus would wear the bridle and he slipped it over the horse's head. Then he sprang once more onto the horse's back. "Take me to the Chimera!" he cried and Pegasus leaped upward, tossing his head with excitement.

They flew for many miles until at last they came to a valley where the grass and trees were trampled and broken. Far below them a village lay in ruins. From the dark hills beyond the valley they heard a thunderous rumbling roar.

"That must be the Chimera," whispered Bellerophon. He leaned forward and reassuringly patted the horse's neck, but his own heart beat faster at

The heroes in myths use reason as well as strength to achieve their goals. How does Bellerophon trick Pegasus into carrying him?

Center:
Athena holding a shield with an image of Pegasus
c. 500–490 B.C. Panathenaic amphora The Metropolitan Museum of Art, New York Rogers Fund, 1907 (Accession no. 07.286.79)

Chimera *second half of the 6th century* B.C. *Detail from Greek kylix* *The British Museum, London*

the thought of what was to come. Pegasus showed no fear, but flew on toward the rumbling sound. Soon they were confronted by a horrible sight. The Chimera rose up before them . . . this was no ordinary beast—the monster had *three heads!*

One head roared—it was the head of a lion. The second head hissed—it was the head of a giant snake. The third and last head bleated like a goat and had two sharp horns.

Bellerophon was terrified. He almost wished he could turn back, but then he remembered Athena. She had sent Pegasus to help Bellerophon and that made him feel much braver.

"Death to the cruel Chimera!" he shouted, and drew out his sword. The lion's head reached out toward him, its mouth ready to swallow him up, but the winged horse darted sideways and Bellerophon cut off the head with one mighty blow. The Chimera's rage was frightful. The snake's head lunged at Bellerophon, hissing loudly, but down came the sword again. Chop! And away rolled the snake's head.

"Two heads gone and one to go!" shouted Bellerophon, but the Chimera was not going to be beaten quite so easily. Without warning it reared up on its hind legs and reached out with its fearsome claws. They sank into the winged horse, who whinnied with pain. Silver feathers floated down and the beautiful white mane was suddenly speckled with blood.

Notice that Bellerophon forgets his terror when he sees that Pegasus is injured. From this we can infer that he is compassionate as well as courageous, two heroic traits.

The sight of the horse's blood made Bellerophon forget his own fear. Without a thought for his own safety he slashed again and again at the goat's head until that too lay bleeding on the ground. Now the Chimera had lost all three of its heads, and it collapsed in a heap.

Bellerophon waited, his sword at the ready, but the Chimera would rise no more.

A great cry went up as the people ran from their hiding places in the ruined village. "The Chimera is dead!" they cried, cheering and waving as Pegasus and Bellerophon flew skyward once more. They watched the young man and the horse as they rose higher and higher and disappeared at last among the rolling clouds.

The grateful people then set about rebuilding their village and replanting their crops. The memory of the beautiful white horse and its <u>valiant</u> rider would live on in their hearts forever. Bellerophon had escaped death, and no one could now doubt that he was indeed a hero.

Myths were intended to entertain, to describe the gods, to preserve history, to teach lessons, or to explain natural phenomena. What purpose do you think this story served?

---

valiant (val′yənt) *adj.* brave; courageous.

MEET PAMELA OLDFIELD

Pamela Oldfield (born 1931) comes from London and lives in a small village in England. A former school teacher, Oldfield is the author of dozens of books for children and adults. Besides retelling Greek myths, she often writes about the supernatural, in books such as *Ghost Stories* and *A Witch in the Summer House*.

More Greek Myths

- *The Golden Fleece* by Padraic Colum (Macmillan, 1921). Greek myths are woven into a continuous tale filled with adventure and suspense.

- *Two Queens of Heaven* by Doris Gates (Puffin, 1983). The myths surrounding the Greek goddesses Aphrodite and Demeter are retold in this book.

- *The Adventures of Ulysses* by Bernard Evslin (Scholastic, 1989). In this retelling of Homer's *Odyssey,* Ulysses faces many dangers.

RESPONDING TO *Literature*

THINK • TALK • WRITE

1 Did you enjoy this myth? How does it compare with others you know? Describe in your journal scenes or ideas that interested you.

2 What is the King of Lycia's problem? How does he solve it? Does this solution seem fair? Explain.

3 What lessons about human nature do you think this myth teaches?

4 Greek myths were passed on orally for generations. Why do you think very different versions of the same myth often exist today?

5 What traits does Bellerophon share with superhuman figures you know, such as Superman?

ACTIVITY

- **Write About Myths** Copy and complete this prediction chart for "Bellerophon and the Flying Horse."

Pages	What I Predicted	What Happened

VOCABULARY PRACTICE

Choose the vocabulary word that best fits in each blank. Write the word on a separate piece of paper.

lavishly   valiant

implore   rash

vilest

The two sisters entertained the three heroes ___**1**___ before explaining what the task was.

"Our village is beset by a horrible worm, ten feet long and two feet around," said the elder sister. "Its mouth is a round hole studded with sharp teeth." She shuddered. "It is the ___**2**___ creature you can imagine. It will take great courage to defeat this monster. Only the most ___**3**___ of you will be able to beat it."

"We ___**4**___ you to destroy the creature for the villagers' sake," continued the younger sister. "But do not make a ___**5**___ decision. Think about it tonight, and give us your answer tomorrow."

With that, the two sisters retired for the night. They left the three would-be heroes to consider their quest.

FOLKLORE

SAVITRI AND SATYAVAN

CONNECT TO LITERATURE

If you could have three wishes, what would you ask for? Record your wishes in your journal. Then, as you read the selection, discover what Savitri, the main character, wishes for and how her wishes are granted.

THINKING ABOUT HEROES/HEROINES

The hero or heroine figure is common to folklore around the world. Even many tales written today feature a brave and clever woman or man with extraordinary, even superhuman, abilities. These heroic abilities are used for good, and the person is admired by others.

As you read the following folk tale, watch for ways in which Savitri demonstrates heroic abilities: extraordinary strength, determination, bravery, and cleverness.

DID YOU KNOW?

- The story of Princess Savitri (sä vē′trē) is one of India's best-loved tales. It appears within *The Mahabharata* (mə hä bär′ə tə), an epic poem that has important religious meaning for Hindus.

- *The Mahabharata* was recounted by oral storytellers for centuries before being written down around the time of Christ. The title means "Great King Bharata," and the epic tells the story of Bharata's descendants. A great battle is fought between two groups of cousins over his kingdom, and many lives are lost. Within the main story, other stories are told, and religious philosophy is discussed.

- The princess's parents named her after the Hindu goddess Savitri, who granted their wish for a child.

Lady Feeding a Bird   *early 17th century   Deccan, Bijapur, India   Chester Beatty Library, Dublin*

Savitri and Satyavan

retold by Madhur Jaffrey

Once upon a time there lived a King and Queen, who after many years of being childless, gave birth to a daughter. She was the most beautiful baby the parents could have hoped for, and they named her Savitri.

When Savitri grew up and it was time for her to marry, her father said to her, "Dearest child, we hate to part with you. You have given us the greatest joy that humans can ever know. But it is time for you to start a family of your own. Is there any man you wish to marry?"

"No, father," replied Savitri, "I have not yet met a man I would care to spend my life with."

"Perhaps we should send for pictures of all the nobles in the country. You might come upon a face you like," said the King and he sent his court painter to bring back portraits of all the nobles and rulers in the country.

Savitri examined the portraits, one after the other, and shook her head. The men in the portraits all looked so very ordinary, even though they were all emperors, kings and princes.

The King then said to his daughter, "It might be best if you went to all the big cities of the world to find a husband for yourself. I will

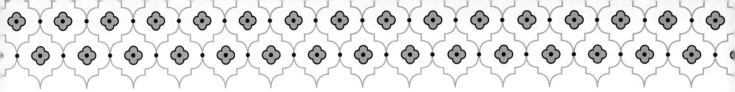

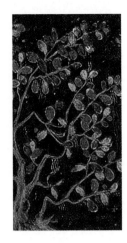

provide you with the proper <u>escort</u> of men, elephants, camels and horses. Good luck. I hope you can find a man to love."

Savitri set out with a large <u>procession</u> of men, elephants, camels and horses. In her effort to visit all the cities of the world, she had to cross many oceans and deserts. She did this fearlessly. But she never found a man she could love.

When she returned home, her father said to her, "You have looked in all the big cities of the world and have found no man that you wish to marry. Perhaps you should now search through all the forests of the world."

Savitri set out again with a large procession of men, elephants, camels and horses, and began searching through all the forests of the world. She did this fearlessly.

She had looked through the last forest and was just about to return home when she came upon a young man who was cutting wood.

"What is your name?" she asked.

"Satyavan, your highness," he replied.

"Please do not address me as 'your highness,'" she said. "My name is Savitri. What do you do for a living?"

"I do nothing much," the young man replied. "I have very old, blind parents. I live with them in a small, thatched cottage at the edge of the forest. Every morning I go out to cut wood and gather food. In the evening I make a fire for my parents, cook their dinner, and feed them. That is all I do."

Savitri returned to her father's palace and said, "Dearest mother and father. I have finally found a man to love and marry. His name is Satyavan and he lives in a cottage by a forest not too far from here."

"But will you be able to live a simple life in a simple cottage?" asked her father. "This young man obviously has no money."

"That makes no difference at all to me," Savitri said. "He is capable, honest, good and caring. That is what I respect and love him for."

The King sent a message to the blind couple's cottage saying that Princess Savitri wished to marry their son, Satyavan. When Satyavan arrived home that evening with his heavy load of wood his

---

escort (es′kôrt) *n.* person or persons who accompany another or others as a courtesy, honor, or protection.
procession (prə sesh′ən) *n.* group of persons or things moving along in a continuous forward movement, especially in a formal or orderly manner.

parents said, "There are messengers here from the King. Princess Savitri wishes to marry you."

"I love the young lady in question," replied Satyavan, "but it will be impossible to marry her. She has money, jewels, elephants, camels and servants. What can *I* offer her?"

Tears rolled down the faces of his blind parents. "Son," cried the mother, "we never told you this, but long ago, before you were born, your father too was a ruler with a kingdom of his own. His wicked brother blinded us and stole our birthright. You should have been born a prince and heir to the kingdom, quite worthy of the beautiful Savitri. We have fallen on hard times, but if you two love each other, why should you not marry? Who knows what the future has in store for anybody?"

So a message was sent back to the King saying that Satyavan had agreed to the match.

On the day of the wedding, the King and Queen held a huge reception. Everyone of any importance was invited.

That is how it happened that the wisest Sage in the kingdom appeared at the scene.

Just before the wedding ceremony, the Sage took the King aside and whispered, "It is my duty to warn you. The young man your daughter is to marry is decent and of good character, but his stars are crossed. He will die very shortly. This marriage would be a tragic mistake."

The King felt ill when he heard this. He called his daughter and told her what the Sage had said, adding, "Perhaps it is best to call the marriage off."

"No, father," Savitri said solemnly, "I will marry Satyavan, whatever our future may hold."

Savitri was no fool, however. She had heard that the Sage knew of heavenly remedies for earthly problems.

"Oh dearest Sage," Savitri said to him, "surely there is a way I can prevent my husband from dying. You, in your great wisdom, must offer me some hope. There must be something I can do?"

The Sage thought deeply, "You can extend your husband's life

---

birthright (bûrth′rīt′) *n.* right, privilege, or possession that a person is entitled to by birth.

reception (ri sep′shən) *n.* social gathering, especially one at which guests are formally received.

solemnly (sol′əm lē) *adv.* in a serious and earnest manner.

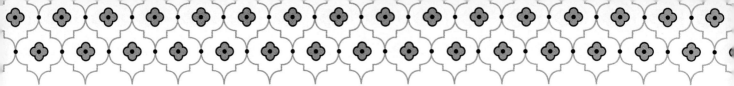

by fasting. Eat nothing but fruit, roots and leaves for a year, and Satyavan will live for those twelve months. After that he *must* die."

With a sense of doom hanging over the bride's family, the wedding did take place. The groom and his parents were told nothing of what the future held for them.

Savitri began to lead a simple life with her husband and parents-in-law. Early each morning, Satyavan set out for the forest to cut wood and to <u>forage</u> for food. When he was gone, Savitri made the beds, swept the house, and shepherded her in-laws around wherever they wished to go. She also prayed and fasted.

One day Savitri's mother-in-law said to her, "Child, we know how rich a family you come from. Since we have lost our kingdom, we can offer you no <u>fineries</u> but Satyavan does collect enough food for all of us. We have noticed that you eat just fruit, roots and leaves and never touch any grain. That is not a healthy diet. We are beginning to worry about you."

"Oh, please do not worry about me," begged Savitri. "I love to eat fruit."

The twelve months were almost over. On the very last day, Savitri got up with her husband and announced that she would accompany him into the forest.

"Child, what will you do in the forest? The work is hard and there are all kinds of dangerous animals," said her mother-in-law.

"Do stay at home," said Satyavan, "the forest is not a comfortable place."

"I have travelled through all the forests of the world. I was not uncomfortable and I was not frightened. Let me go with you today."

Satyavan had no answer for his wife. He loved her a lot and trusted her instincts. "Come along then, we'd better start quickly. The sun is almost up."

So they set out towards the heart of the forest.

Once there, Satyavan climbed a tree and began to saw off its dried-up branches.

It was a scorchingly hot day in May. The trees had shed the last <u>withered</u> yellowing leaves. Savitri looked for a cool spot to sit down

---

forage (fôr′ij) *v.i.* hunt or search for food or supplies.

fineries (fī′nə rēz) *n., pl.* fine or showy clothes or ornaments.

withered (wi<u>th</u>′ərd) *adj.* dried up or shriveled, as from heat or loss of moisture.

Squirrels in a Plane Tree   *c.1610   Abu'l-Hassan and Mansur   The British Library, London*

and just could not find any. Her heart was beating like a two-sided drum. Any moment now the year would end.

"Ahhh . . ." came a cry from Satyavan.

Savitri ran towards him, "Are you all right?"

"I have a piercing headache."

"Come down from the tree. It's the heat. I will run and find some shade." Savitri found a banyan tree and helped Satyavan towards it. Many of the banyan tree's branches had gone deep into the earth and come up again to form a deliciously cool <u>grove</u>. The leaves rustled gently to fan the couple.

"Put your head in my lap," Savitri said to Satyavan, "and rest."

Satyavan put his head down, gave a low moan, and died.

Savitri looked up. There, in the distance coming towards her was Yamraj, the King of the Underworld. He was riding a male water buffalo, and Savitri knew that he was coming to claim Satyavan's soul. She turned to the banyan tree and implored, "Banyan tree, banyan tree, look after my husband. Shield him and keep him cool. I will return one day to claim him."

Yamraj took Satyavan's soul and started to ride away. Savitri followed on foot. She followed for miles and miles. Yamraj finally turned around and said, "Why are you following me, woman?"

"You are taking my husband's soul away. Why don't you take me as well? I cannot live without him."

"Go back, go back to your home and do not bother me," Yamraj said.

But Savitri kept following.

Yamraj turned around again. "Stop following me, woman," he cried.

Savitri paid no <u>heed</u> to him.

"Well, woman," said Yamraj, "I can see that you are quite determined. I will grant you just one wish. As long as you do not ask for your husband's soul."

"May my in-laws have their sight back?" asked Savitri.

"All right, all right," said Yamraj, "now go home."

After several more miles Yamraj glanced back. There was Savitri, still following.

---

grove (grōv) *n.* small group of trees without underbrush.

heed (hēd) *n.* careful attention; notice.

"You really are quite persistent," Yamraj said. "I'll grant you one other wish. Just remember, do not ask for your husband's soul."

"Could my father-in-law get back the kingdom he lost?" Savitri asked.

"Yes, yes," said Yamraj. "Now go, go."

Several miles later, Yamraj looked back again.

Savitri was still following.

"I do not understand you. I've granted you two wishes and yet you keep following me. This is the last wish I am offering you. Remember, you can ask for anything but your husband's soul."

"May I be the mother of many sons?" Savitri asked.

"Yes, yes," Yamraj said. "Now *go*. Go back home."

Several miles later Yamraj looked back only to see Savitri still there. "Why are you still following me?" Yamraj asked. "I have already granted you your wish of many sons."

"How will I have many sons?" Savitri asked. "You are carrying away the soul of the only husband I have. I will never marry again. You have granted me a false wish. It can *never* come true."

"I have had enough," Yamraj said. "I am quite exhausted. Here, take back your husband's soul."

Savitri rushed back to the banyan tree so her husband's body and soul could be joined again.

"Oh banyan tree," she said, "thank you for looking after my husband. In the years to come, may all married women come to you and offer thanks and prayers."

Satyavan opened his eyes and said, "My headache has gone."

"Yes," said Savitri, "thanks to the kind banyan tree that offered us its shade. Let us go home now where a surprise awaits you. I will not tell you what it is."

Satyavan put his arm around his wife's shoulders and they began to walk slowly back home.

Lovers in a Landscape (detail)   *c.1775*
Mir Kalan Khan   The David Collection, Copenhagen

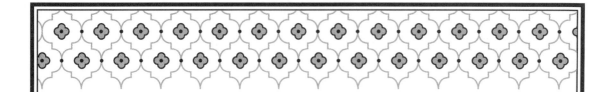

Meet Madhur Jaffrey

Madhur Jaffrey grew up in a large extended family in Delhi, India. With her siblings and her cousins, she spent much of her time "either listening to stories told by the elders or else translating them into live theatre," writes Jaffrey. "Some of the stories we were told were of ancient origin and were drawn from our religious epics. Others had just been told, in my family, generation after generation for centuries." Jaffrey collected some of the tales in her book *Seasons of Splendour,* from which "Savitri and Satyavan" is taken.

Jaffrey has also written several popular cookbooks and won acclaim as an actress in films, on stage, and on radio and television.

More Heroines in Folklore

- *Clever Gretchen and Other Forgotten Folktales* by Alison Lurie (HarperCollins, 1990). Plucky heroines who risk all and back down at nothing populate this offbeat collection of tales from across Europe.

- *The Maid of the North: Feminist Folk Tales from Around the World* by Ethel Johnston Phelps (Holt, 1982). These 21 delightful tales from a variety of cultures feature active and wise heroines who take charge of their own destinies.

- *East of the Sun, West of the Moon* by Mercer Mayer (Aladdin, 1980). In this version of a favorite fairy tale, a determined farmer's daughter is helped by friendly spirits of Nature to rescue her true love.

RESPONDING TO
Literature

THINK • TALK • WRITE

1 Did you find the ending of this tale satisfying? Respond in your journal.

2 Savitri chooses humble Satyavan, not a rich, powerful man. What traits of his does she admire? What does her choice say about her?

3 What are three ways that Savitri exhibits heroic traits such as extraordinary courage, intelligence, strength, or determination?

4 What wish will Yamraj not grant? How does Savitri trick him into granting it? Were you surprised by the twist the tale takes? Explain.

5 Yamraj grants Savitri three wishes. What tales from other cultures do you know in which the hero/heroine is granted three wishes? Why do you think stories from different cultures often have common elements?

ACTIVITIES

• **Write About Heroes/Heroines**
Make a short comic book starring a hero or heroine you create. Keep in mind that your hero or heroine should have amazing abilities that are used for the good of others.

• **Retell the Selection** Retell the story of "Savitri and Satyavan" as if you were a traveling Indian storyteller. Try using dramatic devices such as costumes and changes of voice.

VOCABULARY PRACTICE

On a separate piece of paper, write the vocabulary word that best answers each question.

escort   forage
procession   fineries
birthright   withered
reception   grove
solemnly   heed

1 Which word is most closely associated with inheriting?

2 Which word might name part of a forest?

3 Which verb refers to taking advice?

4 If a flower has dried up, which word would describe it?

5 Which word might describe a man going to a rock concert with his grandson?

6 Which word suggests luxurious clothes and expensive jewelry?

7 Which kind of event is often held to celebrate a wedding?

8 Which word might describe how an animal looks for food?

9 Which word describes the serious way that someone swears an oath?

10 For which noun might you use students marching at a graduation ceremony as an example?

FOLKLORE

THE JEWELS OF THE SEA

CONNECT TO LITERATURE

In your journal, describe a time you lost or broke an item that did not belong to you. How did you feel? What would you have done to recover the item or make up for its loss? Then as you read the selection, notice what the younger prince is willing to do to find something he had borrowed from his brother and lost.

THINKING ABOUT MOTIVATION

Why does a character act in a certain way? What are her thoughts and feelings? Why did he do something or not do something? Answering these questions reveals a character's *motivation,* the reason or reasons behind his or her actions.

In "The Jewels of the Sea," as in much fiction, motivation is a key element. A prince makes a dangerous voyage to recover a lost object. If the item had not been lost, then the prince would have had no reason to undertake his journey.

HAVE YOU EVER?

Have you ever set a goal that seemed nearly impossible? A hero or heroine in pursuit of such a goal, called a *quest,* is common in mythology. A quest often involves a long journey, during which the main character meets various challenges. To succeed, he or she must show courage, strength, and honor.

Quests can be found in literature ranging from Greece to Peru to Ethiopia. Tales of quests date back at least 5,000 years, when the ancient Sumerians told of Gilgamesh's search for eternal life. Quest tales are also as new as today's cartoons. In many cartoons, heroes fight evil forces to obtain a goal.

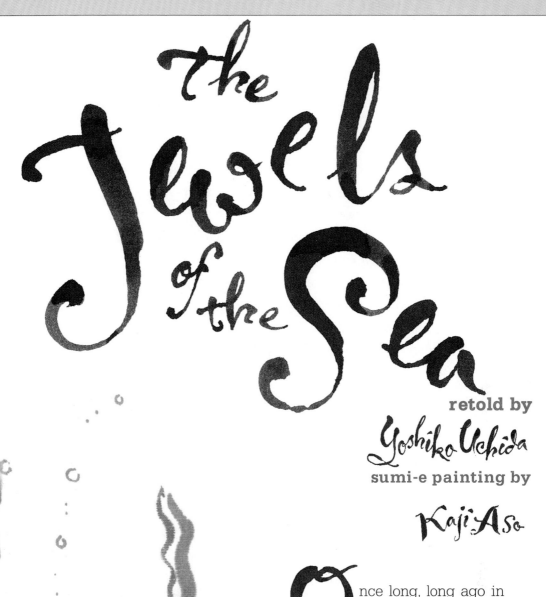

The Jewels of the Sea

retold by
Yoshiko Uchida

sumi-e painting by

Kaji Aso

Once long, long ago in the land of Japan, there lived two young princes. The older prince was an excellent fisherman whose skill no one could ever equal. It was said that he could catch anything that swam in the sea. Now the younger prince was as skilled on land as his brother was at sea. He was the finest hunter in all the land, and feared no animal that stalked through the woods and over the mountains of Japan. Each day the two set out together; the older brother would go toward the sea with his rod and reel, while the younger brother with his bow and a quiver full of arrows set forth for the mountains.

Now one morning as the two princes prepared to go out for the day, the younger brother said, "Each day for many years we have done the very same thing. You go to the sea and I to the mountains. I have grown weary of the same sport each day. Wouldn't you like to go hunting in my place today, while I go fishing in yours?"

"A good idea," said his brother. "I will take your bow and arrow and you shall take my rod and reel. Take care how you use them, however, for they are my most prized possessions."

So the older prince headed for the mountains and the younger prince for the sea. When the young prince reached the edge of the sea, he sat down among some boulders. He baited his hook with clumsy fingers, threw it into the water, and anxiously waited for the fish to bite. Each time the line moved just a little, he pulled it up to see what he had caught, but each time the hook came up empty. Finally the sun began to sink slowly below the rim of the mountains, but still he had not caught a single fish. What's more, he had even lost his brother's very best hook.

"I must find my brother's hook," thought the young prince sadly, and he searched among the crevices of the boulders, and on the sands of the beach. As he was looking for the lost hook, his brother came back from the mountains. He too was empty-handed, for although he was an excellent fisherman, he could not hunt game.

"What are you looking for?" he called crossly to his younger brother.

"I have lost your precious hook," said the young prince, "and I have searched everywhere but cannot find it."

"Lost my hook?" shouted the older brother. "You see, this is what comes of your idea to change tasks for the day. If it hadn't been for your foolish idea, this never would have happened. You are a clumsy, blundering fool, and I shall not return your bow and arrow to you until you find my hook."

The young prince was very sad, and spent long hours searching for the lost hook. At last he began to think he would never find it by the sea, so he took his very best sword and broke it into hundreds of tiny pieces. Then he made five hundred beautiful hooks for his brother with the tiny pieces of his sword. He brought these to his brother saying, "Since I cannot find your lost hook, I have broken my sword and made five hundred new

---

quiver (kwiv′ər) *n.* case for holding arrows.
crossly (krôs′lē) *adv.* in a bad-tempered, peevish manner.
blundering (blun′dər ing) *adj.* moving or acting blindly or clumsily.

hooks for you. Please forgive me for having lost your precious hook."

But his older brother would not forgive him. The young prince made five hundred more hooks, but still his brother would not forgive him. He only said, "Even though you bring me a million hooks, I will not forgive you until you return the one hook you lost!"

So once again the young prince went to the seashore to see if the tide might have washed the lost hook up onto the sand. He <u>roamed</u> about sadly, walking back and forth along the beach where he had fished. Suddenly, from nowhere, there appeared an old man with hair as white as the clouds in the sky.

"Pray tell me, what is the young prince doing all alone, and why do you look so sad?" asked the old man.

So the young prince told him how he had lost his elder brother's hook, and how he could never be forgiven until he found it again.

"But, my dear prince," said the old man kindly. "Surely your lost hook is at the bottom of the sea by this time, or at least in the belly of a fish. You will never find it here on the shore."

"Then what can I do?" asked the young prince.

"Why, the only thing you can do is to go to the King of the Sea and ask him to help you find it," answered the old man.

"That is an excellent idea!" said the prince. "But how will I ever get to his palace at the bottom of the sea?"

"Just leave everything to me," replied the old man. "I will help you get to his palace."

And so the old man made the prince a very special boat which could take him safely to the bottom of the sea. He then told him just how to get there, and wished him luck in finding his lost hook.

"Thank you, old man. You shall surely be rewarded when I return," said the young prince, and he sailed off for the palace of the King of the Sea.

He followed the old man's directions carefully, and before long he saw the <u>sapphire</u> roofs of the palace sparkling in the blue water. A large gate guarded the entrance, and the prince found it was locked tight.

"Oh, dear, how will I get in?" he thought as he looked around. Then he spied a lovely old tree growing by the gate. Its <u>gnarled</u> branches bent low and hung over a beautiful silver well.

"I shall just climb up on one of those branches and rest awhile," thought the prince. "Then someone

---

roamed (rōmd) *v.t.* wandered through a place.
sapphire (saf′īr) *adj.* having the deep blue color of the precious stone.
gnarled (närld) *adj.* having many rough, twisted knots, as a tree trunk or branches.

may come along through the gates soon."

So he climbed up on one of the low branches and sat down to rest. Before long, the big gate of the palace slowly swung open. The prince looked down quickly and saw two beautiful maidens coming out of the gate carrying a lovely golden cup. They hurried toward the well and bent down to fill their cup with the clear, cool water. As they looked into the mirror-like water, they both cried out, for there, reflected in the stillness, was the face of the young prince.

They looked up at the tree in surprise, and saw the prince sitting quietly on one of the branches.

"I didn't mean to startle you," he said to the two maidens. "I have come a long way and just wanted to rest for a few minutes. I am very thirsty, and I see that you have a lovely golden cup. Will you give me a drink of water?"

"Why, of course," answered the two beautiful maidens.

When the prince had had his fill of water, he pulled a precious stone from a chain around his neck and dropped it into the golden cup before he returned it.

"Thank you for your kindness," he said. "I am looking for the King of the Sea. I wonder if you could help me find him?"

"Oh, but of course," answered the two lovely maidens, laughing gaily. "For we are his daughters!"

They hurried to tell their father of this strange visitor whom they had found sitting on the branch of the old tree by the well.

"Surely he is no ordinary mortal, for look at this beautiful stone which he dropped into our cup. It seems to be a *maga-tama,* a stone which is worn only by royalty."

The King of the Sea then called the young prince into his most beautiful room. "Now tell me what I can do for you," he said to the prince.

So the young prince told him who he was, and why he had come. He told him how he had lost his brother's hook and had come down to the bottom of the sea to seek help.

"Will you be good enough, kind sir, to search your kingdom for my brother's fishhook?" he asked.

"By all means, my good friend, by all means," replied the king, and he beckoned to one of his servants. "Call together all my subjects who live in the kingdom of the sea," he said.

The servant disappeared for a few moments and before long, all who lived in the great kingdom of the sea came swimming toward the palace of

---

mortal (môr′təl) *n.* human being; person.
beckoned (bek′ənd) *v.t.* signaled, summoned, or directed (someone) by a sign or gesture.

their king: giant tortoises and little clams; sea horses, crabs, and lobsters with long green claws; mackerels, sea bass, herrings, swordfish, and all the many, many fish in the sea. When they had all gathered in the great courtyard, the king stood before them and called out, "We have a very important visitor with us today—a prince who has come down to the bottom of the sea to search for a lost fishing hook. If any among you have seen it, speak now and tell your king!"

The fish looked at each other and shook their shiny heads; the tortoise looked at the clam and slowly shook his head; the crabs and lobsters wriggled their feelers and looked about on the sand and in the coral. At last, from far back in the group a little silver fish came forward and spoke to the king.

"Oh, good King, I do believe it is my friend, the red snapper, who has swallowed the hook of our visiting prince."

"And why do you say that?" asked the king.

"Because, sir, he has been complaining of a sore throat and has eaten nothing for a long time. And you see, he is not present now, for I fear he is ill at home."

"Hmm, that *is* strange," said the king, "for the red snapper is usually the first to come to all our gatherings.

Have him brought forth immediately."

Soon the red snapper was brought to the meeting. He looked pale and sickly, and his tail drooped on the sand.

"Yes, sir?" he answered in a low, weak voice. "Did you wish to see me?"

"Why did you not come when I called the fish of my kingdom?" asked the king.

"Because, sir, I have been very ill," moaned the red snapper. "I haven't been at all well for some time. My throat is sore, I cannot eat, and see—my fins will not stand up on my back. I fear something is very wrong indeed."

"He's swallowed the hook! He's swallowed the hook!" murmured all the fish of the sea.

---

drooped (drüpt) *v.i.* hung or sunk down.

223

"Then open his mouth and look," commanded the king. Two guards immediately opened wide the red snapper's mouth, and peered down his throat. There they found the prince's shiny hook, and quickly removed it. The red snapper smiled happily, and so did the young prince. He thanked the guards and the king and all the subjects of the kingdom of the sea, for now at last he had recovered his brother's precious hook. Now at last his task was completed and he could return home once more. But the kingdom of the sea was so beautiful, and he was having such a pleasant time that he stayed on and on. Before he quite realized it, three long years had gone by. At last he went to the King of the Sea and said,

"I have spent three long and happy years here in your lovely kingdom of the sea, but I cannot stay forever. I must return to my own kingdom and to my own land above the waters."

The king turned to the young prince and said, "I hope that you of the land and we of the sea shall always be friends. As a <u>token</u> of our friendship, I wish you to take back with you two jewels of the sea." Then he called his servant, who came in with two large and beautiful jewels. They sparkled and glistened as the king held them in his hands.

The king raised the jewel in his right hand and said, "This stone has the power to call forth the waters of the sea. Raise it above your head and great waves will come rushing up about you no matter where you may be."

Then the king held up the jewel in his other hand. "Raise this stone above your head and no matter how high the seas that surround you may be, the waters will <u>recede</u> and be drawn away." Then he gave the two jewels to the prince.

"They are beautiful jewels, sir," said the prince. "And what wonderful powers they possess!"

---

token (tō′kən) *n.* something that serves to indicate or represent some fact, event, object, or feeling; symbol.
recede (ri sēd′) *v.i.* move back or away.

"Keep them with you always," said the king, "and they will protect you from all danger and harm."

The prince thanked the good king and prepared to be on his way. He said farewell to his many friends in the kingdom of the sea, and then the king called a large alligator who was to carry the prince back again to land. This was an even stranger vessel than the one which had brought him to the bottom of the sea, but the alligator swam swiftly and smoothly, and soon the prince was standing safely on the very beach from which he had departed.

He hurried to his palace and holding the hook which he had found, he called to his older brother, "Here I am, back once again, and here is your precious hook at last!"

Now the older brother had seized the throne while the younger prince was away, thinking that his younger brother would never return. He was very happy that he alone was the great and powerful ruler of the land, so when the young prince appeared with the lost hook, he was not at all glad to see him. Dark and evil thoughts cropped up in his jealous mind, and soon he decided that he would kill his younger brother so that he could continue to be the only ruler of the land.

One day as the young prince was strolling about in the field out-side the palace, the older brother crept up behind him with a long dagger. He raised it high in the air and was about to stab the young prince. But the young prince turned quickly and remembered what the King of the Sea had told him. He reached for the jewels of the sea and raised one high over his head. At once great high waves came thundering over the fields. They crashed and roared about the older prince and swept him off his feet.

"Help, help, I'm drowning! Save me, save me!" he cried.

The young prince then reached for the other jewel and held it high over his head. The waters immediately began to recede and the waves rolled gently back again toward the sea. The older brother sat on the ground gasping for breath.

"Thank you for saving my life," he said to the young prince. "You must have a power far greater than I, to be able to command the waters of the sea to come and go when you choose. I have done you a great injustice and I hope you will forgive me."

The kind young prince was quick to forgive his older brother and before long they were once again the best of friends. From that day on, they ruled together over a land of peace and plenty.

meet Yoshiko Uchida

When Yoshiko Uchida (1921–1992) was a child, she loved hearing the Japanese stories that her mother read to her. She retold many of the tales in her first published book, *The Dancing Kettle.* "The Jewels of the Sea" comes from that collection.

Uchida, who was born and raised in California, felt strong ties to the culture of Japan, her parents' homeland. "All my books have been about the Japanese or Japanese Americans," she wrote, "but while I cherish and take pride in my special heritage, I never want to lose my sense of connection with the community of man."

More Folk Tales from Asia

- *The Sea of Gold and Other Tales from Japan* (Creative Arts, 1988) and *The Magic Listening Cap: More Folk Tales from Japan* (Creative Arts, 1987) by Yoshiko Uchida. In these two collections, Uchida has once again brought together tales of adventure from old Japan.

- *The Rainbow People* by Laurence Yep (HarperCollins, 1989). Folk tales were an important bridge between Chinese immigrants in America and their homeland, according to Yep, an award-winning author of young-adult fiction.

- *Sky Legends of Vietnam* retold by Lynette Dyer Vuong (HarperCollins, 1993). Ancient peoples told stories to explain the mysteries of the sun, moon, and stars. This book introduces six such tales from Vietnam.

RESPONDING TO
Literature

THINK • TALK • WRITE

1 Did this tale remind you of any other stories you know? Respond in your journal.

2 How are the princes alike? How are they different? Give examples.

3 What happens when the princes switch tasks for the day? How would the story have been different if they had *not* changed tasks?

4 How does the younger prince decide to treat his older brother at the end of the tale? Do you agree with his decision? Why or why not?

5 Mythical heroes often seek a lost or hard-to-obtain item, such as the fish hook in this tale. What other tales or myths about a quest for a rare, valuable object do you know?

ACTIVITIES

• **Write About Motivation** Here is the first sentence in a paragraph: "Sean took a deep breath and let out a scream." Finish the paragraph, revealing something about Sean's motivation for screaming. Then compare paragraphs with a classmate.

• **Sing a Sea Chantey** Sailors sing sea chanteys to relieve boredom and make their work go faster. Retell "The Jewels of the Sea" as a sea chantey. Try setting your words to a melody you already know.

VOCABULARY PRACTICE

On a separate piece of paper, write the vocabulary word that best completes each sentence.

crossly   blundering
roamed   sapphire
gnarled   mortal
beckoned   drooped
token   recede

1 The old man _____ the child to come closer.

2 I watched the ship _____ into the distance.

3 Her smile disappeared, and her face _____ in disappointment.

4 The _____ shortstop kept dropping the ball.

5 She asked that he accept the gift as a _____ of her gratitude.

6 The _____ old tree had branches that looked like crooked fingers.

7 She lost her temper and exclaimed _____, "Just leave me alone!"

8 The _____ gem sparkled with an inner blue light.

9 He _____ for many years before settling in this country.

10 The gods knew the man was no ordinary _____.

WRITING

Folk tales, fables, and legends are imaginary stories that tell a lot about the people who made them up. Every country has its favorites. Make up your own folk tale, fable, or legend. In your tale, show how certain events or conditions caused others.

PREWRITE

What will your tale be about? Jot down some notes about the characters and plot. Then sketch ideas for your own tale.

> **Characters:** Blue Midnight (a very big blue-black cat)
> Thunder Mouse (a tiny gray mouse with a very deep voice)
>
> Blue Midnight goes hunting field mice. ——→ He finds Thunder Mouse. ——→
> Thunder Mouse runs into a hole.——→ Blue Midnight sticks his paw in the hole.
> ——→ Thunder Mouse uses his bass voice to growl like a big dog. ——→ Blue
> Midnight runs away terrified.

This writer wrote a fable proving that cleverness can overcome physical strength. He planned the events as a series of causes and effects.

Organize your notes. Think about cause-and-effect events in your tale.

DRAFT

Read the beginning of this writer's draft. How much does it tell you about what might happen?

The author sets the stage for the hunting scene that will come next. - - - - - →
When you write your beginning, keep the next scene in mind.

> **Blue Midnight and Thunder Mouse**
>
> Blue Midnight the cat streched his big paws. He felt like going hunting. The idea of a a field mouse made his mouth water

Use your prewriting notes to begin your draft. As you write, think about your tone. Will your tale be funny or scary? How do you want your audience to react?

FOLKLORE

REVISE

Take a moment to reread your draft. Can you picture in your mind's eye what is happening? The writer of our sample made a few changes. Can you see why?

The first change suggests another cause for Blue Midnight's decision to go hunting. He's bored. The second change makes the main cause for Blue Midnight's decision to go hunting even clearer.

> Blue Midnight the cat *yawned and* streched his
> big paws. He felt like going hunting. *was hungry*
> The idea of a a *plump* field mouse made his
> mouth water

It's time to revise your draft. But first, ask a friend what he or she thinks of it. Take notes about the friend's responses.

PROOFREAD

This writer caught all of his errors after proofreading twice. Take a good look at the corrections.

The writer didn't notice the period missing until the second proofread. Proofread your writing more than once to make sure you catch all errors.

> Blue Midnight the cat ~~streched~~ his *yawned and stretched*
> big paws. He felt like going hunting. *was hungry*
> The idea of a a *plump* field mouse made his
> mouth water.

PUBLISH

The writer used a cartoon-style illustration with his fable.

How would you like to share your writing? Check out some books of folk tales, fables, or legends for ideas. A partner may have some suggestions, too.

WRITING

USING SPECIFIC NOUNS

ENRICH YOUR WRITING OF **FOLKLORE.**

Want to get your ideas across? Then choose specific nouns to give a precise picture of events. Using exactly the right noun will mean having to use fewer words to express your ideas.

Read these two paragraphs. Which paragraph gives more than just a general idea?

Paragraph 1

As the man galloped toward the building, his heart beat with emotion. He was worried. What if the other man had already been imprisoned?

Paragraph 2

As the knight galloped toward the castle, his heart beat with terror. He was worried. What if his uncle had already been imprisoned?

PRACTICE 1 Respond on a separate piece of paper.

1 How does the writer of the second paragraph manage to give a more precise idea of what is happening?

2 Change the characters and setting in this paragraph by rewriting it using other specific nouns.

FORMING PLURAL NOUNS

REMEMBER THESE RULES ABOUT PLURAL NOUNS WHEN YOU ARE WRITING **FOLKLORE.**

- Most singular nouns add *s* to form the plural. Singular nouns ending in *s, ss, x, z, ch,* or *sh* add *es* to form the plural.

- Singular nouns ending in a consonant and *y* form the plural by changing *y* to *i* and adding *es.* Singular nouns ending in a vowel and y merely add *s* to form the plural.

- Some irregular nouns, such as *woman* and *mouse,* change their spelling to form the plural. *(women, mice)*

PRACTICE 2 When necessary, change nouns into their plural forms.

1 The knight found his uncle working with a pair of ox.

2 He crept closer to the pasture and hid behind a row of bush.

3 One of the lady of the court saw the knight hiding.

4 The lady told the guards to be ready to use their sword.

FORMING POSSESSIVE NOUNS

USE THESE RULES ABOUT POSSESSIVE NOUNS WHEN YOU ARE WRITING **FOLKLORE.**

- Form the possessive of most singular nouns by adding *'s.*

- Form the possessive of plural nouns ending in *s* by adding *'.*

- Form the possessive of plural nouns that don't end in *s* by adding *'s.*

PRACTICE 3 When necessary, change nouns into their possessive forms.

1 The knight uncle was put in chains.

2 The princes servants came to tell them the news.

3 Before long the king began to fear his people anger.

4 The king sons urged him to change his mind.

WRITING

PROJECT 1

WRITING A POEM

What are you searching for in life? Write a poem about a quest—
either for something practical or for one of your wildest dreams!

PREWRITE

Try using a cluster as a prewriting strategy. Jot down a phrase
describing a quest that interests you. Then see what other ideas,
words, or phrases it suggests.

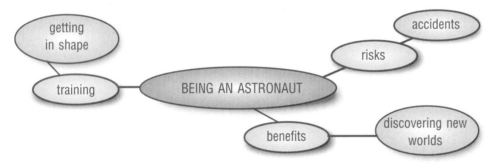

DRAFT Let your thoughts flow when you write. Get words on the
page. You can work on the rhythm and form of the poem later.

REVISE How can you make your poem "sing"? Do you want it to
rhyme? Break up the lines to create a strong rhythm—patterns of
weak and strong beats. Read it aloud to a friend.

PROOFREAD Now that the poem sounds good, check for errors in
spelling, punctuation, and grammar.

PUBLISH Ask your teacher to organize a group poetry reading.
Then collect your poems in a class book.

> ▶ *Proofreading Alert!*
> Use commas to set off appositives. Check page 205 in
> *Spotlight on Success: Writing and Language Handbook.*

PROJECTS

MAKE A SCRAPBOOK

REMEMBER TO: • PREWRITE • DRAFT • REVISE • PROOFREAD • PUBLISH

Make a scrapbook of words and pictures about an exciting, real-life quest.

You can cut out photos from a magazine or newspaper or make your own drawings. Then use captions to tell what happened. Try using a chart to plan your ideas.

Quest	Participants	Events	Ending
hot-air balloon trip	professional balloonist and young hobbyist	smooth ascent; then heavy winds	safe landing

WRITE A PROPOSAL

REMEMBER TO: • PREWRITE • DRAFT • REVISE • PROOFREAD • PUBLISH

What would you like to see accomplished? Work with several class-mates to write a convincing proposal for a class quest. Brainstorm your proposal together. Then try to outline it before you draft. Use an outline like this:

Proposal: Getting Ourselves in Shape

I. Reasons for proposal
   A. Benefits of being in shape
      1. Heart and circulation
      2. Relieves stress
   B. Tie in to sports week in May
II. Planning
   A. Exploring ways to get fit
   B. Choosing exercise leaders

233

FINDERS KEEPERS?

For centuries, explorers have searched all the world over for buried treasure. With the help of high-tech equipment, modern adventurers are discovering valuable treasures. Certainly, the explorers deserve a reward for their hard work. But should that reward be the ancient treasure they find? Or should that treasure remain in the country where it's been buried for so many years?

CONSIDER THIS ISSUE: Your social studies class has been studying the recent discovery of a Spanish ship sunk hundreds of years ago. Divers have recovered gold coins and other valuables. What do you think should happen to the treasures they find? Think about some of the issues involved.

- Shouldn't the people who worked hard to find the treasure keep it?
- Doesn't the treasure belong in a museum, where everyone can see it?
- Is it better to leave the treasure where it is, as a memorial to the sailors who died in the ship?
- What about the rights of the country the ship came from?

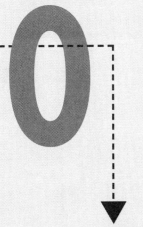

Read the following viewpoints about the ownership of ancient treasures. Decide which opinion is closest to your own. Think of more arguments yourself to support the position you choose.

VIEWPOINT 1 I think the people who find the buried treasure should be allowed to keep it.

- The treasure has been lost for hundreds of years and really doesn't belong to anyone.
- Keeping the treasure is a fair reward for their hard work.
- If the explorers don't keep the treasure, people will stop planning these modern quests.

VIEWPOINT 2 I think the lost treasure should be returned to the country it belonged to originally.

- The treasure is part of that country's heritage.
- If it's returned to the country, it can be exhibited in a museum, where everyone can see it.
- In return for the treasure, the country should give the explorers a reward.

VIEWPOINT 3 I think the treasure should be examined and photographed, and then returned to where it was found.

- The treasure will remain a memorial to the drowned sailors.
- There are enough treasures in museums as it is.
- If the treasure is left as it is, no one can fight over it.

WHAT DO YOU THINK?
Take some time to think about this issue. Do you share one of the viewpoints above, or do you have another? Talk about your opinions with a partner.

HOME • SCHOOL • COMMUNITY

QUESTS: Journeys of discovery help us learn more about the world around us and our own capabilities.

A quest may have an actual destination, or it may be an attempt to reach new knowledge or new understanding. You might begin an underwater quest to discover the secrets of the sunken ocean liner *Titanic.* Or you might share an imaginary journey of courage and determination, such as Bellerophon's quest to find and kill the Chimera. Whatever its purpose, there are no limits to what we can learn during any quest.

Sometimes a quest involves a physical journey. But you can also go on a quest without ever leaving the room. A book and your imagination can take you on the most exciting journeys of all. Would you like to travel across the solar system? Look at the chart.

THE PLANETS

PLANET	RANK IN SIZE	DIAMETER AT EQUATOR (KM)	AVERAGE DISTANCE FROM SUN (millions of km)	PERIOD OF ROTATION		PERIOD OF REVOLUTION	
				earth days	earth hours	earth days	earth hours
Mercury	8	4,874	58	58.6			88
Venus	6	12,104	108	243			225
Earth	5	12,756	150	1		1	
Mars	7	6,794	228		24.6	1.9	
Jupiter	1	142,800	778		9.8	11.9	
Saturn	2	120,000	1,427		10.2	29.5	
Uranus	3	52,000	2,870		16.28	84	
Neptune	4	48,400	4,497		18.20	164.8	
Pluto	9	3,000	5,899	6.3		247.7	

A **chart** is a simple, concise way of organizing important information. Charts present data about a single subject or make comparisons between two or more subjects. The *title* explains the information on the chart. *Headings* identify the categories by which the information is organized.

I O N S

Here are three activities in which you use charts to find or present information. Think of other situations in which you use charts. Then choose an activity below or one of your own and talk or write about it.

PROJECT 1

A PLANET CHART Choose one of the planets from the chart on page 236. Use books from your classroom or school library to find out more information about the planet. Organize this information on a chart. Be sure to include a title that sums up the main idea of the chart and headings that identify the chart's categories. Compare the planets by using information from your classmates' charts.

PROJECT 2

A CHART SUMMARY You can use the information you find on a chart in a variety of ways. First find a chart in a textbook or magazine article. Study it carefully. Then write a paragraph summarizing the information from the chart. Include a topic sentence that states the main idea. Write a title for your paragraph based on the title of the chart.

PROJECT 3

A CHART OF FACTS Charts include key facts about a topic. How many facts about a subject do you think you could find from a chart? Working in small groups, choose a chart from a book or magazine. Then list all the facts about the topic you can find on the chart. Identify all the ways the chart presents facts.

DETERMIN

Abstract Speed + Sound (Velocità astratta + rumore) 1913–1914
Giacomo Balla   The Peggy Guggenheim Collection, Venice, Italy

To James

Do you remember
How you won
That last race . . . ?
How you flung your body
At the start . . .
How your spikes
Ripped the cinders
In the stretch . . .
How you catapulted
Through the tape . . .
Do you remember . . . ?
Don't you think
I lurched with you
Out of those starting holes . . . ?
Don't you think
My sinews tightened
At those first
Few strides . . .
And when you flew into the stretch
Was not all my thrill
Of a thousand races
In your blood . . . ?
At your final drive
Through the finish line
Did not my shout
Tell of the
Triumphant ecstasy
Of victory . . . ?
Live
As I have taught you
To run, Boy—
It's a short dash
Dig your starting holes
Deep and firm
Lurch out of them
Into the straightaway
With all the power
That is in you
Look straight ahead
To the finish line
Think only of the goal
Run straight
Run high
Run hard
Save nothing
And finish
With an ecstatic burst
That carries you
Hurtling
Through the tape
To victory . . .

—Frank Horne

239

DETERMINATION

BEFORE READING

CONNECT TO LITERATURE

"Nothing we really want is easy," says a character in "Petronella." Have you ever really wanted to accomplish something that wasn't easy? Write about your feelings in your journal. Did other people encourage and help you? As you read "Petronella," compare your sense of determination with that of the princess.

THINKING ABOUT PARODY

"Petronella" is a *parody* of a fairy tale. A parody imitates a common literary form in a humorous way. In "Petronella," for example, the author mixes a fairy-tale setting and situation with comic dialog and role reversals. As you will discover, Petronella is no "damsel in distress" as most fairy-tale princesses are. While you read, think about what message the author, Jay Williams, may have intended when he wrote this parody.

DID YOU KNOW?

Though centuries old, many famous European fairy tales were first written or popularized by just a few influential authors, such as

- Charles Perrault, a French writer whose *Tales of Mother Goose* (1697) included "Cinderella" and "Sleeping Beauty." An English author of nursery rhymes later borrowed his title.

- Jacob and Wilhelm Grimm, brothers who published a book of German tales in the early 1800s, including "Rumpelstiltskin."

- Hans Christian Andersen, a 19th-century Danish writer whose tales (such as "The Ugly Duckling" and "The Emperor's New Clothes") rank among the most widely read works in literature.

The Noble Life   *16th century   Tapestry by unknown artist   Musée du Moyen Age (Cluny), Paris*

Petronella

BY JAY WILLIAMS

In the kingdom of Skyclear Mountain, three princes were always born to the king and queen. The oldest prince was always called Michael, the middle prince was always called George, and the youngest was always called Peter. When they were grown, they always went out to seek their fortunes. What happened to the oldest prince and the middle prince no one ever knew. But the youngest prince always rescued a princess, brought her home, and in time ruled over the kingdom. That was the way it had always been. And so far as anyone knew, that was the way it would always be.

ntil now.

Now was the time of King Peter the twenty-sixth and Queen Blossom. An oldest prince was born, and a middle prince. But the youngest prince turned out to be a girl.

"Well," said the king gloomily, "we can't call her Peter. We'll have to call her Petronella. And what's to be done about it, I'm sure I don't know."

There was nothing to be done. The years passed, and the time came for the princes to go out and seek their fortunes. Michael and George said good-bye to the king and queen and mounted their horses. Then out came Petronella. She was dressed in traveling clothes, with her bag packed and a sword by her side.

"If you think," she said, "that I'm going to sit at home, you are mistaken. I'm going to seek my fortune, too."

"Impossible!" said the king.

"What will people say?" cried the queen.

"Look," said Prince Michael, "be <u>reasonable</u>, Pet. Stay home. Sooner or later a prince will turn up here."

Petronella smiled. She was a tall, handsome girl with flaming red hair and when she smiled in that particular way it meant she was trying to keep her temper.

"I'm going with you," she said. "I'll find a prince if I have to rescue one from something myself. And that's that."

The grooms brought out her horse, she said good-bye to her parents, and away she went behind her two brothers.

They traveled into the flatlands below Skyclear Mountain. After many days, they entered a great dark forest. They came to a place where the road divided into three, and there at the <u>fork</u> sat a little, wrinkled old man covered with dust and spiderwebs.

Prince Michael said <u>haughtily</u>, "Where do these roads go, old man?"

---

reasonable (rē′zə nə bəl) *adj.* showing or using good sense; not foolish.
fork (fôrk) *n.* spot where a road splits.
haughtily (hô′tə lē) *adv.* with much pride in oneself and disdain for others.

"The road on the right goes to the city of Gratz," the man replied. "The road in the center goes to the castle of Blitz. The road on the left goes to the house of Albion the enchanter. And that's one."

"What do you mean by 'And that's one'?" asked Prince George.

"I mean," said the old man, "that I am forced to sit on this spot without stirring, and that I must answer one question from each person who passes by. And that's two."

Petronella's kind heart was touched. "Is there anything I can do to help you?" she asked.

The old man sprang to his feet. The dust fell from him in clouds.

"You have already done so," he said. "For that question is the one which releases me. I have sat here for sixty-two years waiting for someone to ask me that." He snapped his fingers with joy. "In return, I will tell you anything you wish to know."

"Where can I find a prince?" Petronella said promptly.

"There is one in the house of Albion the enchanter," the old man answered.

"Ah," said Petronella, "then that is where I am going."

"In that case I will leave you," said her oldest brother. "For I am going to the castle of Blitz to see if I can find my fortune there."

"Good luck," said Prince George. "For I am going to the city of Gratz. I have a feeling my fortune is there."

They <u>embraced</u> her and rode away.

Petronella looked thoughtfully at the old man, who was combing spiderwebs and dust out of his beard. "May I ask you something else?" she said.

"Of course. Anything."

"Suppose I wanted to rescue that prince from the enchanter. How would I go about it? I haven't any experience in such things, you see."

---

enchanter (en chant′ər) *n.* one who casts spells.
embraced (em brāst′) *v.t.* hugged.

The old man chewed a piece of his beard. "I do not know everything," he said, after a moment. "I know that there are three magical secrets which, if you can get them from him, will help you."

"How can I get them?" asked Petronella.

"Offer to work for him. He will set you three tasks, and if you can do them you may demand a reward for each. You must ask him for a comb for your hair, a mirror to look into, and a ring for your finger."

"And then?"

"I do not know. I only know that when you rescue the prince, you can use these things to escape from the enchanter."

"It doesn't sound easy," sighed Petronella.

"Nothing we really want is easy," said the old man. "Look at me—I have wanted my freedom, and I've had to wait sixty-two years for it."

Petronella said good-bye to him. She mounted her horse and galloped along the third road.

It ended at a low, rambling house with a red roof. It was a comfortable-looking house, surrounded by gardens and stables and trees heavy with fruit.

On the lawn, in an armchair, sat a handsome young man with his eyes closed and his face turned to the sky.

Petronella tied her horse to the gate and walked across the lawn.

"Is this the house of Albion the enchanter?" she said.

The young man blinked up at her in surprise.

"I think so," he said. "Yes, I'm sure it is."

"And who are you?"

The young man yawned and stretched. "I am Prince Ferdinand of Firebright," he replied. "Would you mind stepping aside? I'm trying to get a suntan and you're standing in the way."

Petronella snorted. "You don't sound like much of a prince," she said.

Lady and Unicorn: After My Own Desire—Five Senses 1480–1490 *Tapestry from Brussels*
Musée du Moyen Age (Cluny), Paris

"That's funny," said the young man, closing his eyes.
"That's what my father always says."

At that moment the door of the house opened. Out
came a man dressed all in black and silver. He was tall and
thin, and his eyes were as black as a cloud full of thunder.
Petronella knew at once that he must be the enchanter.

He bowed to her politely. "What can I do for you?"

"I wish to work for you," said Petronella boldly.

Albion nodded. "I cannot refuse you," he said. "But I
warn you, it will be dangerous. Tonight I will give you
a task. If you do it, I will reward you. If you fail, you
must die."

Petronella glanced at the prince and sighed. "If I must, I must," she said. "Very well."

That evening they all had dinner together in the enchanter's cozy kitchen. Then Albion took Petronella out to a stone building and unbolted its door. Inside were seven huge black dogs.

"You must watch my hounds all night," said he.

Petronella went in, and Albion closed and locked the door.

At once the hounds began to snarl and bark. They bared their teeth at her. But Petronella was a real princess. She plucked up her courage. Instead of backing away, she went toward the dogs. She began to speak to them in a quiet voice. They stopped snarling and sniffed at her. She patted their heads.

"I see what it is," she said. "You are lonely here. I will keep you company."

And so all night long, she sat on the floor and talked to the hounds and stroked them. They lay close to her, panting.

In the morning Albion came and let her out. "Ah," said he, "I see that you are brave. If you had run from the dogs, they would have torn you to pieces. Now you may ask for what you want."

"I want a comb for my hair," said Petronella.

The enchanter gave her a comb carved from a piece of black wood.

Prince Ferdinand was sunning himself and working at a crossword puzzle. Petronella said to him in a low voice, "I am doing this for you."

"That's nice," said the prince. "What's 'selfish' in nine letters?"

"You are," snapped Petronella. She went to the enchanter. "I will work for you once more," she said.

That night Albion led her to a stable. Inside were seven huge horses.

---

plucked up pulled together; gathered.

"Tonight," he said, "you must watch my steeds."

He went out and locked the door. At once the horses began to <u>rear</u> and neigh. They pawed at her with their iron hoofs.

But Petronella was a real princess. She looked closely at them and saw that their coats were rough and their manes and tails full of burrs.

"I see what it is," she said. "You are hungry and dirty."

She brought them as much hay as they could eat, and began to brush them. All night long she fed them and groomed them, and they stood quietly in their stalls.

In the morning Albion let her out. "You are as kind as you are brave," said he. "If you had run from them they would have trampled you under their hoofs. What will you have as a reward?"

"I want a mirror to look into," said Petronella.

The enchanter gave her a mirror made of silver.

She looked across the lawn at Prince Ferdinand. He was doing exercises leisurely. He was certainly handsome. She said to the enchanter, "I will work for you once more."

That night Albion led her to a loft above the stables. There, on perches, were seven great hawks.

"Tonight," said he, "you must watch my falcons."

As soon as Petronella was locked in, the hawks began to beat their wings and scream at her.

Petronella laughed. "That is not how birds sing," she said. "Listen."

She began to sing in a sweet voice. The hawks fell silent. All night long she sang to them, and they sat like feathered statues on their perches, listening.

In the morning Albion said, "You are as talented as you are kind and brave. If you had run from them, they would have pecked and clawed you without mercy. What do you want now?"

---

rear (rîr) *v.i.* rise on the hind legs.

Detail from *Lady and Unicorn: After My Own Desire—*
Five Senses

"I want a ring for my finger," said Petronella.

The enchanter gave her a ring made from a single diamond.

All that day and all that night Petronella slept, for she was very tired. But early the next morning, she crept into Prince Ferdinand's room. He was sound asleep, wearing purple pajamas.

"Wake up," whispered Petronella. "I am going to rescue you."

Ferdinand awoke and stared sleepily at her. "What time is it?"

"Never mind that," said Petronella. "Come on!"

"But I'm sleepy," Ferdinand objected. "And it's so pleasant here."

Petronella shook her head. "You're not much of a prince," she said grimly. "But you're the best I can do."

She grabbed him by the wrist and dragged him out of bed. She hauled him down the stairs. His horse and hers were in a separate stable, and she saddled them quickly. She gave the prince a shove, and he mounted. She jumped

on her own horse, seized the prince's reins, and away they went like the wind.

They had not gone far when they heard a tremendous thumping. Petronella looked back. A dark cloud rose behind them, and beneath it she saw the enchanter. He was running with great strides, faster than the horses could go.

"What shall we do?" she cried.

"Don't ask me," said Prince Ferdinand grumpily. "I'm all shaken to bits by this fast riding."

Petronella desperately pulled out the comb. "The old man said this would help me!" she said. And because she didn't know what else to do with it, she threw the comb on the ground. At once a forest rose up. The trees were so thick that no one could get between them.

Away went Petronella and the prince. But the enchanter turned himself into an ax and began to chop. Right and left he chopped, slashing, and the trees fell before him.

Soon he was through the wood, and once again Petronella heard his footsteps thumping behind.

She reined in the horses. She took out the mirror and threw it on the ground. At once a wide lake spread out behind them, gray and glittering.

Off they went again. But the enchanter sprang into the water, turning himself into a salmon as he did so. He swam across the lake and leaped out of the water on to the other bank. Petronella heard him coming—*thump! thump!*— behind them again.

This time she threw down the ring. It didn't turn into anything, but lay shining on the ground.

The enchanter came running up. And as he jumped over the ring, it opened wide and then snapped up around him. It held his arms tight to his body, in a magical grip from which he could not escape.

"Well," said Prince Ferdinand, "that's the end of him."

---

grumpily (grump'ə lē) *adv.* in a bad-tempered, complaining way.

Petronella looked at him in <u>annoyance</u>. Then she looked at the enchanter, held fast in the ring.

"Bother!" she said. "I can't just leave him here. He'll starve to death."

She got off her horse and went up to him. "If I release you," she said, "will you promise to let the prince go free?"

Albion stared at her in astonishment. "Let him go free?" he said. "What are you talking about? I'm glad to get rid of him."

It was Petronella's turn to look surprised. "I don't understand," she said. "Weren't you holding him prisoner?"

"Certainly not," said Albion. "He came to visit me for a weekend. At the end of it, he said, 'It's so pleasant here, do you mind if I stay on for another day or two?' I'm very polite and I said, 'Of course.' He stayed on, and on, and on. I didn't like to be rude to a guest and I couldn't just kick him out. I don't know what I'd have done if you hadn't dragged him away."

"But then—" said Petronella, "but then—why did you come running after him this way?"

"I wasn't chasing him," said the enchanter. "I was chasing *you*. You are just the girl I've been looking for. You are brave and kind and talented, and beautiful as well."

"Oh," said Petronella. "I see."

"Hmm," said she. "How do I get this ring off you?"

"Give me a kiss."

She did so. The ring vanished from around Albion and reappeared on Petronella's finger.

"I don't know what my parents will say when I come home with you instead of a prince," she said.

"Let's go and find out, shall we?" said the enchanter cheerfully.

He mounted one horse and Petronella the other. And off they trotted, side by side, leaving Prince Ferdinand of Firebright to walk home as best he could.

---

annoyance (ə noi′əns) *n.* state of being irritated.

MEET Jay Williams

Jay Williams believed that a good story should be "a web of surprises, tension, and wonderment." He loved to write about the way things seem to be and the way they really are.

Williams himself was not always who he seemed to be. Many people who enjoy the mystery books of a writer named Michael Delving do not realize that Delving was actually Williams.

Williams's most famous books are those in a humorous science fiction series about a young inventor named Danny Dunn. Two books in that series won the Young Reader's Choice Award. Another of his award-winning books is The Practical Princess and Other Liberating Fairy Tales, *from which "Petronella" is taken.*

RESPONDING TO *Literature*

THINK • TALK • WRITE

1 Do you think "Petronella" is a successful parody? Why or why not? Write some ideas in your journal.

2 Why does the old man by the forest road help Petronella find a prince? What do you learn about Petronella from this event?

3 Why does Petronella attempt the three tasks at Albion's house? Do you think Petronella really wants to rescue this particular prince? Explain your opinion.

4 Do you think Petronella finds what she is looking for at the end of the story? Why or why not? Why does she release Albion from the ring? What do you think happens next?

5 Fairy tales from many cultures have a main character who must follow specific instructions. For example, after she performs each task, Petronella asks for an object that the old man had named. Why do you think performing specific tasks is an important element in fairy tales throughout the world?

ACTIVITIES

- **Write a Parody** Choose a familiar folk tale or fairy tale, and write a parody of it. Your characters may live in a castle but use current slang. Share your parody with your class.

- **Make a Comic Book** With a small group, create your own comic book version of "Petronella." Draw pictures that capture the mood of the story and show the major events. Write your own dialog or quote some from the selection. Try to give your version of the story an original twist.

VOCABULARY PRACTICE

On a separate piece of paper, write the vocabulary word that is the best substitute for each italicized word.

reasonable   embraced

haughtily   annoyance

enchanter

1 The prince considered himself better than the maid and answered her *disdainfully*.

2 The princess's parents felt great *irritation* when she refused to stay home.

3 The princess whistled for her horse, *hugged* him, and galloped away.

4 The wise old man gave the princess very *sensible* advice.

5 "That *sorcerer* must have cast a powerful spell!" exclaimed the princess.

BEFORE READING

....

BANNER IN THE SKY

CONNECT TO LITERATURE

Have you ever had someone depending on you? How did it make you feel? Did you feel you couldn't let the person down? In your journal, write about how it must feel to be the *only* person who can help. As you read "Banner in the Sky," compare your ideas with Rudi's experience on the glacier.

THINKING ABOUT MOOD

Mood is a feeling an author creates with words. The mood of a story may be light and playful, as in "Petronella," or serious and sad, as in "Last Summer with Maizon." The mood in "Banner in the Sky" comes from the description of the setting. The mountain where this selection is set is a place of great beauty and of great danger. The grandness of the mountain inspires wonder, yet the possibility of injury, even death, creates suspense.

DID YOU KNOW?

Perhaps the most famous peak in Europe is the Matterhorn, a 14,692-foot (4,478-km) mountain on the border of Switzerland and Italy. For centuries, no one even dared to attempt to scale its steep, icy slopes all the way to the top. In 1865, the British explorer Edward Whymper became the first person to climb the Matterhorn, but his triumph came at a terrible cost: four members of his party were killed on the way down.

The novel *Banner in the Sky* was inspired by Whymper's story. This selection comes from the first two chapters. Other parts of the book explain that Rudi's father, a mountain guide, was killed while climbing the Citadel, a Matterhorn-like mountain. Rudi's mother insists that he work in a hotel, where he will be safe. But Rudi, like his father, is drawn to the mountain.

BANNER IN THE SKY

SIXTEEN-YEAR-OLD RUDI MATT WAS BORN IN THE SWISS VILLAGE OF KURTAL, IN THE SHADOW OF THE GREAT MOUNTAIN KNOWN AS THE CITADEL. RUDI HAS STUDIED EVERY RIDGE AND LEDGE OF THE CITADEL AND SEVERAL TIMES HAS ASCENDED BOTH THE DORNEL GLACIER AND THE BLUE GLACIER, WHICH LIE AT THE BASE OF THE MOUNTAIN. ONE SUNNY MIDSUMMER DAY, RUDI CLIMBS BLUE GLACIER ONCE AGAIN.

BY JAMES RAMSEY ULLMAN
ILLUSTRATED BY STEVEN MADSON

Like all glaciers, the Blue was cut through by crevasses: deep splits and chasms caused by the pressures of the slow-moving ice. When hidden by snow these could be a great hazard to climbers; but on this midsummer day no snow had fallen in some time, the crevasses were plain to view, and there was no danger if one kept his eyes open and paid attention. Rudi zigzagged his way carefully upward. On the ice, of course, his smooth-soled shoes were even worse than on the boulders, but by skillful balancing and use of his stick he kept himself from slipping.

As he climbed, a black dot came into view on the high col ahead. This was an old hut, built many years before by the first explorers of the mountain, but now abandoned and all but forgotten by the people of the valleys. Rudi had twice spent nights there during his circuits of the Citadel, and he knew it well. But it was not there, specifically, that he was going now. He was not going anywhere, specifically, but only climbing, watching, studying. Every few paces now, he would stop and stare upward, motionless.

The east face of the Citadel rose above him like a battlement. Cliff upon cliff, it soared up from the glacier, its rock bulging and bristling, its walls veined with long streaks of ice. Far overhead, he could see a band of snow, which marked the mountain's first setback. Beyond it, the sloping walls disappeared for a space, only to bulge out again higher up—incredibly higher up—in a great gray thrust against the empty sky. So vast was it, so steep, so mighty, that it seemed more than a mere mass of rock and ice. More than a mere mountain. It seemed a new world rising up out of the old world that was its mother; a world with a life and a meaning of its own; beautiful and menacing, beckoning and unknown.

But it was not of beauty or terror that Rudi Matt was thinking as he gazed up at it now from the Blue Glacier. It was of a deep cleft, wide enough for a man's body, that slanted up the

---

chasms (kaz′əmz) *n., pl.* deep cracks or gaps.

col (käl) *n.* high, walkable ridge in a mountain range.

specifically (spi sif′i klē) *adv.* in particular.

rock wall before him—and ended. Of a series of ledges, broad enough for a man's feet, that rose one above another toward the high belt of snow—and petered out. His eyes searched up and down, to the right and the left. He climbed on, stopped, and studied the next section of the face. Then he climbed on again.

He moved through absolute silence. Later in the day, when sun and melting snow had done their work, great rock-and-ice masses would break loose from the heights above and come roaring down the mountainside. But it was still too early for this. The Citadel rose up like a tower of iron. There was no movement anywhere. No stirring. No sound.

And then there was a sound. . . .

Rudi stood motionless. It was not the sound of the mountain, of falling rock and ice. It was a voice. He waited; he looked around him; every sense was straining. But he saw nothing. Nothing moved. It was his imagination, he thought: a trick of his mind, or of the stillness. Or was it—and now the cold finger of fear touched him again—was it the voice of a mountain demon?

He stood without breathing. And the sound came again. It seemed at the same time to come from nearby and far away. He waited. Once more it came. And then suddenly he knew where it came from. It was from beneath the ice. From a crevasse in the glacier.

He approached the nearest crevasse and called out. But there was no answer. He went on to a second. No answer. Again he waited and listened. Again the voice came, faintly. Straight ahead was a third chasm in the ice, and, advancing cautiously, he peered over the edge.

The crevasse was about six feet wide at the top and narrowed gradually as it went down. But how deep it was Rudi could not tell. After a few feet the blue walls of ice curved away at a sharp slant, and what was below the curve was hidden from sight.

"Hello!" Rudi called.

"Hello—" A voice answered from the depths.

"How far down are you?"

"I'm not sure. About twenty feet, I'd guess."

"On the bottom?"

"No. I can't even see the bottom. I was lucky and hit a ledge."

The voice spoke in German, but with a strange accent. Whoever was down there, Rudi knew, it was not one of the men of the valley.

"Are you hurt?" he called.

"Nothing broken—no," said the voice. "Just shaken up some. And cold."

"How long have you been there?"

"About three hours."

Rudi looked up and down the crevasse. He was thinking desperately of what he could do.

"Do you have a rope?" asked the voice.

"No."

"How many of you are there?"

"Only me."

There was a silence. When the voice spoke again, it was still quiet and under strict control. "Then you'll have to get help," it said.

Rudi didn't answer. To get down to Kurtal would take at least two hours, and for a party to climb back up would take three. By that time it would be night, and the man would have been in the crevasse for eight hours. He would be frozen to death.

"No," said Rudi, "it would take too long."

"What else is there to do?"

Rudi's eyes moved over the ice-walls: almost <u>vertical</u>, smooth as glass. "Have you an ax?" he asked.

"No. I lost it when I fell. It dropped to the bottom."

"Have you tried to climb?"

"Yes. But I can't get a hold."

There was another silence. Rudi's lips tightened, and when

---

vertical (vûr′ti kəl) *adj.* upright; straight up and down.

he spoke again his voice was strained. "I'll think of something," he cried. "I'll think of *something!*"

"Don't lose your head," the voice said. "The only way is to go down for help."

"But you'll—"

"Maybe. And maybe not. That's a chance we'll have to take."

The voice was as quiet as ever. And, hearing it, Rudi was suddenly ashamed. Here was he, safe on the glacier's surface, showing fear and despair, while the one below, facing almost certain death, remained calm and controlled. Whoever it was down there, it was a real man. A brave man.

Rudi drew in a long, slow breath. With his climbing-staff he felt down along the smooth surface of the ice walls.

"Are you still there?" said the voice.

"Yes," he said.

"You had better go."

"Wait—"

Lying flat on the glacier, he leaned over the rim of the crevasse and lowered the staff as far as it would go. Its end came almost to the curve in the walls.

"Can you see it?" he asked.

"See what?" said the man.

Obviously he couldn't. Standing up, Rudi removed his jacket and tied it by one sleeve to the curved end of the staff. Then, holding the other end, he again lay prone and lowered his staff and jacket.

"Can you see it now?" he asked.

"Yes," said the man.

"How far above you is it?"

"About ten feet."

Again the staff came up. Rudi took off his shirt and tied one of its sleeves to the dangling sleeve of the jacket. This time, as he lay down, the ice bit, cold and rough, into his bare chest; but he scarcely noticed it. With his arms extended, all the shirt and half the jacket were out of sight beneath the curve in the crevasse.

"How near you now?" he called.

"Not far," said the voice.

"Can you reach it?"

"I'm trying."

There was the sound of scraping boot-nails; of <u>labored</u> breathing. But no pull on the shirtsleeve down below.

"I can't make it," said the voice. It was fainter than before.

"Wait," said Rudi.

For the third time he raised the staff. He took off his trousers. He tied the trouser-leg to the loose sleeve of the shirt. Then he pulled, one by one, at all the knots he had made: between staff and jacket, jacket and shirt, shirt and trousers. He pulled until the blood pounded in his head and the knots were as tight as his strength could make them. This done, he stepped back from the crevasse to the point where his toes had rested when he lay flat. With feet and hands he kicked and scraped the ice until he had made two holes. Then, lying down as before, he dug his toes deep into them. He was naked now, except for his shoes, stockings and underpants. The cold rose from the ice into his blood and bones. He lowered the staff and knotted clothes like a sort of crazy fishing line.

The trousers, the shirt and half of the jacket passed out of sight. He was leaning over as far as he could.

"Can you reach it now?" he called.

"Yes," the voice answered.

"All right. Come on."

"You won't be able to hold me. I'll pull you in."

"No you won't."

He braced himself. The pull came. His toes went <u>taut</u> in their ice-holds and his hands tightened on the staff until the knuckles showed white. Again he could hear a scraping sound below, and he knew that the man was clawing his boots against the ice-wall, trying both to lever himself up and to take as much weight as possible off the <u>improvised</u> lifeline. But the wall obviously offered little help. Almost all his weight was on

---

labored (lā′bərd) *adj.* forced; done with effort.

taut (tôt) *adj.* full of tension or strain; tight.

improvised (im′prə vīzd) *adj.* made from whatever materials are on hand.

the lifeline. Suddenly there was a jerk, as one of the knots in the clothing slipped, and the staff was almost wrenched from Rudi's hands. But the knot held. And his hands held. He tried to call down, "All right?" but he had no breath for words. From below, the only sound was the scraping of boots on ice.

How long it went on Rudi could never have said. Perhaps only for a minute or so. But it seemed like hours. And then at last—at last—it happened. A hand came into view around the curve of the crevasse wall: a hand gripping the twisted fabric of his jacket, and then a second hand rising slowly above it. A head appeared. A pair of shoulders. A face was raised for an instant and then lowered. Again one hand moved slowly up past the other.

But Rudi no longer saw it, for now his eyes were shut tight with the strain. His teeth were clamped, the cords of his neck bulged, the muscles of his arm felt as if he were being drawn one by one from the bones that held them. He began to lose his toeholds. He was being dragged forward. Desperately, frantically, he dug in with his feet, pressed his whole body down, as if he could make it part of the glacier. Though all but naked on the ice, he was pouring with sweat. Somehow he stopped the slipping. Somehow he held on. But now suddenly the strain was even worse, for the man had reached the lower end of the staff. The slight "give" of the stretched clothing was gone, and in its place was rigid <u>deadweight</u> on a length of wood. The climber was close now. But heavy. Indescribably heavy. Rudi's hands ached and burned, as if it were a rod of hot lead that they clung to. It was not a mere man he was holding, but a giant; or a block of granite. The pull was unendurable. The pain unendurable. He could hold on no longer. His hands were opening. It was all over.

And then it was over. The weight was gone. There was a scraping sound close beneath him; a hand on the rim of ice; a figure pulling itself up onto the lip of the crevasse. The man was beside Rudi, turning to him, staring at him.

"Why—you're just a boy!" he said in astonishment.

■
deadweight (ded´wāt´) *n.* heavy burden.

Rudi was too numb to move or speak. Taking the staff from him, the man pulled up the line of clothes, untied the knots and shook them out.

"Come on now. Quickly!" he said.

Pulling the boy to his feet, he helped him dress. Then he rubbed and pummeled him until at last Rudi felt the warmth of returning circulation.

"Better?" the man asked, smiling.

Rudi nodded. And finally he was able to speak again. "And you, sir," he said, "you are all right?"

The man nodded. He was warming himself now: flapping his arms and kicking his feet together. "A few minutes of sun and I'll be as good as new."

Nearby, a black boulder lay embedded in the glacial ice, and, going over to it, they sat down. The sunlight poured over them like a warm bath. Rudi slowly flexed his aching fingers and saw that the man was doing the same. And then the man had raised his eyes and was looking at him.

"It's a miracle how you did it," he said. "A boy of your size. All alone."

"It was nothing," Rudi murmured.

"Nothing?"

"I—I only—"

"Only saved my life," said the man.

For the first time, now, Rudi was really seeing him. He was a man of perhaps thirty, very tall and thin, and his face, too, was thin, with a big hawklike nose and a strong jutting chin. His weather-browned cheeks were clean-shaven, his hair black, his eyes deep-set and gray. And when he spoke, his voice was still almost as quiet as when it had been muffled by the ice-walls of the crevasse. He is—what?—Rudi thought. Not Swiss, he knew. Not French or German. English, perhaps? Yes, English. . . . And then suddenly a deep excitement filled him, for he knew who the man was.

"You are Captain Winter?" he murmured.

"That's right."

---

pummeled (pum′əld) *v.t.* hit again and again with the fists; pounded.

embedded (em bed′id) *adj.* set firmly into something.

flexed (flekst) *v.t.* bent; tightened.

"And I—I have saved—I mean—"

Rudi stopped in confusion, and the Englishman grinned. "You've saved," he said, smiling, "one of the worst <u>imbeciles</u> that ever walked on a glacier. An imbecile who was so busy looking up at a mountain that he couldn't even see what was at his feet."

Rudi was wordless—almost stunned. He looked at the man, and then away in embarrassment, and he could scarcely believe what had happened. The name of Captain John Winter was known through the length and breadth of the Alps. He was the <u>foremost</u> mountaineer of his day, and during the past ten years had made more first ascents of great peaks than any other man alive. Rudi had heard that he had come to Kurtal a few days before. He had hoped that at least he would see him in the hotel or walking by in the street. But actually to meet him—and in this way! To pull him from a crevasse—save him. . . . It was incredible!

MEET JAMES RAMSEY ULLMAN

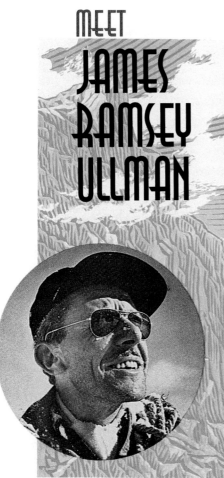

James Ramsey Ullman knew what it was like to face danger in the wilderness. In his lifetime, he climbed many of the world's highest mountains, including Mount Everest. He used his experiences to create exciting works of fiction, such as *The White Tower* and *River of the Sun*. In Ullman's novels, individuals must find the courage to make life-and-death decisions and to overcome great obstacles. *Banner in the Sky* was a Newbery Honor Book in 1955 and was made into a movie.

Ullman also understood the courage it takes to overcome obstacles in everyday life. In 1965, he took part in the Freedom March in Montgomery, Alabama, an important event in the struggle to secure civil rights for African Americans.

---

imbeciles (im′bə silz) *n., pl.* stupid or foolish people.
foremost (fôr′mōst′) *adj.* leading; first in rank or importance.

RESPONDING TO *Literature*

THINK • TALK • WRITE

1 What would you have done if you had been in Rudi's place? You may want to jot some ideas in your journal.

2 Why does Rudi *not* run for help? What does he do to rescue the man? Why is this dangerous? Explain.

3 What does Rudi do while the man struggles up the line made of clothing and his staff? What happens to Rudi during this rescue?

4 Who has more reason to be afraid— Rudi or Captain Winter? Who shows more fear? What lessons about courage might Rudi have learned?

5 Why do you suppose people try to climb mountains? How might they feel if they succeed? If they fail?

ACTIVITIES

- **Write with Mood** Think of a place you like. What is the mood of this place? Is it peaceful yet exciting? Write a few paragraphs capturing the mood of the place.

- **Draw Instructions** Rudi saves Captain Winter following a series of steps. Think of something you like to do. Draw pictures showing the steps in the process. If necessary, write a caption to go with each picture.

VOCABULARY PRACTICE

Write the vocabulary word that best answers each question.

chasms   improvised
specifically   pummeled
vertical   embedded
taut   flexed
labored   foremost

1 Which word describes what a man did as he struggled up a mountain?

2 When Rudi bent his arm, what did his muscles do?

3 Which word describes the line of clothing stretched tight as the captain climbed up?

4 Which word describes how stones are set in cement?

5 What are deep cracks in a mountain or glacier called?

6 Which word would describe walls of ice that run straight up and down?

7 How does Captain Winter rank among mountain climbers?

8 What did Rudi do when he created a lifeline using his clothes and staff?

9 Which adverb would you use when you refer to something in particular?

10 What did the captain do with his fists to help Rudi's circulation?

I May,
I Might,
I Must

by Marianne Moore

If you will tell me why the fen
appears impassable, I then
will tell you why I think that I
can get across it if I try.

Your World

Your world is as big as you make it.
I know, for I used to abide
In the narrowest nest in a corner,
My wings pressing close to my side.

But I sighted the distant horizon
Where the skyline encircled the sea
And I throbbed with a burning desire
To travel this immensity.

I battered the cordons around me
And cradled my wings on the breeze
Then soared to the uttermost reaches
With rapture, with power, with ease!

—Georgia Douglas Johnson

BEFORE READING

BROTHER TO THE WIND

CONNECT TO LITERATURE

Did you ever dream or imagine that you could fly? Did you enjoy the experience, or were you too frightened? In your journal, write about how it might feel to fly. As you read "Brother to the Wind," an African folk tale retold by Mildred Pitts Walter, note how Emeke, the hero, feels about flying.

THINKING ABOUT THEME

The *theme* of a story is its main idea or message. Sometimes writers state the theme directly. More often, writers only imply the theme. Readers must judge the theme from the actions and dialog of the characters. Analyzing how the central character changes or what that person learns can offer helpful clues to theme. Mildred Pitts Walter never defines the message of "Brother to the Wind," but you will understand it if you read the tale carefully. Pay special attention to Emeke's dream and the way he pursues it.

DID YOU KNOW?

Did you know that many African folk tales share remarkable similarities with tales from Asia, Europe, and the Americas? Every culture has folk tales, and certain elements appear in folklore all over the world. For example, animals often talk to people and sometimes have other special powers. Many tales feature a magical spirit who governs all the animals, such as the Good Snake in this selection. Most folk-tale animals can be seen as symbols for different aspects of human nature. The animals help illustrate a lesson about how people should live. Teaching truths is an important goal of all different kinds of folk tales.

Brother to the Wind

Mildred Pitts Walter

pictures by Diane and Leo Dillon

"Good Snake can make any wish come true," Emeke's grandmother often said. And every day in the village of Eronni, Emeke herded his family's goats and dreamed of finding Good Snake. He wanted to make a wish to fly.

Emeke rose early to herd the goats high up on the mountain. Dark clouds clung to the earth. Morning was almost like night. The rains would soon come.

"Say, Emeke," Ndumu shouted in the dim light, "still want to fly like a bird?" Other boys on the road laughed.

"Our friend thinks he can move like the wind," Mongo said.

"No, he really thinks he will find Good Snake and that Good Snake will help him fly." Nizam's words brought great bursts of laughter.

High up on the mountain, alone with his goats, Emeke looked out at the farms and his village below. Fires blazed and sent up smoke as the men cleared thick brush for new farmland. They worked hard to beat the rains. Their clothes, the colors of the rainbow, flowed with the wind.

Finally Emeke sat watching his goats eat greedily. Then, with his knees drawn to his chest and chin, he closed his eyes. He tried to imagine now what he had often felt in dreams. He wanted to feel the wind, to soar up, up, up, then wheel off like a bird. But his mind filled only with the laughter of his friends.

Then he remembered his grandmother's words: "If you find Good Snake, he will help you fly."

If only I could leave my goats for one day, he thought. I would go searching deep in the bush for Good Snake. But Father would never let me do that.

Maybe he should go into the bush at night when the village was asleep. No boy would go there after dark. Secrets of the bush unfold, and the silence of ghosts grows loud in the dark. No. No boy would do that. "But no boy in my village can fly," Emeke said aloud.

He would find Good Snake and make his wish.

Suddenly he heard a low rumbling noise. What could it be? Not thunder. Thunder came only with the rains. Emeke put his ear closer to the ground and heard the sound of many feet.

Then Emeke saw the strangest thing. A swarm of fire-flies moved in a circle in the distance. In their light Emeke saw animals moving toward a tree, not too far from where his goats were feeding.

Emeke jumped up. He saw Elephant, Rhinoceros, Giraffe, and Zebra. He moved closer and saw smaller animals: Turtle, Hyena, Wild Dog, and Hare. There were many birds too. How peacefully and quietly they all moved together. Emeke's goats were calm, still eating the short grass. They will be safe for a little while, Emeke thought.

Curious, he hurried.

Cautiously he fell in line with the animals.

When they reached the tree he saw an unusual thing.

A huge snake was wrapped around the biggest branch. His tail was hidden in the leaves, but his head hung down toward the ground. Emeke's heart beat wildly, his skin went hot, then cold, and his scalp tingled. This is Good Snake, he thought. Emeke wanted to run away, but his feet felt rooted to the spot.

Hyena, Elephant, Rhinoceros, and all the animals, one by one, made wishes. But Turtle stood off to the side, laughing. He did not believe in Good Snake.

As Emeke watched Turtle laughing, he thought of Ndumu, Nizam, and Mongo. Would he dare ask to fly like a bird?

Finally Good Snake nodded at him. Emeke knew it was now his turn. "Oh, Good Snake, I would like to fly."

Good Snake uncurled his tail and brought forth a rock. "Are you sure you want to fly?"

"Oh, yes, Good Snake," Emeke whispered, hardly able to speak.

Good Snake held out the rock. "This is what you must do: Before the rains come, find the bark of a baobab tree and three large bamboo poles. Then make a kite exactly like the one on the back of this rock."

---

baobab (bā′ō bab′) *n.* tropical tree in Africa, having a broad trunk, thick spreading branches, and a fruit resembling a gourd (a fruit related to the pumpkin).

Emeke took the rock and placed it in his pouch. But what did
a rock and a kite have to do with flying, Emeke wondered. He
wanted to say, Why make a kite? All I want to do is fly like a
bird. Instead he listened as Good Snake went on: "Before the feast
of the harvest, you must find the right wind for the kite."

"Good Snake, how will I know the right wind?" Emeke asked.

Good Snake curled up his tail again and looked at Emeke. "The right wind will whisper words that will let you know for sure. Then, on the day of the feast, meet me high on the mountaintop. If you have done all the things that I have asked, then on that day you will fly. One other thing: Keep that rock with you always. It will help you."

Emeke was so happy and excited he almost forgot to thank Good Snake as he hurried back to his goats.

Good Snake called after him. "Be sure you find the bark and bamboo before the rains come."

Turtle laughed. "He, he, he. Beware! Things without wings don't fly."

The dark heavy clouds threatened to overflow. Emeke hurried toward his goats, wondering how he would find bark and bamboo before it rained. He touched the rock and remembered: *The rock will help you.*

When he reached the place where his goats were feeding, he saw Hyena lurking nearby. Emeke hurriedly gathered his goats together to protect them. His goats did not seem at all alarmed. They kept right on eating greedily.

Hyena moved closer.

Emeke became more frightened, and touched the rock.

"Do not be scared," Hyena shouted. "I have come to herd your goats."

"*You?* Herd my goats?" Emeke asked in disbelief.

"Yes. I wished to have more patience and less greed. Be off to the bush to find your bamboo and bark. I'll care for your goats until you return."

Emeke did not trust Hyena.

He was still afraid.

---

lurking (lûr′king) *v.i.* moving about in a sneaky manner.

disbelief (dis′bi lēf′) *n.* refusal to accept the truth or reality of something.

Hyena sensed Emeke's fear and said, "Do you believe Good Snake can help you fly?"

Emeke realized he did not know whether he could trust Good Snake. But his grandmother believed in Good Snake. "Yes," he said. "I believe Good Snake can help me fly."

"Then believe that he can make me a goat herder."

Every few feet Emeke turned to look back, thinking his goats would be eaten. But Hyena was moving among the goats as a caring herder should. I must trust Hyena, he thought, and hurried on toward the bush.

The clouds made the bush almost as dark as night. Emeke stumbled along in the unfriendly quiet.

He must find the bark and bamboo before the rains came.

Suddenly he walked into something that felt like a wall. It moved. Emeke's heart beat wildly. Then he knew. It was not a wall at all. It was Elephant. Emeke was frightened; he squeezed the rock for comfort.

"I am here to help you find the baobab tree," Elephant said.

"How do you know I need bark from the baobab tree?"

"I made a wish too. I wished to be kind and helpful. My wish can come true, if I can help you." Elephant led the way into the bush.

Soon Emeke had enough bark for his kite. Emeke thanked Elephant. Now he must hurry to find the bamboo. His father would be furious if he found the goats left in Hyena's care.

At last Emeke found the watering hole where bamboo grew. To his surprise, Rhinoceros was waiting for him with three neatly cut poles.

"I knew you would come," Rhinoceros said. "I made a wish to be gentle and of service. My wish has come true."

It was night when Emeke returned to the pasture. His goats were gone! Emeke's heart skipped beats. He felt weak and his head seemed to swell. He ran here and there, everywhere, looking. Then, around a curve, he saw his goats. Hyena had gathered them all together.

The goats pushed and shoved around Emeke. Hyena was glad to see Emeke too. Emeke thanked Hyena and hurried down the mountain.

He had not gone far when he saw his father with men from the village. Emeke's friends were with them.

"Where were you?" his father demanded.

"On the mountain."

"No, you were not!" Ndumu shouted.

"We looked all over for you," Nizam said.

"And what is this burden you are carrying?" His father pointed to the bark and bamboo.

"I want to fly, Father, so—"

An <u>explosion</u> of laughter interrupted Emeke. Emeke looked at

---

explosion (ek splō′zhən) *n.* sudden, loud outburst.

his father and knew his father was <u>humiliated</u>. The men laughed because they thought Emeke was a lazy, careless boy who did not take his duties seriously.

"Why do you say foolish things, Emeke?" his father demanded. "Did you ever see humans fly?"

Emeke felt his father was more hurt than angry. He wanted to move closer to his father, but it was as though the laughter had turned him to stone.

Finally, with tears in his voice and with great respect, Emeke tried to explain again.

"Father, I did not leave the goats alone. Hyena cared for them. . . ."

There was another explosion of laughter. Over the laughter Emeke's father shouted, "Let me hear no more of this foolishness. Now, I want you to promise that you will never leave the goats unattended again."

Emeke remembered that he still had to find the right wind. He did not want to promise.

"Emeke," his father said, "if you leave the goats again, I will have to punish you. I want your word that you will not."

"I promise," Emeke said sadly.

Later that night, thunder rumbled and lightning lit up the village. Emeke heard the sound of drops like small pebbles <u>pelting</u> the roof. The rains had come. He had found the bark and bamboo just in time.

Rain fell in gray sheets, soaking the earth, filling the streams. Emeke could not herd his goats. While other children sat around the fire roasting <u>maize</u> and groundnuts, Emeke sat alone working on his kite.

With the rock close by, he worked every day. Soon word spread about the huge kite. Emeke's friends called him bird boy, wing-flapper. People in the village said Emeke was a foolish boy. His family was ashamed of him. Only his grandmother believed he might fly one day.

---

humiliated (hū mil′ē ā tid) *adj.* feeling or showing shame or extreme embarrassment.
pelting (pel′ting) *v.t.* beating against repeatedly.
maize (māz) *n.* corn.

"Why such a heavy kite?" his mother asked.

"You will never fly that one on a string," his father said.

"It will fly me. I will soar in the wind, dive and wheel like a bird without falling," Emeke said proudly.

His grandmother beamed, but his father said, "Put the kite away. Forget this flying foolishness."

Finally the rain fell in drops as thin as needles against the sunlight. White clouds raced away, leaving the sky clean and blue. The sun shone bright and the wind blew cold. Emeke herded his goats at the foot of the mountain and wondered where he would ever find the right wind.

Days grew warmer. After many days and nights, the growing season ended and it was time for the harvest to begin.

The night before the harvest festival, the moon rose like a giant orange ball. The night slowly turned almost as bright as day.

Emeke lay listening to the wind. "Come out, come out, you don't have to break your promise," the wind sighed.

Emeke rushed outside. He hurried to the edge of his village. The grass grew tall, and the wind sang like the sound of the sea. The grass bowed left and right, moving like women's skirts in the dance. Emeke stood still, listening.

Then softly as the flutter of a bird's wing came a whisper: "My brother." Emeke trembled with the excitement that comes with dancing. Be still and listen, he told himself. Again the whisper: "My brother." That is the right wind! He felt light with happiness.

The rest of the night, Emeke slept without dreaming.

The morning of the festival came with the sound of many drums. The air was heavy with excitement. Today I will fly, Emeke thought when he awoke.

Emeke walked with his family to the center of the village. His friends gathered around him, excited about the games and races to be held at the festival.

"I will fly today," Emeke said matter-of-factly. "Look up and you will see me."

"Then look down," Ndumu said. "Oooh, no more Emeke! He is splattered like a bird's egg." Ndumu fell to the ground, arms and legs spread. All the boys bent with laughter.

"I will fly. You will see," Emeke said.

When the center of the village was <u>overrun</u> with people, Emeke slipped away with his kite and rock. He hurried up the mountain to meet Good Snake.

As he came near the top of the mountain, he heard a plodding sound. He looked around and saw Turtle struggling to join him.

"Hey," Turtle shouted. "Beware! Boys were not made to fly."

"With the help of Good Snake, I can, and I will."

---

overrun (ō′vər run′) *v.t.* swarming or overflowing.

285

"What if you drift to the end of the earth or land on your feet in the mouth of Crocodile, or in Lion's lair?"

Emeke became frightened. He had thought only of flying. Then suddenly he heard the wind sighing softly. Emeke's confidence returned. "I am not afraid, Turtle." He hurried to find Good Snake.

High up on the mountain Good Snake was waiting.

"I made the kite and found the wind," Emeke said to Good Snake.

Good Snake turned the kite this way and that to make sure it was made well, safe for flying. Then he led Emeke to the edge of the mountain. "You will fly from here down into your village."

Emeke heard the drums from the distance. He looked down and saw the cloud of dust from dancing feet. He thought of Ndumu's words and of his friends' laughter. Turtle's words echoed: "Boys are not made to fly." Emeke hurriedly backed away from the edge. He looked at Good Snake and said, "I cannot fly."

"But everything is ready."

"With all those people in the center of the village, where will I land safely?" Emeke cried.

"You must think of nothing but flying. Trust me with the rest. Give me the rock. I leave you with the wind."

Emeke pointed the nose of his kite up slightly. Should he trust Good Snake? Would he really fly? He waited. He listened.

"My brother," the wind sighed.

Emeke felt the easy, steady wind. He forgot his fear. He balanced his kite and started running toward the edge of the mountain.

He kept his mind on running and keeping his kite's nose up.

Suddenly he was in the air. He flowed up, then floated down, gliding with the wind. His body seemed to disappear. There was only wind, sky, and the earth far below. He was flying! Soaring, turning, streaming down, then lightly, easily floating. "I am brother to the wind," he shouted.

He floated to his feet as lightly as a feather. His grandmother was the first to reach him. She hugged him, beaming with love. His mother and father smiled with pride. All of his friends rushed to examine the kite. "He did fly like a bird," Nizam said.

Drummers beat their drums, sending up sounds as great as all the thunder in the world. Dancing feet sent up clouds of dust. Emeke danced to the rhythms with his grandmother.

Meet
Mildred Pitts Walter

Being active in a variety of causes has been very much a part of Mildred Pitts Walter's life. Her concern for building a better understanding of the African-American experience has led her to write a number of books for young people that explore themes of going to school and growing up.

Walter is not afraid to make some tough decisions to support her beliefs. In fact, when she was awarded the Coretta Scott King Award for Literature for Justin and the Best Biscuits in the World, *she had to choose between appearing at the awards ceremony and participating in a peace walk in the Soviet Union. She says, "I struggled with the question: Which creates the best image for young people? To be in San Francisco to accept the award, or to walk for peace? . . . My answer came. I chose to walk."*

Meet
Diane and Leo Dillon

Since Leo and Diane Dillon met in art school in the 1950s, they have worked together illustrating books for both children and adults. The Dillons express their feelings about their craft when they say, "We believe in magic. To sit down with a blank piece of paper and see scenes and characters take form . . . it is *magic*."

Two of their books, Why Mosquitoes Buzz in People's Ears and Ashanti to Zulu: African Traditions, won the American Library Association's Caldecott Medal for illustrated books. Another of their books is Aïda, which is based on an opera about an Ethiopian princess.

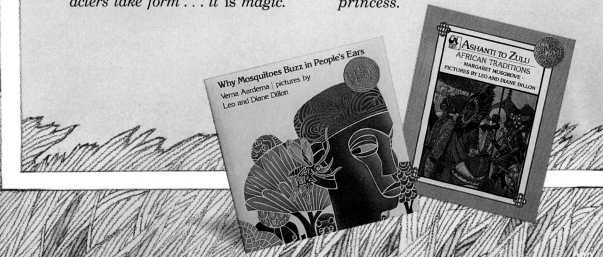

RESPONDING TO Literature

THINK • TALK • WRITE

1 Why do you think it is so important to Emeke to learn to fly? Write your ideas in your journal.

2 What is Emeke's relationship with his grandmother? How does she feel about Emeke? Why does Emeke want to find Good Snake?

3 Why do you think the Turtle tries to discourage Emeke? How do the other animals help the boy? Why do they help him?

4 Does Emeke actually *fly?* Do you think the Good Snake uses magic to help Emeke fly? Why or why not?

5 How do the events and characters in this folk tale reflect the African culture that produced it? Does the tale remind you of any folk tales from other cultures? Explain.

ACTIVITIES

- **Write About Theme** Compare "Brother to the Wind" and "Petronella." Write a paragraph stating the theme of each selection and then a third paragraph comparing the themes.

- **Conduct Experiments** Experiment with things that float or glide. It's easy! First make a parachute:
  —Tie equal lengths of string to the corners of a handkerchief.
  —Gather the loose ends together, and tape a dime to them.
  —Hold the handkerchief at its center, and drop it. What does it do?

Next, test paper airplane designs:
  —With a group of classmates, make paper airplanes as many different ways as you can.
  —Try each design outdoors or in the school gym. Which designs work best? Which work the worst?

VOCABULARY PRACTICE

On a separate piece of paper, write the word from the vocabulary list that best completes each sentence.

lurking   pelting
disbelief   humiliated
explosion

1 The wind wailed like a siren, and heavy rain was _____ the windows.

2 The forecaster felt _____ because he had guaranteed good weather, and instead there was a storm.

3 When lightning struck the paint factory, a tremendous _____ rocked the town.

4 The shocking news left the factory managers speechless with _____.

5 A spy was _____ in the shadows hoping to overhear the owner's secrets.

Autour d'elle   1945   Marc Chagall   Museum of Modern Art, Paris

Since he weighs nothing,

Even the stoutest dreamer

Can fly without wings.

—W. H. Auden

BEFORE READING

LOB'S GIRL

CONNECT TO LITERATURE

Have you ever had a pet? How did the animal feel about you? How did you know? If you haven't had a pet, what kind of pet would you like? Write some thoughts in your journal. As you read "Lob's Girl," compare your feelings with those Sandy has for Lob.

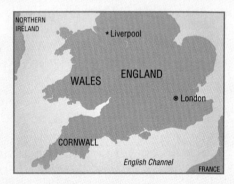

THINKING ABOUT SURPRISE ENDINGS

A surprise ending brings an unexpected conclusion to the events of a story. On your first reading, the final twist may seem sudden. However, when you reread the story, you will probably find clues to what was going to happen.

Why does an author create a surprise ending? One reason is to entertain the reader. Another may be to emphasize the theme of the story. In "Lob's Girl," a dog repeatedly overcomes obstacles to be with a girl. Each time, the obstacles get greater. As you read, think about where this pattern might lead and how the pattern helps to bring out the story's theme.

DID YOU KNOW?

This story is set in a fishing village in the county of Cornwall, located at the southwestern tip of Britain. Many years ago, Cornwall was an independent country, just as England, Scotland, and Wales were. Now, all these are part of the United Kingdom.

For years, fishing and tin mining were the major Cornish industries. Today, Cornwall is a popular holiday resort. In the summer, people from other parts of England visit the region to vacation by the sea. Lob's owner came from Liverpool, which is four hundred miles to the north of Cornwall.

LOB'S GIRL

BY JOAN AIKEN

Some people choose their dogs, and some dogs choose their people. The Pengelly family had no say in the choosing of Lob; he came to them in the second way, and very decisively.

It began on the beach, the summer when Sandy was five, Don, her older brother, twelve, and the twins were three. Sandy was really Alexandra, because her grandmother had

Paddling *Marshall Brown* *Philip Gale Fine Art* *Chepstow, England*

who didn't need it because they were occupied in seeing which of them could wrap the most seaweed around the other one's legs. Father—Bert Pengelly—and Don were up on the Hard painting the bottom boards of the boat in which Father went fishing for pilchards. And Mother—Jean Pengelly—was getting ahead with making the Christmas puddings because she never felt easy in her mind if they weren't made and safely put away by the end of August. As usual, each member of the family was happily getting on with his or her own affairs. Little did they guess how soon this state of things would be changed by the large new member who was going to erupt into their midst.

a beautiful picture of a queen in a diamond tiara and high collar of pearls. It hung by Granny Pearce's kitchen sink and was as familiar as the doormat. When Sandy was born everyone agreed that she was the living spit of the picture, and so she was called Alexandra and Sandy for short.

On this summer day she was lying peacefully reading a comic and not keeping an eye on the twins,

---

tiara (tē ar′ə) *n.* ornament resembling a crown, worn on the head.
living spit exact image or likeness.
Hard *n.* firm sheltered beach or stone path sloping down to the water's edge.

Sandy rolled onto her back to make sure that the twins were not climbing on slippery rocks or getting cut off by the tide. At the same moment a large body struck her forcibly in the midriff and she was covered by flying sand. Instinctively she shut her eyes and felt the sand being wiped off her face by something that seemed like a warm, rough, damp flannel. She opened her eyes and looked. It was a tongue. Its owner was a large and bouncy young Alsatian, or German shepherd, with topaz eyes, black-tipped prick ears, a thick, soft coat, and a bushy black-tipped tail.

"Lob!" shouted a man farther up the beach. "Lob, come here!"

But Lob, as if trying to atone for the surprise he had given her, went on licking the sand off Sandy's face, wagging his tail so hard while he kept on knocking up more clouds of sand. His owner, a gray-haired man with a limp, walked over as quickly as he could and seized him by the collar.

"I hope he didn't give you a fright?" the man said to Sandy. "He meant it in play—he's only young."

"Oh, no. I think he's *beautiful,*" said Sandy truly. She picked up a bit of driftwood and threw it. Lob, whisking easily out of his master's grip,

was after it like a sand-colored bullet. He came back with the stick, beaming, and gave it to Sandy. At the same time he gave himself, though no one else was aware of this at the time. But with Sandy, too, it was love at first sight, and when, after a lot more stick-throwing, she and the twins joined Father and Don to go home for tea, they cast many a backward glance at Lob being led firmly away by his master.

"I wish we could play with him every day." Tess sighed.

"Why can't we?" said Tim.

Sandy explained. "Because Mr. Dodsworth, who owns him, is from Liverpool, and he is only staying at the Fisherman's Arms till Saturday."

"Is Liverpool a long way off?"

"Right at the other end of England from Cornwall, I'm afraid."

It was a Cornish fishing village where the Pengelly family lived, with rocks and cliffs and a strip of beach and a little round harbor, and palm trees growing in the gardens of the little whitewashed stone houses. The village was approached by a narrow, steep, twisting hill-road, and guarded

---

midriff (mid′rif) *n.* part of the body below the breast and above the waist.

atone (ə tōn′) *v.i.* make up, as for a wrong; make amends.

by a notice that said LOW GEAR FOR 1½ MILES, DANGEROUS TO CYCLISTS.

The Pengelly children went home to scones with Cornish cream and jam, thinking they had seen the last of Lob. But they were much mistaken. The whole family was playing cards by the fire in the front room after supper when there was a loud thump and a crash of china in the kitchen.

"My Christmas puddings!" exclaimed Jean, and ran out.

"Did you put TNT in them, then?" her husband said.

But it was Lob, who, finding the front door shut, had gone around to the back and bounced in through the open kitchen window, where the puddings were cooling on the sill. Luckily only the smallest was knocked down and broken.

Lob stood on his hind legs and plastered Sandy's face with licks. Then he did the same for the twins, who shrieked with joy.

"Where does this friend of yours come from?" inquired Mr. Pengelly.

"He's staying at the Fisherman's Arms—I mean his owner is."

"Then he must go back there. Find a bit of string, Sandy, to tie to his collar."

"I wonder how he found his way here," Mrs. Pengelly said, when the reluctant Lob had been led whining away and Sandy had explained about their afternoon's game on the beach. "Fisherman's Arms is right round the other side of the harbor."

Lob's owner scolded him and thanked Mr. Pengelly for bringing him back. Jean Pengelly warned the children that they had better not encourage Lob any more if they met him on the beach, or it would only lead to more trouble. So they dutifully took no notice of him the next day until he spoiled their good resolutions by dashing up to them with joyful barks, wagging his tail so hard that he winded Tess and knocked Tim's legs from under him.

They had a happy day, playing on the sand.

The next day was Saturday. Sandy had found out that Mr. Dodsworth was to catch the half-past-nine train. She went out secretly, down to the station, nodded to Mr. Hoskins, the stationmaster, who wouldn't dream of charging any local for a platform ticket, and climbed up on the footbridge that led over the tracks. She didn't want to be seen, but she did want to see. She saw Mr. Dodsworth get on the train,

---

dutifully (dü'tə fəl lē) *adv.* obediently.

accompanied by an unhappy-looking Lob with drooping ears and tail. Then she saw the train slide away out of sight around the next headland, with a melancholy wail that sounded like Lob's last good-bye.

Sandy wished she hadn't had the idea of coming to the station. She walked home miserably, with her shoulders hunched and her hands in her pockets. For the rest of the day she was so cross and unlike herself that Tess and Tim were quite surprised, and her mother gave her a dose of senna.

A week passed. Then, one evening, Mrs. Pengelly and the younger children were in the front room playing snakes and ladders. Mr. Pengelly and Don had gone fishing on the evening tide. If your father is a fisherman, he will never be home at the same time from one week to the next.

Suddenly, history repeating itself, there was a crash from the kitchen. Jean Pengelly leaped up, crying, "My blackberry jelly!" She and the children had spent the morning picking and the afternoon boiling fruit.

But Sandy was ahead of her mother. With flushed cheeks and eyes like stars she had darted into the kitchen, where she and Lob were hugging one another in a frenzy of joy. About a yard of his tongue was out, and he was licking every part of her that he could reach.

"Good heavens!" exclaimed Jean. "How in the world did *he* get here?"

"He must have walked," said Sandy. "Look at his feet."

They were worn, dusty, and tarry. One had a cut on the pad.

"They ought to be bathed," said Jean Pengelly. "Sandy, run a bowl of warm water while I get the disinfectant."

"What'll we do about him, Mother?" said Sandy anxiously.

Mrs. Pengelly looked at her daughter's pleading eyes and sighed.

"He must go back to his owner, of course," she said, making her voice firm. "Your dad can get the address from the Fisherman's tomorrow, and phone him or send a telegram. In the meantime he'd better have a long drink and a good meal."

Lob was very grateful for the drink and the meal, and made no objection to having his feet washed. Then he flopped down on the hearthrug and slept in front of the fire they had lit because it was a cold, wet evening, with

senna (sen′ə) *n.* dried leaves of any of several tropical plants, used in making a laxative.
disinfectant (dis′in fek′tənt) *n.* substance used to destroy disease-causing germs.

his head on Sandy's feet. He was a very tired dog. He had walked all the way from Liverpool to Cornwall, which is more than four hundred miles.

The next day Mr. Pengelly phoned Lob's owner, and the following morning Mr. Dodsworth arrived off the night train, decidedly put out, to take his pet home. That parting was worse than the first. Lob whined, Don walked out of the house, the twins burst out crying, and Sandy crept up to her bedroom afterward and lay with her face pressed into the quilt, feeling as if she were bruised all over.

Jean Pengelly took them all into Plymouth to see the circus on the next day and the twins cheered up a little, but even the hour's ride in the train each way and the Liberty horses and performing seals could not cure Sandy's sore heart.

She need not have bothered, though. In ten days' time Lob was back—limping this time, with a torn ear and a patch missing out of his furry coat, as if he had met and tangled with an enemy or two in the course of his four-hundred-mile walk.

Bert Pengelly rang up Liverpool again. Mr. Dodsworth, when he answered, sounded weary. He said, "That dog has already cost me two days that I can't spare away from my work—plus endless time in police stations and drafting newspaper advertisements. I'm too old for these ups and downs. I think we'd better face the fact, Mr. Pengelly, that it's your family he wants to stay with—that is, if you want to have him."

Bert Pengelly gulped. He was not a rich man; and Lob was a pedigreed dog. He said cautiously, "How much would you be asking for him?"

"Good heavens, man, I'm not suggesting I'd *sell* him to you. You must have him as a gift. Think of the train fares I'll be saving. You'll be doing me a good turn."

"Is he a big eater?" Bert asked doubtfully.

By this time the children, breathless in the background listening to one side of this conversation, had realized what was in the wind and were dancing up and down with their hands clasped <u>beseechingly</u>.

"Oh, not for his size," Lob's owner assured Bert. "Two or three pounds of meat a day and some vegetables and gravy and biscuits—he does very well on that."

Alexandra's father looked over the telephone at his daughter's swimming

beseechingly (bi sēch'ing lē) *adv.* in an earnest, pleading manner.

Newfoundland *19th century   Edwin Landseer   William Secord Gallery, New York*

home. They'll look after him and see he gets enough exercise. But I can tell you," he ended firmly, "if he wants to settle in with us he'll have to learn to eat a lot of fish."

So that was how Lob came to live with the Pengelly family. Everybody loved him and he loved them all. But there was never any question who came first with him. He was Sandy's dog. He slept by her bed and followed her everywhere he was allowed.

Nine years went by, and each summer Mr. Dodsworth came back to stay at the Fisherman's Arms and call on his <u>erstwhile</u> dog. Lob always met him with recognition and dignified pleasure, accompanied him for a walk or two—but showed no signs of wishing to return to Liverpool. His place, he intimated, was definitely with the Pengellys.

eyes and trembling lips. He reached a decision. "Well, then, Mr. Dodsworth," he said briskly, "we'll accept your offer and thank you very much. The children will be overjoyed and you can be sure Lob has come to a good

---

erstwhile (ûrst′hwīl′) *adj.* former.

299

St. Ives *Gwendoline Mary Hopton   John Noott Galleries   Broadway, England*

home from school—even the twins were at high school now, and Don was a full-fledged fisherman—Jean Pengelly said, "Sandy, your Aunt Rebecca says she's lonesome because Uncle Will Hoskins has gone out trawling, and she wants one of you to go and spend the evening with her. You go, dear; you can take your homework with you."

Sandy looked far from enthusiastic.

"Can I take Lob with me?"

"You know Aunt Becky doesn't really like dogs—Oh, very well." Mrs. Pengelly sighed. "I suppose she'll have to put up with him as well as you."

Reluctantly Sandy tidied herself, took her schoolbag, put on the damp raincoat she had just taken off, fastened Lob's lead to his collar, and set off to walk through the dusk to Aunt Becky's cottage, which was five minutes' climb up the steep hill.

In the course of nine years Lob changed less than Sandy. As she went into her teens he became a little slower, a little stiffer, there was a touch of gray on his nose, but he was still a handsome dog. He and Sandy still loved one another devotedly.

One evening in October all the summer visitors had left, and the little fishing town looked empty and secretive. It was a wet, windy dusk. When the children came

---

trawling (trô′ling) *v.i.* fishing with a strong, usually bag-shaped, net dragged over the ocean bottom.

The wind was howling through the shrouds of boats drawn up on the Hard.

"Put some cheerful music on, do," said Jean Pengelly to the nearest twin. "Anything to drown that wretched sound while I make your dad's supper." So Don, who had just come in, put on some rock music, loud. Which was why the Pengellys did not hear the truck hurtle down the hill and crash against the post office wall a few minutes later.

Dr. Travers was driving through Cornwall with his wife, taking a late holiday before patients began coming down with winter colds and flu. He saw the sign that said STEEP HILL. LOW GEAR FOR 1½ MILES. Dutifully he changed into second gear.

"We must be nearly there," said his wife, looking out of her window. "I noticed a sign on the coast road that said the Fisherman's Arms was two miles. What a narrow, dangerous hill! But the cottages are very pretty—Oh, Frank, stop, *stop!* There's a child, I'm sure it's a child—by the wall over there!"

Dr. Travers jammed on his brakes and brought the car to a stop. A little stream ran down by the road in a shallow stone <u>culvert</u>, and half in the water lay something that looked, in the dusk, like a pile of clothes—or was it the body of a child? Mrs. Travers was out of the car in a flash, but her husband was quicker.

"Don't touch her, Emily!" he said sharply. "She's been hit. Can't be more than a few minutes. Remember that truck that overtook us half a mile back, speeding like the devil? Here, quick, go into that cottage and phone for an ambulance. The girl's in a bad way. I'll stay here and do what I can to stop the bleeding. Don't waste a minute."

Doctors are expert at stopping dangerous bleeding, for they know the right places to press. This Dr. Travers was able to do, but he didn't dare do more; the girl was lying in a queerly crumpled heap, and he guessed she had a number of bones broken and that it would be highly dangerous to move her. He watched her with great concentration, wondering where the truck had got to and what other damage it had done.

Mrs. Travers was very quick. She had seen plenty of accident cases and knew the importance of speed. The first cottage she tried had a phone; in four minutes she was back, and in six an ambulance was wailing down the hill.

Its attendants lifted the child onto a stretcher as carefully as if she were

---

culvert (kul′vərt) *n.* drain for water under roads, sidewalks, and railroads.

made of fine thistledown. The ambulance sped off to Plymouth—for the local cottage hospital did not take serious accident cases—and Dr. Travers went down to the police station to report what he had done.

He found that the police already knew about the speeding truck—which had suffered from loss of brakes and ended up with its radiator halfway through the post office wall. The driver was concussed and shocked, but the police thought he was the only person injured—until Dr. Travers told his tale.

At half-past nine that night Aunt Rebecca Hoskins was sitting by her fire thinking aggrieved thoughts about the inconsiderateness of nieces who were asked to supper and never turned up when she was startled by a neighbor, who burst in, exclaiming, "Have you heard about Sandy Pengelly, then, Mrs. Hoskins? Terrible thing, poor little soul, and they don't know if she's likely to live. Police have got the truck driver that hit her—ah, it didn't ought to be allowed, speeding through the place like that at umpty miles an hour, they ought to jail him for life—not that that'd be any comfort to poor Bert and Jean."

Horrified, Aunt Rebecca put on a coat and went down to her brother's house. She found the family with white shocked faces; Bert and Jean were about to drive off to the hospital where Sandy had been taken, and the twins were crying bitterly. Lob was nowhere to be seen. But Aunt Rebecca was not interested in dogs; she did not inquire about him.

"Thank the lord you've come, Beck," said her brother. "Will you stay the night with Don and the twins? Don's out looking for Lob and heaven knows when we'll be back; we may get a bed with Jean's mother in Plymouth."

"Oh, if only I'd never invited the poor child," wailed Mrs. Hoskins. But Bert and Jean hardly heard her.

That night seemed to last forever. The twins cried themselves to sleep. Don came home very late and grim-faced. Bert and Jean sat in a waiting room of the Western Counties Hospital, but Sandy was unconscious, they were told, and she remained so. All that could be done for her was done. She was given transfusions to replace all the blood she had lost. The broken bones were set and put in slings and cradles.

---

thistledown (this'əl doun') *n.* soft, silky fuzz on a prickly plant, which has red or purple flowers.
concussed (kən kust') *adj.* injured by a blow to the brain or spinal cord.
aggrieved (ə grēvd') *adj.* having hurt feelings or wounded pride.

"Is she a healthy girl? Has she a good constitution?" the emergency doctor asked.

"Aye, doctor, she is that," Bert said hoarsely. The lump in Jean's throat prevented her from answering; she merely nodded.

"Then she ought to have a chance. But I won't conceal from you that her condition is very serious, unless she shows signs of coming out from this coma."

But as hour succeeded hour, Sandy showed no signs of recovering consciousness. Her parents sat in the waiting room with haggard faces; sometimes one of them would go to telephone the family at home, or to try to get a little sleep at the home of Granny Pearce, not far away.

At noon next day Dr. and Mrs. Travers went to the Pengelly cottage to inquire how Sandy was doing, but the report was gloomy: "Still in a very serious condition." The twins were miserably unhappy. They forgot that they had sometimes called their elder sister bossy and only remembered how often she had shared her pocket money with them, how she read to them and took them for picnics and helped with their homework. Now there was no Sandy, no Mother and Dad, Don went around with a gray, shuttered face,

and worse still, there was no Lob.

The Western Counties Hospital is a large one, with dozens of different departments and five or six connected buildings, each with three or four entrances. By that afternoon it became noticeable that a dog seemed to have taken up position outside the hospital, with the fixed intention of getting in. Patiently he would try first one entrance and then another, all the way around, and then begin again. Sometimes he would get a little way inside, following a visitor, but animals were, of course, forbidden, and he was always kindly but firmly turned out again. Sometimes the guard at the main entrance gave him a pat or offered him a bit of sandwich— he looked so wet and beseeching and desperate. But he never ate the sandwich. No one seemed to own him or to know where he came from; Plymouth is a large city and he might have belonged to anybody.

At tea time Granny Pearce came through the pouring rain to bring a flask of hot tea with brandy in it to her daughter and son-in-law. Just as she reached the main entrance the guard was gently but forcibly shoving out a large, agitated, soaking-wet Alsatian dog.

---

coma (kō′mə) *n.* state of deep unconsciousness from which a person cannot easily be aroused.

"No, old fellow, you can *not* come in. Hospitals are for people, not for dogs."

"Why, bless me," exclaimed old Mrs. Pearce. "That's Lob! Here, Lob, Lobby boy!"

Lob ran to her, whining. Mrs. Pearce walked up to the desk.

"I'm sorry, madam, you can't bring that dog in here," the guard said.

Mrs. Pearce was a very determined old lady. She looked the porter in the eye.

"Now, see here, young man. That dog has walked twenty miles from St. Killan to get to my granddaughter. Heaven knows how he knew she was here, but it's plain he knows. And he ought to have his rights! He ought to get to see her! Do you know," she went on, bristling, "that dog has walked the length of England—*twice*—to be with that girl? And you think you can keep him out with your fiddling rules and regulations?"

"I'll have to ask the medical officer," the guard said weakly.

"You do that, young man." Granny Pearce sat down in a determined manner, shutting her umbrella, and Lob sat patiently dripping at her feet. Every now and then he shook his head, as if to dislodge something heavy that was tied around his neck.

Presently a tired, thin, intelligent-looking man in a white coat came downstairs, with an impressive, silver-haired man in a dark suit, and there was a low-voiced discussion. Granny Pearce eyed them, biding her time.

"Frankly . . . not much to lose," said the older man. The man in the white coat approached Granny Pearce.

"It's strictly against every rule, but as it's such a serious case we are making an exception," he said to her quietly. "But only *outside* her bedroom door—and only for a moment or two."

Without a word, Granny Pearce rose and stumped upstairs. Lob followed close to her skirts, as if he knew his hope lay with her.

They waited in the green-floored corridor outside Sandy's room. The door was half shut. Bert and Jean were inside. Everything was terribly quiet. A nurse came out. The white-coated man asked her something and she shook her head. She had left the door ajar and through it could now be seen a high, narrow bed with a lot of gadgets around it. Sandy lay there, very flat under the covers, very still. Her head was turned away. All Lob's attention was riveted on the bed. He strained toward it, but Granny Pearce clasped his collar firmly.

"I've done a lot for you, my boy, now you behave yourself," she whispered grimly. Lob let out a faint whine, anxious and pleading.

At the sound of that whine Sandy stirred just a little. She sighed and moved her head the least fraction. Lob whined again. And then Sandy turned her head right over. Her eyes opened, looking at the door.

"Lob?" she murmured—no more than a breath of sound. "Lobby, boy?"

The doctor by Granny Pearce drew a quick, sharp breath. Sandy moved her left arm—the one that was not broken—from below the covers and let her hand dangle down, feeling, as she always did in the mornings, for Lob's furry head. The doctor nodded slowly.

"All right," he whispered. "Let him go to the bedside. But keep a hold of him."

Granny Pearce and Lob moved to the bedside. Now she could see Bert and Jean, white-faced and shocked, on the far side of the bed. But she didn't look at them. She looked at the smile on her granddaughter's face as the groping fingers found Lob's wet ears and gently pulled them. "Good boy," whispered Sandy, and fell asleep again.

Granny Pearce led Lob out into the passage again. There she let go of him and he ran off swiftly down the stairs.

She would have followed him, but Bert and Jean had come out into the passage, and she spoke to Bert fiercely.

"*I* don't know why you were so foolish as not to bring the dog before! Leaving him to find the way here himself—"

"But, Mother!" said Jean Pengelly. "That can't have been Lob. What a chance to take! Suppose Sandy hadn't—" She stopped, with her handkerchief pressed to her mouth.

"Not Lob? I've known that dog nine years! I suppose I ought to know my own granddaughter's dog?"

"Listen, Mother," said Bert. "Lob was killed by the same truck that hit Sandy. Don found him—when he went to look for Sandy's schoolbag. He was—he was dead. Ribs all smashed. No question of that. Don told me on the phone—he and Will Hoskins rowed a half mile out to sea and sank the dog with a lump of concrete tied to his collar. Poor old boy. Still—he was getting on. Couldn't have lasted forever."

"*Sank him at sea?* Then what—?"

Slowly old Mrs. Pearce, and then the other two, turned to look at the trail of dripping-wet footprints that led down the hospital stairs.

In the Pengellys' garden they have a stone, under the palm tree. It says: "Lob. Sandy's dog. Buried at sea."

MEET JOAN AIKEN

"I always knew I wanted to be a writer," says Joan Aiken (born 1924). The daughter of poet Conrad Aiken, she bought her own thick notebook when she was five and began writing "poems, stories, and thoughts as they occurred." Some of her early work was published in her school magazine. At 17, a story she wrote was read on a radio show for children.

As an adult, Aiken worked as a secretary, a librarian, and an editor, before taking a chance at writing full-time. Within a few years, she published a novel, *The Wolves of Willoughby Chase,* which won a Lewis Carroll Shelf Award in 1965. The success of the book allowed her to continue writing.

Aiken has published more than 80 books of all kinds—novels, plays, short stories. But she most enjoys writing fantasy short stories such as "Lob's Girl," because to her, short stories "come closest to free flight." Her collections include *A Whisper in the Night* and *A Fit of the Shivers.*

RESPONDING TO *Literature*

THINK • TALK • WRITE

1 Would you like to have a dog like Lob? Why or why not? Write some ideas in your journal.

2 How does Sandy meet Lob? What happens to both the girl and the dog at this meeting?

3 How does Lob return to Cornwall from Liverpool? Why is this so astonishing? After he returns the second time, what do the adults decide to do?

4 Whom does Granny Pierce believe the dog at the hospital to be? Why do the Pengellys say she must be wrong? How would you explain this mystery?

5 Sandy, her siblings, and parents live in England. What are some things they do or say that seem distinctively English? How would the story have been different if it had taken place in the United States?

ACTIVITIES

• **Write a Surprise Ending** With a partner, brainstorm to come up with a personal experience or a short story idea with a surprise ending. Write the story, and then read it to your classmates. How surprised were they by your ending?

• **Make an Animal Diorama** Choose an animal that interests you. Use an encyclopedia or your library to research facts about the animal. Look for unusual characteristics. Then make a diorama showing the animal in action. On an index card, explain what is happening in your diorama.

VOCABULARY PRACTICE

On a separate sheet of paper, write the vocabulary word that best answers each question.

atone   beseechingly

dutifully   aggrieved

disinfectant

1 A puppy wants to be friends. How does the puppy look at you?

2 A girl accidentally throws a baseball through a neighbor's window. She agrees to do yard work to earn enough money to pay for the window. What does she plan to do?

3 A friend has lied to you. How do you feel?

4 Your friend has cut a foot. What do you use to help?

5 A young boy looks both ways before crossing the street—just as his mother has told him. How is he acting?

SP⊙T on

BIOGRAPHY

If you wanted to express to someone what your best friend was like, how would you do it? If you like painting, you might paint a portrait. A portrait can be a painting of a person, either famous or little known. Look carefully at the portrait of the child below. Think about how the artist conveys the child's character.

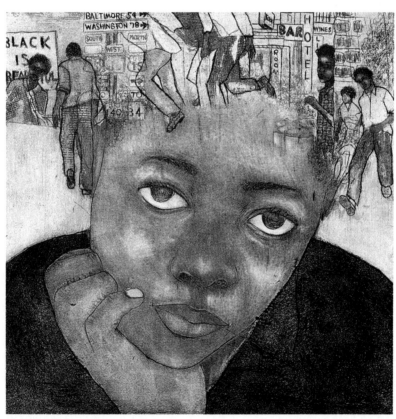

Gemini I *1969 Lev T. Mills Collection Evans-Tibbs*

Who is the subject of this portrait? What, if anything, do you know about this subject? What adjectives might you use to describe him or her?

What details do you notice in the background of the portrait? What do these details suggest about the child's life?

Biographies tell the stories of real-life people. In what ways is this portrait like a biography?

LIGHT

ELEMENTS OF A BIOGRAPHY

A biography is the true story of a real person's life written by someone else. Here are some important parts of a biography.

SUBJECT is the person described in the biography. The subject may be famous or little known, alive or dead, but he or she is always someone who has actually existed.

CHARACTERIZATION is the way in which the writer brings to life the subject of the biography.

- *Direct characterization* takes place when the writer tells you how the subject looks, behaves, and thinks.
- *Indirect characterization* takes place when the writer lets you draw your own conclusions about the subject. For example, the writer might show you how other people react to the subject.

CONFLICT is a clash between opposing forces. The biographer tells how the subject has handled an internal or external conflict.

- *Internal conflict* takes place in the subject's mind, for example, a struggle to make a decision.
- *External conflict* takes place between the subject and another person or a force of nature.

CHRONOLOGICAL ORDER is the order in which events occur in real life. Most biographies are organized in this way and cover the major events of the subject's life from birth to death.

SOURCES OF INFORMATION are the materials from which biographers obtain their facts. Sources can include letters, diaries, interviews, and other writings on the subject.

AUTHOR'S POINT OF VIEW is the biographer's attitude toward the subject. For example, this point of view can be admiring or critical.

In the following biographies, you will learn more about these elements. What you learn will enrich your understanding and enjoyment of biographies and will help you in writing a biography yourself.

BIOGRAPHY

AT LAST!

CONNECT TO LITERATURE

If you could travel anywhere, where would you go? Would you like to visit the Arctic with its freezing cold and miles of ice and snow? Write some ideas in your journal. As you read "At Last!" notice what Matthew Henson endured because he was determined to be among the first group to reach the North Pole.

INTRODUCTION TO THE MODEL BIOGRAPHY

A *biography* tells about a real person's life. As you read the biographies in this unit, you will find that they contain similar elements. For example, each biography includes details from the person's life, uses a variety of information sources, and provides a sequence of events. A biography may also include characterization, setting, and the author's attitude, or tone.

As you read "At Last!" look at the notes in the margin. The notes will help you see the structure of the selection and the way the basic elements of biography are connected. While reading, you may want to jot down ideas and impressions in your journal.

DID YOU KNOW?

"At Last!" is the second-to-last chapter in the biography *Matthew Henson* by Michael Gilman. Henson and Robert Peary made several trips to the Arctic over a 20-year span. During this time, Henson's Inuit friends taught him how to survive in their frozen land. The Inuit loved Henson and even adopted one of his expressions, *Ahdoolo,* into their language. Henson called out this word each morning to wake people up for another tough day of arctic travel. To the Inuit, the word means "endurance" or "courage."

AT LAST!

BY MICHAEL GILMAN

For 17 years, the explorer Matthew Henson (1866-1955) had worked with Admiral Robert Peary to achieve a goal many people considered impossible: reaching the North Pole, the top of the world. In 1908, they set out to make another attempt. This time they were determined to let nothing come between them and the Pole.

The new members of Peary's team were George Borup, Dr. J. W. Goodsell, and Donald MacMillan. Returning from the 1906 expedition were Ross Marvin and Captain Bob Bartlett, both of whom had become veterans of Arctic Sea ice travel during the previous trek. All of the men were young, and they were extremely confident that the expedition would be a success. Henson looked upon the younger men with a practiced eye, trying to judge their capabilities. He was 42 years old, and he had no illusions about life in the Arctic or the dangers that the team would be facing. He had seen too many disfiguring injuries and had been near death too many times to face the new venture with anything except extreme caution.

The expedition left New York on July 6, 1908, stopping first at Oyster Bay, New York. President Theodore Roosevelt, who was on vacation at his nearby family estate, came aboard the ship that bore his name and gave his good wishes to each member of the team. The president told Peary, "If any man succeeds in reaching the Pole, you'll be that man."

Henson prayed that he would be with Peary all the way to the end of the journey. He knew that this would be his last adventure, his last chance to win glory for himself and all black Americans.

Again, the usual preparations were made on the voyage north. Eskimo helpers and dog teams were taken aboard in Greenland, and equipment was readied for the expedition. On September 5, 1908, the *Roosevelt* was anchored off Cape Sheridan.

As Henson looked out over the Arctic Sea ice, he reflected that even with all his years of experience in arctic exploration, he had no way of knowing whether the trip back from Cape Sheridan would be made in joy or sorrow. In choosing a life of adventure, he knew that few things could ever be certain for him. His work

---

trek (trek) *n.* journey, especially one that is difficult or slow.
illusions (i lü′zhenz) *n., pl.* false or misleading ideas.

duties soon removed any time he had for further reflection. He gave the newcomers to the team thorough instruction in how to live and work in the Arctic. As part of the training, the men transported supplies farther west down the coast to Cape Columbia, establishing a camp there called Crane City.

On February 27, Peary gathered the men at Crane City and gave them a pep talk. His words, while not rousing, did inspire them with confidence. Later, the men met in Bartlett's igloo. They toasted each other with brandy and sang their college songs. Henson slipped out into the night. These songs had no meaning to him. His college had been the Arctic. The time had come to prove how well he had mastered its lessons.

The chronological order, or the sequence of events, is often important in a biography. As you read on, notice how biographer Michael Gilman keeps you informed about the date and order of events.

The next day, Bartlett and Borup started out with the advance party that would break the trail for the other groups. Henson and his Eskimo helpers followed one day later. For a quarter of a mile, they followed the advance party's path over the jagged ice near the shore. Almost immediately, they had to pull out axes and chop their way through particularly rough areas. Henson's <u>sledge</u> split after only a mile, and he was forced to make emergency repairs in the face of a tremendous wind.

At the end of the first day of travel, they took shelter in an igloo that Bartlett and Borup had made at the end of their first march. The igloo was only 12 miles from shore. They still had more than 400 miles to go. In a diary account he was keeping, Henson wrote about how ferocious the wind had been on the first day. "No other but a Peary party would have attempted to travel in such weather," he noted. He also wrote that temperatures on the sea ice were especially frigid: "All through the night I would wake from the cold and beat my arms or feet to keep the <u>circulation</u> going."

Notice that the author includes an excerpt from Henson's diary. The people, books, and other materials authors turn to for facts and ideas about their subjects are called their **sources of information.**

sledge (slej) *n.* sled or sleigh.
circulation (sûr′kyə lā′shən) *n.* movement of blood to and from the heart through the blood vessels of the body.

Matthew Henson

In a few days, the traveling improved greatly, and Henson noted that he had never seen smoother sea ice. They finally caught up to the advance party, which had been stopped by a wide lead. With the exception of the rear party led by Marvin and Borup, the other groups soon reached the lead, and a camp of igloos began to grow.

Just as in fiction, the **setting** in a biography affects events. The date and the temperature were crucial for Henson.

On March 5, the sun became visible for the first time that year—a crimson sphere skimming just above the southern horizon. The weather became frustratingly warm, with temperatures reaching almost 0°F. Before them, the open water spread a mile or more into the distance. Henson sat there impatiently, knowing that they needed to travel 20-25 miles a day to keep on schedule. He wrote: "We eat and sleep, and watch the lead and wonder. . . . Are we to be <u>repulsed</u> again?"

---

repulsed (ri pulst′) *v.t.* beaten or driven back.

Bartlett fumed during the delay, calling their camp "hell on earth." Only MacMillan remained cheerful, and he tried to keep the other men amused with his endless supply of stories and jokes. With Henson's help, MacMillan organized games and competitions among the Eskimos to keep them interested in the expedition. The prizes that MacMillan offered to winners of various events were parts of the *Roosevelt:* the rudder, spars, anchors, and keel. No one cared that the prizes were all nonsense; the games had cut through the tension.

Finally, on March 11, the temperature plunged to nearly –50°F, and ice formed on the lead. Bartlett's group crossed first, and the other groups followed a few hours later. The Marvin and Borup party, which was bringing the last of the supplies, still had not appeared. Peary left a note in one of the igloos telling them to hurry.

The ice remained fairly smooth, and the groups traveled fast. On the morning of March 14, Marvin and Borup overtook Henson and Peary's groups, bringing them badly needed supplies. Shortly after the rear party arrived, Peary sent Goodsell and some Eskimos back to the *Roosevelt* with a sledge that carried just enough supplies to get the team back to shore. The commander had begun the process of thinning down the expedition. After every march of five days, he planned to send one of the team members back to land with a group of Eskimos. He was calculating on preserving just enough supplies to allow a few men to reach the Pole. However, no one—not even Henson— knew who Peary would choose to stay with him until the end.

As the march continued, the weather remained extremely cold. For 12 hours a day, Henson and the others lifted and dragged their sledges through hip-deep snow, over small leads, and across jagged ice floes. Two sledges split in half, forcing the men to stop and make time-consuming repairs. In the bitter cold, Henson worked without gloves on his hands, drilling holes to fit leather <u>thongs</u> through the sledges.

MacMillan, whose heel became badly frozen, went south on March 15. Borup's turn came five days later. The tension between the remaining explorers mounted, although they all were too dedicated to the success of the team to demand to know who would be asked to go to the Pole. Bartlett and Henson continued ahead as the trailblazers. In addition to his work advancing the trail, Bartlett was making measurements with a sextant to determine their <u>latitude</u>. After Bartlett and Henson advanced the trail a day's march ahead, they would build an igloo, eat, and go to sleep. While they slept, Peary, Marvin, and the Eskimos marched on the trail that the advance group had created. Thus, at least one party was traveling at all times.

On March 25, Peary gave Marvin and two Eskimos orders to return to land. Henson breathed a sigh of relief. He knew that one more party would be sent back and either he or Bartlett would be put in charge of it. He hoped that Peary would choose Bartlett.

Peary, Henson, and Bartlett each took command of one of the sledges as they continued their advance on the Pole. All three parties had healthy dogs and plenty of food and fuel. For days they sped along, averaging 16 miles a march. On March 28, they passed beyond the farthest point that they had reached on the 1906 trek. Now every mile covered set a new record.

Five more days of travel passed, and on March 30, Peary told Bartlett to return south. Peary, Henson, and four Eskimos—Seegloo, Ootah, Egingwah, and

thongs (thôngz) *n., pl.* narrow strips of leather or other material, used especially as fastenings.

latitude (lat′i tüd′) *n.* distance north or south of the equator, expressed in degrees measured from the earth's center.

Robert Peary on board the Roosevelt

Ooqueah—would make the final dash to the Pole.
Bartlett was disappointed, but he congratulated Henson.

"There's no man in the world right this minute with
a greater responsibility than you, Henson," Bartlett
said. "The commander is tired. We've done all we can.
The rest is up to you. History will be made in these
next few days."

Henson well understood Bartlett's frustration about
coming so close to the Pole only to have to turn back.

He said, "Don't worry, Captain. We'll make it."

They shook hands, and Bartlett left with his group
on the long journey back. Soon all they could see of
his team was the steamy breath of his dogs hanging
in the air to the south.

On April 1, the six men who would make the final
march started their trek. For Peary and Henson, the

ultimate prize and the reason for all their efforts and sacrifices during the last 18 years lay only 130 miles away. Peary had to travel much of the way riding on a sledge because he was unable to march for long on his crippled feet. But his determination to achieve his goal propelled him onward. Henson set a ferocious pace on the last five-day march. In order to cover the distance to the Pole, they needed to average an incredible 26 miles a day.

The temperature rose to almost –15°F. Henson was worried that the team would encounter an uncrossable lead, and he pushed his companions to work 20 hours a day. At the end of April 5, Henson estimated that they had only 35 miles to go.

That night, only the Eskimos could sleep deeply. Henson and Peary tossed restlessly all night. After a few hours, Peary woke up Henson. It was time to go. Henson rose immediately, roused Seegloo and Ootah, and began breaking the final trail. Peary followed a while later with Ooqueah and Egingwah.

A few hours into the march, Henson came close to losing his life. Forsaking caution, he stepped out onto thin ice covering a lead. His feet broke through the ice, and he sank up to his mouth in the frigid water. Ootah pulled Henson clear and helped to get him dried off and warm. Henson thanked his rescuer, telling him, "Ootah is very strong." The Eskimo replied sternly that he was not crazy like Henson. He knew better than to go out on thin ice.

They finally managed to cross the lead. Hours later, Henson stopped and backtracked a ways before making camp. He believed that he might have overshot the Pole. Henson knew Peary would not be pleased to hear this because of a conversation they had earlier. Peary had told him to stop a little distance from the approximate position of the Pole.

Even the hard-working and capable Henson made mistakes. By showing readers another side of Henson, the author makes him a more interesting, multi-dimensional character.

---

ultimate (ul′tə mit) *adj.* final; greatest possible.
forsaking (fôr sāk′ing) *v.t.* giving up completely.

The commander had said, "I'll take one of the boys [Eskimos] and go on from there." Amazed, Henson had asked Peary whether or not he would be joining the commander. "I meant we'll take one of the boys," Peary responded. But Henson thought that Peary had let slip his real intentions: to have his black companion wait behind so that he could claim to have been the very first man at the North Pole.

When Peary arrived at the final camp, Henson was surprised to see that the commander showed no <u>jubilation</u> at reaching his destination. He said hardly a word to Henson and made no effort to congratulate his assistant. Despite the strain between the two men, they had achieved their goal. On the morning of April 7, Peary made one sighting with his sextant at the camp. He then drove off with two of the Eskimos to make more observations from different points in the area. Henson was left behind at the camp. When the commander returned, he announced that his sightings showed them to be on the approximate position of the North Pole.

Peary had Henson and the four Eskimos stand on a nearby pressure ridge while he photographed them. Henson stood in the middle with the American flag in his hands. The Eskimos held flags representing the U.S. Navy, the Red Cross, and other organizations that Peary wished to honor.

Henson said to Ootah, "We have found what we hunt."

Ootah looked at Henson strangely and then looked all around him. "There is nothing here. Just ice," he replied, and shrugged his shoulders.

There was little time to savor the triumph. Because the amount of daylight hours was increasing every day, the temperature might rise, causing unpassable leads to open up. They might soon become trapped hundreds of miles from land.

---

jubilation (jü'bə lā'shən) *n.* feeling of joyful happiness or triumph.

Henson (center) with Seegloo, Ootah, Egingwah, and Ooqueah at the North Pole

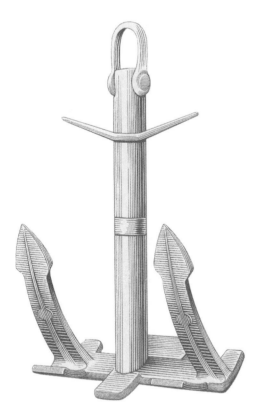

On April 7, Peary's small band of explorers began the journey back across the sea ice. As usual, Henson led the dash back to land. Peary rode on a sledge for most of the way. Even though this time they had plenty of supplies, Henson pushed the team very hard.

The lead that had delayed the men on the trek north was frozen solid, and on April 21, they crossed it and sped onward. Two days later they reached Cape Columbia. As soon as they stepped on land again, the Eskimos leaped up and down and laughed until they had to sink to the ground and gasp for breath. Henson laughed along with them, kidding them good-naturedly about their fear of the devil Tahnusuk. Ootah said the devil must have been asleep or having trouble with his wife to have let them come and go so easily.

After resting at the camp at Cape Columbia for two days, they marched eastward toward the *Roosevelt*. On April 25, they were greeted on the trail by Bartlett, who had returned to the ship a few days before. All the other members of the expedition had arrived back on land safely—except for Marvin. The Eskimos who had traveled back with Marvin said that he had fallen into a lead and drowned. Many years later, one of the Eskimos would confess that he had killed Marvin. The murderer claimed that he had been driven mad by the strain of traveling on the sea ice. In any event, the loss of Marvin cast a <u>pall</u> over the celebration on the ship.

Henson had toiled with remarkable energy, endurance, and courage to achieve his life's goal. He was 42 years old when he succeeded in traveling to the top of the world. Now he could rest, feeling that when he returned to the United States he would be widely honored as a national hero.

The way a biographer writes about the details and events in a subject's life conveys his or her own feelings about that person. This feeling is called the author's **tone,** or attitude.

pall (pôl) *n.* covering of darkness and gloom.

MEET MICHAEL GILMAN

Author Michael Gilman was born and raised in New York City. Besides writing, he enjoys rock climbing. He wrote *Matthew Henson,* the book from which "At Last!" is taken, as part of Chelsea House's Black Americans of Achievement series. It was his first published book. His "fast-paced and readable" style won him praise from *Publishers Weekly.*

More Biographies About Determined People

- *Around the World in a Hundred Years: From Henry the Navigator to Magellan* by Jean Fritz (Putnam, 1994). Here are the stories of 15th-century Europeans who were determined to find a water route to the riches of Asia.

- *Nelson Mandela: Determined to Be Free* by Jack L. Roberts (Millbrook Press, 1995). Even during his 26 years in prison, Nelson Mandela battled the tyranny of apartheid in South Africa.

- *Living Dangerously: American Women Who Risked Their Lives for Adventure* by Doreen Rappaport (HarperCollins, 1991). From shooting Niagara Falls in a barrel to hunting prehistoric human bones beneath the ocean, these six women sought out adventure.

RESPONDING TO Literature

THINK • TALK • WRITE

1 Did reading this selection make you want to explore the Arctic? Explain why or why not in your journal.

2 What did Henson have to teach the newcomers in the expedition? Why do you think he was the one who did the training?

3 How did Ootah save Henson's life? Why do you think Henson had made this dangerous mistake?

4 Who actually seems to have reached the North Pole first? Why do you think Peary did not appear happy when he arrived at camp?

5 At the Pole, Henson told Ootah, "We have found what we hunt." Ootah replied there was nothing but ice. How does this show a difference between the way the American explorers thought and the way the Inuit thought?

ACTIVITY

● **Write About Biography** Skim the selection. Then copy the chart below. Fill in some important events that happened on the expedition's way to the Pole.

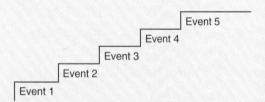

VOCABULARY PRACTICE

Choose the vocabulary word that best fits in each blank. Write the word on a separate sheet of paper.

trek	ultimate
circulation	forsaking
repulsed	jubilation
thongs	pall
latitude	illusions

Explorers in the Arctic face many difficulties and dangers. ___**1**___ the comforts of warmer climates, they begin a ___**2**___ across the ice. When the temperature is very low, a person may have trouble keeping the ___**3**___ of his blood going. The dogsleds have to be held together with walrus hide ___**4**___, since metal nails could crack in the cold. If the temperature rises and the ice melts, the explorers may be ___**5**___ in their attempts to continue. Experienced arctic travelers have no ___**6**___ about the danger of falling through thin ice. Any accident can cast a ___**7**___ over the whole expedition. Using instruments to check ___**8**___ and longitude, the explorers continue on toward their ___**9**___ destination. When they succeed in reaching it, there is much ___**10**___.

BIOGRAPHY

OPERA, KARATE, AND BANDITS

CONNECT TO LITERATURE

What do you know about your grandparents' lives? In your journal, note
some things your grandparents have
told you, or write about your feelings
for them. As you read "Opera, Karate,
and Bandits," compare your feelings
with the feelings the author has for
his grandmother.

THINKING ABOUT CHRONOLOGICAL ORDER

When an author uses *chronological order,* he or she relates events
in the time order that they actually happened. In a biography, this
means the author writes about the person's childhood, youth, and
adulthood in order. However, in "Opera, Karate, and Bandits," the
author does not strictly follow chronological order. He relates several anecdotes about his grandmother, but they are not written
in the sequence they happened. His purpose is not to tell the
whole story of his grandmother's life, but to reveal her personality
as he remembers her from his childhood. He includes incidents
out of order because each one illustrates a characteristic he
remembers about his grandmother.

DID YOU KNOW?

"Opera, Karate, and Bandits" is a chapter from *The Land I Lost*
by Huynh Quang Nhuong. In this book, the author relates his life
as a boy in a remote village in Vietnam. The villagers worked hard
as farmers and hunters and faced many dangers from wild animals in the jungle. However, they remained close and helped one
another. This way of life was changed by the many years of the
Vietnam War, in which Mr. Huynh fought when he grew up.

OPERA, KARATE & BANDITS

from THE LAND I LOST
Adventures of a Boy in Vietnam

by Huynh Quang Nhuong
illustrated by Robert Roth

I was born on the central highlands of Vietnam in a small <u>hamlet</u> on a riverbank that had a deep jungle on one side and a chain of high mountains on the other. Across the river, rice fields stretched to the slopes of another chain of mountains.

There were fifty houses in our hamlet, scattered along the river or propped against the mountainsides.

hamlet (ham′lit) *n.* cluster of houses in the country; small village.

325

The houses were made of bamboo and covered with coconut leaves, and each was surrounded by a deep trench to protect it from wild animals or thieves. The only way to enter a house was to walk across a "monkey bridge"—a single bamboo stick that spanned the trench. At night we pulled the bridges into our houses and were safe.

There were no shops or marketplaces in our hamlet. If we needed supplies—medicine, cloth, soaps, or candles—we had to cross over the mountains and travel to a town nearby. We used the river mainly for traveling to distant hamlets, but it also provided us with plenty of fish.

During the six-month rainy season, nearly all of us helped plant and cultivate fields of rice, sweet potatoes, Indian mustard, eggplant, tomatoes, hot peppers, and corn. But during the dry season, we became hunters and turned to the jungle.

Wild animals played a very large part in our lives. There were four animals we feared the most: the tiger, the lone wild hog, the crocodile, and the horse snake. Tigers were always trying to steal cattle. Sometimes, however, when a tiger became old and slow it became a maneater. But a lone wild hog was even more dangerous than a tiger. It attacked every creature in sight, even when it had no need for food. Or it did crazy things, such as charging into the hamlet in broad daylight, ready to kill or to be killed.

The river had different dangers: crocodiles. But of all the animals, the most hated and feared was the huge horse snake. It was sneaky and attacked people and cattle just for the joy of killing. It would either crush its victim to death or poison it with a bite.

Like all farmers' children in the hamlet, I started working at the age of six. My seven sisters helped by

working in the kitchen, weeding the garden, gathering eggs, or taking water to the cattle. I looked after the family herd of water buffaloes. Someone always had to be with the herd because no matter how carefully a water buffalo was trained, it always was ready to nibble young rice plants when no one was looking. Sometimes, too, I fished for the family while I guarded the herd, for there were plenty of fish in the flooded rice fields during the rainy season.

I was twelve years old when I made my first trip to the jungle with my father. I learned how to track game, how to recognize useful roots, how to distinguish edible mushrooms from poisonous ones. I learned that if birds, raccoons, squirrels, or monkeys had eaten the fruits of certain trees, then those fruits were not poisonous. Often they were not delicious, but they could calm a man's hunger and thirst.

My father, like most of the villagers, was a farmer and a hunter, depending upon the season. But he also had a college education, so in the evenings he helped to teach other children in our hamlet, for it was too small to afford a professional schoolteacher.

My mother managed the house, but during the harvest season she could be found in the fields, helping my father get the crops home; and as the wife of a hunter, she knew how to dress and nurse a wound and took good care of her husband and his hunting dogs.

I went to the lowlands to study for a while because I wanted to follow my father as a teacher when I grew up. I always planned to return to my hamlet to live the rest of my life there. But war disrupted my dreams. The land I love was lost to me forever.

These stories are my memories. . . .

—H.Q.N.

---

edible (ed′ə bəl) *adj.* fit to eat.
disrupted (dis rup′tid) *v.t.* broke apart; upset.

When she was eighty years old my grandmother was still quite strong. She could use her own teeth to eat corn on the cob or to chew on sugar plants to <u>extract</u> juice from them. Every two days she walked for more than an hour to reach the marketplace, carrying a heavy load of food with her, and then spent another hour walking back home. And even though she was quite old, traces of her beauty still lingered on: Her hands, her feet, her face revealed that she had been an attractive young woman. Nor did time do much damage to the youthful spirit of my grandmother.

One of her great passions was theater, and this passion never <u>diminished</u> with age. No matter how busy she was, she never missed a show when there was a group of actors in town. If no actors visited our hamlet for several months, she would organize her own show in which she was the manager, the producer, and the young leading lady, all at the same time.

My grandmother's own plays were always <u>melodramas</u> inspired by books she had read and by what she had seen on the stage. She always chose her favorite grandson to play the role of the hero, who would, without fail, marry the heroine at the end and live happily ever after. And when my sisters would tell her that she was getting too old to play the role of the young heroine anymore, my grandmother merely replied: "Anybody can play this role if she's young at heart."

When I was a little boy my grandmother often took me to see the opera. She knew Chinese mythology by heart, and the opera was often a dramatization of this mythology. On one special occasion, during the Lunar New Year celebrations—my favorite holiday, because children could do anything they wanted and by

---

extract (ek strakt′) *v.t.* draw or pull out by effort or force.
diminished (di min′isht) *v.i.* got smaller or less in size or importance.
melodramas (mel′ə drä′məz) *n., pl.* sentimental plays acted out with exaggerated emotions.

tradition no one could scold them—I accompanied my grandmother to the opera.

When we reached the theater I wanted to go in immediately. But my grandmother wanted to linger at the entrance and talk to her friends. She chatted for more than an hour. Finally we entered the theater, and at that moment the "Faithful One" was onstage, singing sadly. The "Faithful One" is a common character in Chinese opera. He could be a good minister, or a valiant general, or someone who loved and served his king faithfully. But in the end he is unjustly <u>persecuted</u> by the king, whose opinion of him has been changed by the lies of the "Flatterer," another standard character.

When my grandmother saw the "Faithful One" onstage she looked upset and gave a great sigh. I was too interested in what was happening to ask her the reason, and we spent the next five hours watching the rest of the opera. Sometimes I cried because my grandmother cried at the pitiful situation of the "Faithful One." Sometimes I became as angry as my grandmother did at the wickedness of the "Flatterer."

When we went home that night my grandmother was quite sad. She told my mother that she would have bad luck in the following year because when we entered the theater, the "Faithful One" was onstage. I was puzzled. I told my grandmother that she was confused. It would be a good year for us because we saw the good guy first. But my mother said, "No, son. The 'Faithful One' always is in trouble and it takes him many years to <u>vindicate</u> himself. Our next year is going to be like one of his bad years."

So, according to my mother's and grandmother's logic, we would have been much better off in the new year if we had been lucky enough to see the villain first!

persecuted (pûr′si kū′tid) *v.t.* given cruel, harmful, or unjust treatment.
vindicate (vin′di kāt′) *v.t.* clear (someone) of suspicion or charges of wrongdoing.

331

My grandmother had married a man whom she loved with all her heart, but who was totally different from her. My grandfather was very shy, never laughed loudly, and always spoke very softly. And physically he was not as strong as my grandmother. But he excused his lack of physical strength by saying that he was a "scholar."

About three months after their marriage, my grandparents were in a restaurant and a <u>rascal</u> began to insult my grandfather because he looked weak and had a pretty wife. At first he just made insulting remarks, such as, "Hey! Wet chicken! This is no place for a weakling!"

My grandfather wanted to leave the restaurant even though he and my grandmother had not yet finished their meal. But my grandmother pulled his shirt sleeve and signaled him to remain seated. She continued to eat and looked as if nothing had happened.

Tired of yelling insults without any result, the rascal got up from his table, moved over to my grandparents' table, and grabbed my grandfather's chopsticks. My grandmother immediately wrested the chopsticks from him and struck the rascal on his cheekbone with her elbow. The blow was so quick and powerful that he lost his balance and fell on the floor. Instead of finishing him off, as any street fighter would do, my grandmother let the rascal recover from the blow. But as soon as he got up again, he kicked over the table between him and my grandmother, making food and drink fly all over the place. Before he could do anything else, my grandmother kicked him on the chin. The kick was so swift that my grandfather didn't even see it. He only heard a heavy thud, and then saw the rascal tumble backward and collapse on the ground.

All the onlookers were surprised and delighted, especially the owner of the restaurant. Apparently the

---

rascal (ras′kəl) *n.* mischievous or mean, dishonest person.

rascal, one of the best karate fighters of our area, came to his restaurant every day and left without paying for his food or drink, but the owner was too afraid to confront him.

While the rascal's friends tried to revive him, everyone else surrounded my grandmother and asked her who had taught her karate. She said, "Who else? My husband!"

After the fight at the restaurant people assumed that my grandfather knew karate very well but refused to use it for fear of killing someone. In reality, my grandmother had received special training in karate from my great-great uncle from the time she was eight years old.

Anyway, after that incident, my grandfather never had to worry again. Anytime he had some business downtown, people treated him very well. And whenever anyone happened to bump into him on the street, they bowed to my grandfather in a very respectful way.

When my father was about ten years old a group of bandits attacked our house. There had been a very poor harvest that year, and bandits had already attacked several homes in other hamlets. My grandmother had a premonition this would also happen to them, so she devised a plan. In case of danger, she would carry the children to safety, and my grandfather would carry the bow and arrows, a bottle of poison, and the box containing the family jewels.

It was night when the bandits came. My grandfather became scared to death and forgot his part of the plan, but my grandmother remained very calm. She led her husband and children to safety through a secret back door that opened into a double hedge of cactus

that allowed a person to walk inside, undetected, to the banana grove. When they were safely inside the banana grove, my grandfather realized that he had forgotten the bow and arrows and the bottle of poison. So my grandmother stole back into the house and retrieved the weapons.

The bandits were still trying to smash through our very solid front door when she sneaked out of the house for the second time. She dipped one arrow in poison and crawled around to the front of the house near the bandits. But, upon second thought, she put the poisoned arrow aside and took another arrow and carefully aimed at the leg of the bandit leader. When the arrow hit his thigh the bandit let out a loud cry and fell backward.

The night was so dark that none of the bandits knew where the arrow had come from. And moments later, friends started arriving and began to attack them from the road in front of our house. The bandits panicked and left in a hurry. But my grandmother spent the rest of the night with her family in the banana grove, just in case the bandits came back.

When my grandmother became older she felt sick once in a while. Before the arrival of the doctor, she would order everybody in the house to look sad. And during the consultation with the doctor she acted as if she were much sicker than she really was. My grandmother felt that she had to make herself look really sick so that the doctor would give her good medicine. She told the doctor that she had a pain in the head, in the shoulders, in the chest, in the back, in the limbs—pain everywhere. Finally the doctor would become confused and wouldn't know what could be wrong with her.

---

consultation (kon′səl tā′shən) *n.* meeting to get advice, ideas, or opinions.

Whenever the doctor left, my mother would sneak out of the house, meet him at the other side of the garden, and tell him exactly where my grandmother hurt.

Two or three days later my grandmother usually felt much better. But before the doctor arrived for another visit she ordered us to look sad again—not as sad as the first time, but quite sad. She would tell the doctor that her situation had improved a little bit but that she still felt quite sick. My grandmother thought that if she told the doctor she had been feeling much better he would stop giving her good medicine. When the doctor left my mother sneaked out of the house again and informed him of the real condition of my grandmother.

I don't think my grandmother ever guessed it was my mother's reports to the doctor, and not her acting, that helped her get well.

One morning my grandmother wanted me to go outside with her. We climbed a little hill that looked over the whole area, and when we got to the top she looked at the rice field below, the mountain on the horizon, and especially at the river. As a young girl she had often brought her herd of water buffaloes to the river to drink while she swam with the other children of the village. Then we visited the graveyard where her husband and some of her children were buried. She touched her husband's tombstone and said, "Dear, I will join you soon." And then we walked back to the garden and she gazed at the fruit trees her husband had planted, a new one for each time she had given birth to a child. Finally, before we left the garden my sister joined us, and the two of them fed a few ducks swimming in the pond.

That evening my grandmother did not eat much of her dinner. After dinner she combed her hair and put on her best dress. We thought that she was going to go out

336

again, but instead she went to her bedroom and told us that she didn't want to be disturbed.

The family dog seemed to sense something was amiss, for he kept looking anxiously at everybody and whined from time to time. At midnight my mother went to my grandmother's room and found that she had died, with her eyes shut, as if she were sleeping normally.

It took me a long time to get used to the reality that my grandmother had passed away. Wherever I was, in the house, in the garden, out on the fields, her face always appeared so clearly to me. And even now, many years later, I still have the feeling that my last conversation with her has happened only a few days before.

---

amiss (ə mis′) *adj.* not as it should be; wrong.

Meet
HUYNH QUANG NHUONG

Many people might have given up in despair if they had lost their homeland and had been disabled in a war. But not Huynh Quang Nhuong. After leaving Vietnam for medical treatment, he made a new home in the United States and went on to earn two college degrees as well as to become a prizewinning author and playwright.

Nhuong's first book, *The Land I Lost: Adventures of a Boy in Vietnam,* has won many awards. His plays have been produced in several cities, including his new hometown of Columbia, Missouri. In 1990, he received a grant from the National Endowment for the Arts to encourage his creative writing.

RESPONDING TO *Literature*

THINK • TALK • WRITE

1 Did you like the author's grandmother? Why or why not? Write your feelings in your journal.

2 What problems does the "Faithful One" in Chinese opera have? Why did the grandmother say she would have bad luck after seeing the opera?

3 Who taught the grandmother karate? Why did she say that her husband had taught her? What effect did this have on the way people treated him? Why?

4 Why do you think the grandmother walked around her village on the morning before she died? How did the author feel about her death?

5 In what ways do the characters' lives seem different from yours? In what ways are their lives similar?

ACTIVITIES

- **Write with Chronological Order**
  Write about an anecdote from your own life. Before you begin, make a list of the events in your anecdote. Then write, putting the events in chronological order.

- **Tell a Story** Ask an older family member to tell anecdotes about his or her childhood. Share the anecdotes with classmates.

VOCABULARY PRACTICE

On a separate piece of paper, write the vocabulary word that is the best substitute for each italicized word or phrase.

hamlet	edible
disrupted	extract
diminished	persecuted
vindicate	rascal
consultation	amiss

1 They live in a remote *village* near a river.

2 The children learned to gather *nonpoisonous* plants in the area.

3 A wild pig ran through the village, which *upset* the harvest celebration.

4 If the birds stop singing, something may be *wrong*.

5 The hunter knows how to *pull out* the snake's fangs.

6 Sometimes a *mischiefmaker* tries to steal one of the animals.

7 The farmers requested a *meeting to get advice* from the village elders.

8 A person the villagers dislike may be *treated unjustly*.

9 The family hopes to *clear the name of* the suspect.

10 Time has not *lessened* his memories of the village.

BIOGRAPHY

ALEXANDER THE GREAT

CONNECT TO LITERATURE

Which teachers have made the biggest difference in your life? Make notes in your journal
about how those teachers have influenced
you. The following selection from *The Golden
Days of Greece* is a biography of Alexander
the Great, a ruler of ancient Greece. Author
Olivia Coolidge describes two men who taught
Alexander when he was a child. As you read
the selection, think about what characteristics his
teachers share with yours.

THINKING ABOUT CHARACTERIZATION

Characterization is the way an author presents a person's traits,
motives, and feelings. In a biography of a man who lived over 2,000
years ago, this task may seem impossible. However, Coolidge uses
stories about Alexander and records of his deeds to tell the conqueror's story. Learning about his childhood, goals, and vision of
himself helps readers discover the man behind the legends.

DID YOU KNOW?

Alexander conquered much of Europe and parts of Asia and Africa
as well. He claimed that his true father was Zeus, the chief Greek
god. Among the other characters in the selection are

* Philip, the ruler of Macedon (mas'i don'), a kingdom north of
  Athens, the Greek capital. Philip conquered Greece and was
  planning to invade Persia when he was murdered.

* Xenophon, a learned Greek whose book *The Education of Cyrus*
  outlines his ideas about how to train a future king.

* Demosthenes, a democrat from Athens known for his commitment to Greek, and especially Athenian, freedom.

MEET
OLIVIA COOLIDGE

A good biography, according to Olivia Coolidge, is "concerned with the effect its hero has on other people, with environment and background, with the nature of the great man's achievements and their value." She says, "Facts are the bricks with which a biographer builds," and stresses that it is important to "distinguish a fact from a judgment."

Coolidge was born in England in 1908. She taught English, Latin, and Greek in Europe and the United States. Her many books include *Greek Myths, The Trojan War,* and *Lives of Famous Romans,* as well as biographies of Abraham Lincoln and Gandhi. Several of her books received the American Library Association Notable Book award and were on the *Horn Book* honor list.

More Biographies About People from the Ancient World

- *Alexander the Great* by Maureen Ash (Children's Press, 1991). Read more about the life of the young king who was determined to prove himself and succeeded in uniting much of the world under his rule.

- *Cleopatra* by Diane Stanley and Peter Vennema (Morrow, 1994). Cleopatra, a young queen of Egypt, joined forces with Roman generals Julius Caesar and Mark Antony in an ambitious plan to conquer the world.

- *The Librarian Who Measured the Earth* by Kathryn Lasky (Little, Brown, 1994). How can one measure the earth? Certainly not with a ruler! It took the curiosity and intelligence of an ancient Greek named Eratosthenes to come up with the solution. Amazingly, he was off by only two hundred miles.

Alexander in Battle 1st century A.D. Detail from a Roman mosaic National Museum Naples, Italy

ALEXANDER
THE
GREAT

BY OLIVIA
COOLIDGE

Alexander (356–323 B.C.) was twenty years old when his father was murdered, the only son of the queen Olympias, who had long ago quarreled with Philip over his custom of taking extra wives like the king of Persia. Partly for this reason, and partly because Philip was busy with his wars, the boy's education was left to his mother, who chose for him a stern tutor. Leonidas would allow no softness in the boy. He used to look through the chest where Alexander kept his clothes and blankets to be sure that the queen had not provided anything costly. He only allowed the plainest food, and he taught the prince that the best "cook" for a good breakfast was an all-night walk, and for a good dinner was a light breakfast. In fact, he gave Alexander the sort of training which <u>Xenophon</u> praised in *The Education of Cyrus*.

When Alexander was about twelve, legend says, an incident attracted Philip's attention. A dealer had a great black horse for sale, which he called Bucephalus, or Bull's-head, because of the shape of a white mark on his forehead. He was indeed a splendid creature, but he would let nobody mount him. Philip told the owner to take him away, but Alexander said it was a shame to lose such an animal because nobody had the skill to ride him.

Philip was angry at his <u>impudence</u>, but the boy offered to bet the price of the horse that he could ride it. He had noticed that Bucephalus was frightened by his own shadow dancing on the ground in front of him. He turned him to face the sun and patted him until he quieted down. Suddenly he sprang on his back, and the horse <u>bolted</u> madly. Philip, who had never thought

---

Xenophon (zen′ə fən)

impudence (im′pyə dəns) *n.* act of being rudely bold or forward.

bolted (bōl′tid) *v.i.* broke away from control; started and ran off.

the boy would mount, was afraid for him now. Alexander, however, clung on until Bucephalus was tired enough to be guided safely home.

We shall never know if the story of how Alexander won his horse is a true one, but it gives a good picture of his cleverness and daring. Philip began to take interest in the boy, and shortly afterward he arranged another tutor for him who was in his own way the most famous man in the Greek world.

Aristotle had come to Plato's Academy when he was seventeen and had proved himself the best pupil Plato had. He had stayed there another seventeen years, learning and teaching, until Plato died. At this point he left the Academy to form a school of his own. Aristotle was a different kind of man from Plato. He did not have as much imagination, but he was more practical. When Plato, for instance, wanted to know what the ideal government might be, he started to consider what the soul of a man was like. When Aristotle asked himself the same question, he collected a hundred and fifty-eight different constitutions which had been set up by the Greek states; and he tried to compare them.

Now Aristotle, as it chanced, had been born in one of the Greek towns on the Macedonian coast. His father had been a doctor and was actually court physician to King <u>Amyntas</u> of Macedonia, Philip's father. Philip and he were about the same age, and shared childhood memories. Since then, Aristotle had learned in the Academy that Plato's purpose was to train the rulers of the future. For both these reasons, Aristotle

---

Amyntas (ə min′təs)

Above: Alexander on a horse fighting Poros on an elephant 323 B.C. Bronze coin from Babylon

was willing to tutor Alexander. Thus on top of the education described by Xenophon, Alexander received some of the training of Plato.

He never became a philosopher, but he was clever and eager to learn. Aristotle's position as tutor gave a special interest to the young heir of Macedon, as many remembered Plato saying that the ruler of the future must have this sort of education. Statesmen like Demosthenes who visited the court of King Philip thought it worthwhile to meet the boy.

They were nearly all impressed. Alexander was striking-looking, with blue eyes and golden curls. He was tall for his age, and good at every sport. He loved poetry and music; and he liked to compare himself with his legendary ancestor Achilles, hero of the *Iliad*, who won great glory from his earliest years.

Philip soon gave his son military training. When Alexander commanded a wing in the battle of Chaeronea, he was only eighteen years old; but he had been fighting since he was sixteen, and he had also governed Macedonia while his father was absent.

When Philip died, his son was only twenty. Demosthenes urged the Athenians to regain their freedom. But his plans were upset by the energy of Alexander. The Athenians were forced to receive him as their master. They did not like him. Philip at least, many felt, had been a great man. The Athenians, who were unused to kings, sneered at this untried boy who wanted to be treated like a hero. When Alexander went onto Corinth, everyone laughed at what happened to him there.

There was a philosopher in Corinth called Diogenes who felt that nothing mattered except a

---

Demosthenes (di mäs′thə nēz′)

Iliad (il′ē əd) *n.* ancient Greek epic poem describing some of the events of the Trojan War. It is believed to have been composed by Homer.

Chaeronea (ker′ō nē′ə)

sneered (snîrd) *v.i.* had a facial expression showing hatred or contempt.

man's own soul. To show his contempt for the world, he dressed in rags, was unshaven and dirty, and had no home but a big tub laid on its side in which he took shelter when the weather forced him to do so. He lost no chance of telling the Corinthians what he thought of them for caring about useless things, and he had become famous for his rude remarks.

Curious, Alexander went to see him. They made a strange contrast as the golden-haired young man in the royal costume stood looking down at the rough philosopher who was squatting in front of his tub. Diogenes took no notice of the king until Alexander asked if he could do anything for him.

There probably was no one in Corinth who would not have been glad to ask a favor of the master of all Greece. Diogenes looked up frowning at the tall young man in front of him and said, "Yes. Stop standing between me and the sun."

The Greeks laughed, but Alexander was not angry. He admired the philosopher's spirit and said to his friends, "If I were not Alexander I should have liked to be Diogenes."

The war which Philip had planned against Persia was only delayed two years by his death. In 334, Alexander invaded Asia Minor with about thirty-five thousand troops. Nearly half were Macedonians, the rest hired soldiers or troops sent by the Greek cities. The army took with it engineers for making bridges or siege towers, well diggers, surveyors to find out about routes and camp grounds, geographers to make maps, botanists and other learned men to collect specimens

---

surveyors (sər vā′ərz) *n., pl.* persons who find shape, area, and boundaries of a region or tract of land by taking measurements.
botanists (bot′ə nists) *n., pl.* specialists in the science or study of plants.

and find out more about the country they conquered. There was a baggage train, of course, and a military council of high officers trained by Philip. Everything was planned to go like clockwork.

Philip had merely meant to conquer Asia Minor. The Greek cities on the coast would be easily won over, and they would dry up the stream of hired soldiers on which the Persians relied. The great landowners of the country districts made splendid <u>cavalry</u> in the Persian style; but the peasants, though loyal to their lords and personally warlike, were too poor to afford the armor of Greek <u>infantry</u>. Hard fighting lay ahead of Alexander, but he was victorious.

After a while he found that he could not hold his gains without going further. Control of Asia Minor with its long seacoast depended on a fleet. The fleet of the Persians came from Egypt and the great Phoenician city of Tyre on the Syrian coast. Alexander advanced against Tyre because he had to, descending from mountainous country into the plain where Asia Minor borders on Syria.

Darius III, who had succeeded <u>Artaxerxes</u>, was a weak ruler, but he came of fighting stock and knew that he must battle for his kingdom. He could not, however, get together an army which was larger than the countryside would support. His native infantry was not equal to the Greeks, and his leadership was poor. When he met Alexander at the battle of Issus, the Macedonian charged at the head of his men, while the Persian hovered in a <u>chariot</u> in the rear and speedily fled. Darius's leaderless men were cut to pieces, and Alexander found himself master of Syria.

---

cavalry (kav′əl rē) *n.* military unit trained to fight on horseback.

infantry (in′fən trē) *n.* soldiers trained and equipped to fight on foot.

Artaxerxes (är′tə zərk′sēz)

chariot (char′ē ət) *n.* two-wheeled vehicle drawn by two, three, or four horses and driven from a standing position, used in ancient times in warfare, processions, and races.

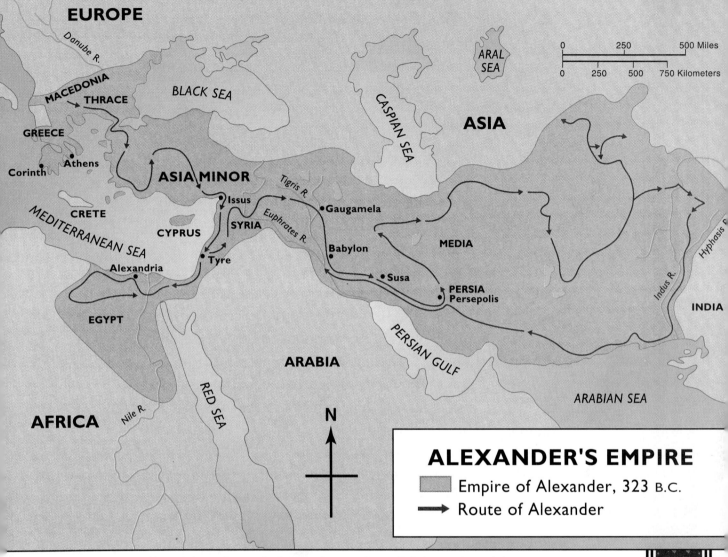

ALEXANDER'S EMPIRE

▨ Empire of Alexander, 323 B.C.
➜ Route of Alexander

Alexander's empire stretched across three continents. Babylon was its capital.

He hurried to blockade Tyre, but found it difficult. The Tyrians kept his warships off by piling great boulders under water. Alexander sent merchant ships to haul these away, but the Tyrians ventured out in their own warships to attack them. Alexander brought up his fleet to protect his <u>dredgers</u>, but Tyrian divers

---

dredgers (drej´ərz) *n., pl.* boats equipped for scooping up or removing mud, sand, and other substances from the bottom of a body of water.

cut their cables under water. Meanwhile, on the land side his engineers were unable for a long while to make the slightest progress. Tyre held out for seven months, but King Darius did not dare face Alexander again. Unaided, the city fell at last in July, 332. By November, Alexander was in Egypt, where he was received with joy, since the Egyptians had long desired to be free from the Persians. Alexander controlled the whole eastern end of the Mediterranean.

Once more his only defense lay in attack. The true center of the Persian empire lay across the Euphrates, in Media, Babylonia, and Persia. In Susa, long the capital, and in Persepolis, where the kings had built their palaces in the days of their pride, lay uncounted treasure piled up from the tribute of two hundred years. For this even Darius must fight. Eighteen months had gone by since his defeat, and he had by now refitted his forces. The cavalry, which had always been superb, was better armed. For the infantry less could be done, seeing that to make new equipment took much time, and to drill fighters even longer. Darius was relying on chariots whose wheels had long knives sticking out. A few hundred of these might well be able to break up massed infantry if skillfully handled.

Darius gave battle on the flat plain of Gaugamela, since he was anxious to give his chariots a chance. There on the first of October, 331, Alexander found him. The chariots made their charge, but Alexander had screened his infantry by javelin men and slingers.

---

tribute (trib'ūt) *n.* money paid by one ruler or nation to another to show submission or to ensure peace or protection.

Above: Alexander the Great c. 300 B.C.   Silver coin from Thrace

For the sake of speed, the chariots had little armor. Men and horses crashed to the ground, and very few of them reached the infantry. The rest of the battle swayed back and forth. The Persians had the greater numbers, but the Greeks the better army. They had a tradition of victory, too, and a finer commander.

Once more Darius took to flight. He might have spared himself the effort, for he had lost his kingdom by now and even his life. The Persian nobles whom he had twice deserted in battle were finished with him. He was arrested; and as the pursuit of Alexander came close, he was finally murdered.

There was now no king in the empire but Alexander. The men of Babylon came out to surrender. The satrap of Persia tried to keep him from entering his homeland but was swept aside. Alexander took Susa and Persepolis. He sat on the Great King's throne and seized his treasure. As a sign to the whole East, he set fire to the palace of King Xerxes and burned it to the ground. The miracle had come to pass. Greece had conquered the empire.

We need not follow Alexander farther east across the steppes of Turkestan, through the foothills of the Himalayas, into India. Susa had been only the center of an empire which stretched as far east as it did west. There were adventures ahead for Alexander with tribes, in lands, and on rivers which he had never heard of. But before he pursued his way, he had to face the problem of holding what he had won. It is what Alexander did to found an empire as much as his generalship that made him great.

---

satrap (sā′trap) *n.* governor of a province in the ancient Persian empire.

Greeks generally thought that barbarians, which is what they called non-Greeks, were fit to be <u>plundered</u> or made slaves, rather than to rule. Alexander, however, was half barbarian himself; and he had seen the wonders of Babylonia and Egypt, as well as the splendor of Persian kings. He understood that East and West must be mingled into a greater whole and that he, Alexander, must have a share in both.

The first thing that he did was found many cities through the eastern world where homeless Greek soldiers found a new place to live and build their temples. Those cities acted as market places for country villages or stages on the trade routes which had run far in Persian times and were soon to be thronged with travelers. Alexandria in Egypt has always been the greatest of the towns that Alexander founded, but there were many others, including one called after Bucephalus, his horse. From these cities Greek ways spread all over the East. When the Romans came to rule two hundred years later they found that Greek had become a second language through the eastern part of their whole empire. They were content to let it remain so and to speak it themselves; for the Romans, like the eastern peoples, had much to learn from the Greeks.

All this Alexander did, but in actually governing the peoples of the East he relied on themselves. He split up the power of the satraps, to be sure; and he left trusty Macedonian generals here and there with troops. All the same, he tried to employ the great Persian nobles, got to know them, dressed in eastern clothes himself, and liked his friends to do so. He married an eastern princess called Roxana and encouraged his friends to follow his example.

---

plundered (plun'dərd) *v.t.* looted or robbed, as during a war.

He did not want men to think of him as a conqueror, but rather as a godlike hero, born to rule. There is often something of this feeling about kingship. Philip's image had been carried in procession with those of the gods. Egyptian kings were thought divine, and the Persians could claim at least to be God's servants. Alexander had found these ideas in the East and was eager to adopt them because he needed loyalty. They meant something special to him, too. Achilles, his ancestor, was half divine. During the quarrels between his mother and Philip, Queen Olympias made a mystery of his birth, pretending that he was more than Philip's son. It is likely also that his victories had gone to his head. No one had ever done what he had done, and he was not yet thirty. Alexander gave out that he was not really Philip's son, but was born of a god.

It was a wise political stroke, but his Macedonian friends did not like it. They were many years away from home and they may have been tired of adventures. Perhaps they had their ambitions, too; and they did not wish Alexander to show favor to native princes. At all events, there were plots against him.

Alexander was noble and trusting by nature. Early in his campaigns his doctor was mixing a drink of medicine for him when a letter was brought in. He read it. It warned him that the doctor was planning to poison him. Alexander stretched out one hand for the drink, while with the other he offered the letter to his doctor. While the startled man read it, the king drained the medicine down.

After this, it is sad to discover that years later this very doctor took part in an attempt on Alexander's life. Alexander's new position was making him so lofty that he could trust no one.

The strain had begun to tell on him. If he made mistakes, his empire might collapse even more quickly than it had been won. At feasts he began to drink deeply, as his father had once done. His royal rages became terrible to endure. But victory followed him all the same wherever he went.

In 323, he was back from India in Babylon, preparing to conquer Arabia; but his amazing career was over at last. He fell sick of a fever and, weakened by battle wounds, could not throw it off. He died in the palace of the kings of Babylon on June 13, 323 B.C. He was only thirty-two years old and in the thirteenth year of his reign. He had conquered nearly all of the world then known to the Greeks.

Alexander the Great   *Bronze statuette from Roman Imperial period   British Museum, London*

RESPONDING TO *Literature*

THINK • TALK • WRITE

1 Do you admire Alexander the Great? Why or why not? Jot some ideas in your journal.

2 According to legend, how did Alexander obtain Bucephalus, his horse? What does the legend suggest about Alexander? How did he later pay tribute to his horse?

3 What was unusual about the people who accompanied Alexander's army to Asia Minor? Why do you think Alexander brought these people along?

4 How far east in Asia did Alexander and his armies get? What steps did Alexander take to hold on to his empire?

5 What ideas did Alexander adopt from the Persians and the other cultures that he conquered? If Alexander had lived, do you think his plan to unite the people of the east and the west would have succeeded? Why or why not?

ACTIVITIES

- **Write with Characterization** Choose one character trait of Alexander. Invent a legend that shows this side of his personality.

- **Do a Dialog** With a partner, brainstorm about a scene between Alexander and another character.

Look in the selection for ideas about the characters. Then improvise a dialog. Practice and perform it for the class.

VOCABULARY PRACTICE

Read each book title below. Choose the vocabulary word that best fits the subject of each book. On a separate piece of paper, write the word you chose for each title.

impudence	bolted
sneered	surveyors
botanists	cavalry
infantry	chariot
tribute	plundered

1 *Endangered Plants of the Rain Forest*

2 *A History of Horse-Drawn Vehicles*

3 *Armies on Horseback*

4 *The Dog That Fled*

5 *Redrawing the Line: Changing Town Borders*

6 *Facial Expressions in Different Cultures*

7 *Correcting the Rude Child*

8 *Looting the Enemy: How Theft Follows War*

9 *Foot Soldiers Throughout History*

10 *Gifts Given to Powerful Kings*

WRITING

Hard work and sheer determination can overcome huge obstacles. Write a biographical sketch about someone who proved this. It can be a famous person or a friend or relative.

PREWRITE

How will you brainstorm for your biographical sketch? List a few people whose determination you admire. Write some of their accomplishments next to their names. This writer chose to write about her aunt. She used an outline to organize some of her aunt's accomplishments.

Pull together your notes. Try organizing them into an outline.

> ### AUNT ROSA
> **I.** Her brave childhood
>   **A.** Helping the family
>   **B.** Getting an education
>   1. Studying at night on her own
>   2. How she got to college
> **II.** Aunt Rosa now
>   **A.** Her career
>   **B.** How she inspires me

DRAFT

Here's the beginning of the draft about Aunt Rosa. Has the writer considered her audience? If so, Aunt Rosa should seem interesting to you.

This writer has her audience in mind. She has tried to imagine what they would think of her aunt when they first saw her.

> ### My Amazing Aunt Rosa
>
> You might not notice Aunt Rosa first of all. But just try talking to her, for a wile. She's a tiny woman with a quiet voice. Inside Aunt Rosa is a very big person.

Use your outline or other prewriting notes to begin your draft. If other ideas come to mind, include them, too.

BIOGRAPHY

REVISE

When the writer of our sample reread the opening paragraph, she decided to change the order of the sentences.

The writer realizes that she should keep together the sentences describing first impressions of Aunt Rosa.

> You might not notice Aunt Rosa first *at* of all. But just try talking to her, for a wile. She's a tiny woman with a quiet voice. Inside Aunt Rosa is a very big person.

Now revise your draft. Will your readers want to meet the person you describe? Ask a partner if your sentences are in the right order.

PROOFREAD

The writer made some corrections in spelling and punctuation when she reread her draft.

Pay special attention to where you place commas. A mistake can confuse the meaning of the sentence.

> You might not notice Aunt Rosa first *at* of all. But just try talking to her for a *while* wile. She's a tiny woman with a quiet voice. Inside Aunt Rosa is a very big person.

Try different techniques for proofreading your sketch. Read it aloud. Read it backward, word by word, to catch spelling errors.

PUBLISH

How will you present your writing? Ask a partner for some ideas. Consider including a photo or drawing.

WRITING

VIVID VERBS

ENRICH YOUR WRITING OF **BIOGRAPHICAL SKETCHES.**

Vivid, precise verbs will help your reader imagine the scenes you are describing. Use vivid verbs to make your writing "sing"! They will bring the action in your writing to life.

How effectively does each of these paragraphs describe the action?

Paragraph 1

Uncle Jim walked into the water and swam clumsily to the raft. My cousin and I smiled at the sight of Uncle Jim before going in ourselves. Then we heard him asking for us.

Paragraph 2

Uncle Jim waded into the water and paddled clumsily to the raft. My cousin and I smirked at the sight of Uncle Jim before diving in ourselves. Then we heard him shouting for us.

PRACTICE 1 Respond on a separate piece of paper.

 What words in the second paragraph make the action easier to picture? More exciting?

 Replace the verbs in the second paragraph. Have you made the action more or less exciting?

356

& LANGUAGE

SUBJECT-VERB AGREEMENT

REMEMBER THESE RULES ABOUT VERBS WHEN YOU ARE WRITING
BIOGRAPHICAL SKETCHES.

- A verb must always agree with its subject. A singular subject takes a singular verb, and a plural subject takes a plural verb.

- Compound subjects joined by *and* take a plural verb. When they are joined by *or,* the verb agrees with the subject closest to it.

PRACTICE 2 Choose the correct form of the verb to complete these sentences. Then rewrite the sentences on a separate piece of paper.

1 My cousins and she always (listens, listen) to my uncle's advice.

2 People on the beach (watches, watch) us help him to shore.

3 My sisters or Jim (was, were) the one to see him first.

4 The whole village (are, is) concerned about what happened.

PRESENT, PAST, AND FUTURE TENSES

USE THESE RULES ABOUT TENSES WHEN YOU ARE WRITING
BIOGRAPHICAL SKETCHES.

- Use present tense to show something that is happening now.

- Use past tense to show something that has already happened.

- Use future tense to show something that is going to happen.

PRACTICE 3 Change the verb to the correct tense. Then rewrite the sentence on a separate piece of paper.

1 Right now she (understand) how close my cousins and I (to be).

2 Next summer we (be) more careful in the water.

3 Last summer nobody (want) to spend time with my uncle.

4 Tomorrow I (tell) you the whole story of the accident.

PROJECT 1

WRITING A SCIENCE REPORT

Use scientific thinking and some determination to solve a problem in your community. What needs fixing? What can be done about it?

PREWRITE

Brainstorm with a partner about a problem in your community. Do some research about how it could be fixed. Then organize all your information in a chart. Suppose your problem was the gradual disappearance of a nearby beach. Your chart might look like this:

Problem	Cause	Solution
our beach gets narrower every year	erosion of sand and rocks by waves	wind fence; plant grasses

DRAFT Start your draft by clearly stating the main idea. Then begin writing, keeping your conclusion in mind.

REVISE Take a fresh look at your report. Are the problem and solution thoroughly explained? Is your report well organized?

PROOFREAD Use a dictionary to check your spelling, and use other reference books to check grammar and punctuation.

PUBLISH Who would benefit from your ideas? Consider sending your science report to a community group or town council. If you are determined enough, your ideas may cause some changes!

▶ *Proofreading Alert!*

Use correct verb forms. Check page 170 in *Spotlight on Success: Writing and Language Handbook.*

PROJECTS

PROJECT 2

MAKE A VIDEO

REMEMBER TO: • PREWRITE • DRAFT • REVISE • PROOFREAD • PUBLISH

Videotape an interview with someone you think has determination. Before you begin, decide what kinds of questions to ask.

You could use the "5 W's and H" questions in your interview: Who is this person? Why do I think this person has determination? What is an example of that determination? Where and when did the example take place? How can I best get this person to talk about determination? Use the questions as guidelines, but let the person talk freely. Write your questions on three-by-five-inch cards and have them handy when you conduct the interview.

"5 W'S AND H" QUESTIONS

Why?
Who?
Where?
How?
What?
When?

PROJECT 3

TEST YOUR CLASSMATES' DETERMINATION

REMEMBER TO: • PREWRITE • DRAFT • REVISE • PROOFREAD • PUBLISH

Create a puzzle or game to find out just how determined your classmates are. To solve your puzzle or game, they will need to do the right steps in the right order. Map the steps out on a flowchart like this. Give a copy to those who can't figure out your puzzle.

TYING A BOWLINE KNOT

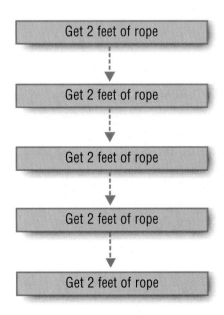

Get 2 feet of rope

Get 2 feet of rope

Get 2 feet of rope

Get 2 feet of rope

Get 2 feet of rope

V I E W P

Have you ever heard the saying "There are two sides to every story"? Think about a current issue in your community—perhaps a new park or highway. Different groups probably have very different ideas about what to do. If people discuss their ideas, an imaginative solution is more likely. But there won't be any solution if they don't listen to and respect each other's viewpoints. Without this respect, serious conflicts occur.

CONSIDER THIS ISSUE: The students in your class have worked hard to earn money for a class trip. Most students had been planning to have a picnic at a state park. But now some students have other ideas. Tomorrow there will be a class meeting to decide where to go. If students can't agree, the trip will be canceled. How should your class handle this disagreement? Consider some of the issues involved.

- What's the best way to let all the students have a say in the decision?
- Should students ask an adult to make the decision for them?
- Is it possible to satisfy everyone without causing hard feelings?

Read the following viewpoints about how to handle the conflict caused by the class trip. Decide which opinion is closest to your own. Think of more arguments yourself to support the position you choose.

VIEWPOINT 1 I think the majority should decide what to do.

- It's not fair to change the students' plans at the last minute.
- A few students shouldn't be allowed to cause problems for the entire class.
- Most students have been looking forward to a picnic all year.

VIEWPOINT 2 All the students should express their opinions at the class meeting and then vote on each suggestion.

- Everyone helped to earn the money for the trip and is entitled to express a point of view.
- Students have to learn to listen to each other's opinions before making up their minds.
- Letting everyone speak out will make sure that everyone feels a part of the final decision.

VIEWPOINT 3 I think it's best for the class teacher to make the final decision for the group.

- The students would be more willing to listen to a teacher than to one of their classmates.
- The teacher is aware of all the issues and is more likely to reach a fair decision.
- By letting the teacher decide, no group can blame another for the final choice.

WHAT DO YOU THINK?

Think about this issue on your own. Do you agree with one of these viewpoints, or do you have another? Share your opinion with a classmate.

real life
CONNECT

DETERMINATION: It is a fixed and firm purpose. It can be the fuel that drives us to our goals.

With determination, you can do anything—even achieve goals that seem unlikely at first. Without fierce determination, Matthew Henson and Robert Peary would never have reached the North Pole. In the same way, the loyal dog in "Lob's Girl" is determined to be Sandy's dog even if he must travel hundreds of miles to find her.

That same determination to succeed, despite the odds, helps many athletes reach their goals. To find out about athletes and how they train, you might refer to a book with an index like this one.

An **index** is an alphabetical listing of the topics in a book. An index—found at the back of a book—is more detailed than the Table of Contents, found in the front. An index *entry* includes the subject heading and all the subheadings related to it. There are also page references for each listing. For example, in this sample index, you would find information about *elbow injuries* on pages 356–358.

IONS

Here are three activities that require you to use an index. Think of other situations in which an index would be helpful. Then choose an activity below or one of your own and talk or write about it.

PROJECT 1

USE AN INDEX Looking up a topic in the index of a book helps you locate information quickly. Work in small groups. Each student should bring a book about sports. Cover the titles of the books. Practice finding topics in the index. How do subheadings help you find information? After using the index, try to guess the subject of each book. Check the titles to see how accurately you guessed.

PROJECT 2

YOU ARE THERE An index can help you find useful facts for your writing. Find a book in your library about a famous exploration, such as Peary's journey to the North Pole. Use the index to look up information about one event during that journey. Then write a paragraph about the event. Use the point of view of a person on the expedition. Write your paragraph in the first person.

PROJECT 3

FIND INDEXES Books are not the only places you will find indexes. They are found in a variety of information sources, from newspapers to telephone books. Bring in at least three common examples of indexes, and explain how they help you locate information on a daily basis.

T I M
T T I M
T I M

The Clock and the Lantern   1915   Joan Miró   Private Collection

How Many Seconds?

How many seconds in a minute?
Sixty, and no more in it.

How many minutes in an hour?
Sixty for sun and shower.

How many hours in a day?
Twenty-four for work and play.

How many days in a week?
Seven both to hear and speak.

How many weeks in a month?
Four, as the swift moon runn'th.

How many months in a year?
Twelve the almanack makes clear.

How many years in an age?
One hundred says the sage.

How many ages in time?
No one knows the rhyme.

—Christina Rossetti

T I M E

BEFORE READING

YOUR THREE MINUTES ARE UP

CONNECT TO LITERATURE

How long should a phone call last? What should you do when someone is overusing the telephone? Explain your opinions in your journal. As you read "Your Three Minutes Are Up," notice how the main characters disagree about fair use of the phone.

THINKING ABOUT A CHARACTER'S POINT OF VIEW

In this short story, telephone time becomes a quarrelsome issue for a girl and her parents. In fiction—as in real life—each person has a different *point of view,* or way of looking at things. You can understand a character's point of view by thinking about what he or she says and does. You can also ask yourself, "How would *I* feel in this character's place?" Understanding each character's point of view clarifies the story's conflict, or problem.

DID YOU KNOW?

- In 1876, Alexander Graham Bell was about to test an invention. He spilled acid and cried to his assistant, "Mr. Watson, come here. I want you!" In the next room, Watson heard Bell through the invention. Bell had made the first telephone call.

- Granville T. Woods, an African American inventor, made key contributions to the development of the telephone transmitter.

- Today, the average American home has three telephones. That's more than 200 million telephones in the United States.

- A facsimile, or fax, machine can transmit images and text over phone lines. Early fax machines were used by news services in the 1930s to send photos quickly over long distances.

YOUR three minutes ARE UP

by ellen conford

Illustrated by Nancy Nimoy

"And you're sure he was talking about me? You actually heard him say 'Libby Kalman'? I mean, maybe he was talking about Renee Kaplan. Our names sound alike. . . . Sure they do, if you say them fast—"

"Elizabeth, get off that phone!"

Libby held her hand over the mouthpiece and looked pleadingly at her mother. "Just two more minutes, Mom. Just two minutes."

"You've been talking for forty-five minutes already, and your father's expecting—"

"Mother, *please*. This call is really important. It could affect the entire course of my future."

"If you're not off that phone in two minutes you won't *have* a future."

Her mother strode out of the kitchen, her spine ramrod straight, like a soldier. Libby frowned. Whenever her mother squared her shoulders off like that, she meant business. But Libby couldn't worry about that now.

She gazed dreamily at the note pad next to the phone. She'd written the name Mark on it thirteen times. Some Marks were printed in capital letters, some all in small letters. Some she wrote out in her ordinary handwriting, and some she tried to do in elegant italic, like calligraphy.

She wrote the fourteenth Mark in block letters and began shading the *M*.

---

calligraphy (kə lig′rə fē) *n.* art of beautiful or elegant handwriting.

"But did he know you heard him? I mean, do you think he said it because he knew you were right there and would hear him? And then he'd know you'd tell me, because he knows we're friends? I mean, I think he knows we're friends, doesn't he? Actually, maybe he doesn't. How would he know? . . . You think so? . . . Well, I mean, did he want me to know he said it, or did you just sort of overhear it? . . . Well, because if he knows that I know he said it, he'd expect me to act entirely different than if he didn't know I knew he said it. . . . Sure. And see, if he *didn't* know I knew he said it, and I started acting different, he'd be suspicious, right? And then he'd think, she knows, and what if he really didn't *want* me to know? I mean, you have to deal with a whole other situation, right? Okay, so tell me again, right from the beginning, and don't leave anything out, because even the smallest detail might be—"

"Elizabeth!"

Her father and mother were suddenly looming over her, their faces purple and red—respectively—with rage.

"Get off that phone!" her father roared.

"Instantly!" her mother added.

Libby rolled her eyes toward the ceiling. "Look, Stace, I'll have to call you back—"

"You'll call no one back!" her father exploded. "You'll get off that phone and stay off!"

Her mother glared at her, arms folded, face red, shoulders squared. "In two seconds," she said dangerously, "I am going to rip that phone off the wall and *clobber you with it.*"

"Uh, Stace, listen, my mother is going berserk here, and my father's about to have a coronary, so I have to get off. Yeah, I know you heard. I'm sure the whole eastern seaboard heard."

Her mother reached for the phone cord.

"Bye, Stace!" Libby slammed the receiver down. "Okay, okay, I'm off."

---

respectively (ri spek′tiv lē) *adv.* with respect to each of two or more in the order presented.
berserk (bər sûrk′) *adv.* into a wild or violent rage.
coronary (kôr′ə ner′ē) *n. Slang.* heart attack.

"I have had it," her father said. "Your mother has had it. Your brother has had it. He'd be here telling you in person he's had it, but he's afraid to come near you because he might kill you, so he's upstairs ripping apart a pillow with his bare hands."

"Fed up, Libby," her mother said. "Absolutely fed up to *here.* You don't own this phone. There are three other people in the house who need to use it and you haven't shown the slightest <u>consideration</u> for any of us."

"I get business calls, Elizabeth," her father went on. "Important calls. When people can't reach me for three hours, they stop trying. That's bad for business. Bad for my career. Bad for all of us. And I have to *make* calls. And I can't pick up that phone without you hanging over me asking when I'll get off, how long will I take, can I please hurry it up, because you're expecting another <u>vitally</u> important call."

"Well, if you'd just get me my own phone—"

"You can get your own phone when you're earning the money to pay your own phone bill!" her father shouted.

The phone rang. Libby lunged for it, but her father snatched up the receiver before she could get to it.

"No, Libby can't come to the phone now."

Libby's eyes opened wide in horror. "I'm *here,*" she whispered desperately. "I'm *right here.*"

"No, you'd better try her tomorrow. Sorry."

"How could you *do* that?" Libby cried. "Who was it? Was it a boy or a girl?"

"A boy, I suppose. And I did it because I had to. It's a matter of self-preservation. I'm expecting a very important call—"

"Mark!" Libby wailed. "It was Mark, I just know it. Do you realize what you've done? You've ruined my life, that's all. Just ruined my life. You've destroyed my one chance for happiness. I might as well just go upstairs and swallow everything in the medicine cabinet."

---

consideration (kən sid′ə rā′shən) *n.* regard for others and their feelings; respect.

vitally (vī′tə lē) *adv.* extremely; essentially.

"Good luck with the shaving cream," her mother said drily.

"I can't believe it," Libby said. "I can't believe you did that to me."

"If you can't believe that," her mother said, "you're going to hate this next part."

"What next part?" What could be worse, Libby wondered bitterly, than what her father had already done?

"Look, Libby, I'm sorry, but this business with the phone has gotten completely out of hand." Her mother sat down next to her. "You no sooner get home from school than you're on the phone for three hours with people you've been talking to all day."

"You can't talk to people in *school!*"

"Why not?" her father demanded. "That's ridiculous."

"You just can't," Libby insisted. How could she explain it? It was hopeless to expect her parents to understand what would have been obvious to any teenager.

"Well, you're going to have to," he said, "because from now on you'll have a limit on your calls."

"What do you mean? Like no more than five a day?"

Her father laughed, but it was a short, humorless laugh.

"No, not just the number of calls you make, but the amount of time you spend on each one. Tomorrow I'm getting three egg timers, and I'm going to put one next to each extension. When you make a call, you turn over the egg timer. When the salt runs out of the top, you get off the phone. *Immediately.*"

"How long does it take," Libby asked, her voice weak with shock, "for the salt to run out?"

"Three minutes."

"*Three minutes!* That's impossible! That's crazy! How can you have a conversation in three minutes?"

Libby's father looked at her thoughtfully. "Look at it this way," he said. "Every time we ask you to get off the phone you say, 'Just two more minutes, just two more minutes.'"

Libby squirmed. He did a pretty good imitation of her.

"So we figure, when the pressure's on, you can wrap up these life-and-death matters in two minutes. When you really have to. We're giving you three minutes—an extra minute more than you always ask for. Anything vitally important that you have to say to anybody can be said in three minutes."

For a moment Libby was too stunned to speak. How could they do this to her? It was humiliating. It was <u>barbaric</u>. There are plenty of vitally important things that can't be said in three minutes. And even if *she* talked fast, what about the person on the other end of the phone? What if he was shy and hesitant and talked slowly, trying to work up his nerve, sort of build up to what he actually called about? Like, say, someone like Mark? Not that Mark would ever call her again, after tonight, but just as an example.

---

barbaric (bär bar′ik) *adj.* savage; brutal.

Of course, if they weren't going to limit the number of calls she made—Libby's eyes brightened for a moment. "Then what you're saying is, I have to hold each *individual* call down to three minutes, right?"

Her mother smiled. "Forget it, Libby. No more than three calls a day. You can't just hang up and call back, hang up and call back."

"But what about people who call me?"

"Incoming calls will be timed, too."

"Oh, no! You can't do that! It's not fair! I have *rights.* This is *America.*"

"The Constitution," her father said, "does not give you the <u>inalienable</u> right to a telephone. And we've tried to be understanding and fair, but *you* haven't. We just can't think of any other way to solve this problem."

Dazed, Libby pulled herself out of the chair.

"I can't believe you're doing this to me." She shook her head. "I can't believe my own parents could be so . . . I've got to call Stacey. She'll never believe it either."

"Libby!" her father said. "You can tell Stacey tomorrow. The bad news will wait eight hours."

Libby turned to stare back at him, her face pale with the shock of betrayal. Then she trudged up to her room, shoulders slumping, to do her homework.

What else was there to do?

• • •

On the second day after the "Invasion of the Egg Timers," as Libby called it, she thought she'd found a loophole.

"My time is up," she said to Stacey loudly. She looked around <u>furtively</u>, then hunched over the phone. "Wait ten minutes," she whispered, "and call me back."

When the phone rang ten minutes later, Libby grabbed it. "Now look, when I have to get off, do the same thing again. Wait ten minutes and call me back."

---

inalienable (in āl′yə nə bəl) *adj.* that cannot be given up or taken away.
furtively (fûr′tiv lē) *adv.* slyly; sneakily.

"This is no way to hold a conversation."

"What can I do?" moaned Libby. "They've driven me to this."

The third time Stacey called, Libby's mother got to the phone first.

"Hello, Stacey. Yes, just a minute." She handed the phone to Libby with a knowing look. She held up three fingers.

"I know, I know," Libby grumbled. "Three minutes."

Her mother shook her head. "No. Three strikes and you're out."

"What?" Libby clamped her hand over the mouthpiece. "What do you mean?"

"That's the third time Stacey's called. No more. You may be sticking to the letter of the law, but you're <u>violating</u> the spirit of it."

"*What?*"

"In plain English: You can't get around it that way, but nice try."

"Why don't you just lock me in my room and throw away the key?" Libby wailed. "You're cutting off my lifeline to the outside world!"

Her brother came clumping down the stairs. "Are you still on that phone?"

"What do you mean, *still?*" Libby demanded. "I haven't even said hello yet."

"Then say hello," said her mother, and carefully turned over the egg timer.

• • •

What her parents did to her was bad enough, Libby felt, but what her friends did seemed even a worse betrayal. Within a week after the "Invasion of the Egg Timers," the grumbling started.

"Boy, Libby, you really loused things up for everybody," Renee Kaplan said, sitting down next to her in algebra.

"Me? What did I do?"

---

violating (vī'ə lā'ting) *v.t.* failing to obey; breaking.

"You and those three-minute phone calls. My mother has me on egg timers now."

"But that's not my fault!" Libby said, outraged. "My parents did that, not me!"

"They're *your* parents," Renee said. "It all started with you."

"What all?"

"Suzanne's parents, Lauri's mother—you started an epidemic of egg timers."

"*I* didn't start anything!" Libby couldn't believe it. It was bad enough that her parents had turned on her, but now this? Her friends, too?

"Renee, I'm sorry, but really, it's not fair to blame me. What can I do?"

"Well, if you've got any AT&T stock," Renee said coldly, "I suggest you sell."

• • •

Libby hadn't forgotten about Mark, though she was sure she might as well.

---

epidemic (ep′i dem′ik) *n.* rapid spread or sudden, widespread appearance.

He was in only one of her classes, where he sat way in the back of the room next to his friend John Kelly, so she didn't even get to see him unless she got there early and watched him walk in or hung around after the bell and watched him walk out.

Libby began to think that Stacey had been mistaken—that day she thought she heard Mark talking about Libby, he was actually talking about Renee Kaplan. Either that or her father really *had* ruined everything the night he hung up on Mark, making her sound like a two year old who'd been <u>banished</u> to her room for throwing spinach at the cat.

Why Mark should like her she didn't know. Just because *she* liked him? Just because she thought he was cute? But she did. And he was. And there was no hope for it now, if there ever had been. If, by some remote chance, Mark finally called her one night, he'd barely have enough time to say who it was before she had to hang up. And a shy person like Mark might need a good ten minutes to relax enough to sort of casually work whatever it was he *really* wanted to say into the conversation.

So between rounds of nursing her bruised feelings and snapping at her family, Libby sighed a lot and thought about what was never to be but might have been.

And wrote *Mark* a few hundred times on the memo pad on top of her desk.

•   •   •

Monday night when the phone rang, Libby didn't even run for it. She was too <u>disheartened</u>. Her spirit had been broken. And it probably wasn't for her, anyhow. Half of her friends had had their phone lines cut off, and most of them blamed it on Libby. Those people who were still speaking to her—mostly the ones who *hadn't* been invaded by egg timers—didn't call her because what kind of a satisfying talk could you have in three minutes?

---

banished (ban′isht) *v.t.* forced to leave one place, and restricted to another place.
disheartened (dis här′tənd) *v.t.* discouraged; weakened in hope or will.

"It's for you," her brother said, pounding on the door. "Don't forget to turn your timer."

"I won't forget to turn my timer," Libby mimicked. "I probably won't even have to. It's just someone who wants to know what the homework is. That's all we have time to say anymore."

Libby went into her parents' bedroom and picked up the phone.

"Hello," she said dully.

"Uh, hi, Libby?" It was a boy's voice. A boy's shy, hesitant voice.

Libby exhaled so hard she was sure he must have heard her.

The egg timer slipped out of her fingers and rolled under the bed.

"Yes, this is me," she said softly. Wow, did that sound dumb. Well, what could you expect? She wasn't getting much practice in the art of telephone conversation lately.

"It's Mark Welch. Uh"—he cleared his throat—"I know you can't stay on the phone very long. . . ."

The whole world knows my problems, Libby thought bitterly. This is humiliating.

"So I'll—uh—get right to the point."

He probably wants to know what the homework is in earth science, Libby thought.

"You know they're having this—uh—Sixties Dance in school next Saturday, and I was wondering if you'd—I mean, I don't dance really well or anything, but—well, you know, if you want to—"

I don't believe it! Libby thought. I'm going to faint. Faint later! she told herself. Your three minutes are almost up. She felt for her heart; it was still beating. Very rapidly.

"I mean, what I thought was maybe we could go, you know, together, if you want."

"That would be really nice," Libby said. How calm she sounded! Just as if Mark called her every day! Just as if she hadn't been waiting and hoping for weeks for this moment. "I'd really like that."

"You would?" Mark sounded like he couldn't believe it. Like he'd expected her to say no. "Oh, good. Great. I'll pick you up about eight, okay?"

"Eight is fine."

"Well. Well, okay. I guess you have to get off now."

"Right, right," Libby said, dazed. "I guess I'd better. Bye."

"Bye. Take care."

Libby dropped the receiver back on the hook and threw herself across her parents' bed. *Now* she was going to faint. She was going to faint from shock and then die of happiness.

No. Not yet.

First she had to call Stacey.

"Stace? Stace, you're not going to believe this—"

"He called?" Stacey asked excitedly. "Did he call yet?"

"What? How did you know—"

"He did call! Did he ask you?"

"Stacey, how do you know all this?" Libby demanded.

"John sort of hinted around at it—I wormed most of it out of him."

"Why didn't you tell me?"

"Because John said he was so nervous about it he might chicken out at the last minute, and I didn't want to get your hopes up for nothing. But he really called?"

"Yes," sighed Libby. "Yesss. . . ."

"Well, it's really bizarre, Lib. Listen, you're not going to believe this. He tried to call you for two weeks."

"What?"

"But your line was always busy." Stacey giggled. "Isn't that <u>ironic</u>?"

"What?"

"And he was too shy to talk to you in school, with people all around. And when he finally did reach you, your father said you couldn't come to the phone. So he gave up.

---

ironic (ī ron′ik) *adj.* odd, as an outcome of events that is the opposite of what might have been expected.

He figured you were so popular you'd never go out with him. All those phone calls and all."

"What?"

"You're repeating yourself, Libby. So anyhow, when this thing with the time limit came up, he figured he'd be able to get you now, but he was still sure you wouldn't be interested in him. It took a whole week for John to help him work up the nerve to try."

In a haze, Libby slid off the bed and down to the floor. Still holding onto the receiver, she groped around under the bed till she found the egg timer. She put it down carefully on the night table.

"Libby? You still there?"

"Yeah, I'm still here. My time's almost up, though. I don't believe this."

"I told you you wouldn't. Oh, Lib, did you die? Were you surprised? I would have died."

"No, no, I'm saving that for later," Libby said distractedly.

Her mother walked into the room. She looked at the egg timer, which had never been turned over, and saw that all the salt was on the bottom, as if it had run out. She stared <u>pointedly</u> at Libby.

"I have to go, Stace. Talk to you later. I mean, tomorrow."

"Okay. Take care."

Libby hung up the phone and walked dreamily toward the door.

She paused just before leaving the bedroom and looked at her mother almost fondly.

"You know," she murmured, "you might be right."

"About what?" her mother asked, startled.

Libby trailed her fingers gently around the doorknob.

"Maybe you *can* say anything you have to say in three minutes . . . if it's important enough." ●

---

pointedly (poin′tid lē) *adv.* forcefully; with emphasis.

meet ELLEN Conford

Ellen Conford (born 1942) wants to entertain her readers. She explains, "I don't write to pound home a message, or to teach a lesson. . . . I want to write books that are fun to read."

One of the things that makes Conford's books entertaining is her use of humor. She believes that we laugh when we read about people like ourselves or about situations that we have been in.

Conford often writes about problems and situations that her readers might face—how to get someone you like to notice you, how to adjust to a new school, what to do when you get the worst part in a school play. "I write books about things that could or do happen to 75 percent of the kids I know who face the normal problems of growing up," she says.

Conford's first book was *Impossible, Possum,* a children's book about a possum who can't seem to hang by his tail like every other possum. Another of her popular books is *Dreams of Victory,* in which Victory Benneker's imagination helps her cope with everyday disappointments. Both *Impossible, Possum* and *Dreams of Victory* were Junior Literary Guild selections.

RESPONDING TO *Literature*

THINK • TALK • WRITE

1 Which character in this story did you like best? Why? Jot some reasons in your journal.

2 Why do you think Libby talks so long on the telephone? Do you think her friends appreciate her calls? Explain your opinions.

3 What is the most important thing in Libby's life as the story begins? How do you think this affects the plot? Is it still the most important thing by the end of the story?

4 Is it fair for Libby's parents to limit her telephone time? Why or why not? What other solutions can you think of for the Kalmans' problem?

5 In some parts of the world, telephones are considered a luxury. How might your life be different if your home didn't have a phone?

ACTIVITIES

• **Write with Point of View**
Imagine that Libby writes an advice column for her school newspaper. A reader writes to ask for advice on dealing with the three-minute-telephone-call rule. What do you think Libby would say? Write an answer for Libby.

• **Pantomime** Sometimes Libby talks too much for her own good. With a group, try to retell her story without talking at all. Act out a silent three-minute version of this selection. Use such things as movement, facial expressions, costumes, and props in place of dialog.

VOCABULARY PRACTICE

On a separate piece of paper, write the root word of each vocabulary word. If there is no root word, write the word itself. Then give the meaning of each word you wrote. Use a dictionary if you need help.

1 respectively
root word:
meaning:

2 consideration
root word:
meaning:

3 berserk
root word:
meaning:

4 vitally
word:
meaning:

5 furtively
word:
meaning:

6 violating
root word:
meaning:

7 epidemic
root word:
meaning:

8 banished
root word:
meaning:

9 disheartened
root word:
meaning:

10 ironic
root word:
meaning:

BEFORE READING

CALENDAR ART

CONNECT TO LITERATURE

What kinds of activities require the use of a calendar? Why do you even *need* a calendar? Jot down your thoughts in your journal. As you read the following selection, note the different ways that people have divided the solar year (the time it takes Earth to make one revolution around the sun).

THINKING ABOUT EXPOSITION

Many articles and books give an overview of one topic. This kind of informative writing is called *exposition.* To present the information clearly, authors often organize each section around a *main idea,* a key fact or concept. Authors support these main ideas with details or examples. Another expository technique is to compare similar items, people, events, or systems. In "Calendar Art," the author shows how some ancient calendars were alike and different.

HAVE YOU EVER?

Have you ever wished that a week could have an extra day? That summer could last an extra month? Well, you're not the first! People in other cultures have measured time in many ways. There have been weeks with 5 days, 8 days, and 10 days. There have been years with 18 months and months with 20 days. Some years lasted as long as 445 days, and others were as short as 260 days. There have been calendars to suit almost every need. Each calendar has been an attempt to measure time so that people would know when to plant, to harvest, to pray, or to celebrate. Eventually, most societies settled on the 365¼-day year, for reasons you will discover as you read the following excerpts from the book *Calendar Art.*

CALENDAR

Gregorian sun and moon (upper left); Mayan month (upper right); Babylonian sun (lower left); Egyptian solar disc (lower right)

by
Leonard
Everett
Fisher

Days, Weeks, Months, and Years

Throughout the <u>existence</u> of humankind, people have been aware of the special rhythms of the sun and the moon. Primitive humans saw that the sun rose in one place, turning night into day, and that it set in another place, turning day into night. To them the moon, too, seemed to emerge from one position, move across the star-strewn sky, and disappear with the night at another position. They believed, then, that each day and each night the sun and the moon traveled an endless, <u>repetitive</u> course.

In other words, early people thought that the earth stood still as heavenly objects circled around it. Their knowledge was limited in this way from the dawn of the human <u>epoch</u>, about 500 thousand years ago, until about 440 years ago. It was then that the astronomer Nicolaus Copernicus

(1473–1543) offered a startling idea: that the sun stood still, that the earth was one of a group of heavenly bodies moving around it, and that as the earth moved in a measurable orbit around the sun, the moon traveled around the earth in its own measurable path.

Whatever the limits of early people's knowledge of the heavens, they knew there was a passage of time—from sunrise to sunset. And they knew that aging, growing from young to old, was a process of time. While they did not measure a day in seconds, minutes, and hours, they knew when it began and ended, and that it took 365¼ days for the sun to appear and disappear at identical positions—a solar year. Early people knew, too, that in some mysterious way the position of the sun determined the seasons.

The moon also provided a broad measure of timekeeping for these people. In the darkness they watched the moon change from no shape at all—the invisible new moon—to a slim crescent, a half-moon, an oval, or *gibbous,* a full moon, then back to a gibbous, half-moon, and crescent, before it became the shadowy new moon again. These phases of the moon always spanned 29½ days.

WINTER

This was the length of time it took the moon to orbit the earth once—the lunar month.

Our word *month* derives from *moon.* Early people knew that 12 lunar months nearly equaled one solar year, falling short by about 11 days. And as civilization evolved, people realized that they had to try to compensate for those days. A rough estimate of nature's timing was

no longer good enough. People needed a chart to tell them with certainty when to plant and harvest their crops, when to work, and when to pray. They needed a time-measuring system—a calendar.

The Greek and Roman civilizations gave us the word *calendar.* Its roots are in the Greek *kalend,* "I shout," and in the Roman *calends,* the first day of a Roman month. The ancient Greek who shouted *kalend* was a public timetable who informed the people when to pay their taxes, when the magistrates would try criminals, and when marketing days and religious and athletic events would take place.

SPRING

Other cultures—Aztec, Chinese, Jewish, Moslem—used varying systems to calculate days, weeks, months, and years. There was no standard calendar in use

---

evolved (i volvd′) *v.i.* developed slowly.
compensate (kom′pən sāt′) *v.t.* balance out; make up.

anywhere in the ancient world. And most of these systems, if not all, were based on either the lunar month or the solar year.

The ancient Sumerians devised the first lunar calendar

SUMMER

about 5,000 years ago. Later, Babylonians divided months into weeks and a week into 7 days. The Jews, once captive in Babylonia, used the Babylonian 7-day week, as did the sun-worshiping Egyptians, who developed a 52-week solar calendar based on the 7-day week.

The schemes were too complicated, however, and calendar dates and seasons became mismatched. The problem worsened each year. Farmers could not rely on these calendars to plant crops. Religious celebrants never knew the right day for a particular festival. Fall weeks of one year would become winter weeks the next year.

Julius Caesar (circa 100–44 B.C.) tried to adjust the calendar so that it would repeat itself the same way every year. Progress was made, but not enough. Then early Christians modified Caesar's "Julian" calendar so that all years following year 1, when Jesus Christ was born, would be known as A.D., or *anno domini,* "in the year of the Lord," and those that came before as B.C., before Christ, or B.C.E., before the common era. Still, calendar errors continued to multiply.

Finally, Pope Gregory XIII (1502–1585) corrected the calendar. Now its dates would <u>conform</u> year after year to the proper seasons with almost no error. The "Gregorian" calendar continues to be the calendar of our modern world.

FALL

On the following pages, you will read about the calendars of various cultures. The examples represent ancient as well as modern attempts to keep track of time.

---

conform (kən fôrm´) *v.i.* be the same or similar; correspond.

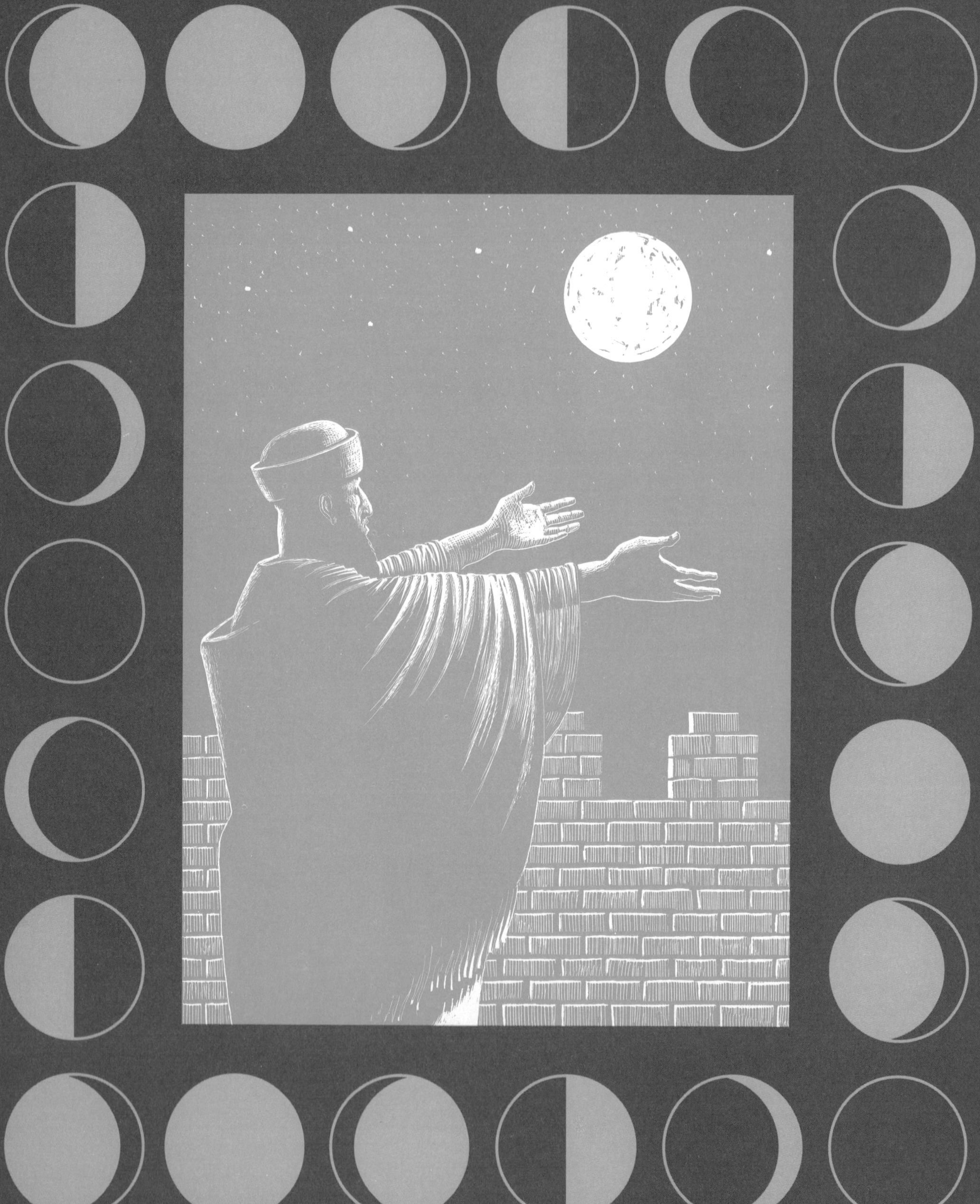

BABYLONIAN

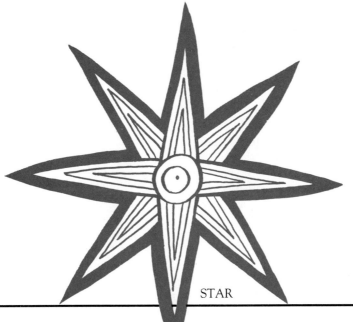

STAR

About 3000 B.C., long before the Greeks named the hot desert region between the Tigris and Euphrates rivers Mesopotamia, "the land between rivers," <u>nomadic</u> tribes quit wandering and formed farming towns. Chief among these towns was Ur, located on the banks of the Euphrates River at the northern rim of the Persian Gulf. The area was called Sumer. To help them deal with the dry land, the Sumerian farmers relied on their priest-astronomers to interpret the movement of the stars. They developed a 30-day lunar calendar and used it to plan their farming. These same Sumerians invented the first writing system, *cuneiform*. With it came the beginning of history: the written record.

Ur and the Sumerians faded after a 700-year presence. Babylon—the biblical Babel—and Babylonians arose in their place. However, during the kingdom of Hammurabi, circa 1750 B.C., a revised Sumerian calendar emerged as a Babylonian calendar.

---

nomadic (nō mad'ik) *adj.* wandering from place to place.

The Babylonians <u>devised</u> a 354-day lunar calendar with 12 alternating months of 29 and 30 days. But it fell 11¼ days short of the 365¼-day solar year. To correct the calendar so that the seasons matched their dates somewhat each year, they *intercalated,* or "inserted," two extra months seven times within every 19-year period.

MOON

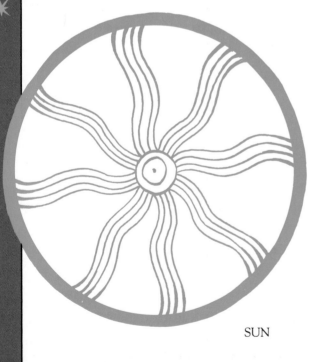

SUN

Also, the Babylonians were among the first civilizations to divide their year into 7-day weeks. The Babylonian week was based solely on the worship of the sun, moon, and five planets: Shamash (Sun/Sunday), Sin (Moon/Monday), Nebo (Mercury/Tuesday), Ishtar (Venus/Wednesday), Nergal (Mars/Thursday), Marduk (Jupiter/Friday), and Ninurta (Saturn/Saturday).

---

devised (di vīzd′) *v.t.* invented.

BABYLONIAN MONTHS

Υ 1. NISANU	ΥΥ 2. AIARU	ΥΥΥ 3. SIMANU
ΥΥΥ 4. Υ DUZU	ΥΥΥ 5. ΥΥ ABU	ΥΥΥ 6. ΥΥΥ ULULU
ΥΥΥ 7. ΥΥΥ Υ TASHRITU	ΥΥΥ 8. ΥΥΥ ΥΥ ARAHSAMNU	ΥΥΥ 9. ΥΥΥ ΥΥΥ KISLIMU
⟨ 10. TEBETU	⟨Υ 11. SHABATU	⟨ΥΥ 12. ADDARU

Intercalated months: ULULU II (29 days) ADDARU II (30 days)

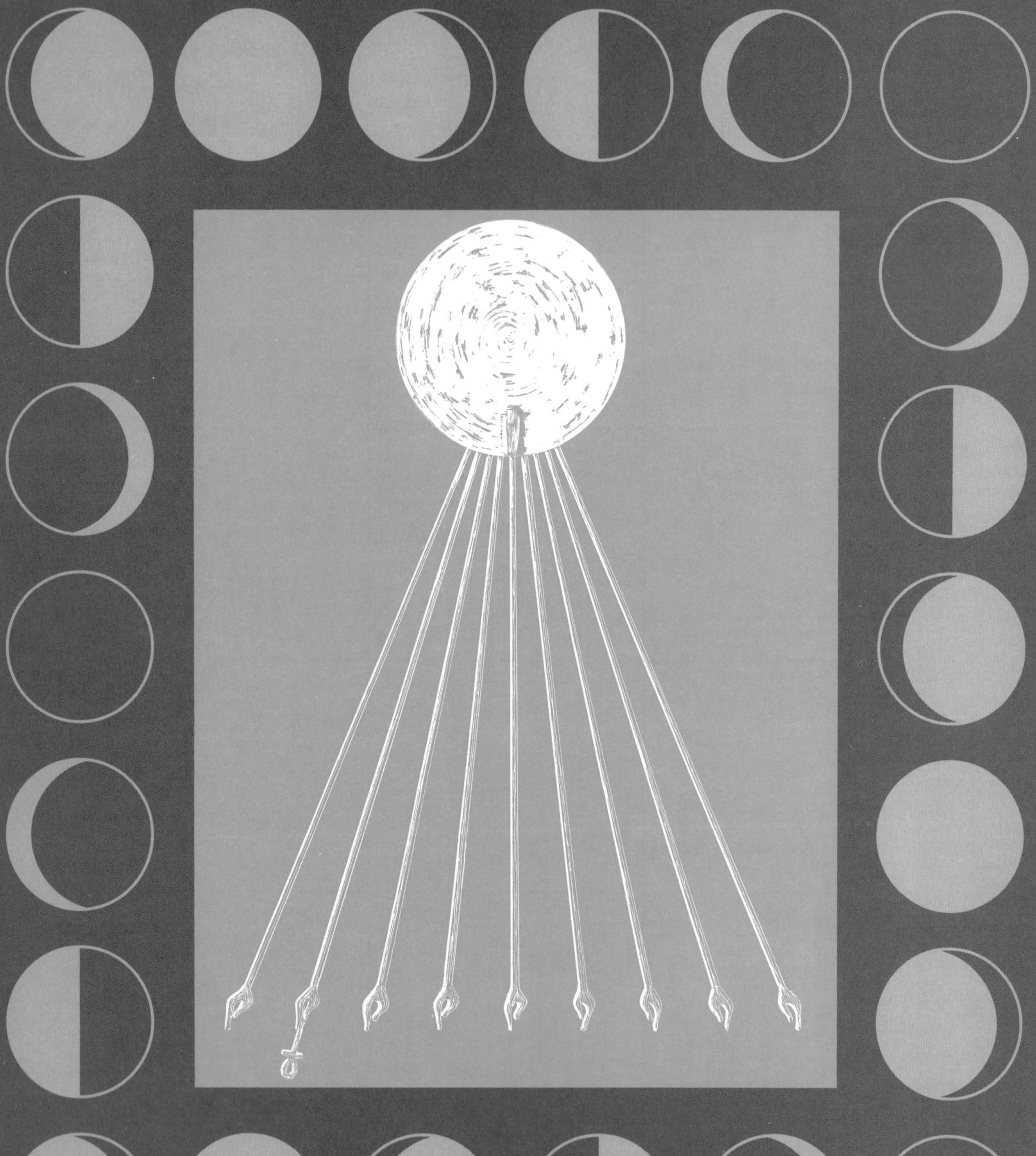

EGYPTIAN

| FIRST MONTH OF SUMMER | FIRST MONTH OF WINTER | FIRST MONTH OF SPRING |

An object of ancient worship, the Nile River is the spirit and lifeblood of Egypt. For without that great wash of water flowing from Ethiopia to the Mediterranean Sea, Egypt would be a desert. Once each year for the past 5,000 years of Egyptian recorded time, the Nile has flooded the 600-mile-long valley to create a green and <u>fertile</u> tract for planting.

Early Nile Valley farmers had to know when the river would flood in order to save their crops, their property, and even their lives. They knew that the flooding would begin whenever the brightest fixed star, Sirius (Sothis to the Egyptians), rose on the eastern horizon. This took place about once every 365 days, just before sunrise. So they developed a lunar calendar in which a year began with the first new moon following the appearance of Sirius. The lunar calendar year, containing 12 months with 29½ days each, covered 354 days, 11 short of 365. To make sure the flooding of the Nile and the calendar date always matched, they added an extra month every so often.

---

fertile (fûr′təl) *adj.* able to produce abundant crops.

In time the Egyptians created a more accurate 360-day solar calendar with 12 months of 30 days each, along with the 7-day week favored by Jews and Babylonians. Since this, too, fell short, they added 5 days to the last month of the year. Of course, Egyptian

ANCIENT EGYPTIAN MONTHS (named after Egyptian gods)

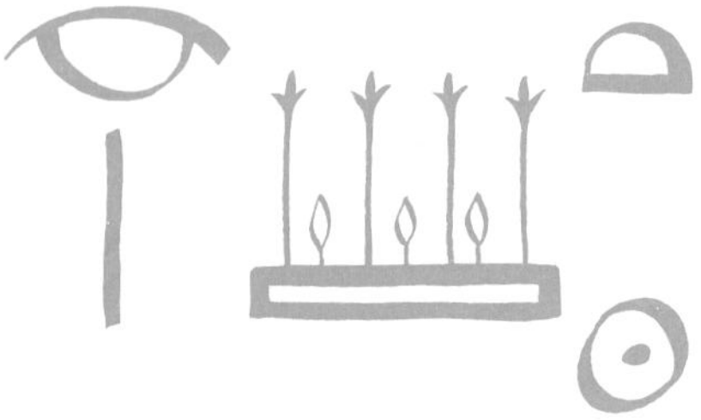

THOTH

PAOPI

TOBI

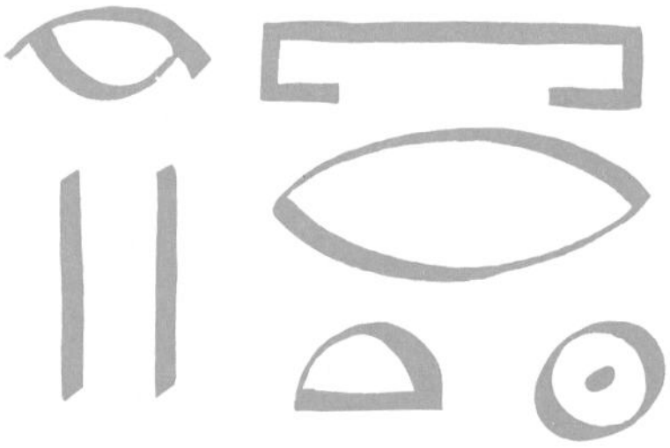

MEKHIR

PAKHON

PAONI

astronomers knew that a year was 365¼ days long. But their priests, guardians of centuries of tradition, forbade them to correct the calendar by adding an extra day every four years—a leap year. Eventually the calendar fell out of line with the seasonal flooding.

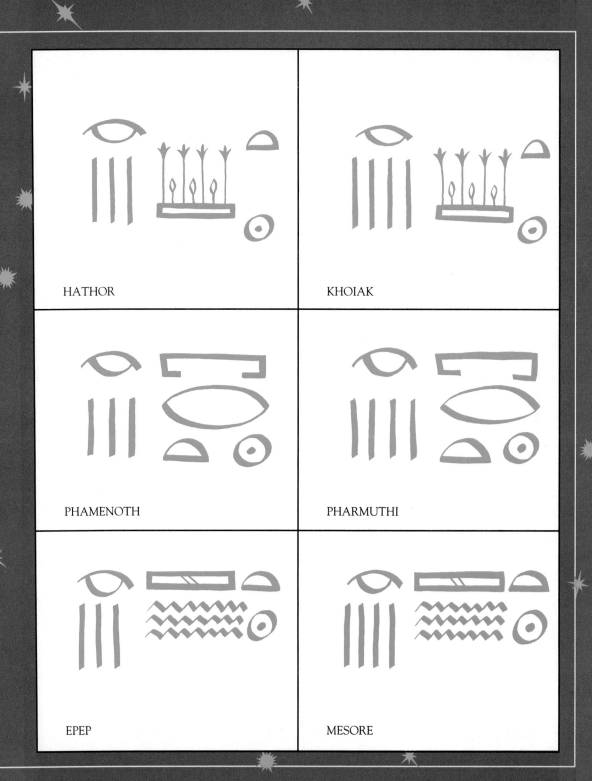

HATHOR

KHOIAK

PHAMENOTH

PHARMUTHI

EPEP

MESORE

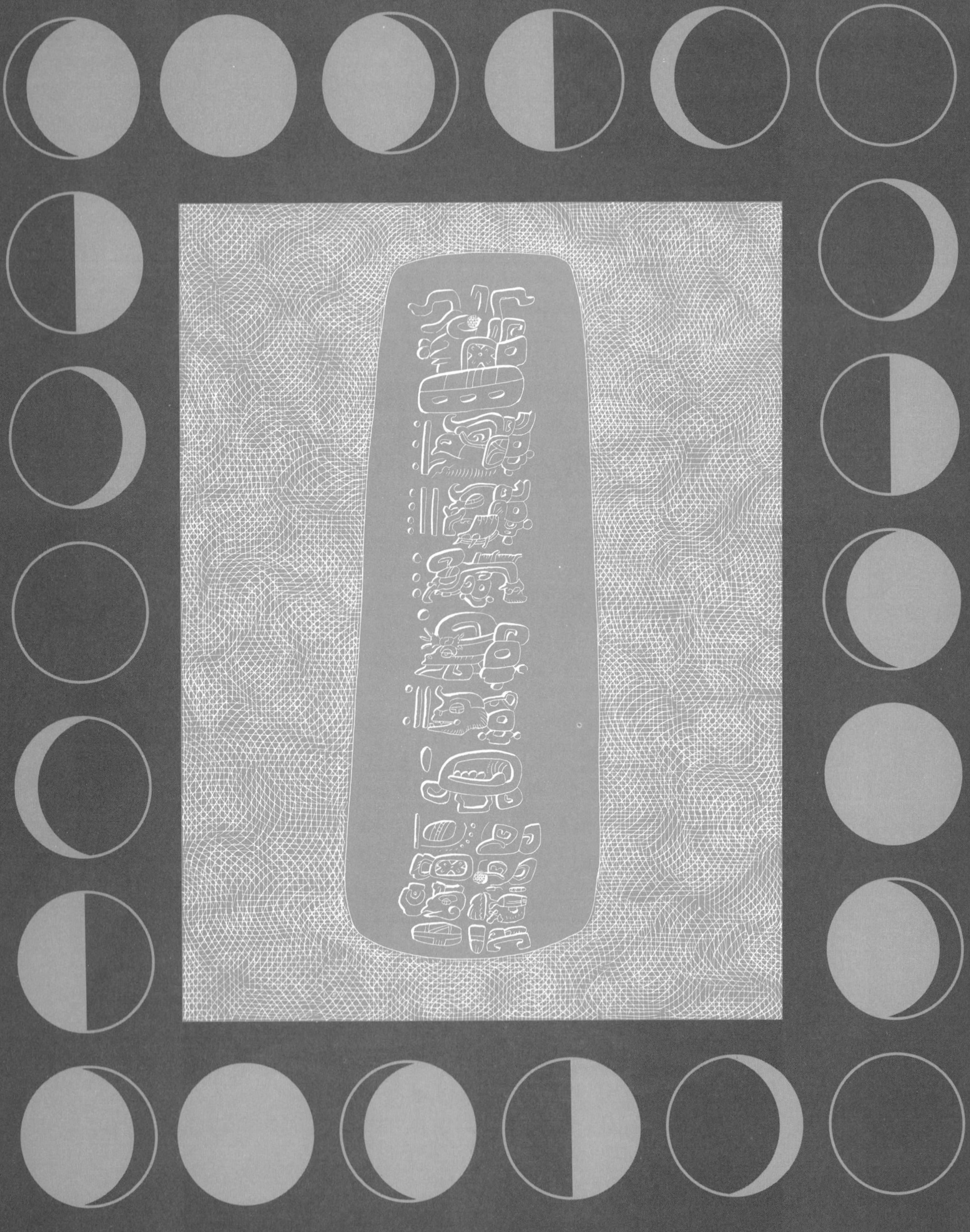

MAYAN

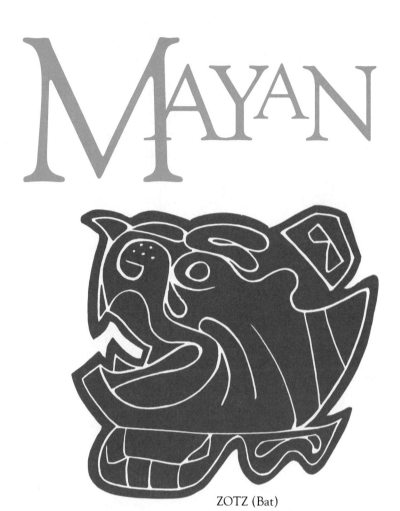

ZOTZ (Bat)

exico's Yucatan Peninsula and present-day Honduras and Guatemala were once the lands of the Maya. Long before Europeans arrived in the Western Hemisphere during the 1500s, the Mayan Indians had achieved a <u>distinctive</u> civilization. Their large cities —Copan, Chichen Itza, Tikal, and others—were administered by priests whose writings and astronomical observations, carved in stone or set down on tree-bark paper, provided a record of history, science, medicine, and religion, including human sacrifice. The priest-astronomers had developed a precise numbering system to manage Mayan lives at least 300 years before the birth of Christ, some 2,300 years ago. It enabled them precisely to measure planetary movements, time, and eclipses, and to develop a calendar for religious and civil affairs.

distinctive (di stingk′tiv) *adj.* unique; different in kind from others.

Mayan dating indicates that an accurate solar calendar was in use by them early in the common era in Europe, about the year 300. The Maya relied on two calendars working together in 52-year cycles called the *xiuhmolpilli*. One was the *haab*, a 365-day civil calendar having 18 months of 20 days each, plus a nineteenth month of 5 days. An extra day was added every fourth year. The 18-month period was called a *tun*.

MAYAN MONTH GLYPHS

Question marks indicate that researchers have been unable to translate glyphs.

Tun

Katun

1. Pop (mat)

2. Uo (frog)

3. Zip (goddess)

4. Zotz (bat)

4. Zotz (bat)

5. Tzec (?)

6. Xul (?)

7. Yaxkin (summer)

8. Mol (?)

9. Chen (?)

9. Chen (?)

10. Yax (green)

11. Zac (white)

12. Ceh (deer)

13. Mac (?)

14. Kankin (ribs)

14. Kankin (ribs)

15. Muan (falcon)

16. Pax (?)

17. Kayab (turtle)

17. Kayab (turtle)

18. Cumku (?)

19. Uayeb (?)

Twenty tuns were a *katun*. The other was a religious calendar, or *tzolkin*, having 260 sacred days.

The Maya did not have a written language that expressed sound. Instead, like the Egyptians, they used symbols called *hieroglyphs*, or *glyphs*, to express an idea. And they used a variety of number, word, and name glyphs to work out their calendar and <u>convey</u> its meaning.

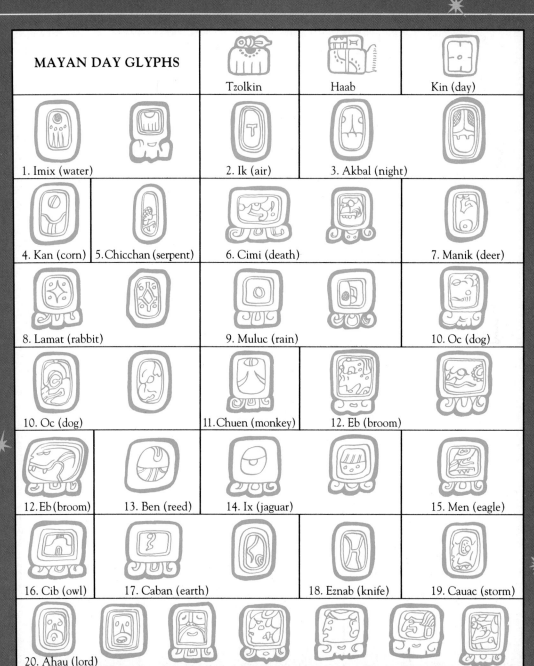

MAYAN DAY GLYPHS		Tzolkin	Haab	Kin (day)
1. Imix (water)		2. Ik (air)	3. Akbal (night)	
4. Kan (corn)	5. Chicchan (serpent)	6. Cimi (death)		7. Manik (deer)
8. Lamat (rabbit)		9. Muluc (rain)		10. Oc (dog)
10. Oc (dog)		11. Chuen (monkey)	12. Eb (broom)	
12. Eb (broom)	13. Ben (reed)	14. Ix (jaguar)		15. Men (eagle)
16. Cib (owl)	17. Caban (earth)		18. Eznab (knife)	19. Cauac (storm)
20. Ahau (lord)				

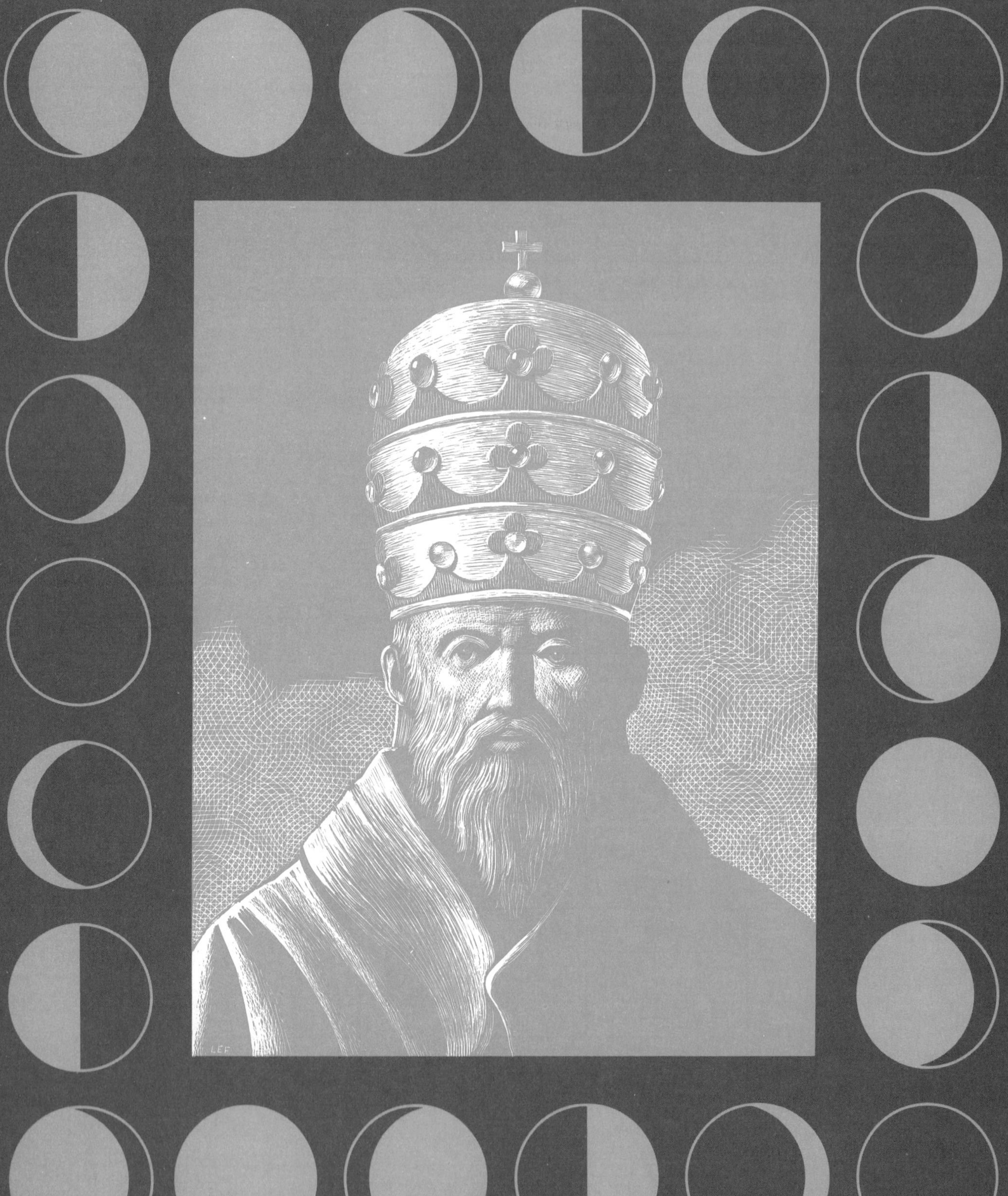
LEF

GREGORIAN

SUN AND MOON

By the sixteenth century, errors in the Julian calendar had become a problem for the Catholic Church. Easter was supposed to be celebrated on the vernal equinox, the day the sun crosses the equator, turning winter into spring in the Northern Hemisphere, summer to fall in the Southern Hemisphere. And the vernal equinox was supposed to occur on the first Sunday after the first full moon after March 21. But March 21 had moved 10 days ahead of the equinox. While the vernal equinox would occur every 365¼

days, as usual, March 21 would soon be in midsummer.

Pope Gregory XIII ordered the calendar changed to correct the errors. After ten years of study, the Pope decreed that October 5, 1582, would become October 15, 1582, to bring the dates into line with the sun's position. Ten days were dropped from the calendar. Also, though January 1 would continue to be New Year's Day, leap year would no longer be any year divisible by four. While a leap year still would occur every four years by adding one day to February, the last year of a century could not be a leap year unless it was divisible by 400. The year 1900, for example, could not be a leap year. The year 2000 would be a leap year. Now it would be 30,000 years before the calendar would become 10 days out of line.

It took two hundred years for Protestant Europe, namely, England and Germany, to accept the Gregorian calendar. The Russians did not adopt it until 1918. Moslems, Jews, and Greek Orthodox people continue to use their own ancient calendars for religious events. But the business of nearly the entire modern world is conducted by the Gregorian calendar.

DAYS OF THE WEEK AROUND THE MODERN WORLD						
ENGLISH	LATIN	FRENCH	SPANISH	ITALIAN	DANISH	DUTCH
Sunday	Dies Dominica Lord's Day	Dimanche	Domingo	Domenica	Soendag	Zondag
Monday	Dies Lunae Moon's Day	Lundi	Lunes	Lunedì	Mandag	Maandag
Tuesday	Dies Martis Mars's Day	Mardi	Martes	Martedì	Tirsdag	Dinsdag meeting day
Wednesday	Dies Mercurii Mercury's Day	Mercredi	Miércoles	Mercoledì	Onsdag	Woensdag Woden's day
Thursday	Dies Jovis Jupiter's Day	Jeudi	Jueves	Giovedì	Torsdag	Donderdag thunder day
Friday	Dies Veneris Venus's Day	Vendredi	Viernes	Venerdì	Fredag	Vrijdag
Saturday	Dies Saturni Saturn's Day	Samedi	Sábado sabbath	Sabato sabbath	Loerdag bath day	Zaterdag

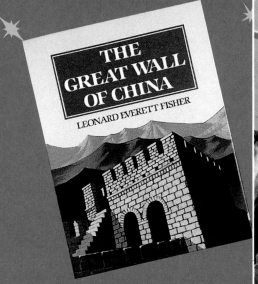

MeeT
LEONARD EVERETT FISHER

Painting and illustration are central to the books Leonard Everett Fisher creates. "I want to present art in nonfiction— to have people look at the power and dynamics of art. . . ."

Winner of a Pulitzer Prize for his painting, Fisher uses a variety of techniques and color schemes in his books. The illustrations in *Calendar Art* were created using the scratchboard technique. White board was covered with blue ink that was then scratched away to reveal the white underneath. In other books, such as *The Blacksmith*, Fisher used black ink.

Full-color paintings illustrate the book *Celebrations* by Myra Cohn Livingston, a poet Fisher has collaborated with for several collections. In *The Great Wall of China*, Fisher used black, white, and gray to create dramatic effects. He also used red blocks called "chops" to sign his work, just as Chinese artists have done since ancient times.

As Fisher says, "I design according to the idea."

RESPONDING TO *Literature*

THINK • TALK • WRITE

1 What did you learn from this selection? Write some of the more interesting facts in your journal.

2 How would you sum up the main idea of "Calendar Art"?

3 What is the Gregorian calendar? Why do you think it is used so widely throughout the world today?

4 Why did people need calendars in the past? Why do people need calendars today?

5 What are some special days that your family or culture celebrates? Research one special day, and explain its meaning.

ACTIVITIES

• **Write About Exposition** Write a letter from Pope Gregory XIII explaining the new Gregorian calendar. compare it to the Julian calendar, and show how it will correct the Julian calendar's mistakes.

• **Make Scratchboard Art** Design a symbol to represent each day of the week. Then try copying your designs using Fisher's scratchboard technique. You can use special scratchboard paper from an art supply store, or you can try making your own.

VOCABULARY PRACTICE

On a separate piece of paper, write the vocabulary word that best completes each sentence.

existence	repetitive
evolved	compensate
conform	nomadic
devised	fertile
distinctive	convey

1 Sara doubted the animal's _____ until she saw it with her own eyes.

2 The actor could _____ strong emotion with just a simple look.

3 What began as a minor annoyance _____ into a major conflict.

4 Agriculture is a major Ohio industry due to the state's _____ soil.

5 Zak quit the club when he realized that he couldn't _____ to its rules.

6 Some wrist injuries are caused by performing _____ motions such as typing or chopping too many times.

7 Sailors lead a _____ life as duty takes them from place to place.

8 Tan promised to _____ the library for the book's loss.

9 The inventor _____ a unique windshield wiper.

10 Nick's mother said she would know his _____ hairstyle anywhere.

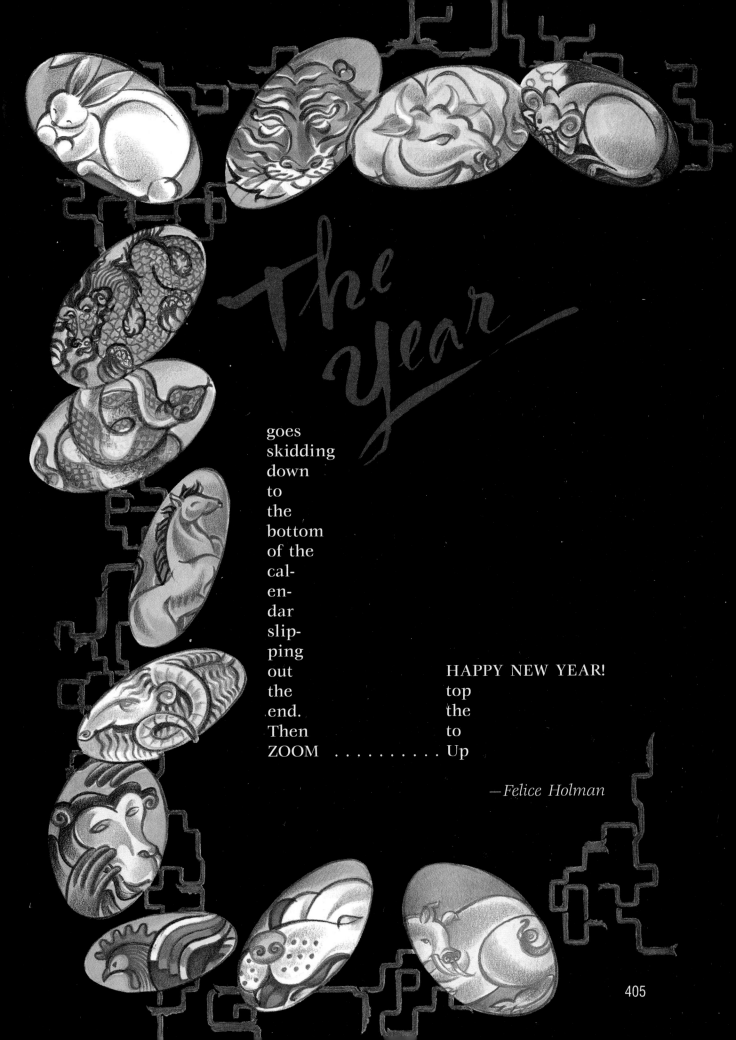

The Year

goes
skidding
down
to
the
bottom
of the
cal-
en-
dar
slip-
ping
out
the
end.
Then
ZOOM . . . . Up

HAPPY NEW YEAR!
top
the
to
Up

—*Felice Holman*

TODAY I'M Going YESTERDAY

BY JACK PRELUTSKY

Relativity 1953 M. C. Escher

Today I'm going yesterday
as quickly as I can,
I'm confident I'll do it,
I've devised a clever plan,
it involves my running backward
at a constant rate of speed,
if I'm mindful of my timing,
I'll undoubtedly succeed.

Today I'm going yesterday,
I'm moving very fast
as I'm putting off the future
for the rather recent past,
I can feel the present fading
as I hastily depart,
and look forward to arriving
on the day before I start.

Today I'm going yesterday,
I'm slipping out of sight
and anticipate I'll vanish
just a bit before tonight,
when I reach my destination,
I'll compose a note to say
that I'll see you all tomorrow,
which of course will be today.

BEFORE READING

....

THIS BOOK IS ABOUT TIME

CONNECT TO LITERATURE

Why are some people "early birds" and others "night owls"? Why is one person always late and another person always early? Write some ideas in your journal. Then read this excerpt from Chapter 8 of *This Book Is About Time* to find out more about inner clocks and other human rhythms.

THINKING ABOUT DIRECT ADDRESS

Hey, you! Now that I have your attention . . . Addressing the reader as "you" is a technique called *direct address*. Talking directly to the reader is a good way to involve the reader. A writer might ask a question or make general statements such as "Scientists have discovered you need less sleep as you grow older." Notice how author Marilyn Burns uses direct address in the selection. Think about why she chose to use this technique.

HAVE YOU EVER?

Have you ever seen time fly? Wanted to turn back the clock? There are many expressions about time in our culture. Do you know where these famous sayings or quotations came from?

- To every thing there is a season, and a time to every purpose under heaven. (the Bible, Ecclesiastes 3:1)

- A people without history is like the wind on the buffalo grass. (Sioux saying)

- There is a time and place for everything. (Aesop, c. 600 B.C.)

- It is better to be late than never. (Publilius Syrus, c. 42 B.C.)

- Today is the first day of the rest of your life. (wall slogan, 1970s)

THIS BOOK

IS ABOUT

TIME

THE INSIDE STORY
ON PEOPLE TIME

BY MARILYN BURNS

You have your own inner clocks. They do the inside job of timing what goes on in your body. They're not like the clocks that help you time your activities during the day. Those clocks are out where you can easily see them—on walls, on wrists, sitting on table tops. Those timekeepers sometimes need your attention for winding or resetting.

But your inner clocks aren't visible to you. They don't need to be wound. You don't have to check them to see how time is moving. They do their job, day in and day out, automatically, with no help needed from you.

Inner clocks are what keep your biological rhythms well timed. They keep the inside parts of your body working together and timed with the outside world too. Do you know what some of your biological rhythms are?

Scientists have the same questions about human biological rhythms that they've had about the inner clocks of plants and animals. Even though your rhythms aren't as noticeable as plant and animal rhythms, they're there. And you can learn a great deal about them.

This article has information on what people have found out about human cycles. There are also activities and experiments, so you can try out some of what scientists have learned firsthand. Here's a chance for you to take a look at your own inner timing.

THE CLOCK IN YOU

How is your own sense of time? Take a quick check. Try guessing what time you think it is right now. Don't look at a clock yet. First make your guess as accurate as you think you can. Now go and check the clock. How close were you?

Investigate the time sense of some other people in your family. Try asking them what time they think it is. Do this on and off during the next several days. See how close their guesses are.

Some people set an alarm clock at night to be sure they'll get up in the morning by a certain time. Do you? Lots of people have reported that they always seem to wake up just before the alarm goes off. Has this ever happened to you? Has it happened to people you know? Ask your parents. Check with other people who use alarm clocks; see if this is generally true or untrue for them. If it's true for them, ask how come they still keep on setting the alarm at night?

Do you have a dog or a cat? If you do, try to observe their time sense. Some people notice that their pets seem to ask to be fed just about the same time every day. If you have a pet, check the times it shows up around the kitchen sniffing for some supper.

Not everyone's inner timing works with the same accuracy. Maybe you could improve your time sense. Try guessing the time on and off during the day whenever you remember. See if you can get more accurate. Do you think it's possible to sharpen your inner timekeeping?

---

biological (bī′ə loj′i kəl) *adj.* having to do with life processes; bodily.

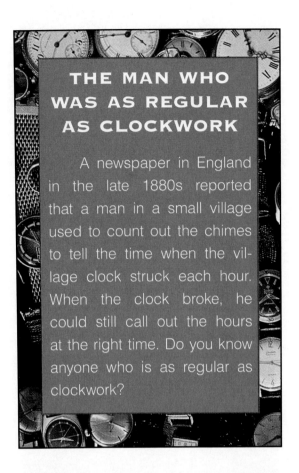

THE MAN WHO WAS AS REGULAR AS CLOCKWORK

A newspaper in England in the late 1880s reported that a man in a small village used to count out the chimes to tell the time when the village clock struck each hour. When the clock broke, he could still call out the hours at the right time. Do you know anyone who is as regular as clockwork?

PEOPLE'S PACEMAKERS

Some scientists feel that there is a pacemaker in everyone's brain that gives people some sense of time. Scientists don't know too much about this pacemaker. They do know that it's not a very trustworthy or accurate time-keeper for most people. They also know that humans don't do nearly as well as plants and animals do in keeping track of time. Maybe that's why people have spent so much of their energy inventing clocks to keep the time for them.

Scientists know that people's timing abilities are easily thrown off by changes. Heat is one of those changes. Have you ever had the feeling on a hot, hot day that time seems to be moving very slowly? Heat speeds up your pacemaker so your own sense of time is moving faster than time really is. Then things seem to take longer, as if they're happening in slow motion.

When you've got the flu or some nasty sickness that gives you a fever, the fever will have the same effect. Being sick in bed for a day with a fever often makes a day feel very long and slow.

When Frank Brown investigated the fiddler crab, heat changes had no effect whatsoever on the crab's daily color changes. When Henri-Louis Duhamel experimented with the plants that opened and closed their leaves on a daily cycle, temperature changes didn't change the plants' cycles at all. Your inner clocks just aren't that reliable.

ARE YOU AN ON-TIME PERSON?

Are you a punctual person? Are you usually an early arriver, or are you a latecomer? Most people fit clearly into one of those three timely groups. What about you?

---

pacemaker (pās′mā′kər) *n.* device that controls timing.
punctual (pungk′chü əl) *adj.* on time; prompt.

Here are some questions to ask yourself if you're not sure which you are. When your mom or dad tells you to be home at 5:00 P.M., do you get home on time? Is it a struggle to do so, racing at the last minute to get there, or is it something you just plan for, so it's no big <u>hassle</u>?

Do you get ready to leave for school on time in the morning easily, or do you depend on someone else to keep you moving? Are you the one who always has to wait for someone else to finish getting ready?

What about the other people you live with or your friends? Predict whether you think they are on-timers, early arrivers, or latecomers. Then ask them what they think, and see if your opinions agree.

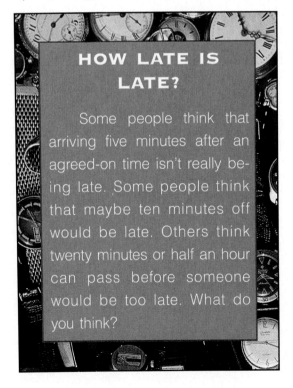

HOW LATE IS LATE?

Some people think that arriving five minutes after an agreed-on time isn't really being late. Some people think that maybe ten minutes off would be late. Others think twenty minutes or half an hour can pass before someone would be too late. What do you think?

THE HUMAN RHYTHMS

One thing scientists have learned from their experiments to investigate human biological cycles is this: Many of your body rhythms operate on a twenty-four-hour cycle. These are daily rhythms. They operate automatically, without any effort from you.

These daily body rhythms are called circadian rhythms. The word *circadian* comes from two Latin words. *Circa* means "about" and *dies* means "day." Here's a listing of some of the circadian rhythms that are part of your everyday life.

1. Your sleep-awake cycle. This is an easy cycle for you to notice. Your brain controls your sleep-awake rhythm, and some of your other circadian rhythms are keyed to this one.

2. Your body-temperature cycle. Your temperature is regulated by the part of your brain called the hypothalamus. During a twenty-four-hour period, your temperature rises and falls about $1\frac{1}{2}$ to 2 degrees Fahrenheit. It's lowest when you're asleep. And for most people, it's highest in the late afternoon.

Do you ever notice that when you're up watching a late movie on TV, you get really cold and need to huddle under a blanket? That's because your temperature is dropping for the night.

---

hassle (has′əl) *n.* irritation; struggle.

3. Your oxygen-use rhythm. Your cells need oxygen. How much oxygen they require varies in a daily cycle. When you run or exercise a lot, you breathe harder because your cells need more oxygen then. During the time of day that you're usually most active, your body's oxygen consumption is higher. When is this time of day for you? What's interesting is that even when you're not so active on some days, your rhythm of oxygen increase continues.

4. The rhythm of your heartbeats. The rate of your heartbeats changes on a daily cycle. When you're asleep, your heart beats slowest. Scientists have measured people's pulses and have found that they're usually lowest between 10 P.M. and 7 A.M. During the day, your pulse will vary according to how active you are. But even when you're resting or napping in the daytime, it won't be as low as it is at night.

5. Your kidney-excretion cycle. Your kidneys filter out the waste products from your blood. They expel these waste products in your urine. Your kidneys do most of this work during the day and less of it at night, when you're asleep. That's convenient, so you usually don't have to get up during the night to urinate.

6. Your taste, smell, and hearing rhythms. For most people, the sense of taste and smell and hearing are sharpest in late afternoon or evening. That's when people seem to be more aware of how good the dinner that's cooking smells, and how good it is to sit down and eat a yummy meal, and how sounds seem so much clearer or louder. Have you ever noticed any of these for yourself?

There are other body rhythms that scientists have discovered too. The ones listed are the ones you can observe most easily in yourself and in the people around you. Later in this article some experiments will help you take a closer look at your own cycles.

A REMINDER ABOUT RHYTHMS

It's important to remember that people's individual cycles aren't all exactly the same. Living in a family where people's rhythms aren't all tuned in together makes for differences. Talk about these human rhythms with the other people in your family. Maybe you can get them interested in trying some of the activities that follow. That may give all of you another way to understand your differences and similarities.

consumption (kən sump′shən) *n.* amount that is used up.

excretion (ek skrē′shən) *n.* discharge of waste matter from the body.

YOUR SLEEPING-AWAKE CYCLE

Everyone needs to sleep. That's a biological law. When you sleep, your body gets a chance to restore the energy you've used up. When you don't have enough sleep, you act tired, you can't keep your attention on things well, you can't react as fast as you normally can, and you get generally grumpy.

How many hours do you sleep daily? Figure this out. If you're not sure, keep a record for a week. You can do that by making a chart like this and writing down the time you go to bed every night and when you get up every morning. Do you get up a different time on days that you don't have to go to school? Does that change how much sleep you get?

	Went to Bed	Got Up	Hours
MONDAY			
TUESDAY			
WEDNESDAY			
THURSDAY			
FRIDAY			
SATURDAY			
SUNDAY			

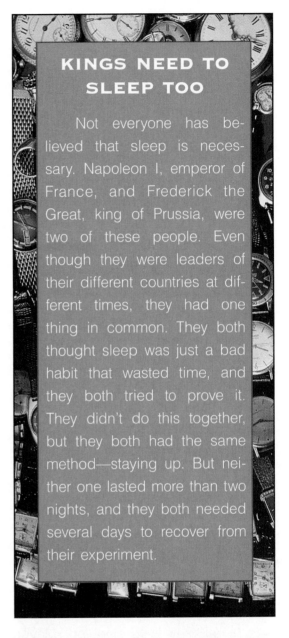

KINGS NEED TO SLEEP TOO

Not everyone has believed that sleep is necessary. Napoleon I, emperor of France, and Frederick the Great, king of Prussia, were two of these people. Even though they were leaders of their different countries at different times, they had one thing in common. They both thought sleep was just a bad habit that wasted time, and they both tried to prove it. They didn't do this together, but they both had the same method—staying up. But neither one lasted more than two nights, and they both needed several days to recover from their experiment.

SLEEPING AGES WITH TIME

The amount of sleep people need varies for individuals, but experiments have shown that age makes a big difference too. When you were a newborn baby, you slept on and off all during the day and night. You were asleep twice as much as you were awake, which meant you were sleeping about sixteen hours a day.

As you grow older, you need less and less sleep. Up until the time you are a teenager, you may sleep an average of about ten hours every night.

Grownups don't all need the same amount of sleep, but on an average, adults are awake twice as long as they are asleep. That means they sleep about eight hours out of every day. When grownups get older, they need even less sleep than that. People who are over sixty years old usually need only five to six hours.

Check these sleep times with people you know—friends, parents, grandparents, other relatives. See if the information you find agrees with what the experts have learned.

SLEEPY STATISTICS

People spend about 33 percent of their lives asleep. Cows spend only 3 percent of their lives sleeping. Maybe that's because they have four stomachs, and they've got to spend a lot more time chewing than humans do.

Horses sleep just a little less of their lives than humans do, about 29 percent. But gorillas are asleep 70 percent of the time.

THERE ARE DIFFERENT KINDS OF SLEEP

Scientists have also discovered that there are cycles you go through as you sleep. You plunge down into deep sleep, up to lighter sleep, and down again to deep sleep. This happens all the time you're sleeping, in cycles that last about an hour and a half each. Scientists have learned this from studying people's brain waves while they're asleep. Here's the difference in how brain waves look when you're awake and when you're asleep, including different stages. Scientists have also learned that you do your dreaming when you're in the light-sleep stage.

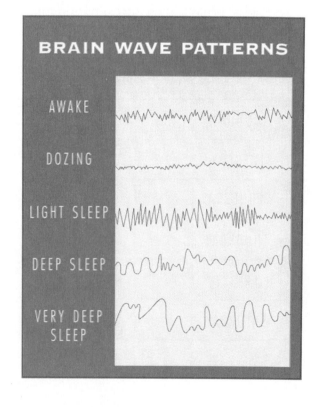

BRAIN WAVE PATTERNS

AWAKE

DOZING

LIGHT SLEEP

DEEP SLEEP

VERY DEEP SLEEP

TWO-TIMING

Here's a way to take a look at two of your daily cycles—your temperature cycle and your heartbeat cycle. The best time to do this experiment is on a day when you're not in school, so you can keep a record all through the day at regular times.

Get ready the night before you'll be doing the experiment. First make a recording chart, like the one shown. A piece of notebook-size paper will do fine. Notice that the chart is marked off every two hours. You'll start recording on your chart at the time listed that is closest to when you get up. Then take measurements at the other times listed during the day, stopping when you go to bed at night. Notice the space for answering the ten follow-up questions. You'll do that after you've taken all your <u>statistics</u> for the day.

The next thing to do is collect the equipment you'll need. You'll need a thermometer for taking your temperature, a thumbtack, a short piece of a straw—an inch or less—for taking your pulse. You'll also need a clock or watch with a second hand to time both your temperature taking and your pulse.

It's a good idea to practice taking both of these measurements once just to make sure you know how to do it. Here's how.

Date_____			Follow-up Questions
Time	Temperature	Pulse	
6AM			1.
8AM			2.
10AM			3.
12Noon			4.
2PM			5.
4PM			6.
6PM			7.
8PM			8.
10PM			9.
			10.

TAKING YOUR TEMPERATURE

1. Clean the thermometer. Use soapy water or alcohol. Rinse well.

2. Shake the thermometer down until it reads less than 96 degrees.

3. Put the bulb under your tongue. It needs to stay there for a good three minutes, so time that with the clock or watch. (Notice how long three minutes seem like too.)

4. Read your temperature.

5. Clean the thermometer before putting it away.

---

statistics (stə tis′tiks) *n.* information represented in numbers.

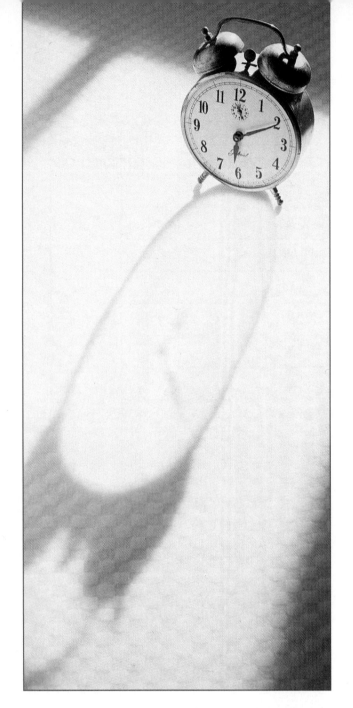

1. Put the piece of straw on the point of the thumbtack.

2. Place one hand, palm up, on a table top.

3. Put the straw-thumbtack apparatus on your wrist, on the outside edge. Move it about until you find the spot where your pulse is the strongest. You can tell because the straw moves more.

4. Count each time the straw moves up. Do this for fifteen seconds.

5. Multiply the number you counted by four. This will give you the number of times your heart beats in one minute.

If you know another way to take your pulse, that's fine too. When you do the experiment, take your temperature readings and pulse counts carefully all through the day. When you've got your chart completed, see how your information measures up to these follow-up questions.

Check with your parents for a quickie lesson about how to take your temperature and read the thermometer, if you're not sure. The average human body temperature is 98.6 degrees Fahrenheit, but not everyone has exactly that temperature normally. Don't be concerned if yours is a degree or two above or below this figure.

WHAT DOES YOUR CHART SHOW?

1. What's the lowest temperature you recorded all day?

2. What's the highest temperature?

3. How big a difference is there between these two readings?

4. At what time was the highest reading?

5. When was your temperature the lowest?

6. What was the slowest pulse reading you took?

7. What was the fastest pulse measurement?

8. When was your pulse the fastest?

9. When was it the slowest?

10. Can you see any relationship between when your pulse was fastest and when your temperature was highest?

According to scientists, your temperature should have been highest late in the afternoon or in the evening, and lowest in the early morning. Does your cycle agree with this? Also scientists say that most people have a 1½ to 2 degree <u>variation</u> all day. Was this true for you? Your pulse should have been lowest when you first got up, according to scientists. It should be highest at your usual time of greatest activity.

A STATISTICAL CAUTION

Remember, scientists did many, many tests before they came up with their conclusions. What you've done is just one sample of your daily cycle of temperature and pulse changes. Not only can your cycles differ somewhat from what the reported averages are, your own rhythms can change a bit from day to day. You've got a lifetime to spend with your body rhythms. Trying the experiment on another day will give you a chance to take another look.

---

variation (vâr′ē ā′shən) *n.* amount of change.

MEET

MARILYN BURNS

Time flies when you're having fun and drags miserably when you've got the flu. Marilyn Burns explains why in this excerpt from *This Book Is About Time.*

Burns's humor and chatty writing style are evident throughout the book, which is dedicated to "the tortoise, the hare, and anyone else who has ever had a run-in with time." Burns is one of a group of writers who works with educators and artists to create the Brown Paper School book series. The group believes that "learning happens only when it is wanted, that it can happen anywhere and doesn't require fancy tools." One book in this series, *The I Hate Mathematics! Book,* was named an Outstanding Science Book for Children.

RESPONDING TO Literature

THINK • TALK • WRITE

1 What did you learn in this selection? Note in your journal some facts you learned.

2 What is the main idea of this selection? Give details to support your opinion.

3 What are some of the things that affect our sense of time? Do you agree with the author's examples? Use examples from your own life to explain your opinion.

4 A *generalization* is a broad statement based on given facts. Based on the information in this selection, what is at least one generalization you can make?

5 The meaning of "lateness" varies from country to country. In some cultures, it is polite to be early for a party. In others, it is good manners to be late. How might this cause problems when people of different cultures meet? What solutions can you suggest?

ACTIVITIES

● **Write with Direct Address**
Some people are always late to the movies. Others talk during the film. Work in small groups to write a list of rules for a theater chain. Tell customers how to use the movie theater properly. Use direct address in the list of rules you write. Remember to be polite. You want people to continue to come to your theaters!

● **Clock Yourself** Keep a log of your most important daily activities for one week. Note each activity and how long it takes. Then assemble the results into a report about your daily cycles. In your report, include at least one chart, such as the amount of time you spend eating meals.

VOCABULARY PRACTICE

On a separate piece of paper, write the vocabulary word that is the best substitute for each italicized word or phrase.

biological   hassle
consumption   statistics
variation

1 You may see a *difference* in your pulse if you take it early one day and late the next.

2 Some people find it a real *problem* to wait for someone who is late.

3 The need to sleep is *related to the science of living things.*

4 The scientists made a chart to display *information in numbers.*

5 Your *intake* of food is linked to how much energy you use.

BEFORE READING

THE PHANTOM TOLLBOOTH

CONNECT TO LITERATURE

What do you do when you are bored? In your journal, record a surefire cure for a boring day. Then read the selection and see how Milo, the main character, escapes from the Doldrums.

THINKING ABOUT STYLE

Part of the fun of reading is finding an author whose style you like. *Style* is an author's own special way of writing. Style is revealed through sentence structure, sentence length, and word choice. For example, the author of this selection, Norton Juster, uses many synonyms—some of them quite silly—to increase the humor of the Lethargarians' language. Juster also emphasizes the humor of Milo's problem by using phrases or words *literally*. This means common phrases mean *exactly* what the words say. For example, his "watchdog" is a dog with the body of a watch. Look for other examples of the author's style as you read.

HAVE YOU EVER?

Have you ever thought about the phrases we use every day? Why is someone "under the weather"? Why do people ask if the cat has "got your tongue"? This selection features many common expressions. Such phrases sometimes come from history. For instance, a signature is a "John Hancock" because Hancock was the first signer of the Declaration of Independence and he wrote *very* large! Other common phrases are based on a mistake. That's why some people sign their "John Henry," not "John Hancock"! In a reference book of common phrases, find a "horse of a different color" and "birds of a feather." These phrases make English a colorful and fascinating language.

Meet Norton Juster

An architect who writes in his spare time, Norton Juster says about the book *The Phantom Tollbooth,* "I began to write what I thought was a short story—for my own relaxation. Before I knew it, it had created its own life and I was hooked. *The Phantom Tollbooth* was the result."

Juster says, "I am always a little embarrassed to call myself a writer." For, as he puts it, "The way I see things and think about things is as an architect." However, Juster has written a number of other books in addition to *The Phantom Tollbooth.*

The New York Times listed *The Phantom Tollbooth* as a best-selling children's book in 1962, as well as one of the fifty best books of 1960–1965. The book was made into a movie in 1970.

THE PHANTOM TOLLBOOTH

by Norton Juster
illustrated by David Goldin

*Milo comes home from school one day to find a
mysterious package waiting for him. In it he finds
a ready-to-assemble phantom tollbooth, complete with
a rule book and a map to strange lands that Milo has
never heard of before. Milo chooses Dictionopolis as
his destination, drives his toy car up to the tollbooth,
deposits a coin, and takes off on his fantastic voyage.
As Milo drives along, the unfamiliar landscape gets
grayer and grayer, Milo gets sleepier and sleepier, and
the car moves slower and slower until it finally stops.*

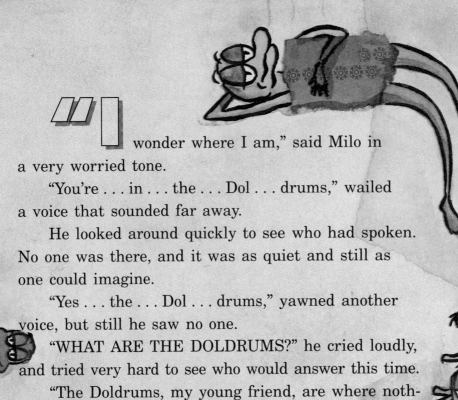

"I wonder where I am," said Milo in a very worried tone.

"You're . . . in . . . the . . . Dol . . . drums," wailed a voice that sounded far away.

He looked around quickly to see who had spoken. No one was there, and it was as quiet and still as one could imagine.

"Yes . . . the . . . Dol . . . drums," yawned another voice, but still he saw no one.

"WHAT ARE THE DOLDRUMS?" he cried loudly, and tried very hard to see who would answer this time.

"The Doldrums, my young friend, are where nothing ever happens and nothing ever changes."

This time the voice came from so close that Milo jumped with surprise, for, sitting on his right shoulder, so lightly that he hardly noticed, was a small creature exactly the color of his shirt.

"Allow me to introduce all of us," the creature went on. "We are the Lethargarians, at your service."

Milo looked around and, for the first time, noticed dozens of them—sitting on the car, standing in the road, and lying all over the trees and bushes. They were very difficult to see, because whatever they happened to be sitting on or near was exactly the color they happened to be. Each one looked very much like the other (except for the color, of course) and some looked even more like each other than they did like themselves.

"I'm very pleased to meet you," said Milo, not sure whether or not he was pleased at all. "I think I'm lost. Can you help me please?"

"Don't say 'think,' " said one sitting on his

shoe, for the one on his shoulder had fallen asleep. "It's against the law." And he yawned and fell off to sleep, too.

"No one's allowed to think in the Doldrums," continued a third, beginning to doze off. And as each one spoke, he fell off to sleep and another picked up the conversation with hardly any interruption.

"Don't you have a rule book? It's local ordinance 175389-J."

Milo quickly pulled the rule book from his pocket, opened to the page, and read, "Ordinance 175389-J: It shall be unlawful, illegal, and unethical to think, think of thinking, surmise, presume, reason, meditate, or speculate while in the Doldrums. Anyone breaking this law shall be severely punished!"

"That's a ridiculous law," said Milo, quite indignantly. "Everybody thinks."

"We don't," shouted the Lethargarians all at once.

"And most of the time *you* don't," said a yellow one sitting in a daffodil. "That's why you're here. You weren't thinking, and you weren't paying attention either. People who don't pay attention often get stuck in the Doldrums." And with that he toppled out of the flower and fell snoring into the grass.

Milo couldn't help laughing at the little creature's strange behavior, even though he knew it might be rude.

"Stop that at once," ordered the plaid one clinging to his stocking. "Laughing is against the law. Don't you have a rule book? It's local ordinance 574381-W."

Opening the book again, Milo found Ordinance 574381-W: "In the Doldrums, laughter is frowned upon and smiling is permitted only on alternate Thursdays. Violators shall be dealt with most harshly."

---

ordinance (ôr′də nəns) *n.* regulation or law made by a city or town government.

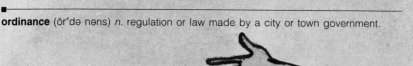

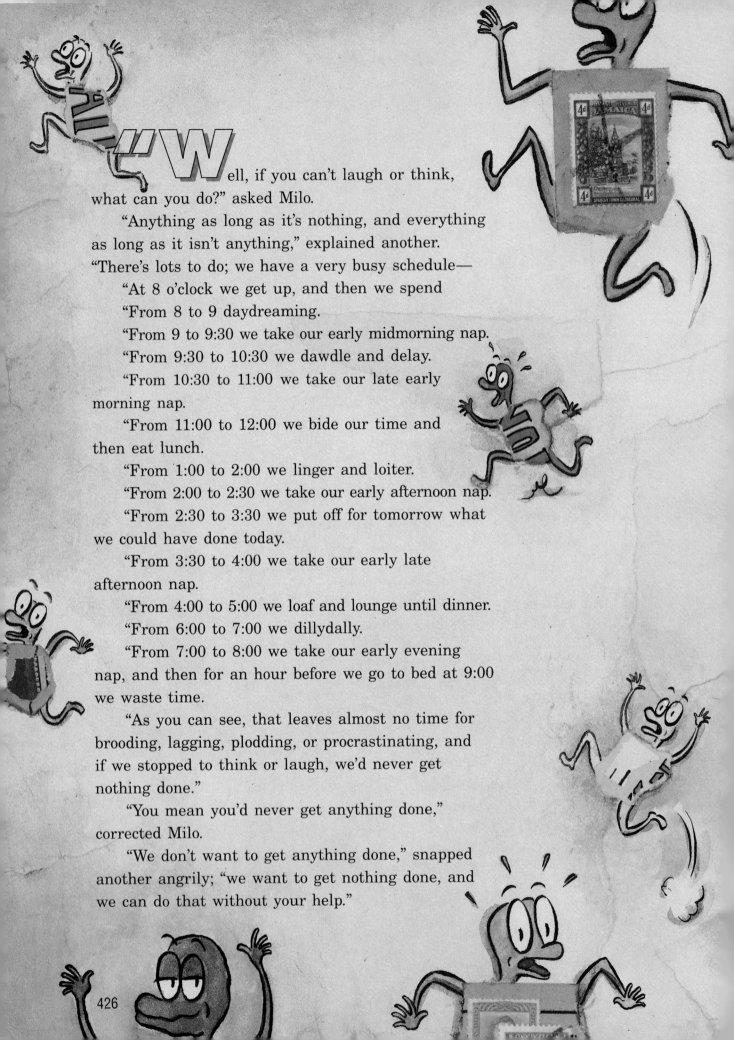

"Well, if you can't laugh or think, what can you do?" asked Milo.

"Anything as long as it's nothing, and everything as long as it isn't anything," explained another. "There's lots to do; we have a very busy schedule—

"At 8 o'clock we get up, and then we spend

"From 8 to 9 daydreaming.

"From 9 to 9:30 we take our early midmorning nap.

"From 9:30 to 10:30 we dawdle and delay.

"From 10:30 to 11:00 we take our late early morning nap.

"From 11:00 to 12:00 we bide our time and then eat lunch.

"From 1:00 to 2:00 we linger and loiter.

"From 2:00 to 2:30 we take our early afternoon nap.

"From 2:30 to 3:30 we put off for tomorrow what we could have done today.

"From 3:30 to 4:00 we take our early late afternoon nap.

"From 4:00 to 5:00 we loaf and lounge until dinner.

"From 6:00 to 7:00 we dillydally.

"From 7:00 to 8:00 we take our early evening nap, and then for an hour before we go to bed at 9:00 we waste time.

"As you can see, that leaves almost no time for brooding, lagging, plodding, or procrastinating, and if we stopped to think or laugh, we'd never get nothing done."

"You mean you'd never get anything done," corrected Milo.

"We don't want to get anything done," snapped another angrily; "we want to get nothing done, and we can do that without your help."

426

"You see," continued another in a more conciliatory tone, "it's really quite strenuous doing nothing all day, so once a week we take a holiday and go nowhere, which was just where we were going when you came along. Would you care to join us?"

"I might as well," thought Milo; "that's where I seem to be going anyway."

"Tell me," he yawned, for he felt ready for a nap now himself, "does everyone here do nothing?"

"Everyone but the terrible watchdog," said two of them, shuddering in chorus. "He's always sniffing around to see that nobody wastes time. A most unpleasant character."

"The watchdog?" said Milo quizzically.

"THE WATCHDOG," shouted another, fainting from fright, for racing down the road barking furiously and kicking up a great cloud of dust was the very dog of whom they had been speaking.

"RUN!"

"WAKE UP!"

"RUN!"

"HERE HE COMES!"

"THE WATCHDOG!"

Great shouts filled the air as the Lethargarians scattered in all directions and soon disappeared entirely.

**-R-R-G-H-R-O-R-R-H-F-F,"**
exclaimed the watchdog as he dashed up to the car,
loudly puffing and panting.

Milo's eyes opened wide, for there in front of him
was a large dog with a perfectly normal head, four
feet, and a tail—and the body of a loudly ticking
alarm clock.

"What are you doing here?" growled the watchdog.

"Just killing time," replied Milo <u>apologetically</u>.
"You see—"

"KILLING TIME!" roared the dog—so furiously
that his alarm went off. "It's bad enough wasting time
without killing it." And he shuddered at the thought.
"Why are you in the Doldrums anyway—don't you have
anywhere to go?"

"I was on my way to Dictionopolis when I got
stuck here," explained Milo. "Can you help me?"

"Help you! You must help yourself," the dog
replied, carefully winding himself with his left hind
leg. "I suppose you know why you got stuck."

"I guess I just wasn't thinking," said Milo.

"PRECISELY," shouted the dog as his alarm went
off again. "Now you know what you must do."

"I'm afraid I don't," admitted Milo, feeling
quite stupid.

"Well," continued the watchdog impatiently, "since
you got here by not thinking, it seems reasonable to
expect that, in order to get out, you must start thinking." And with that he hopped into the car.

"Do you mind if I get in? I love automobile rides."

Milo began to think as hard as he could (which
was very difficult, since he wasn't used to it). He
thought of birds that swim and fish that fly. He
thought of yesterday's lunch and tomorrow's dinner.

---

apologetically (ə pol′ə jet′i klē) *adv.* in a regretful way.

He thought of words that began with J and numbers that end in 3. And, as he thought, the wheels began to turn.

"We're moving, we're moving," he shouted happily.

"Keep thinking," scolded the watchdog.

The little car started to go faster and faster as Milo's brain whirled with activity, and down the road they went. In a few moments they were out of the Doldrums and back on the main highway. All the colors had returned to their original brightness, and as they raced along the road Milo continued to think of all sorts of things; of the many <u>detours</u> and wrong turns that were so easy to take, of how fine it was to be moving along, and, most of all, of how much could be accomplished with just a little thought. And the dog, his nose in the wind, just sat back, watchfully ticking.

"You must excuse my gruff conduct," the watchdog said, after they'd been driving for some time, "but you see it's traditional for watchdogs to be ferocious . . ."

Milo was so relieved at having escaped the Doldrums that he assured the dog that he bore him no ill will and, in fact, was very grateful for the assistance.

"Splendid," shouted the watchdog. "I'm very pleased—I'm sure we'll be great friends for the rest of the trip. You may call me Tock."

"That is a strange name for a dog who goes tick-tickticktickticktick all day," said Milo. "Why didn't they call you—"

---

detours (dē′tŭrz) *n., pl.* roundabout or indirect ways taken instead of the main road.

"**D**on't say it," gasped the dog, and Milo could see a tear well up in his eye.

"I didn't mean to hurt your feelings," said Milo, not meaning to hurt his feelings.

"That's all right," said the dog, getting hold of himself. "It's an old story and a sad one, but I can tell it to you now.

"When my brother was born, the first pup in the family, my parents were overjoyed and immediately named him Tick in expectation of the sound they were sure he'd make. On first winding him, they discovered to their horror that, instead of going tickticktickticktick, he went tocktocktocktocktocktock. They rushed to the Hall of Records to change the name, but too late. It had already been officially <u>inscribed</u>, and nothing could be done. When I arrived, they were determined not to make the same mistake twice and, since it seemed <u>logical</u> that all their children would make the same sound, they named me Tock. Of course, you know the rest—my brother is called Tick because he goes tocktocktocktocktocktocktock and I am called Tock because I go tickticktickticktickticktick and both of us are forever burdened with the wrong names. My parents were so <u>overwrought</u> that they gave up having any more children and devoted their lives to doing good work among the poor and hungry."

"But how did you become a watchdog?" interjected Milo, hoping to change the subject, as Tock was sobbing quite loudly now.

"That," he said, rubbing a paw in his eye, "is also traditional. My family have always been watchdogs— from father to son, almost since time began.

"You see," he continued, beginning to feel better, "once there was no time at all, and people found it

---

inscribed (in skrībd´) *v.t.* written, marked, or engraved on.

logical (loj´i kəl) *adj.* sensible; reasonable.

overwrought (ō´vər rôt´) *adj.* extremely excited or nervous.

very inconvenient. They never knew whether they were eating lunch or dinner, and they were always missing trains. So time was invented to help them keep track of the day and get places when they should. When they began to count all the time that was available, what with 60 seconds in a minute and 60 minutes in an hour and 24 hours in a day and 365 days in a year, it seemed as if there was much more than could ever be used. 'If there's so much of it, it couldn't be very valuable,' was the general opinion, and it soon fell into disrepute. People wasted it and even gave it away. Then we were given the job of seeing that no one wasted time again," he said, sitting up proudly. "It's hard work but a noble calling. For you see"—and now he was standing on the seat, one foot on the windshield, shouting with his arms outstretched—"it is our most valuable possession, more precious than diamonds. It marches on, it and tide wait for no man, and—"

At that point in the speech the car hit a bump in the road and the watchdog collapsed in a heap on the front seat with his alarm again ringing furiously.

"Are you all right?" shouted Milo.

"Umphh," grunted Tock. "Sorry to get carried away, but I think you get the point."

RESPONDING TO Literature

THINK • TALK • WRITE

1 Would you like to read the rest of the novel? Explain why or why not in your journal.

2 Describe the settings where Milo finds himself at the beginning and end of the selection. How is each setting important to the plot?

3 Do you know what the word *lethargy* means? If not, look it up in a dictionary. Why do you think Norton Juster called the creatures in the Doldrums "Lethargarians"?

4 Although Milo is surrounded by fantasy characters, he is a realistic character. Give at least three examples in which Milo acts as a typical boy might. Why do you think Juster used a realistic character in his fantasy story?

5 Milo suffers "culture shock" in the strange world of the Lethargarians. He is puzzled by the customs he sees there. How are his experiences like those of anyone who enters a new culture?

ACTIVITIES

- **Write with Style** Choose a common place-related phrase, such as "on cloud nine." Write a story in which the phrase is literally true. Use a writing style that makes your story entertaining to read.

- **Create a Travel Brochure** Work in small groups to design and illustrate a travel brochure for the Doldrums. Try to give the feeling of a place where nothing happens. Include drawings of local spots of interest. Display your brochure in class.

VOCABULARY PRACTICE

Choose the vocabulary word that best fits in each blank. Write the word on a separate piece of paper.

apologetically   detours

inscribed   overwrought

logical

The __1__ rabbit glanced at his watch anxiously and muttered, "I'm late. I don't have time to chat."

"I'm sorry to bother you again," Alice said __2__. "I just wondered if you could tell me why this stone is __3__ with such a strange saying."

"It's for persons who are taking __4__ from the regular path," the rabbit explained reluctantly.

"Then why does it make no sense?" asked the __5__ child. "It says, 'Turn left if you're right, and turn right if you've been left.'"

"It makes sense if you have cents," the rabbit said. Then he scurried off, leaving Alice even more puzzled than before.

Marie Lucille

That clock is ticking

Me away!

The me that only

Yesterday

Ate peanuts, jam and

Licorice

Is gone already.

And this is

'Cause nothing's putting

Back, each day,

The me that clock is

Ticking away.

—Gwendolyn Brooks

Ruby Green Singing *1928 James Chapin Norton Museum of Art, West Palm Beach, Florida*

SP⊙T on

DRAMA

When journalists describe an event as "dramatic," they usually mean exciting and memorable. Originally the word *dramatic* referred to events onstage—in dramas or plays. Plays depict a full range of exciting and memorable events, and thus the word *dramatic* has taken on a broader meaning.

King Kong atop the Empire State Building from the movie King Kong *1933*

Do you recognize this scene? What is the basic plot of the movie from which this scene is taken? If you have never seen the movie, what do you think the story might be like?

What is the setting of the scene? Why is the setting important?

What kind of character is King Kong? Which do you suspect is more important to the movie's plot—Kong's struggles with himself or his struggles with outside forces, including other characters?

Try to remember other movies and plays you have seen. What elements of those works apply to this photograph?

LIGHT

ELEMENTS OF DRAMA

ACTS AND SCENES are the way dramas are divided. Acts are like chapters in a book. Scenes are subdivisions of acts.

CHARACTERS are the people or animals who take part in a drama. The playwright can portray these characters in different ways.

- *Direct characterization* takes place when the playwright tells you how a character looks, acts, and thinks.
- *Indirect characterization* takes place when the playwright lets you draw your own conclusions about a character by how others react to him or her.

DIALOG is a conversation between two or more characters. In the script, or written version of a play, dialog is not in quotation marks, but follows the speaker's name.

PLOT is the series of connected events in a drama. Plot centers on conflict, which is a struggle between opposing forces.

- *External conflict* shows characters struggling against an outside force.
- *Internal conflict* shows characters battling a force within.

SETTING is the time and place in which the action of a drama occurs. Usually the setting of each scene is described directly.

STAGE DIRECTIONS instruct the actors where and how to move and speak. Stage directions are enclosed in parentheses and/or set in italic type in the script. Stage directions often describe *props,* the physical objects the actors use; *scenery,* the objects that help create the setting; and *lighting,* the degree and type of light used onstage.

THEME is the central message about life revealed in the drama.

- *Stated themes* are mentioned directly in the play.
- *Implied themes* must be inferred from the characters and their actions, the setting, and the conflict.

In the following play, you will explore these elements in greater depth.

DRAMA

RIP VAN WINKLE

CONNECT TO LITERATURE

What makes you lose all sense of time: Playing with friends? Reading? Watching sports? In your journal, write about an activity that turns hours into minutes for you. Then read the play "Rip Van Winkle," which Adele Thane adapted from Washington Irving's classic story. For Rip Van Winkle years passed like hours.

INTRODUCTION TO THE MODEL DRAMA

Every play shares certain elements. Like all works of fiction, plays usually have characters, setting, plot, and a theme. Because a play is meant to be performed, it also has stage directions. Most of the story is told through dialog spoken by the characters. A play is divided into acts, similar to chapters in a book.

As you read "Rip Van Winkle," use the notes in the margin. The notes point out and describe important elements in a play. As you read, jot down thoughts and impressions in your journal.

DID YOU KNOW?

• Washington Irving adapted *Rip Van Winkle* from a European folk tale. He reset the story in the Catskill Mountains in southeastern New York.

• King George III reigned over Great Britain from 1760 to 1820. He was king at the time of the American Revolution, or War of Independence, which lasted from 1775 to 1783.

• In 1765, the British Parliament passed the Stamp Act to raise tax money from the British colonies. Many colonists refused to pay the tax or to buy English goods. Parliament repealed the Stamp Act in 1766, but other taxes led to the American Revolution.

Rip Van Winkle

BY WASHINGTON IRVING   DRAMATIZED BY ADELE THANE
ILLUSTRATED BY GARY KELLEY

CHARACTERS

RIP VAN WINKLE

DAME VAN WINKLE, *HIS WIFE*

JUDY, *HIS DAUGHTER*

LUKE GARDENIER

KATCHEN } *JUDY'S PLAYMATES*

MEENIE, *A GIRL*

JACOB

NICHOLAS VEDDER, *LANDLORD OF THE KING GEORGE TAVERN*

DERRICK VAN BUMMEL, *THE SCHOOLMASTER*

PETER VANDERDONK } *MEN OF THE VILLAGE*

BROM DUTCHER

OFFSTAGE VOICE

HENDRIK HUDSON

SAILORS, *HUDSON'S CREW*

ORATOR

JONATHAN DOOLITTLE, *PROPRIETOR OF THE UNION HOTEL*

JUDITH GARDENIER, *JUDY GROWN UP*

LITTLE RIP, *HER SON*

TOWNSPEOPLE

CHILDREN

Notice the list of characters. Why do you think that plays include this list? The list of characters' names at the beginning of a play is called the **cast of characters.**

orator (ôr′ə tər) *n.* skilled public speaker.
proprietor (prə prī′i tər) *n.* owner or operator of a small business.

SCENE 1

TIME: *Early autumn, a few years before the Revolutionary War.*

SETTING: *A village in the Catskill Mountains. At left, there is an inn with a sign,* KING GEORGE TAVERN, *and a picture of King George III. A British Union Jack hangs on the flagpole.*

AT RISE: NICHOLAS VEDDER, DERRICK VAN BUMMEL, BROM DUTCHER *and* PETER VANDERDONK *are seated outside the tavern.* VEDDER *is sprawled back in his chair.* DUTCHER *and* VANDERDONK *are at the table, playing a game of checkers.* VAN BUMMEL *is reading aloud from a newspaper. From time to time, a rumble of thunder can be heard in the distance.*

VAN BUMMEL *(reading):* ". . . and it has been learned that Massachusetts favors a Stamp Act Congress to be held in New York to protest English taxation in the Colonies."

DUTCHER *(looking up from his game):* Good! It's high time we did something about this English taxation.

VANDERDONK: Taxes and more taxes! The English are a pack of rascals with their hands in our pockets.

VAN BUMMEL: There's even a <u>revenue stamp</u> on our newspapers. One of these days the people here in the American Colonies will revolt, you mark my words.

VEDDER *(pointing off right as a merry whistle is heard):* Well, here comes one man who is not troubled by these problems—Rip Van Winkle. (RIP VAN WINKLE *enters, a wooden bucket in one hand, his gun in the other. He props his gun against the tree trunk, then crosses to the group of men.)*

---

revenue stamp stamp indicating that the tax due on an item has been paid to the government.

Most plays are divided into **acts** and **scenes**. "Rip Van Winkle" is a one-act play with three scenes. As you read on, notice how the **setting,** or time and place, changes in each scene.

In a play, the words that describe the set and the actors' movements are called **stage directions.** Often, as here, stage directions are printed in italics.

Look at the words in lines next to the characters' names. These lines, called **dialog,** tell the actors what to say. Stage directions, enclosed in parentheses, are mixed in with dialog.

RIP: Good afternoon, Nick Vedder—Brom—Peter. *(to* VAN BUMMEL*)* Good afternoon, Mr. Schoolmaster. *(They return his greeting. There is a loud rumble of thunder and* RIP *cocks his head.)* Just listen to that, will you!

DUTCHER: We're probably in for a storm after this heat all day.

VEDDER: Sit down, Rip. Derrick is reading us the news.

VANDERDONK: How about a game of checkers, Rip?

RIP *(hesitating):* I don't know. Dame Van Winkle sent me for a bucket of water, but—maybe *one* game. *(He sets down the bucket and draws a stool up to the table, as* VANDERDONK *rises.)*

DUTCHER: Your move, Rip. *(Suddenly* DAME VAN WINKLE'S *voice is heard from off right.)*

DAME VAN WINKLE *(calling from off right):* Rip! R-i-p! *Rip Van Winkle!*

RIP: Oh, my galligaskins! It's my wife! *(Before he can get to his feet,* DAME VAN WINKLE *enters with a broom. She looks at the men, then crosses directly to* RIP.*)*

DAME VAN WINKLE: So this is how you draw water from the well! Sitting around with a lot of lazy good-for-nothing loafers. *(She tries to hit* RIP *with the broom.)* Pick up that bucket, you <u>dawdling</u> Dutchman, and fill it with water!

RIP *(snatching up the bucket and dodging out of the way):* Hey there, Dame, I'm not an old rug to be beaten with a broomstick.

DAME VAN WINKLE: Well, you might better be. An old rug is more use than you. At least it would keep our feet warm in winter, which is more than you can do. Little you care that your family is starving and the cow is gone.

RIP: The cow gone?

DAME VAN WINKLE: Aye, the cow is gone and the cabbage trampled down. When are you going to mend the fence?

RIP: It rained yesterday—

DAME VAN WINKLE: If excuses were <u>shillings</u>, we'd be rich!

RIP: I'll mend the fence—tomorrow.

DAME VAN WINKLE: Tomorrow, tomorrow! All your work is going to be done tomorrow! *(*RIP *goes to the well as she starts off right, still talking.)* You show enough energy when there's a <u>husking bee</u> or an errand to run for the neighbors, but here at home . . . *(She exits.* RIP *lowers his bucket into the well. The other men rise to go into the tavern.)*

VEDDER: Poor Rip! His wife has the scoldingest tongue in the Hudson Valley.

In a play, unlike other forms of fiction, the plot and the personalities of the characters are revealed largely through dialog. What does the dialog here tell you about Rip and his wife?

■
dawdling (dô′dling) *adj.* time-wasting; lingering.
shillings (shil′ingz) *n., pl.* former coins of the United Kingdom.
husking bee social event at which neighbors help peel the coverings off corn.

VAN BUMMEL: A sharp tongue is the only tool that grows <u>keener</u> with use.

DUTCHER: What would you do, Derrick, if you had a wife like Van Winkle's?

VAN BUMMEL: War could be no worse. I would enlist. *(They all laugh and exit through the door of the tavern.* RIP *turns to leave, then stops and smiles, as children's voices are heard off left.* JUDY, LUKE, KATCHEN, MEENIE, *holding a kite, and* JACOB, *carrying a bow, run in, left, and shout with delight when they see* RIP.*)*

CHILDREN *(ad lib):* There he is! There's Rip Van Winkle! *(etc. They surround him, chattering excitedly.)*

JUDY: Hello, Father, I've brought some of my friends.

RIP: Glad to see you, children.

JACOB *(holding out bow):* Oh, Rip, there's something wrong with my bow. Every time I go to shoot, the cord slips. *(*RIP *takes the bow, draws his knife from his pocket and cuts the notch deeper for the cord.)*

RIP: There, Jacob, try that, and see if it doesn't work.

JACOB *(pretending to shoot):* Yes, it's all right now.

MEENIE *(holding out kite):* My kite won't stay up, Rip.

RIP *(taking off part of the tail):* Now it will, Meenie—and this breeze is just right for it. *(He hands kite to* MEENIE.*)*

KATCHEN: My mother wants you to plug up her rain barrel, so she'll be able to wash next week.

RIP: Tell her I'll fix it tonight, Katchen.

LUKE: Rip, will you see what's the matter with my whistle? I made it just the way you showed me, but it isn't any good. *(He hands* RIP *a whistle.)*

RIP *(examining it):* You haven't whittled it right there, Luke. Here, I'll fix it for you. *(He sits on the bench under the tree and begins to whittle.)*

JUDY: Tell us a story, Father!

LUKE: Yes, you tell better stories than anybody in the Catskills. *(The children all gather around* RIP, *sitting on the ground.)*

---

keener (kē´nər) *adj.* sharper.

Rip: What shall it be about?

Jacob: Indians!

Katchen: I like witches and goblins best. *(A long roll of thunder is heard.)*

Judy: Oh, Father, hear that! Hear the thunder!

Rip: Why, don't you know what that is, Judy? That's <u>Hendrik Hudson</u> and his famous crew, playing ninepins up in the mountains. *(More thunder is heard.)*

Meenie: Oh, what a noise they make!

Rip: Yes, they are jolly fellows. They sail the wide sea over in their ship, the *Half-Moon,* then every twenty years they come back to the Catskills.

Jacob: What do they do that for?

Rip: Oh, old Hendrik Hudson likes to revisit the country he discovered and keep a watchful eye over his river, the Hudson.

Jacob: I wish I could see Hendrik Hudson and his crew.

Rip: Peter Vanderdonk says his father saw them once in their funny <u>breeches</u>, playing at ninepins up in the hills. (A loud peal of thunder is heard.) Listen to their balls rolling! That must be Hendrik Hudson himself, the Flying Dutchman! *(*DAME VAN WINKLE *enters with broom as* RIP *is speaking.)*

Dame Van Winkle: So! Here you are, telling stories without a word of truth in 'em! Oh, *I* could tell a story or two myself—about a <u>shiftless</u> husband who does nothing but whittle and whistle. Whittle and whistle! What a job for a grown man! *(She snatches the whistle from* RIP.*)*

Luke *(pleadingly):* It's my whistle! Please don't break it, Dame Van Winkle.

Dame Van Winkle: Take it and begone! *(She gives* LUKE *the whistle and he runs off.)* Judy, you go and ask Dame Vedder for an armful of wood. Your father is too busy spinning yarns to split wood for *our* fire. (JUDY *goes off behind the tavern.)* As for the rest of you, go home if you have any homes, and don't keep hanging around here like stray dogs for bones. *(She*

Hendrik Hudson, *also known as Henry Hudson* (d. 1611) English explorer of North America.
breeches (brich′iz) *n., pl.* trousers reaching to just below the knees.
shiftless (shift′lis) *adj.* lazy; lacking in ambition or energy; good-for-nothing.

sweeps the children off the stage with her broom.) Get along! Begone, all of you! Go home now! *(With arms akimbo, she faces* RIP.*)* Well, what do you have to say for yourself? *(*RIP *shrugs, shakes his head and says nothing.)* Nothing as usual. *(*RIP *goes to the tree for his gun.)* What are you getting your gun for? Going off to the mountains, no doubt. Anything to keep you out of the house.

RIP *(good-naturedly):* Well, wife, you have often told me—*my* side of the house is the *out*side. Where's my dog? Where's Wolf?

DAME VAN WINKLE: Wolf is tied up in the cellar.

RIP: You didn't tie up Wolf?

DAME VAN WINKLE: I certainly did. That dog tracked up my kitchen floor right after I'd finished scrubbing it. Well, if you're going hunting, go, and don't come back until you bring us something for supper. And if you can't bring any supper, don't bring yourself.

JUDY *(re-entering from up left, her arms full of logs):* But, Mother, it's going to rain.

DAME VAN WINKLE *(taking the wood):* Pooh! Your father won't get as wet as we will in the house, with the roof leaking and the windows broken. You hurry home now. And bring that bucket of water your father managed to get this far. *(DAME VAN WINKLE starts right, but JUDY stays behind with* RIP.*)*

RIP *(calling after his wife):* Wife, turn Wolf loose when you get home. *(DAME VAN WINKLE looks back at him angrily, tosses her head, and exits right.)*

JUDY *(starting to cry as she puts her hand in* RIP'S*):* Father, where will you go if it rains?

RIP: I'll find a place. Don't cry, Judy. Remember your little song? Come, we'll sing it together. *(They sing an appropriate folk song, such as "Rosa, Will We Go Dancing?")*

JUDY *(hugging* RIP*):* Oh, Father, I hope you have wonderful luck. Then Mother won't be so cross.

RIP: I don't blame her for being cross with me sometimes. I guess I don't do much work around here. But I'm going to do better, Judy. I'm going to do all the jobs your mother has been after me about.

DAME VAN WINKLE (*calling from off*): Ju-dee! Ju-dee!

RIP: There's your mother. I'd better be off. Goodbye, Judy dear. (*He walks left, whistling for his dog.*) Come, Wolf! Come, boy! (*A dog's bark is heard off left, as RIP turns, waves to JUDY, and exits.*)

JUDY (*waving*): Goodbye, Father. (LUKE *enters from right and joins* JUDY *as loud crash of thunder is heard. Startled,* JUDY *clings to* LUKE.) Oh, Luke, listen to that thunder!

LUKE: It's only Hendrik Hudson's men playing ninepins. Don't be scared, Judy.

JUDY: I'm not—that is, not very.

DAME VAN WINKLE (*calling from off*): Judy! Ju-dee!

LUKE: You'd better go in or you'll catch it. Your mother is getting awfully free with her broomstick lately. Here, I'll carry your bucket for you. (*He exits right with the bucket of water.* JUDY *lingers behind to look off in direction her father has taken as the thunder gets louder. Then humming softly to herself, she exits right.*)

CURTAIN

SCENE 2

TIME: *Later the same afternoon.*

SETTING: *A forest glade, high in the Catskill Mountains. There is a tree stump at right center, and a large bush at far left. This scene may be played before the curtain.*

AT RISE: RIP, *carrying his gun, enters left, dragging his feet wearily. He sinks down on the stump.*

RIP: Whew! That was a climb! All the way up the mountain. How peaceful it is up here. No one to scold me, no one to wave a broomstick. Ah, me! (*He gives a big sigh of* contentment.) I wonder where Wolf is. Wolf! Here, boy! (*He whistles and a dog barks off left.*) That's it, Wolf, sick 'em! I hope we get something this time. We can't go home until we do. (*A loud crash of thunder is heard.*) That thunder sounds much louder up here in the mountains than down in the valley. Maybe it's going to rain after all.

---

contentment (kən tent′mənt) *n.* state of being happy and content; satisfaction.

Voice *(calling from off, high-pitched, like a bird-call)*: Rip Van Winkle! *(Rip looks around wonderingly.)* Rip Van Winkle!

Rip *(rising)*: That's my name. Somebody is calling me.

Voice *(off)*: Rip Van Winkle!

Rip: Is it Dame Van Winkle? No—she would never follow me up here. *(Sound of a ship's bell is heard from off right.)* What was that? *(Bell rings again.)* A ship's bell! But how can that be? A ship? Up here in the mountains? *(He gazes off right, in astonishment.)* It *is* a ship! Look at it! Sails all set—a Dutch flag at the masthead. *(Ship's bell is heard again, fainter.)* There, it's gone. I must have imagined it. *(1ST SAILOR with a keg on his back, enters from right and goes to center, as RIP watches him in amazement.)* By my galligaskins, what a funny little man! And how strangely he's dressed. Such old-fashioned clothes! *(1ST SAILOR stops at center. RIP goes to meet him.)* Hello, old Dutchman. That keg looks heavy. Let me carry it for you. *(He relieves 1ST SAILOR of the keg.)* By golly, it is heavy! Why did you bring this keg all the way up here to the top of the mountain? And who are you, anyhow?

1st Sailor *(gruffly)*: Don't ask questions. Set it down over there. *(He points left to a spot beside the bush.)*

Rip *(obeying cheerfully)*: Anything to oblige. *(There is a commotion off right, and HENDRIK HUDSON and his crew enter, capering and shouting. They carry bowling balls and ninepins and a drum. 2ND SAILOR has a burlap bag containing drinking mugs thrown over his shoulder. RIP turns to 1ST SAILOR.)* Why, bless my soul! Here are a lot of little fellows just like yourself. *(to SAILORS, as they gather at center)* Who are you?

Sailors *(shouting)*: Hendrik Hudson and his merry crew!

Hudson *(stepping forward)*: Set up the ninepins, men, and we'll have a game. *(Two or three sailors set up the ninepins at extreme right. HUDSON speaks to the 1ST SAILOR.)* You there, fill up the flagons! *(2ND SAILOR opens sack and passes out the mugs. HUDSON turns to RIP.)* Now then, Rip Van Winkle, will you drink with us?

Rip: Why, yes, thank you, Captain Hudson. I'm quite thirsty after my long climb up the mountain. *(The mugs are filled from keg.)*

2nd Sailor *(raising his mug in toast)*: To Hendrik Hudson, the *Half-Moon*, and its merry crew!

ALL *(as they raise their mugs)*: To Hendrik Hudson, the *Half-Moon*, and its merry crew!

RIP *(lifting his mug)*: Well, gentlemen, here's to your good health. May you live long and prosper. (RIP *drinks and smacks his lips.*) Ah! This is the best drink I ever tasted, but it makes me feel very sleepy. (HUDSON *and his men begin to bowl. As they roll the balls, the thunder increases.* RIP *yawns.*) Ho, hum! I can't keep my eyes open. I guess I'll lie down—*(Carrying his gun, he goes behind bush at left, and lies down out of sight.* NOTE: *Unseen by audience,* RIP *may go offstage for necessary costume changes and return in time for his awakening.)*

HUDSON *(to* SAILORS*)*: Now, men, let's stop our game of nine-pins, and have a merry dance. Then we'll be off, to return again in twenty years. *(One of the men beats the drum, and* SAILORS *dance. At the end of the dance,* 1ST SAILOR *points to bush where* RIP *is sleeping.)*

1ST SAILOR: Look! Rip Van Winkle is asleep.

HUDSON: Peace be with the poor fellow. He needs to take a good long rest from his nagging wife. Sh-h-h-h! *(He places his finger to his lips and they all go about quietly gathering up the ninepins, balls, mugs, keg, etc., then they tiptoe off the stage, their voices dying away to a whisper. The lights may dim briefly to indicate the passage of twenty years, and recorded music may be played. When the lights come up,* RIP *is heard yawning behind the bush, then he stands up with great difficulty. He limps to center, carrying a rusty gun. His clothes are shabby, and he has a long white beard.)*

RIP *(groaning)*: Ouch, my back! It's so stiff. And my legs—just like pokers. My, my, but I'm shaky! I feel as if I'd grown to be an old man overnight. It must be <u>rheumatism</u> coming on. Oh, won't I have a blessed time with Dame Van Winkle if I'm laid up with rheumatism. Well, I'd better get along home to Dame Van Winkle. *(He looks at the gun he is carrying.)* Why, this rusty old thing is not my gun! Somebody has played a trick on me. *(suddenly <u>recollecting</u>)* It's that Hendrik Hudson and his men! They've stolen my gun, and left this rusty one for me! *(He puts his hand to his*

---

rheumatism (rü′mə tiz′əm) *n.* any of several diseases characterized by inflammation, swelling, and stiffness of the muscles and joints.

recollecting (rek′ə lek′ting) *v.t.* calling back to mind; remembering.

head.) Another scolding in store from the Dame. *(He whistles.)* Wolf! Here, Wolf! Have those scamps stolen my dog, too? He'd never leave me. *(He whistles again.)* Come on, old boy! Maybe he found it too cold and went home to be warmed by his mistress' broomstick. Well, I will follow after and get my hot welcome, too. *(He shoulders the rusty gun and totters off.)*

CURTAIN

SCENE 3

TIME: *Twenty years after Scene 1.*

SETTING: *Same as Scene 1, except that the sign above the tavern door reads:* UNION HOTEL—PROPRIETOR, JONATHAN DOOLITTLE. *A picture of George Washington has replaced that of King George III. Washington's name is printed below the picture and an American flag flutters on a pole above it.*

AT RISE: *An* ORATOR *is standing on a bench,* haranguing *a crowd of* TOWNSPEOPLE.

ORATOR: Remember the Boston Tea Party! Remember Bunker Hill! Who saved this country? Who is the father of this country?

TOWNSPEOPLE: George Washington! Washington for President! *(etc. They sing "Yankee Doodle.")*

> Father and I went down to camp
> Along with Captain Good'in,
> There we saw the men and boys
> As thick as hasty puddin'.
>
> Yankee Doodle keep it up.
> Yankee Doodle Dandy.
> Mind the music and the step
> And with the girls be handy.

*(*RIP *enters with a troop of children, who laugh and jeer at him.)*

---

haranguing (hə rang'ing) *v.t.* addressing with a long, noisy, often pompous speech.

CHILDREN *(ad lib):* Look at him! He looks like a scarecrow! Where did you come from, Daddy Long-legs? Where did you get that gun? *(etc.* RIP *and* CHILDREN *go to center.* 1ST CHILD *stands in front of* RIP, *and crouches down, pulling on an imaginary beard.)*

1ST CHILD: Billy goat, billy goat! (CHILDREN *begin stroking imaginary beards until* RIP *does the same. He is amazed to find he has a beard.)*

RIP: By my galligaskins, what's this?

2ND CHILD: It's a beard, old Father Time. Didn't you know you had a beard?

RIP: But I didn't have one last night. (CHILDREN *laugh and mock him.)*

ORATOR *(to* RIP*):* What do you mean by coming here at election time with a gun on your shoulder and a mob at your heels? Do you want to cause a riot?

RIP: Oh, no, sir! I am a quiet man and a loyal subject of King George!

CHILDREN AND TOWNSPEOPLE *(shouting, ad lib):* A spy! Away with him! Lock him up. *(etc.)*

JONATHAN DOOLITTLE *(stepping forward from crowd):* Hold on a minute! We must get to the bottom of this. *(to* RIP*)* Aren't you a supporter of Washington for President?

RIP *(puzzled):* Eh? Supporter of Washington? *(shaking his head, wholly bewildered)* I don't understand. I mean no harm. I only want to find my friends. They were here at the tavern yesterday.

DOOLITTLE: Who are these friends of yours? Name them.

RIP *(hesitantly):* Well, one is the landlord—

DOOLITTLE: *I* am the landlord of this hotel—Jonathan Doolittle.

RIP: Why, what happened to Nicholas Vedder?

1ST WOMAN *(pushing her way out of the crowd):* Nicholas Vedder? Why, he's dead and gone these eighteen years.

RIP: No, no, that's impossible! Where's Brom Dutcher? And the schoolmaster, Van Bummel—?

1ST MAN: Brom Dutcher was killed in the war at Stony Point.

2ND MAN: And Van Bummel went off to the war, too. He became a great general, and now he's in Congress.

RIP: War? What war?

2ND MAN: Why, the war we fought against England, and won, of course.

RIP: I don't understand. Am I dreaming? Congress? Generals? What's happened to me?

DOOLITTLE *(impatiently):* Now, we've had enough of this nonsense. Who are you, anyway? What is your name?

RIP *(utterly confused):* I don't know. I mean, I was Rip Van Winkle yesterday, but today—

DOOLITTLE: Don't try to make sport of us, my man!

RIP: Oh, indeed, I'm not, sir. I was myself last night, but I fell asleep on the mountain, and Hendrik Hudson and his crew changed my gun, and everything's changed, and I'm changed, and I can't tell what my name is, or who I am! *(*TOWNSPEOPLE *exchange significant glances, nod knowingly, and tap their foreheads.)*

2ND MAN *(shaking his head):* Hendrik Hudson, he says! Poor chap. He's mad. Let's leave him alone.

RIP *(in great distress):* Isn't there anybody here who knows who I am?

2ND WOMAN *(soothingly):* Why, you're just yourself, old man. Who else do you think you could be? *(*JUDITH GARDENIER *enters from left, leading* LITTLE RIP *by the hand. He hangs back, whimpering.)*

JUDITH: Hush, Rip! The old man won't hurt you.

RIP *(turning in surprise):* Rip? Who said Rip?

JUDITH: Why, I did. I was just telling my little boy not to be frightened.

RIP *(scanning her face):* And what is your name, my good woman?

JUDITH: My name is Judith, sir.

RIP: Judith? Did you say Judith? *(in great excitement)* And your father—what was his name?

JUDITH: Ah, poor man, his name was Rip Van Winkle. It's twenty years since he went away from home. We never heard of him again.

RIP *(staggered):* Twenty years!

JUDITH: Yes, it must be all of that. His dog came back without him. I was a little girl then.

RIP: And your mother—where is she?

JUDITH: My mother is dead, sir.

RIP *(sighing):* Ah, but that woman had a tongue! Well, peace be with her soul. Did you love your father, Judith?

JUDITH: With all my heart. All the children in the village loved him, too.

RIP: Then look at me. Look closely, my dear Judy. I am your father.

JUDITH *(incredulously):* You? My father?

RIP: We used to sing a little song together, remember? *(He sings a few lines from the folk song sung in Scene 1.)*

---

significant (sig nif′i kənt) *adj.* having special value or importance.
incredulously (in krej′ə ləs lē) *adv.* with disbelief.

JUDITH *(slowly):* Yes, my father used to sing that song with me, but many people know it.

RIP: Do you remember, Judy, that I told you the story of how Hendrik Hudson and his crew played ninepins in the mountains just before I went off hunting with Wolf?

JUDITH *(excitedly):* Yes! And Wolf *was* our dog's name! Oh, Father, it's really *you!*

RIP *(taking her in his arms):* Yes, my little Judy—young Rip Van Winkle once, old Rip Van Winkle now. (TOWNSPEOPLE *talk excitedly among themselves as they watch* RIP *and* JUDITH.)

JUDITH: Dearest Father, come home with me. Luke and I will take good care of you.

RIP: Luke?

JUDITH: Luke Gardenier, my old playmate. You used to make whistles for him and take him fishing. We were married when he came back from the war.

RIP: Ah, the war. There is so much I have to catch up with.

JUDITH: You will have plenty of time to do that—and you must tell us what happened to you.

RIP: Maybe you won't believe what happened to me, Judy— it was all so strange. (RIP *reaches out a hand to* LITTLE RIP, *who shyly takes it, and they start off left,* JUDITH *following. A loud clap of thunder stops them.* RIP *turns front and shakes his fist toward the mountains.)* Oh, no you don't, Hendrik Hudson! You don't get me back up there again. *(There is an answering roll of thunder that sounds like a deep rumble of laughter as the curtain falls.)*

THE END

Meet Washington Irving

Washington Irving (1783–1859) was born in New York City, the youngest of eleven children. His father, a veteran of the Revolutionary War, named his last-born after his commander-in-chief, George Washington.

As an adult, Irving worked as a lawyer for a few years, then considered becoming a painter. At the same time, he was writing essays and stories, but it wasn't until his mid-thirties that he published *The Sketch Book,* which contains the two stories for which he is best known, "The Legend of Sleepy Hollow" and "Rip Van Winkle."

Historic Hudson Valley, Tarrytown, New York

Meet Adele Thane

Adele Thane (born 1904) was bitten by the acting bug as a child growing up in Massachusetts. From 1953 to 1965 Thane directed and acted in a series of plays for children produced by a Boston television station. During this time, she began to publish one-act plays for children and teenagers. She has since written numerous one-act plays, including many adaptations of literary classics such as "Rip Van Winkle."

More Plays

- *Plays Children Love, Volume II: A Treasury of Contemporary and Classic Plays for Children,* edited by Coleman A. Jennings and Aurand Harris (St. Martin's Press, 1988). From "Charlotte's Web" to "Treasure Island," here are dramatizations of works of children's literature that have stood the test of time.

- *A Thousand Cranes,* drama by Kathryn Schultz Miller (Dramatic Publishing, 1990). Time has not erased the memory of Sadako Saski, a Japanese girl who developed radiation sickness as a result of the atomic bombing of Hiroshima at the end of World War II. This is the moving story of her struggle to survive.

- *Plays from Famous Stories and Fairy Tales* by Adele Thane (Plays, Inc., 1967). In this collection of twenty-eight plays, adapted by a well-known director of children's theater, you will find many to read and to perform.

RESPONDING TO *Literature*

THINK • TALK • WRITE

1 Think about the ending of the play. How do you think Rip Van Winkle feels after he gets used to the changes? Do you think he is happy? Why or why not? Jot some ideas in your journal.

2 Describe Rip from Dame Van Winkle's point of view. Then describe him from his own point of view. Is either point of view more accurate than the other? Explain why or why not.

3 Look back at the beginning of Scene 3 on page 449. Imagine you are watching the play. What are at least three clues that would help you figure out what has happened to Rip?

4 What is Rip Van Winkle's most important problem before he falls asleep? How have his problems changed when he wakes up? Explain your answers.

5 Over the course of twenty years, many changes took place in Rip Van Winkle's village. Compare and contrast the world Rip lives in when he goes to sleep with the world he sees when he wakes up. How are the two worlds different? How are the two worlds similar?

ACTIVITY

- **Write About a Play** Copy this story map onto a separate piece of paper. Use what you have learned about the elements of a play to complete the map for "Rip Van Winkle."

	Scene 1	Scene 2	Scene 3
Setting:			
Characters:			
Conflict:			

VOCABULARY PRACTICE

On a separate piece of paper, write whether the following pairs of words are *synonyms* or *antonyms*.

1 shiftless—hardworking

2 'orator—speechmaker

3 incredulously—disbelievingly

4 rushing—dawdling

5 proprietor—owner

6 unimportant—significant

7 sharper—keener

8 haranguing—calming

9 unhappiness—contentment

10 recollecting—remembering

WRITING

Have you ever seen a play, movie, or TV show that kept you on the edge of your seat? Have you ever seen one that you thought could have been done a lot better? Write a review of a play, movie, or TV show. Try to win your audience over to your point of view.

PREWRITE

How will you decide on what to review? In your writer's journal, list some plays, movies, or TV shows that come to mind. Jot down a few opinions about each. Then choose one.

The writer of our sample used this organizer to plan her review:

Position Statement	Sundays with Uncle Henry was the funniest, most entertaining play of the season at the Barkerville Children's Theater.	
Reasons	many hilarious moments, but it was also touching	the surprise ending of the play had everybody spellbound
Examples	Uncle Henry's birthday disguise	the stillness in the theater near the end; you could hear a pin drop
Conclusion	Sundays with Uncle Henry was an example of a perfect children's play: entertaining yet with a deep message.	

DRAFT

The author of our sample wanted a dramatic beginning for her review. Does it grab your attention?

The writer tries to make the reader feel what it was like to be at the play. Involving the feelings of the reader is a good strategy for persuasive writing.

> ### Sundays with Uncle Henry
>
> We laughed. We howled, tears came to our eye. During the performance of Sundays with Uncle Henry the audience went through every emotion.

Use your prewriting notes and organizer to begin your draft. Keep in mind how your audience will probably react to what you are writing.

A REVIEW

REVISE

Take a break. Then reread your draft. Does it read like a review? Will it win the audience over to your point of view? The writer thought adding these phrases would make the opening even stronger.

This detail makes the writer's meaning more precise. ----------▶ We laughed. We howled, tears *of tenderness* came to our eye. During the performance of

Using a phrase with the word *you* involves the reader directly with the writer's opinion. ----------▶ <u>Sundays with Uncle Henry</u> the audience went through every emotion. *you could imagine*

It's time to revise your draft. Are your reasons for liking or disliking the performance clear? Are they backed up by good examples?

PROOFREAD

Take note of the proofreading corrections the writer made. Does your review have any similar errors?

The author almost missed this run-on sentence. Check each of your sentences carefully to make sure they are not really two sentences. ----------▶ We laughed. We howled, tears *of tenderness* came to our eye. During the performance of <u>Sundays with Uncle Henry</u> the audience went through every emotion. *you could imagine*

Fix all the errors that could prevent others from enjoying your work. Find and correct spelling, punctuation, and grammar mistakes.

PUBLISH

The author submitted her review to the school newspaper. They accepted it for publication! How will you publish your writing? Could you combine it with the reviews of other classmates to create a collection of reviews? Discuss your publishing ideas together.

WRITING

ADDING INTERROGATIVE SENTENCES

ENRICH YOUR WRITING OF **REVIEWS.**

An interrogative sentence is a sentence that asks a question. Sometimes adding interrogative sentences to your reviews can help draw in your readers. Interrogative sentences can make readers feel as if their reactions to your ideas are important.

These paragraphs are the same except that Paragraph 2 has interrogative sentences at the end. How do these sentences affect the reader?

Paragraph 1

For most people, the joy of ballet comes from the acrobatic skill of the dancers. But there are those who want something more from this kind of dancing. Different people look for different things.

Paragraph 2

For most people, the joy of ballet comes from the acrobatic skill of the dancers. But there are those who want something more from this kind of dancing. How about you? What do you look for when you go the ballet?

PRACTICE 1 Respond on a separate piece of paper.

1 How does Paragraph 2 succeed in placing you "in" the review?

2 Substitute your own interrogative sentences for the end of the paragraph. Have you made the paragraph more interesting? Why or why not?

PRONOUN-ANTECEDENT AGREEMENT

REMEMBER THESE RULES ABOUT PRONOUNS AND ANTECEDENTS WHEN YOU ARE WRITING **REVIEWS.**

- A word or group of words that is referred to or replaced by a pronoun is known as the antecedent of the pronoun.

- Pronouns and their antecedents must agree in person, number, and gender.

PRACTICE 2 Substitute a pronoun for each italicized word or phrase. Then rewrite the sentence on a separate piece of paper.

1 The lights were bright, and the *lights* twinkled.

2 The ballerina won wild applause, and even the other dancers seemed to admire the *ballerina*.

3 Afterward, the dancers invited us to talk with the *dancers*.

4 Ballet looks easy, but *ballet* takes years of practice.

INDEFINITE PRONOUNS

USE THESE RULES ABOUT INDEFINITE PRONOUNS WHEN YOU ARE WRITING **REVIEWS.**

- An indefinite pronoun is a pronoun that does not refer to any particular person, place, or thing.

- Singular indefinite pronouns—such as *anyone,* take a singular verb. Plural indefinite pronouns—such as *all,* take a plural verb.

PRACTICE 3 Choose the correct verb. Then rewrite the sentence on a separate piece of paper.

1 Both of us (agree, agrees) with the review of the film.

2 No one (enjoy, enjoys) a poorly directed play.

3 Few (know, knows) what it takes to become a ballerina.

4 Each of us (has, have) a list of favorite films.

PROJECT 1

WRITING A SOCIAL STUDIES REPORT

In what time in the past would you like to have lived? What were the causes of some of the events of that period? Write a social studies report about something that happened during your favorite period in history.

PREWRITE

Read books or articles on your favorite period. Focus on a few major events. Make notes on what caused these events to happen. If you were writing about the Boston Tea Party in 1773, you might organize your events in a chain of cause and effect as in the diagram on the right:

DRAFT Discuss your piece with a partner. Is your topic specific enough? Should you narrow it down to a less complex historical event?

REVISE How does your piece read? Are there any missing details? Is it well organized and accurate?

PROOFREAD Check the spelling of historical names and places. Check dates, too.

PUBLISH Tell other students about your piece. Maybe your work could be combined into a collection of readings about that particular time in history.

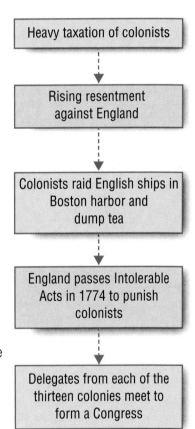

Heavy taxation of colonists

Rising resentment against England

Colonists raid English ships in Boston harbor and dump tea

England passes Intolerable Acts in 1774 to punish colonists

Delegates from each of the thirteen colonies meet to form a Congress

---

▶ *Proofreading Alert!*

Never use an apostrophe with possessive pronouns. Check page 157 in *Spotlight on Success: Writing and Language Handbook.*

PROJECTS

USE PHOTOS TO SHOW HOW TIME PASSES

REMEMBER TO: • PREWRITE • DRAFT • REVISE • PROOFREAD • PUBLISH

Use photos and captions to show the passage of time in your life or a friend's life. Gather a series of photos of yourself or a friend. Arrange them from earliest to most recent. If the photos show a friend, have him or her check the order and help with the captions.

A time line might help you organize your photos and write your captions. Note something about each photo on your time line:

1	**2**	**3**	**4**	**5**
August 1986: at 1 year	August 1991: 6th birthday party	February 1993: Ellen and I, 4th grade	June 1994: the class picnic	March 1995: with the flu

MAKE A CALENDAR ABOUT THE SEASONS

REMEMBER TO: • PREWRITE • DRAFT • REVISE • PROOFREAD • PUBLISH

How does your town or city change with the seasons? Make a calendar for the year to come.

Divide into twelve groups and have each group decide how to decorate its page. Group members can call out words and phrases associated with their month and put their suggestions in a "word bank." Use the "word bank" as a source of ideas for what to put on your calendar page.

WORD BANK FOR OCTOBER		
red leaves and wind	apples	Halloween
acorn squash	football	blankets
election campaigns	sweaters	raking lawn

VIEWP

YEAR-ROUND SCHOOL

The time you spend in school is important for your future. You're not just getting an education; you're also learning how to work with your classmates. Think about how much you learn and do while you're in school. Now think about how little time you actually spend there throughout the year. If you count up all your vacation days and the long summer break, you probably spend four months of every year away from school. If learning is so important, then why are students spending so much time off from it?

CONSIDER THIS ISSUE: Everyone in your community wants to improve the quality of education in the schools. One suggestion is to make the school year twelve months long. What do you think about year-round school? Consider both sides of the issue.

- Don't students deserve a long vacation away from school during the summer?
- Wouldn't all students learn more if they spent more time in school?
- Isn't it better for teachers to be able to offer more in-depth courses and to devote more time to each student?
- Isn't it easier for parents to know their children are being supervised at school all year?

O I N T S

Read the following viewpoints about the issue of year-round school. Decide which opinion is closest to your own. Think of more arguments yourself to support the position you choose.

VIEWPOINT 1   I don't think students should go to school year-round.

- Teachers and students need a break from each other. Time to rest from schoolwork is as important as studying.
- Many students use their summer vacations to do things such as going to camp or spending time with their families.
- For students who work hard during the school year, the summer vacation is a reward for their efforts.

VIEWPOINT 2   I think there should be year-round school.

- We go to school to learn, and the more time we spend there the better educated we'll be.
- Students who have problems with schoolwork would benefit from a slower learning pace and more time to practice.
- More advanced students could use the extra time to work on their own projects or to take special courses.

VIEWPOINT 3   Year-round school would benefit parents, teachers, and students.

- Working parents would rather have their children in school than have them waste their time watching television or hanging out.
- Teachers would have more time to work with their students and could give them extra help when necessary.
- Students would work harder throughout the school year. Under the current system, many students begin to slow down in the spring because of the coming summer vacation.

WHAT DO YOU THINK?

Spend a few minutes thinking about this issue. Do you share one of the viewpoints above, or do you have another? Discuss your opinion with a small group of students.

real life
CONNECT

TIME: It's both the dimension in which we live our lives and the yardstick with which we measure them.

"Time's money!" "Have you got time?" "Just in time!" Time means different things to different people. For some, it's a measurement that locates the events of their lives. We can value time or waste it. It can pass slowly, as it does for Libby in "Your Three Minutes Are Up" when she is waiting for Mark to call. On the other hand, as Rip Van Winkle found out, twenty years can seem like an afternoon's nap!

No matter how time affects you, you have to have some way of measuring it. People have been trying to do exactly that for centuries. Look at this ad. It shows one way people keep time.

A good **advertisement** works like the topic sentence of a paragraph. It highlights important facts briefly and clearly. Ads are designed to attract attention and persuade consumers to buy particular products or services. Print ads, combining a picture with a brief description, are found in many places, including newspapers, magazines, catalogs, and the Yellow Pages.

466

I O N S

Here are three activities that use advertisements. Think of other ways in which ads are important to you. Then choose an activity below or one of your own and talk or write about it.

PROJECT 1

AN AD COLLAGE The same object, service, or place can be advertised in a variety of ways. Make a collage of print ads that refer to one product or service. Use a variety of sources, including newspapers, magazines, and catalogs. Paste the ads on a piece of heavy cardboard or posterboard. You can include your own ads in the collage as well. Display your completed collage in class.

PROJECT 2

WRITE AN AD Advertisements attract our attention in a variety of ways. Write an ad for an object that you use every day. Come up with an interesting way to present the object so that the ad will attract attention. You can include a picture or photograph in addition to a brief description of the item. Display your ads, and discuss in class how they are alike and how they are different.

PROJECT 3

COMPARE ADS Some ads are more effective than others. Work in small groups to brainstorm a list of questions for evaluating an ad. For example: What is the ad trying to get you to do? What do you remember about the ad? Each student in the group should use the list of questions to evaluate the same ad. Discuss reactions to the ads.

Belo

Early Carolina Morning *1978 Romare Bearden Private Collection*

nging

PAST

I have all these parts stuffed in
                                                    me
like mama's chicken
                            and
                    biscuits,
                            and
daddy's apple pie, and a tasty
                                        story
from the family
            tree.
But I know that tomorrow
                            morning
        I'll wake up
            empty, and hungry for that
                                                next
                                                    bite
        of my new
                    day

—Arnold Adoff

Belonging

BEFORE READING

TALKING ABOUT STEPFAMILIES

CONNECT TO LITERATURE

Do you know any stepfamilies—
either your own or a friend's? How
are stepfamilies like other families?
How are they different? Describe
your thoughts in your journal, and
then read the selection to find out
more about the adjustments involved
in joining a stepfamily.

THINKING ABOUT AUTHOR'S PURPOSE

Every author has a reason for writing. This reason is called the
author's purpose. Different authors have different purposes—to
entertain, to inform, to persuade.

Maxine B. Rosenberg shows the same stepfamily from the point
of view of two of its members. Each person describes his feelings and experiences as part of a stepfamily. As you read the
selection, see if you think the author has achieved her purpose
for writing.

DID YOU KNOW?

This selection is an excerpt from the book *Talking About Stepfamilies.* The number of stepfamilies in our country continues
to increase.

- In the United States, one out of five children under the age of
  18 is a stepchild.

- About one out of four children under the age of 18 lives with
  only one parent.

- About one-half of all marriages in the United States today end
  in divorce.

Maxine B. Rosenberg

"A handicapped child, an adopted one, a twin, a child emigrating from another country or a child born of two races, all have joys and pains they want to share. By putting their feelings in books," Maxine Rosenberg says, "I offer children in special situations the comfort of knowing there are others like them." Many people have told Rosenberg that her books have helped them feel better about themselves.

Rosenberg's desire to be a writer began when she adopted a Korean child and recorded the experience in a journal. Now the author of several books, she declares, "I'm so happy with what I do that often I have to remind myself that this is my job." Two of her books, *My Friend, Leslie* and *Growing Up Adopted*, were named American Library Association Notable Books.

MANY YOUNG PEOPLE IN THIS COUNTRY— ALMOST ONE-FIFTH OF THOSE UNDER THE AGE OF 18—LIVE IN STEPFAMILIES. IN THIS SELECTION, DOUGLAS AND OWEN SHARE THEIR THOUGHTS AND FEELINGS ABOUT THEIR STEPFAMILY.

TALKING About STEPFAMILIES

by Maxine B. Rosenberg

DOUGLAS

"A house should be peaceful."

"About five years ago, my parents got divorced. When they decided to break up, I felt miserable most of the time. Suddenly, after doing so well in school, I lost interest in my work, and my grades began to slip. Mostly I dreaded hearing my parents argue with each other. They just couldn't get along, and that's why their marriage fell apart.

"It was also hard not knowing any other children in the same situation. My friends acted as if I was weird. They couldn't understand what was going on in my life, but neither could I. A year and a half later, when Dad told me he was marrying Pat, I was relieved to be back in a family. I thought he and Pat could make things work. In my mind, marriage was supposed to last. It was my parents who were strange for divorcing."

Since his parents' separation and divorce, Douglas and his older brother, Daniel, have alternated homes each week. "When their marriage broke up, Mom moved into her own apartment, while Dad kept the house. Because they lived so close to each other, joint custody worked out.

"In my opinion, switching homes every week is rotten. Of all the things that happened because of the divorce, that's been the hardest for me. I'm better adjusted to it than I was, but it's still confusing.

"At Dad's I live with three rowdy brothers—Daniel plus my stepbrothers, Owen and Eric— and our dog, Rudy. There, my bedtime is eleven o'clock. When I go to Mom's, I'm in a totally different atmosphere. Her house is so quiet with just the two of us, since Daniel's usually off with his friends. Bedtime at Mom's is ten o'clock. After having been at Dad's, I'm not tired then, so for the first night or two, I have trouble falling asleep. When I finally get settled in, I have to move again."

To make his life easier, Douglas keeps clothing at both places. But each week he has to bring some extras, depending upon the weather or school activities. "It never fails that I forget one small thing and have to

---

rowdy (rou′dē) *adj.* lively and rough; disorderly.
stepbrothers (step′bru<u>th</u>′ərz) *n., pl.* sons of one's stepparents by a former marriage.

475

go back to the other house to get it. That can be a real pain, especially for the person who has to drive me.

"Having two different homes can be embarrassing, too. Sometimes in school I'm asked to write on forms that don't have enough lines for my two different addresses. It's annoying having to explain why I need another sheet of paper."

Once his father married Pat, Douglas had another adjustment to make: living with two stepbrothers. In the beginning there were many awkward situations. "Although I feel close to Owen and Eric today, it didn't happen overnight. During those early months, I had no idea what to talk about with them or how we should play together. Gradually, we worked things out.

"One thing in particular helped us get along better—our dog, Rudy. From the moment he arrived, we shared responsibilities: feeding and walking him, and cleaning up his mess. Rudy was the one subject we didn't fight about. We even played with him together without arguing."

When Douglas and Daniel's father remarried, Owen and Eric began attending their stepbrothers' school. "Owen and I were both in fourth grade, but in different classes. On the first day of school, I introduced him to my friends as my stepbrother, not knowing how they would react.

"One thing in particular helped us get along better— our dog, Rudy."

"We're good athletes. The only time we compete is when we're playing on opposite teams."

Fortunately, Owen gets along well with everybody and was quickly accepted. Since he's also good in sports, it made it easier for him to join in. Pretty soon I started thinking of him as my school friend, rather than my stepbrother.

"Now Owen and I are in seventh grade, and we do well. We both have lots of friends; some we share, and some we don't. And we're good athletes. The only time we compete is when we're playing on opposite teams.

"The best thing about having Owen for a stepbrother is that we're the same age. That means we can help each other in math or go to parties together. Although we're not biologically related, Owen's definitely part of my family.

"Having lived with him and Eric for four years, I'm glad they're my stepbrothers. Even though we have different last names I consider them my brothers.

"Still, the stepfamily arrangement is not always easy. For one thing, being the youngest and smallest of the kids, I get all the hand-me-downs. Of course, if I *really* need something, Mom or Dad will get it for me, but first I have to explain why it has to be something new.

"Also, because Owen is seven months older than I, he thinks of himself as my big brother and sometimes acts a little <u>cocky</u>. And because he's older, things happen to him first. Although I started Hebrew school before he moved here, he had his Bar Mitzvah and got all the attention and gifts ahead of me. While I'm looking forward to my celebration, I wish it had come before his."

As for his relationship with Pat, Douglas liked her from the start—even before she married his father. "I'd see Pat when I was staying at Dad's house and she'd come to visit. One weekend, after Pat and Dad had been dating for a while, her family and ours got together and played baseball. While I can't remember anything about the wedding day, I'll never forget that baseball game. It was great.

"Of all the adults in my family now, I have the most fun with Pat. She's home more than the others because she doesn't work, so I get to do a lot of things with her. Since we're the only two who like eating Thai food, we go to those restaurants together. More than that, Pat gives me a lot of attention. Besides being a nice person and a great cook, she's a good listener."

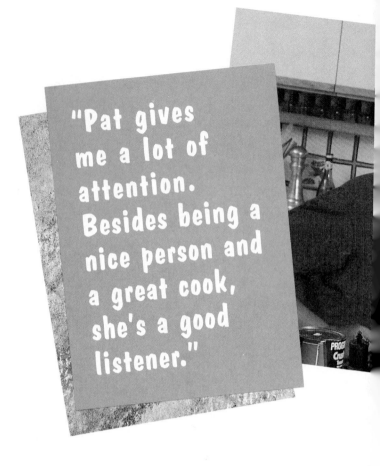

"Pat gives me a lot of attention. Besides being a nice person and a great cook, she's a good listener."

The only time Douglas becomes uncomfortable with his stepmother is when the subject of his parents' divorce comes up. "Pat takes my father's side and sees things from his point of view. But I remember *both* of my parents arguing all the time, so I can't say who's most at fault.

"Anyhow, my mother will always be my parent, and that will never change. I guess that's why I don't like anyone talking badly about her. Sometimes Mom does things that upset me, but other times she's there when I need her. While I realize that she and Dad couldn't make it together, at least I know they both love me.

---

cocky (kok′ē) *adj. Informal.* too confident; self-confident in a swaggering way.

"When Dad married Pat, I thought I'd finally be in a normal family. In my head, a divorced family was peculiar. Thinking about my life today, I see that I've landed in a more unusual setup than I expected. But fortunately, things have turned out all right.

"Still, I have some questions about my future. After all I've been through, marriage might be a problem for me. I wouldn't want to get divorced and go through the kind of arguing I heard between Mom and Dad. I'll never forget how upset Mom was at that time."

Arguing—especially between his parents—continues to make Douglas anxious. "Once in a while Mom and Dad have a fight on the phone. Usually they disagree about small things. Even so, I don't like to hear them raise their voices. It reminds me of what went on during the divorce years. Thank goodness they're much better than they used to be, and I can count on them getting along in public.

"Pat and Dad have fights, too, but just little ones. Still, that makes me nervous. I think, What if *they* don't make it?"

In Douglas's <u>fantasies</u>, the ideal family would include a dog like Rudy, a cute baby girl like his new cousin, two nice brothers who have the same ability in sports and can have fun together, and, to make life easier, the original parents. "Most important, everyone has to get along. I realize families have to have an occasional fight, but a house should be peaceful.

"As for being in a stepfamily, I've pretty much gone with the flow. Now I can't imagine what I'd be like if Pat, Owen, and Eric hadn't come into my life. Surely I'd be a different person than I am today, and I'm happy to be me. That alone makes me believe that everything will work out in my future."

---

fantasies (fan′tə sēz) *n., pl.* imaginative hopes and dreams.

Owen's father died when he was six months old. "I have a lot of pain when I think about my dad. And for a long time I was angry that he died. Mom took me to a <u>therapist</u> when I was in second grade, and after going for three years, I felt much better."

While Owen was in therapy, his mother started dating Ron. "Mom had gone out with lots of guys, but she liked Ron the best. Still, I had no idea how serious she was with him or what the man was really like. The few times I spoke to him were when he came to our apartment to pick Mom up. He seemed nice.

"Then one day Mom told me that Ron had invited the three of us to his house. I suspected something was up because my older brother, Eric, agreed to come along. That Sunday visit made an impression on me. Even though Eric and I had never met Daniel and Douglas—Ron's two boys—before, we all had a lot of fun playing baseball."

After that weekend the two families went on ski trips together, visited museums, and even shared holidays. When Owen's mother had known Ron for a year, she told Owen and Eric that she would be getting married the following September. "Mom also announced that, three weeks before the wedding, we would be moving into a new house in the suburbs. That way Eric and I could begin the school year with everyone else. Although Eric was upset about leaving the city, it didn't bother me. In a way, I was ready for the change. In fact, I had no objections to anything she told us. Having never been in a stepfamily, I couldn't imagine what it would be like—good or bad—and decided to wait and see.

"But moving before the wedding scared me to death. What if Mom suddenly decided not to go through with the marriage, after giving up our apartment and her job, and switching our schools? Thank goodness everything turned out well, but those were three long weeks.

"After that, my life changed. Until Mom's marriage, there were just three people in my house. Within minutes, our family doubled in size."

Before Owen's mother married Ron, the two families met a few times so everybody could talk about their concerns. While

---

therapist (ther'ə pist) *n.* doctor or other person who treats stress, grief, or mental disorders.

OWEN

"There's no way to predict how things will work out."

Owen doesn't remember what was discussed at these meetings, he says they at least helped him feel more comfortable with his future stepfather. "There's no way to predict how things will work out. You have to live with people to understand what they're about. For me, the biggest issue became getting used to a second adult in the house. For almost my entire life, I only had to listen to my mother. Now suddenly Ron was in charge, too, and he did things differently from the way I had been brought up.

"From the start, Ron was stricter than Mom. While he wasn't real harsh, he grounded me or sent me to my room when I misbehaved. Even today, he punishes me that way.

"Mom, on the other hand, was always lenient with Eric and me. As soon as she remarried, though, *she* started disciplining us more, too. It took me a while to get used to this, and I'm still not thrilled with how she's changed.

"What makes it harder is that my stepfather relaxes the rule when it comes to disciplining Douglas. I admit that Douglas doesn't talk back to his father as much as I do, but it's still not fair."

Despite these feelings, Owen has no fantasies about living with his biological father instead. "Maybe if I had known my dad better, I would feel differently. But there's no sense wishing for the kind of person who may never have existed. I was so young when Dad died that I have no memories of him. Whatever I create in my mind about him is just make-believe.

---

misbehaved (mis′bi hāvd′) *v.t.* conducted oneself badly.

lenient (lē′nē ənt, lēn′yent) *adj.* not harsh; tolerant.

"At least with all the people in my family today, I don't get bored around here. But at times it's hard living with so many different personalities. I never realized how much energy it takes learning how to behave with each individual. It can be years before some things are worked out. Truthfully, if I had to do it over, I would have been less cautious with my stepbrothers. It's easy to say that now, because I trust them and like them a lot. When I first met them, though, I kept my distance."

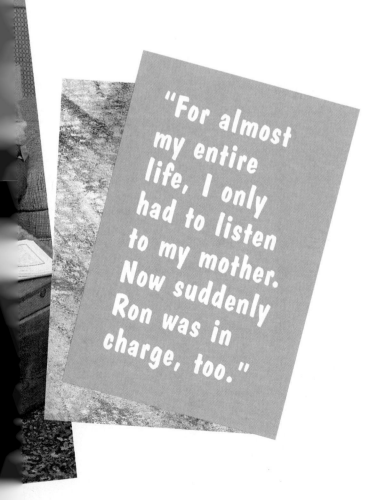

"For almost my entire life, I only had to listen to my mother. Now suddenly Ron was in charge, too."

Owen's acceptance of his stepbrothers was complicated by the fact that he and Douglas were in the same grade (as were Eric and Daniel). And Owen's stepbrothers live alternate weeks with their mother. "Even though it's hectic with the four of us together, in some ways it's easier for me. The weeks Douglas and Daniel are away, Eric and I fight. But when Eric has Daniel to hang out with, my brother and I get along pretty well.

"I've discovered other advantages to having a big family, too. For one, there's a variety of people around, and always someone to do something with. If I want to shoot baskets, I ask Eric and Daniel, who are stronger and more challenging. If I want to walk around the village, I choose Douglas, since we're in the same grade and have a lot in common. When I need to talk to somebody, I go to Daniel, who's interested in what I have to say. I have fun with my brother, Eric, too, but unfortunately he insists on treating me like a kid."

Owen noticed a big change in his feelings about his family after they spent a summer

> "We all agree about what's good for our dog. Nobody complains when it's his turn to take Rudy out."

vacation together. "Two years ago, the six of us went to the beach. With everyone away from the house, school, and work, we were all much calmer. By the end of the holiday I started thinking about Douglas and Daniel as my real family.

"Other changes—some big, some little—helped me enjoy being with the family more, too. For one, I disliked family meals because they were so noisy. Then, a few months ago, Mom started serving in the dining room. Somehow the formal setting quieted everyone down. Although we haven't turned into

saints, we have fewer arguments than before. Now when Mom calls us to eat, I think of the event as a special occasion.

"Getting a dog—Mom's idea—helped cement the combined families. When Rudy came to our house, everyone was immediately attached to him. Even Eric, who's not the most gentle, laid-back person, acted mellow around Rudy. While we're a family that can argue over silly things, we all agree about what's good for our dog. Nobody complains when it's his turn to take Rudy out.

"Another thing that helped my family become closer was my interest in Judaism, and my Bar Mitzvah. I owe that to Ron and

---

laid-back (lād′bak′) *adj. Slang.* casual; relaxed; easy-going.

his sister's strong religious feelings. Mom was never all that religious and she hadn't bothered to enroll Eric or me in Hebrew school. But Ron took Douglas and Daniel to Sunday school. I watched them go each week and, having nothing to do, asked Mom if I could join, too. From the start I enjoyed the whole experience. While a lot of the kids in the class griped that Hebrew school was a drag, I didn't mind it at all. In fact, I'm still going, even though I already had my Bar Mitzvah."

At Owen's Bar Mitzvah, all of Ron's relatives and Owen's, too, were together in one place for the first time. "It meant so much to me that I decided to make that the subject of my speech. And now that I know a lot about the holidays, celebrating them is more special. Sometimes Ron's parents, Grandpa Lou and Grandma Belle, come up from Florida, which is even better.

"Because all of us have worked so hard, my stepfamily situation has improved. Years back, I never would have dreamed that I could feel the way I do about everyone I live with today. Now that I'm getting older I understand that, although my stepfamily and I are not related by birth, it's still possible to feel very close to each person."

---

griped (grīpd) *v.i. Informal.* complained; grumbled.

"I never would have dreamed that I could feel the way I do about everyone I live with today".

RESPONDING TO *Literature*

THINK • TALK • WRITE

1 Suppose you could ask Douglas and Owen one question each. What would you ask? Jot your questions in your journal.

2 Whose points of view are presented in "Talking About Stepfamilies"? Why do you think that Rosenberg chose these people to represent their family?

3 Compare and contrast Douglas's and Owen's feelings about their blended family. In what ways do they agree? In what ways do they disagree?

4 Think about the selection. What advice would you give a friend who was about to live in a stepfamily? Support your advice with quotes from the selection.

5 Do you remember reading about Owen's Bar Mitzvah? This is a Jewish coming-of-age ceremony. After a Bar Mitzvah, a Jewish boy is treated as a man. What other coming-of-age ceremonies do you know about? Have you attended any? Does your family celebrate any? Write about your experiences.

ACTIVITIES

● **Write About Author's Purpose** A newspaper contains pieces meant to entertain (features, arts articles), inform (news stories), and persuade (editorials, letters to the editor). Work in small groups to create a class newspaper that contains at least one example of each type of writing.

● **Make a Family Tree** Make a family tree—for your own family or for Douglas and Owen's.

VOCABULARY PRACTICE

rowdy   fantasies

misbehaved   lenient

griped

On a separate sheet of paper, write the letter of the word that is *least* like the other words in the set.

1 **a.** peaceful   **b.** rowdy
    c. calm   **d.** relaxed

2 **a.** griped   **b.** complained
    c. argued   **d.** complimented

3 **a.** fantasies   **b.** dreams
    c. illusions   **d.** reality

4 **a.** polite   **b.** courteous
    c. misbehaved   **d.** controlled

5 **a.** harsh   **b.** easygoing
    c. friendly   **d.** lenient

BEFORE READING

MANIAC MAGEE

CONNECT TO LITERATURE

What would you do if a bully tried to pick a fight with you? In your journal, write how you might handle a difficult situation with a bully. Then read "Maniac Magee" to see what happens when Maniac, the main character, runs into two bullies in one day.

THINKING ABOUT EXAGGERATION

An *exaggeration* is a deliberate overstatement—for example, "It's so hot outside that you could fry an egg on the sidewalk." This does not mean that you could *actually* fry an egg on the sidewalk. It just means it is very hot outside. This sort of overstatement is often humorous.

Writers use exaggeration to help their readers imagine a scene better or understand the feelings of a character more deeply. As you read the selection, watch for examples of exaggeration.

HAVE YOU EVER?

Have you ever tried to make a new person in your class or neighborhood feel welcome? How do most people treat a new kid in town? This selection—which comes from early in the novel *Maniac Magee*—tells the story of a homeless boy's search for a place to call his own. Think about the challenge of moving to someplace where you don't know anyone. What could you and your friends do to help a boy in that situation? What could your school do to make the first few weeks easier for new students? Think about these issues as you discover how Maniac makes his way in the town of Two Mills.

MANIAC

BY JERRY SPINELLI

Jeffrey Magee is orphaned at three and runs
away from his aunt and uncle at eleven. A
year later, he shows up in the town of Two Mills,
where he immediately begins to become a
legend. He runs everywhere instead of
walking; he hits six home runs off Giant
John McNab, who had struck out thirty-
five Little League players. His first
friend is Amanda Beale, who so loves
books that she carries hers in a suitcase to and from school every day in
order to protect them. He convinces her
to lend him a book, promising to return it to her
house at 728 Sycamore Street.

Illustrated by Oscar Hernandez

The town was buzzing. The schools were buzzing.
Hallways. Lunchrooms. Streets. Playgrounds. West
End. East End.

Buzzing about the new kid in town. The stranger kid.
Scraggly. Carrying a book. Flap-soled sneakers.

The kid who intercepted Brian Denehy's pass to Hands
Down and punted it back longer than Denehy himself ever
threw it.

The kid who rescued Arnold Jones from Finsterwald's
backyard.

The kid who tattooed Giant John McNab's fastball for
half a dozen home runs, then circled the sacks on a
bunted frog.

Nobody knows who said it first, but somebody must have:
"Kid's gotta be a maniac."

And somebody else must have said: "Yeah, reg'lar maniac."

And somebody else: "Yeah."

And that was it. Nobody (except Amanda Beale) had any
other name for him, so pretty soon, when they wanted to
talk about the new kid, that's what they called him: Maniac.

The legend had a name.

But not an address. At least, not an official one, with
numbers.

What he did have was the deer shed at the Elmwood Park
Zoo, which is where he slept his first few nights in town.
What the deer ate, especially the carrots, apples, and day-
old hamburger buns, he ate.

He started reading Amanda Beale's book his second day
in town and finished it that afternoon. Ordinarily, he would
have returned it immediately, but he was so fascinated by
the story of the Children's Crusade that he kept it and read
it the next day. And the next.

---

scraggly (skrag′lē) *adj.* having a ragged or rough appearance.

intercepted (in′tər sep′tid) *v.t.* seized or stopped on the way.

maniac (mā′nē ak′) *n.* someone who is or seems wildly insane; lunatic.

When he wasn't reading, he was wandering. When most people wander, they walk. Maniac Magee ran. Around town, around the nearby townships, always carrying the book, keeping it in perfect condition.

This is what he was doing when his life, as it often seemed to do, took an unexpected turn.

John McNab had never in his life met a kid he couldn't strike out. Until the runt. Now, as he thought about it, he came to two conclusions:

1. He couldn't stand having this <u>blemish</u> on his record.
2. If you beat a kid up, it's the same as striking him out.

So McNab and his pals went looking for the kid. They called themselves the Cobras. Nobody messed with them. At least, nobody in the West End.

The Cobras had heard that the kid hung around the park and the tracks, and that's where they spotted him one Saturday afternoon, on the tracks by the path that ran from the Oriole Street dead end to the park. He was down by Red Hill and heading away from them, book in hand, as usual.

But the Cobras just stood there, stunned.

"I don't believe it," one Cobra said.

"Must be a trick," said another.

"I heard about it," said another, "but I didn't believe it."

It wasn't a trick. It was true. The kid was *running* on the rail.

McNab scooped up a handful of track stones. He launched one. He snarled, "He's dead. Let's get 'im!"

By the time Maniac looked back, they were almost on him. He wobbled once, leaped from the rail to the ground, and took off. He was at the Oriole Street dead end, but his <u>instincts</u> said no, not the street, too much open space. He

---

blemish (blem′ish) *n.* something that spoils perfection; stain.
instincts (in′stingkts′) *n., pl.* natural tendencies to act a certain way.

stuck with the tracks. Coming into view above him was the house on Rako Hill, where he had eaten spaghetti. He could go there, to the whistling mother, the other kids, be safe. They wouldn't follow him in there. Would they?

Stones clanked off the steel rails. He darted left, skirted the dump, wove through the miniature mountain range of stone piles and into the trees . . . skiing on his heels down the steep bank and into the creek, frogs plopping, no time to look for stepping rocks . . . yells behind him now, war whoops, stones pelting the water, stinging his back . . . ah, the other side, through the trees and picker bushes, past the <u>armory</u> jeeps and out to the park boulevard, past the Italian restaurant on the corner, the bakery, screeching tires, row houses, streets, alleys, cars, porches, windows, faces staring, faces, faces . . . the town whizzing past Maniac, a blur of faces, each face staring from its own window, each face in its own personal frame, its own house, its own address, someplace to be when there was no other place to be, how lucky to be a face staring out from a window . . .

And then—could it be?—the voices behind him were growing faint. He slowed, turned, stopped. They were lined up at a street a block back. They were still yelling and shaking their fists, but they weren't moving off the curb. And now they were laughing. Why were they laughing?

The Cobras were standing at Hector Street. Hector Street was the boundary between the East and West Ends. Or, to put it another way, between the blacks and whites. Not that you never saw a white in the East End or a black in the West End. People did cross the line now and then, especially if they were adults, and it was daylight.

But nighttime, forget it. And if you were a kid, day *or* night, forget it. Unless you had business on the other side,

---

armory (är′mə rē) *n.* headquarters of a National Guard or other military reserve unit.

such as a sports team or school. But don't be just *strolling* along, as if you *belonged* there, as if you weren't *afraid*, as if you didn't even *notice* you were a different color from everybody around you.

The Cobras were laughing because they figured the dumb, scraggly <u>runt</u> would get out of the East End in about as good shape as a bare big toe in a convention of snapping turtles.

Of course, Maniac didn't know any of that. He was simply glad the chase was over. He turned and started walking, catching his breath.

East Chestnut. East Marshall. Green Street. Arch Street. He had been around here before. That first day with the girl named Amanda, other days jogging through. But this was Saturday, not a school day, and there was something different about the streets—kids. All over.

One of them jumped down from a front step and planted himself right in front of Maniac. Maniac had to jerk to a stop to keep from plowing into the kid. Even so, their noses were practically touching.

Maniac blinked and stepped back. The kid stepped forward. Each time Maniac stepped back, the kid stepped forward. They traveled practically half a block that way. Finally Maniac turned and started walking. The kid jumped around and plunked himself in front again. He bit off a chunk of the candy bar he was holding. "Where *you* goin'?" he said. Candy bar flakes flew from his mouth.

"I'm looking for Sycamore Street," said Maniac. "Do you know where it is?"

"Yeah, I know where it is."

Maniac waited, but the kid said nothing more. "Well, uh, do you think you could tell me where it is?"

---

runt (runt) *n.* weak, undersized person or animal.

Stone was softer than the kid's glare. "No."

Maniac looked around. Other kids had stopped playing, were staring.

Someone called: "Do 'im, Mars!"

Someone else: "Waste 'im!"

The kid, as you probably guessed by now, was none other then Mars Bar Thompson. Mars Bar heard the calls, and the stone got harder. Then suddenly he stopped glaring, suddenly he was smiling. He held up the candy bar, an inch from Maniac's lips. "Wanna bite?"

Maniac couldn't figure. "You sure?"

"Yeah, go ahead. Take a bite."

Maniac shrugged, took the Mars Bar, bit off a chunk, and handed it back. "Thanks."

Dead silence along the street. The kid had done the unthinkable, he had chomped on one of Mars's own bars. Not only that, but white kids just didn't put their mouths where black kids had had theirs, be it soda bottles, spoons, or candy bars. And the kid hadn't even gone for the unused end; he had chomped right over Mars Bar's own bite marks.

Mars Bar was confused. Who *was* this kid? *What* was this kid?

As usual, when Mars Bar got confused, he got mad. He thumped Maniac in the chest. "You think you bad or somethin'?"

Maniac, who was now twice as confused as Mars Bar, blinked. "Huh?"

"You think you come down here and be bad? That what you think?" Mars Bar was practically shouting now.

"No," said Maniac, "I don't think I'm bad. I'm not saying I'm an angel, either. Not even real good. Somewhere in between, I guess."

Mars Bar jammed his arms downward, stuck out his chin, sneered. "Am I bad?"

Maniac was befuddled. "I don't know. One minute you're yelling at me, the next minute you're giving me a bite of your candy bar."

The chin jutted out more. "Tell me I'm bad."

Maniac didn't answer. Flies stopped buzzing.

"I said, tell me I'm bad."

Maniac blinked, shrugged, sighed. "It's none of my business. If you're bad, let your mother or father tell you."

Now it was Mars Bar doing the blinking, stepping back, trying to sort things out. After a while he looked down. "What's that?"

Before Maniac answered, "A book," Mars Bar had snatched it from his hand. "This ain't yours," he said. He flipped through some pages. "Looks like mine."

"It's somebody else's."

"It's mine. I'm keepin' it."

With rattlesnake speed, Maniac snatched the book back—except for one page, which stayed, ripped, in Mars Bar's hand.

"Give me the page," said Maniac.

Mars Bar grinned. "Take it, fishbelly."

Silence. Eyes. The flies were waiting. East End vultures.

Suddenly neither kid could see the other, because a broom came down like a straw curtain between their faces, and a voice said, "I'll take it."

It was the lady from the nearest house, out to sweep her steps. She lowered the broom but kept it between them. "Better yet," she said to Mars Bar, "just give it back to him."

Mars Bar glared up at her. There wasn't an eleven-year-old in the East End who could stand up to Mars Bar's glare. In the West End, even high-schoolers were known to crumble under the glare. To old ladies on both sides of Hector Street,

---

befuddled (bi fud'əld) *adj.* completely confused or bewildered.
jutted (ju'tid) *v.i.* stuck out; protruded.

it was all but <u>fatal</u>. And when Mars Bar stepped off a curb and combined the glare with his super-slow dip-stride slumpshuffle, well, it was said he could back up traffic all the way to Bridgeport while he took ten minutes to cross the street.

But not this time. This time Mars Bar was up against an East End lady in her prime, and she was matching him eyeball for eyeball. And when it was over, only one glare was left standing, and it wasn't Mars Bar's.

Mars Bar handed back the torn page, but not before he crumpled it into a ball. The broom pushed him away, turned him around, and swept him up the street.

The lady looked down at Maniac. A little of the glare lingered in her eyes. "You better get on, boy, where you belong. I can't be following you around. I got things to do."

Maniac just stood there a minute. There was something he felt like doing, and maybe he would have, but the lady turned and went back inside her house and shut the door. So he walked away.

Now what?

Maniac uncrumpled the page, flattened it out as best he could. How could he return the book to Amanda in this condition? He couldn't. But he had to. It was hers. Judging from that morning, she was pretty finicky about her books. What would make her madder—to not get the book back at all, or to get it back with a page ripped out? Maniac cringed at both prospects.

He wandered around the East End, jogging slowly, in no hurry now to find 728 Sycamore Street. He was passing a vacant lot when he heard an all-too-familiar voice: "Hey, fishbelly!" He stopped, turned. This time Mars Bar wasn't alone. A handful of other kids trailed him down the sidewalk.

Maniac waited.

---

fatal (fā′təl) *adj.* causing death, destruction, or ruin.

Coming up to him, Mars Bar said, "Where you runnin', boy?"

"Nowhere."

"You runnin' from us. You afraid."

"No, I just like to run."

"You wanna run?" Mars Bar grinned. "Go ahead. We'll give you a head start."

Maniac grinned back. "No thanks."

Mars Bar held out his hand. "Gimme my book."

Maniac shook his head.

Mars Bar glared. "Gimme it."

Maniac shook his head.

Mars Bar reached for it. Maniac pulled it away.

They moved in on him now. They backed him up. Some high-schoolers were playing basketball up the street, but they weren't noticing. And there wasn't a broom-swinging lady in sight. Maniac felt a hard flatness against his back. Suddenly his world was very small and very simple: a brick wall behind him, a row of <u>scowling</u> faces in front of him. He clutched the book with both hands. The faces were closing in. A voice called: "That you, Jeffrey?"

The faces parted. At the curb was a girl on a bike—Amanda! She hoisted the bike to the sidewalk and walked it over. She looked at the book, at the torn page. "Who ripped my book?"

Mars Bar pointed at Maniac. "He did."

Amanda knew better. "*You* ripped my book."

Mars Bar's eyes went big as headlights. "I did *not!*"

"You *did*. You lie."

"I *didn't!*"

"You *did!*" She let the bike fall to Maniac. She grabbed the book and started kicking Mars Bar in his beloved sneakers. "I got a little brother and a little sister that crayon all over my books, and I got a dog that eats them

---

scowling (skou'ling) *adj.* angrily frowning.

and poops on them and that's just inside my own family, and I'm *not*—gonna have *nobody*—else *messin'*—with my *books!* You under-*stand?"*

By then Mars Bar was hauling on up the street past the basketball players, who were rolling on the asphalt with laughter.

Amanda took the torn page from Maniac. To her, it was the broken wing of a bird, a pet out in the rain. She turned misty eyes to Maniac. "It's one of my favorite pages."

Maniac smiled. "We can fix it."

The way he said it, she believed. "Want to come to my house?" she said.

"Sure," he said.

When they walked in, Amanda's mother was busy with her usual tools: a yellow plastic bucket and a sponge. She was scrubbing purple crayon off the TV screen.

"Mom," said Amanda, "this is Jeffrey—" She whispered, "What's your last name?"

He whispered, "Magee."

She said, "Magee."

Mrs. Beale held up a hand, said, "Hold it," and went on scrubbing. When she finally finished, she straightened up, turned, and said, "Now, what?"

"Mom, this is Jeffrey Magee. You know."

Amanda was hardly finished when Maniac zipped across the room and stuck out his hand. "Nice to meet you, Mrs. . . . Mrs. . . . ."

"Beale."

"Mrs. Beale."

They shook hands. Mrs. Beale smiled. "So you're the book boy." She started nodding. "Manda came home one day— 'Mom, there's a boy I loaned one of my books out to!' 'Loaned a *book? You?'* 'Mom, he practically *made* me. He really likes books. I met him on—'"

"Mo-om!" Amanda screeched. "I never said all *that!"*

Mrs. Beale nodded solemnly—"No, of course you didn't"— and gave Maniac a huge wink, which made Amanda screech louder, until something crashed in the kitchen. Mrs. Beale ran. Amanda and Maniac ran.

The scene in the kitchen stopped them cold: one little girl, eyes wide, standing on a countertop; one little boy, eyes wide, standing just below her on a chair; one shattered glass jar and some stringy pale-colored glop on the floor; one growing cloud of sauerkraut fumes.

The girl was Hester, age four; the boy was Lester, age three. In less than five minutes, while Mrs. Beale and Amanda cleaned up the floor, Hester and Lester and their dog Bow Wow were in the backyard wrestling and tickling and jumping and just generally going wild with their new buddy—and victim—Maniac Magee.

Maniac was still there when Mr. Beale came home from his Saturday <u>shift</u> at the tire factory.

He was there for dinner, when Hester and Lester pushed their chairs alongside his.

He was there to help Amanda mend her torn book.

He was there watching TV afterward, with Hester riding one knee, Lester the other.

He was there when Hester and Lester came screaming down the stairs with a book, Amanda screaming even louder after them, the kids shoving the book and themselves onto Maniac's lap, Amanda finally calming down because they didn't want to crayon the book, they only wanted Maniac to read. And so he read *Lyle, Lyle, Crocodile* to Hester and Lester and, even though they pretended not to listen, to Amanda and Mr. and Mrs. Beale.

And he was there when Hester and Lester were herded upstairs to bed, and Mrs. Beale said, "Don't you think it's about time you're heading home, Jeffrey? Your parents'll be wondering."

---

shift *n.* scheduled work time.

So Maniac, wanting to say something but not knowing how, got into the car for Mr. Beale to drive him home. And then he made his mistake. He waited for only two or three blocks to go by before saying to Mr. Beale, "This is it."

Mr. Beale stopped, but he didn't let Maniac out of the car. He looked at him funny. Mr. Beale knew what his passenger <u>apparently</u> didn't: East End was East End and West End was West End, and the house this white lad was pointing to was filled with black people, just like every other house on up to Hector Street.

Mr. Beale pointed this out to Maniac. Maniac's lip started to quiver, and right there, with the car <u>idling</u> in the middle of the street, Maniac told him that he didn't really have a home, unless you counted the deer shed at the zoo.

Mr. Beale made a U-turn right there and headed back. Only Mrs. Beale was still downstairs when they walked into the house. She listened to no more than ten seconds' worth of Mr. Beale's explanation before saying to Maniac, "You're staying here."

Not long after, Maniac was lying in Amanda's bed, Amanda having been carried over to Hester and Lester's room, where she often slept anyway.

Before Maniac could go to sleep, however, there was something he had to do. He flipped off the covers and went downstairs. Before the puzzled faces of Mr. and Mrs.

Beale, he opened the front door and looked at the three cast-iron digits nailed to the door frame: seven two eight. He kept staring at them, smiling. Then he closed the door, said a cheerful "Goodnight," and went back to bed.

Maniac Magee finally had an address.

---

apparently (ə par′ənt lē) *adv.* plainly; obviously.
idling (ī′dling) *v.i.* parked with the motor running.

meet JERRY SPINELLI

As unlikely as it may seem, some fried chicken played a part in launching Jerry Spinelli's career as a writer of books for young people. His plan to eat the leftover fowl for lunch was foiled when one of his children beat him to it. Spinelli chose to write about the experience. From that piece of writing grew *Space Station Seventh Grade,* Spinelli's first published book.

It was not the first time that Spinelli had been prompted to write about events in his own life. At sixteen, he celebrated his high school football team's victory by composing a poem. Spinelli remembers, "The poem was published in the local newspaper, and I've been a writer ever since."

Spinelli's attempts at writing for adults proved unsuccessful. However, with the publication of his first book for young adults, he realized that his memories of growing up in Norristown, Pennsylvania, were rich sources of material. Inspired by those memories and by the experiences of his children, he has been writing successfully for young people since 1982. His novels are often funny but also deal honestly with the concerns, feelings, and problems that go with being young.

Maniac Magee won the 1991 Newbery Medal. Spinelli's other books include *Who Put That Hair in My Toothbrush?* and *Dump Days.*

RESPONDING TO Literature

THINK • TALK • WRITE

1 How did you feel when Maniac finds a home? What do you think might happen to him next? Jot your thoughts in your journal.

2 How did Jeffrey Magee get his nickname? What other nickname(s) might have been appropriate?

3 Compare John McNab and Mars Bar. What do you think would happen if these two bullies ever met?

4 Why did the Beales invite Maniac to stay with them? Do you think Maniac will fit in well with the family? Explain why or why not.

5 In Two Mills, African Americans and whites mostly live on opposite sides of town. Why do you think that happened? Do you think it happens in many communities?

ACTIVITIES

- **Write with Exaggeration** In small groups choose a phrase that uses exaggeration and then create a cartoon that expresses its exact meaning. Under the cartoon, write a caption using the exaggeration.

- **Draw a Map** Draw a map of Two Mills. Include streets, the park, the railroad tracks, and a map key. Check a real map for style. Display your map in the classroom.

VOCABULARY PRACTICE

On a separate piece of paper, write the vocabulary word that best completes each sentence.

scraggly   intercepted
blemish   instincts
runt   jutted
fatal   scowling
apparently   idling

1 The tiny puppy was the _____ of the litter.

2 Heidi _____ the poorly aimed pass.

3 The window had _____ been forced open since there were scratches on the sill.

4 The mountain _____ like a dark fist into the pale blue sky.

5 She is dead; she had a _____ heart attack.

6 The child's _____ face clearly indicated his unhappiness.

7 The gardener trimmed the _____ bushes into smooth, neat shapes.

8 I could hardly see the _____, but Carl said it spoiled his looks.

9 The cat's _____ warned it to jump out of the way of the bicycle.

10 Leaving an engine _____ for more than a minute wastes gas.

BEFORE READING

....

CHILD OF THE OWL

CONNECT TO LITERATURE

Do you know one of your grandparents particularly well, or do you have a special elderly friend? Describe this person in your journal. As you read "Child of the Owl," try to decide how the main character, Casey, feels toward her grandmother, Paw-Paw.

THINKING ABOUT FIRST-PERSON POINT OF VIEW

"Child of the Owl" is written in the *first person.* The narrator, Casey, tells about her own experiences. She uses the first-person pronouns *I* and *me.*

An author uses the first-person point of view to help readers understand the narrator. This point of view can make readers feel the narrator is talking directly to them. On the other hand, using a first-person narrator limits readers' knowledge of the other characters, because they learn about them only through the thoughts and reactions of the narrator.

HAVE YOU EVER?

Have you ever met someone who was very different from what you expected? Perhaps the person was a relative you had only heard about. That's what happens to Casey in this selection.

This excerpt comes from the opening chapter of Laurence Yep's novel *Child of the Owl.* When the novel begins, Casey is visiting her father, Barney, in the hospital. Because her mother died when she was little, Casey must go to stay with relatives until her father is better. First she stays with her unpleasant uncle, Phil. Now she is going to live with her grandmother, Paw-Paw, whom she has never met.

C asey was just
a small child when her
mother, Jeanie, died.
Since then, Casey has
been brought up by her
father, Barney. When
Barney is hospitalized,
Casey goes to stay with
her uncle Phil and his
family. Used to a free-
spirited life with her
father, Casey is uncom-
fortable in Phil's strict
household. In turn,
Phil's family is unwill-
ing to accept Casey's at-
titudes, ideas, and
behavior. The situation
is tense for everyone,
so Phil decides to take
Casey to San Francisco's
Chinatown to live with
Paw-Paw, her grand-
mother. On the way,
Casey is nervous. She
has never met Paw-Paw,
and she feels alone and
out of place in the unfa-
miliar setting.

ILLUSTRATED BY
WINSON TRANG

507

Phil headed up Sacramento Street—a steep, slanting street that just zoomed on and on to the top of Nob Hill, where the rich people lived and where they had the <u>swanky</u> hotels. Phil turned suddenly into a little dead-end alley wide enough for only one car. On one side was a one-story Chinese school of brick so old or so dirty that the bricks were practically a purple color. On the other side as we drove by was a small parking lot with only six spaces for cars. Phil stopped the car in the middle of the alley and I could see the rest of it was filled with apartment houses. Somewhere someone had a window open and the radio was blaring out "I Want to Hold Your Hand" by that new group, the Beatles. I couldn't find the place where it was coming from but I did see someone's diapers and shirts hung in the windows and on the fire escape of one apartment.

"Why do they hang their laundry in the windows?" I asked Phil.

"That's what people from Hong Kong use for curtains," Phil grumbled.

The sidewalk in front of Paw-Paw's house was cracked like

---

swanky (swang′kē) *adj. Slang.* very elegant; stylish; luxurious.

someone had taken a sledgehammer to it, and there were iron grates over the lower windows. The steps up to the doorway were old, worn concrete painted red. To the left were the mailboxes, which had Chinese words for the names or had no labels at all. To the right were the doorbells to all the nine apartments. Phil picked out the last and rang. He jabbed his thumb down rhythmically. Three short. Three long. Three short.

"Why are you doing that?" I asked.

"Signaling your Paw-Paw," he grumbled. "She never answers just one buzz like any normal person, or even just three bursts. It's got to be nine buzzes in that way or she doesn't open the door. She says her friends know what she means."

So did I. It was Morse code for SOS. The buzzer on the door sounded like an angry bee. Phil the Pill opened the door, putting his back against it and fighting against the heavy spring that tried to swing it shut. "Go on. Up three flights. Number nine."

I walked into an old, dim hallway and climbed up the wooden steps. As I turned an angle on the stairs, I saw light burning fierce and bright from a window. When I came to it, I looked out at the roof of the Chinese school next door. Someone had thrown some old 45's and a pair of sneakers down there. If I were some kind of kid that felt sorry for herself, I would almost have said that was the way I felt: like some piece of old, ugly junk that was being kicked around on the discard pile while Barney was getting better.

I didn't stay by the window long, though, because Phil was coming up the stairs and I didn't want to act like his kids' stories about Paw-Paw had scared me. Anybody could be better than Phil the Pill and his family . . . I hoped. I stopped by the number-nine room,

discard (dis'kärd) *n.* useless, worthless, rejected item.

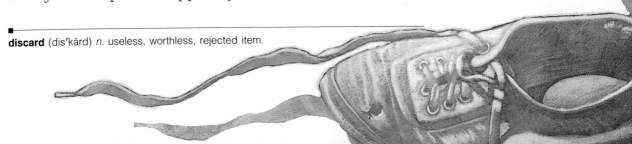

afraid to knock. It could not be the right place because I could hear "I Want to Hold Your Hand" coming through the doorway. I scratched my head and checked the numbers on the other doors on the landing. Phil the Pill was still a flight down, huffing and puffing up the steps with my <u>duffel bag</u>—it wasn't that heavy; Phil was just that much out of shape. "Go on. Go on. Knock, you little idiot," he called up the stairwell.

I shrugged. It wasn't any of my business. I knocked at the door. I heard about six bolts and locks being turned. Finally the door swung open and I saw a tiny, pleasant, round-faced woman smiling at me. Her cheeks were a bright red. Her gray hair was all curly and frizzy around her head and a pair of rimless, thick eyeglasses perched on her nose. She was round and plump, wearing a sweater even on a hot day like this, a pair of cotton black slacks, and a pair of open-heeled, flat slippers.

"Paw-Paw?" I asked.

"Hello. Hello." She opened up her arms and gave me a big hug, almost crushing me. It was funny,

duffel bag cylindrical bag, usually of canvas, used for carrying clothes, equipment, or other belongings.

but even though it was like I said—Barney and me never went in much for that <u>sentimental</u> stuff like hugging and kissing—I suddenly found myself holding on to her. Underneath all the soft layers of clothing I could feel how hard and tough she was. She patted me on the back three times and then left me for a moment to turn down her radio. It really was her old, white, beat-up radio playing rock music.

"Hey, how about a hand?" Phil puffed as he finally got to the landing.

Paw-Paw shuffled out to the landing in her slippered feet and made shooing motions. "You can go home now. We can do all right by ourselves."

Phil heaved his shoulders up and down in a great sigh and set the bag down. "Now, Momma—"

"Go on home," she said firmly. "We need time by ourselves."

I saw that Phil must have had some fine speech all prepared, probably warning Paw-Paw about me and warning me about <u>ingratitude</u>. He was not about to give up such an opportunity to make a speech.

"Now, Momma—"

"Go on. You're still not too old for a swat across the backside."

Phil ran his hand back and forth along the railing. "Really, Momma. You oughtn't—"

"Go on." Paw-Paw raised her hand.

Phil gulped. The thought of having a former district president of the lawyers spanked by his own mother must have been too much for him. He turned around and started down the steps. He still had to get in the last word though. "You mind your Paw-Paw, young lady. You hear me?" he shouted over his shoulder.

---

sentimental (sen′tə men′təl) *adj.* characterized by emotion, especially exaggerated or foolish emotion.

ingratitude (in grat′i tüd′) *n.* lack of appreciation, as for a kindness or favor.

I waited till I heard the door slam. "Do you know what those buzzes stand for?"

"Do you?" Her eyes crinkled up.

"It stands for SOS. But where did you learn it?"

"When I worked for the American lady, her boy had a toy. . .what do you call it?" She made a tapping motion with her finger.

"Telegraph?"

"Yes. It's a good joke on such a <u>learned</u> man, no?" Her round red face split into a wide grin and then she began to giggle and when she put her hand over her mouth, the giggle turned into a laugh.

I don't think that I had laughed in all that time since Barney's accident a month ago. It was like all the laughter I hadn't been able to use came bubbling up out of some hidden well—burst out of the locks and just came up. Both of us found ourselves slumping on the landing, leaning our heads against the banister, and laughing.

Finally Paw-Paw tilted up her glasses and wiped her eyes. "Philip always did have too much dignity for one person. Ah." She leaned back against the railing on the landing before the stairwell, twisting her head to look at me. "You'll go far," she nodded. "Yes, you will. Your eyebrows are beautifully curved, like silkworms. That means you'll be clever. And your ears are small and close to your head and shaped a certain way. That means you're adventurous and win much honor."

"Really?"

She nodded solemnly. "Didn't you know? The face is the map of the soul." Then she leaned forward and raised her glasses and pointed to the corners of her

---

learned (lûr′nid) *adj.* knowledgeable; well-educated.

eyes where there were two small hollows, just shadows, really. "You see those marks under my eyes?"

"Yes." I added after a moment, "Paw-Paw."

"Those marks, they mean I have a temper."

"Oh." I wondered what was to happen next.

She set her glasses back on her nose. "But I will make a deal with you. I can keep my temper under control if you can do the same with your love of adventure and intelligence. You see, people, including me, don't always understand a love of adventure and intelligence. Sometimes we mistake them for troublemaking."

"I'll try," I grinned.

I went and got my bag then and brought it inside Paw-Paw's place and looked around, trying to figure out where I'd put it. Her place wasn't more than ten by fifteen feet and it was crowded with her stuff. Her bed was pushed lengthwise against the wall next to the doorway leading out to the landing. To the right of the door was another doorway, leading to the small little cubicle of a kitchen, and next to that door was her bureau. The wall opposite the bed had her one window leading out to the fire escape and giving a view of the alley, which was so narrow that it looked like we could have shaken hands with the people in the apartment house across from us. Beneath the window was a stack of newspapers for wrapping up the garbage. Next to the window was a table with a bright red-and-orange-flower tablecloth. Paw-Paw pulled aside her chair and her three-legged stool and told me to put my bag under the table. A metal cabinet and stacks of boxes covered the rest of the wall and the next one had hooks from which coats and other stuff in plastic bags hung.

In the right corner of the old bureau were some statues and an old teacup with some dirt in it and a half-burnt <u>incense</u> stick stuck into it. The rest of the top, though, was covered with old photos in little cardboard covers. They filled the bureau top and the mirror too, being stuck into corners of the mirror or actually taped onto the surface.

Next to the photos were the statues. One was about eight inches high in white porcelain of a pretty lady holding a flower and with the most patient, peaceful expression on her face. To her left was a statue of a man with a giant-sized, bald head. And then there were eight little statues, each only about two inches high. "Who are they?" I asked.

---

incense (in′sens′) n. substance that produces a fragrant aroma when burned.

515

"Statues of some holy people," Paw-Paw said <u>reluctantly</u>.

There was something familiar about the last statue on Paw-Paw's bureau. It was of a fat, balding god with large ears, who had little children crawling over his lap and climbing up his shoulders. "Hey," I said. "Is that the happy god?"

Paw-Paw looked puzzled. "He's not the god of happiness."

"But they call him the happy god. See?" I pulled Barney's little plastic charm out of my pocket and pointed to the letters on the back.

Paw-Paw didn't even try to read the lettering. Maybe Barney had already shown it to her long ago. "He's not the god of happiness. He just looks happy. He's the Buddha—the Buddha who will come in the future. He's smiling because everyone will be saved by that time and he can take a vacation. The children are holy people who become like children again."

"What about the others, Paw-Paw?"

"I don't have the words to explain," Paw-Paw said <u>curtly</u>, like the whole thing was embarrassing her.

---

reluctantly (ri luk′tənt lē) *adv.* with hesitation or unwillingness.

curtly (kûrt′lē) *adv.* abruptly; rudely to the point.

516

I sat down by the table on the stool, which was painted white with red flowers. "Sure you do. I think your English is better than mine."

"You don't want to know any of that stuff." With her index finger Paw-Paw rubbed hard against some spot on the tablecloth. "That stuff's only for old people. If I tell you any more, you'll laugh at it like all other young people do." There was bitter hurt and anger in her voice.

I should have left her alone, I guess; but we had been getting close to one another and suddenly I'd found this door between us—a door that wouldn't open. I wasn't so much curious now as I was desperate: I didn't want Paw-Paw shutting me out like that. "I won't laugh, Paw-Paw. Honest."

"That stuff's only for old people who are too stupid to learn American ways," she insisted stubbornly.

"Well, maybe I'm stupid too."

"No." Paw-Paw pressed her lips together tightly; and I saw that no matter how much I pestered her, I wasn't going to get her to tell me any more about the statues on her bureau. We'd been getting along so great before that I was sorry I'd ever started asking questions.

We both sat, each in our own thoughts, until almost apologetically Paw-Paw picked up a deck of cards from the table. "Do you play cards?"

"Some," I said. "Draw poker. Five-card stud. Things like that."

Paw-Paw shuffled the cards expertly. "Poker is for old men who like to sit and think too much. Now I know a game that's for the young and quick."

"What's that?"

"Slapjack." She explained that each of us took half

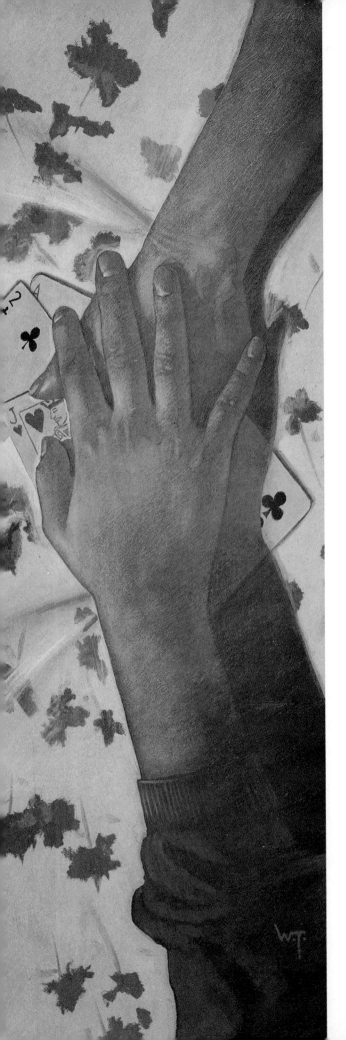

of a deck and stacked it in front
without looking at it. Then we
would take turns taking the top
card off and putting it down in
the middle. Whenever a jack appeared, the first one to put her
hand over the pile of cards got it.
She then mixed the new cards
with all the cards she still had in
front of her. The first one to get
all the cards won the game. It
would sound like the advantage
was with the person who was
putting out the card at that time,
but she was supposed to turn
up the card away from her so
she couldn't see it before the
other player.

Paw-Paw had played a lot
of card games, since she lived by
herself, so she seemed to know
when the jacks were going to come
up. For a while all you could hear
was the *slap-slap-slap*ping of cards
and sometimes our hands smack-
ing one another trying to get the
pile. And sometimes I'd have
more cards and sometimes Paw-
Paw would. Eventually, though,
she beat me. She shuffled the
deck again. "You're a pretty good
player," she grudged.

"Not as good as you, though."

---

advantage (ad van′tij) *n.* useful or helpful
circumstance; benefit; asset.
grudged (grujd) *v.t.* allowed unwillingly.

Paw-Paw shuffled the cards, tapping them against the table so the cards in the pack were all even. "We used to play all the time. Your mother, Phil, everyone. We'd hold big contests and make plenty of noise. Only when Phil got older, he only wanted to play the games fancy Americans played like—what's that word for a road that goes over water?"

"A bridge? Phil wanted to play bridge."

"Yes." Paw-Paw put the deck on the table. I wandered over to the bed.

The radio was in a little cabinet built into the headboard of the bed. I lay down on the bed and looked at the radio dial. "Do you like rock music, Paw-Paw?"

"It's fun to listen to," Paw-Paw said, "and besides, *Chinese Hour* is on that station every night."

"Chinese Hour?"

"An hour of news and songs all in Chinese." Paw-Paw slipped the cards back carefully into their box. "They used to have some better shows on that station like mystery shows."

"I bet I could find some." I started to reach for the dial.

"Don't lose that station." Paw-Paw seemed afraid suddenly.

"Don't worry, Paw-Paw, I'll be able to get your station back for you." It was playing "Monster Mash" right then. I twisted the dial to the right and the voices and snatches of song slid past and then I turned the dial back to her station, where "Monster Mash" was still playing. "See?"

"As long as you could get it back," Paw-Paw said reluctantly.

I fiddled with the dial some more until I got hold of *Gunsmoke.* It'd gone off the air three years ago but

some station was playing <u>reruns</u>. Paw-Paw liked that, especially the deep voice of the marshal. It was good to sit there in the darkening little room, listening to Marshal Dillon inside your head and picturing him as big and tall and striding down the dusty streets of Dodge City. And I got us some other programs too, shows that Paw-Paw had never been able to listen to before.

Don't get the idea that Paw-Paw was stupid. She just didn't understand American machines that well. She lived with them in a kind of <u>truce</u> where she never asked much of them if they wouldn't ask much of her.

"It's getting near eight," Paw-Paw said anxiously. It was only when I got the station back for her that she began to relax. "I was always so worried that I would not be able to get back the station, I never tried to listen to others. Look what I missed."

"But you have me now, Paw-Paw," I said.

"Yes," Paw-Paw smiled briefly, straightening in her chair. "I guess I do."

---

reruns (rē′runz′) *n., pl.* taped performances shown again after their original showings.
truce (trüs) *n.* temporary halt to fighting by mutual agreement.

MEET
Laurence Yep

For much of his early life, Laurence Yep knew what it was like to feel that he did not belong. He lived in a neighborhood where he was the only Chinese-American boy, and, despite his Chinese heritage, he was one of the few Chinese-American students at his school who could not speak Chinese.

Yep's feeling of being an outsider led him to read science fiction. There, he found characters and situations that seemed familiar, he says, "because in those books children were taken to other lands and other worlds where they had to learn strange customs and languages—and that was something I did every time I got on and off the bus."

Yep sold his first story when he was eighteen and was paid a penny per word. Not surprisingly, that piece was science fiction, as are many of Yep's later works. He also writes realistic novels, often drawing upon his Chinese-American background. One of these is *Dragonwings,* which was a Newbery Honor Book. Another is *Child of the Owl,* which won the Boston Globe–Horn Book Award in 1979.

RESPONDING TO
Literature

THINK • TALK • WRITE

1 What would you tell a friend about this selection? Note your thoughts in your journal.

2 How does Casey feel at the beginning of this selection? How does she feel at the end? Explain why she has changed.

3 Why doesn't Paw-Paw want to tell Casey about her statues? What might have happened in the past to make Paw-Paw cautious about talking about these objects?

4 Do you predict that Casey and Paw-Paw will get along well? Explain why or why not.

5 Although Casey is Chinese American, she has not spent a lot of time in Chinese American communities. Do you think she will have a hard time fitting into Chinatown? Explain.

ACTIVITIES

- **Write a First-Person Narrative** Write a letter from Casey to Barney describing Casey's thoughts and feelings on meeting Paw-Paw. Include details from the story about events as well as Casey's feelings.

- **Record Oral History** Become an oral historian. Interview and tape record a relative or an older neighbor about life 20 years ago.

VOCABULARY PRACTICE

Match the words or phrases on the right with the words on the left that have the same meaning. Write the number and letter on a separate piece of paper.

1 discard
2 ingratitude
3 incense
4 truce
5 advantage
6 sentimental
7 learned
8 reluctantly
9 curtly
10 grudged

a resented
b overly emotional
c wise
d lack of appreciation
e unwillingly
f temporary peace
g throw away
h benefit
i rudely
j substance that emits a pleasant odor

Grandmother

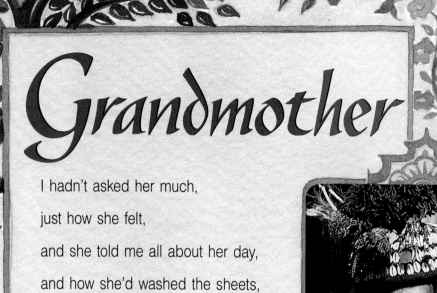

I hadn't asked her much,

just how she felt,

and she told me all about her day,

and how she'd washed the sheets,

and how she could not understand

why the towel got so heavy

when it was wet.

She'd also sunned the mattresses,

such tired bones and so much to do,

and my eyes filled with tears

when I thought of how I was simply

going to say "Salaam" and walk away

and so many words would have been

trapped inside her.

I would have passed by as if

what lay between those bedclothes

was just old life

and not really my grandmother.

—Sameeneh Shirazie

Just in Time 1981 Elizabeth Murray Philadelphia Museum of Art

Becoming the Tea

by Joyce Carol Thomas

Brown honey and broomwheat tea
Sweetwater, Daddy calls me
Liquid ambrosia with fire
"Be careful what you
     ponder," Granny smiles,
"Over a cup of steaming leaves
     for it will surely come to pass."
So I think on
     joy, love, peace,
     patience, grace
Yet I'm sometimes
     impatient, sad, angry,
     awkward
But like the steeping brew
The longer I stand
The stronger I stay

BEFORE READING

....

ANNE OF GREEN GABLES

CONNECT TO LITERATURE

Do you know what an *orphan* is? In our country, what happens to children who have no parents? Describe your own family in your journal. Then read the following selection about an orphan in search of a family.

THINKING ABOUT PLOT: COMPLICATION

A typical plot in fiction involves one or more *complications,* or problems. A good plot keeps you reading until the complications are resolved. A plot complication creates a more exciting story because it makes it more difficult to predict the ending.

The plot complication in this selection involves an important decision. See if you can predict how the complication will be resolved as you read.

DID YOU KNOW?

This selection is an excerpt from the early part of the novel *Anne of Green Gables* by L. M. Montgomery. The setting is Prince Edward Island in Canada. The novel opens when the Cuthberts of Green Gables decide to adopt a boy. Much to their surprise, the orphanage sends high-spirited Anne instead. The novel, an instant bestseller, led to more books about Anne as well as to television and film versions of her story.

There are very few orphanages in the United States and Canada today. Some homeless children are placed in foster homes or group homes. Almost 1,000,000 children under age 18 in the United States are adopted.

Anne
of
Green
Gables

When Marilla Cuthbert and her brother, Matthew, learned that their friend Mrs. Spencer was adopting a child from the orphan asylum, they decided to adopt a young boy themselves. They reasoned that they could give the child a good home and also have someone to help with the work at Green Gables, their farm on Prince Edward Island. Much to the Cuthberts' surprise, the orphan who arrives turns out to be a girl named Anne. Marilla insists that Anne be returned to the orphanage, but Matthew is not so sure.

by L. M. Montgomery

Illustrations by
Roberta Ludlow

It was broad daylight when Anne awoke and sat up in bed, staring confusedly at the window through which a flood of cheery sunshine was pouring and outside of which something white and feathery waved across glimpses of blue sky.

For a moment she could not remember where she was. First came a delightful thrill, as of something very pleasant; then a horrible remembrance. This was Green Gables and they didn't want her because she wasn't a boy!

But it was morning and, yes, it was a cherry tree in full bloom outside of her window. With a bound she was out of bed and across the floor. She pushed up the sash—it went up stiffly and creakily, as if it hadn't been opened for a long time, which was the case; and it stuck so tight that nothing was needed to hold it up.

Anne dropped on her knees and gazed out into the June morning, her eyes glistening with delight. Oh, wasn't it beautiful? Wasn't it a lovely place? Suppose she wasn't really going to stay here! She would imagine she was. There was <u>scope</u> for imagination here.

A huge cherry tree grew outside, so close that its boughs tapped against the house, and it was so thick-set with blossoms that hardly a leaf was to be seen. On both sides of the house was a big orchard, one of apple trees and one of cherry trees, also showered over with blossoms; and their grass was all sprinkled with dandelions. In the garden below were lilac trees purple with flowers, and their dizzily sweet fragrance drifted up to the window on the morning wind.

Below the garden a green field lush with clover sloped down to the hollow where the brook ran and where scores of white birches grew, upspringing airily out of an undergrowth suggestive of delightful possibilities in ferns and mosses and woodsy things generally. Beyond it was a hill, green and feathery with spruce and fir; there was a gap in it where the gray gable end of the little house she had seen from the other side of the Lake of Shining Waters was visible.

scope (skōp) *n.* opportunity or room for expression or development.

527

Off to the left were the big barns and beyond them, away down over green, low-sloping fields, was a sparkling blue glimpse of sea.

Anne's beauty-loving eyes lingered on it all, taking everything greedily in; she had looked on so many unlovely places in her life, poor child; but this was as lovely as anything she had ever dreamed.

She knelt there, lost to everything but the loveliness around her, until she was startled by a hand on her shoulder. Marilla had come in unheard by the small dreamer.

"It's time you were dressed," she said curtly.

Marilla really did not know how to talk to the child, and her uncomfortable <u>ignorance</u> made her crisp and curt when she did not mean to be.

Anne stood up and drew a long breath.

"Oh, isn't it wonderful?" she said, waving her hand comprehensively at the good world outside.

"It's a big tree," said Marilla, "and it blooms great, but the fruit don't amount to much never—small and wormy."

"Oh, I don't mean just the tree; of course it's lovely—yes, it's *radiantly* lovely—it blooms as if it meant it—but I meant everything, the garden and the orchard and the brook and the woods, the whole big dear world. Don't you feel as if you just loved the world on a morning like this? And I can hear the brook laughing all the way up here. Have you ever noticed what cheerful things brooks are? They're always laughing. Even in wintertime I've heard them under the ice. I'm so glad there's a brook near Green Gables. Perhaps you think it doesn't make any difference to me when you're not going to keep me, but it does. I shall always like to remember that there is a brook at Green Gables even if I never see it again. If there wasn't a brook I'd be *haunted* by the uncomfortable feeling that there ought to be one. I'm not in the depths of despair this morning. I never can be in the morning. Isn't it

---

ignorance (igˈnər əns) *n.* state of lacking knowledge or education.

a splendid thing that there are mornings? But I feel very sad. I've just been imagining that it was really me you wanted after all and that I was to stay here for ever and ever. It was a great comfort while it lasted. But the worst of imagining things is that the time comes when you have to stop and that hurts."

"You'd better get dressed and come downstairs and never mind your imaginings," said Marilla as soon as she could <u>get a word in edgewise</u>. "Breakfast is waiting. Wash your face and comb your hair. Leave the window up and turn your bedclothes back over the foot of the bed. Be as smart as you can."

Anne could <u>evidently</u> be smart to some purpose for she was downstairs in ten minutes' time, with her clothes neatly on, her hair brushed and braided, her face washed, and a comfortable consciousness <u>pervading</u> her soul that she had fulfilled all Marilla's requirements. As a matter of fact, however, she had forgotten to turn back the bedclothes.

"I'm pretty hungry this morning," she announced, as she slipped into the chair Marilla placed for her. "The world doesn't seem such a howling wilderness as it did last night. I'm so glad it's a sunshiny morning. But I like rainy mornings real well, too. All sorts of mornings are interesting, don't you think? You don't know what's going to happen through the day, and there's so much scope for imagination. But I'm glad it's not rainy today because it's easier to be cheerful and bear up under <u>affliction</u> on a sunshiny day. I feel that I have a good deal to bear up under. It's all very well to read about sorrows and imagine yourself living through them heroically, but it's not so nice when you really come to have them, is it?"

"For pity's sake hold your tongue," said Marilla. "You talk entirely too much for a little girl."

Thereupon Anne held her tongue so obediently and thoroughly that her continued silence made Marilla rather nervous, as if in the presence of something not exactly natural.

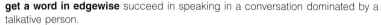

get a word in edgewise succeed in speaking in a conversation dominated by a talkative person.
evidently (evʹi dənt lē) *adv.* clearly; obviously.
pervading (pər vāʹding) *v.t.* spreading through every part of.
affliction (ə flikʹshən) *n.* misery; suffering; misfortune.

Matthew also held his tongue—but this at least was natural—so that the meal was a very silent one.

As it progressed Anne became more and more <u>abstracted</u>, eating mechanically, with her big eyes fixed unswervingly and unseeingly on the sky outside the window. This made Marilla more nervous than ever; she had an uncomfortable feeling that while this odd child's body might be there at the table her spirit was far away in some remote airy cloudland, borne aloft on the wings of imagination. Who would want such a child about the place?

Yet Matthew wished to keep her, of all unaccountable things! Marilla felt that he wanted it just as much this morning as he had the night before, and that he would go on wanting it. That was Matthew's way—take a <u>whim</u> into his head and cling to it with the most amazing silent persistency—a persistency ten times more potent and effectual in its very silence than if he had talked it out.

When the meal was ended Anne came out of her <u>reverie</u> and offered to wash the dishes.

"Can you wash dishes right?" asked Marilla distrustfully.

"Pretty well. I'm better at looking after children, though. I've had so much experience at that. It's such a pity you haven't any here for me to look after."

"I don't feel as if I wanted any more children to look after than I've got at present. *You're* problem enough in all conscience. What's to be done with you I don't know. Matthew is a most ridiculous man."

"I think he's lovely," said Anne reproachfully. "He is so very sympathetic. He didn't mind how much I talked—he seemed to like it. I felt that he was a <u>kindred</u> spirit as soon as ever I saw him."

"You're both queer enough, if that's what you mean by kindred spirits," said Marilla with a sniff. "Yes, you may wash the dishes. Take plenty of hot water, and be sure you dry them well. I've got enough to attend to this morning for I'll have to drive

---

abstracted (ab strak′tid) *adj.* lost in thought.

whim (hwim) *n.* sudden or unexpected notion or fanciful idea.

reverie (rev′ə rē) *n.* daydream.

kindred (kin′drid) *adj.* similar; alike.

over to White Sands in the afternoon and see Mrs. Spencer. You'll come with me and we'll settle what's to be done with you. After you've finished the dishes go upstairs and make your bed."

Anne washed the dishes <u>deftly</u> enough, as Marilla, who kept a sharp eye on the process, discerned. Later on she made her bed less successfully, for she had never learned the art of wrestling with a feather tick. But it was done somehow and smoothed down; and then Marilla, to get rid of her, told her she might go out-of-doors and amuse herself until dinner time.

Anne flew to the door, face alight, eyes glowing. On the very threshold she stopped short, wheeled about, came back and sat down by the table, light and glow as effectually blotted out as if someone had clapped an extinguisher on her.

"What's the matter now?" demanded Marilla.

"I don't dare go out," said Anne, in the tone of a <u>martyr</u> relinquishing all earthly joys. "If I can't stay here there is no use in my loving Green Gables. And if I go out there and get acquainted with all those trees and flowers and the orchard and the brook I'll not be able to help loving it. It's hard enough now, so I won't make it any harder. I want to go out so much—everything seems to be calling to me, 'Anne, Anne, come out to us. Anne, Anne, we want a playmate'—but it's better not. There is no use in loving things if you have to be torn from them, is there? And it's *so* hard to keep from loving things, isn't it? That was why I was so glad when I thought I was going to live here. I thought I'd have so many things to love and nothing to hinder me. But that brief dream is over. I am resigned to my fate now, so I don't think I'll go out for fear I'll get unresigned again. What is the name of that geranium on the windowsill, please?"

"That's the apple-scented geranium."

"Oh, I don't mean that sort of a name. I mean just a name you gave it yourself. Didn't you give it a name? May I give it one then? May I call it—let me see—Bonny would do— may I call it Bonny while I'm here? Oh, do let me!"

deftly (deft′lē) *adv.* skillfully and nimbly.

martyr (mär′tər) *n.* person who suffers or sacrifices greatly for a belief, principle, or cause.

"Goodness, I don't care. But where on earth is the sense of naming a geranium?"

"Oh, I like things to have handles even if they are only geraniums. It makes them seem more like people. How do you know but that it hurts a geranium's feelings just to be called a geranium and nothing else? You wouldn't like to be called nothing but a woman all the time. Yes, I shall call it Bonny. I named that cherry tree outside my bedroom window this morning. I called it Snow Queen because it was so white. Of course, it won't always be in blossom, but one can imagine that it is, can't one?"

"I never in all my life saw or heard anything to equal her," muttered Marilla, beating a retreat down cellar after potatoes. "She *is* kind of interesting, as Matthew says. I can feel already that I'm wondering what on earth she'll say next. She'll be casting a spell over me, too. She's cast it over Matthew. That look he gave me when he went out said everything he said or hinted last night over again. I wish he was like other men and would talk things out. A body could answer back then and argue him into reason. But what's to be done with a man who just *looks?*"

Anne had relapsed into reverie, with her chin in her hands and her eyes on the sky, when Marilla returned from her cellar pilgrimage. There Marilla left her until the early dinner was on the table.

"I suppose I can have the mare and buggy this afternoon, Matthew?" said Marilla.

Matthew nodded and looked wistfully at Anne. Marilla intercepted the look and said grimly:

"I'm going to drive over to White Sands and settle this thing. I'll take Anne with me and Mrs. Spencer will probably make arrangements to send her back to Nova Scotia at once. I'll set your tea out for you and I'll be home in time to milk the cows."

Still Matthew said nothing and Marilla had a sense of having wasted words and breath. There is nothing more aggravating than a man who won't talk back—unless it is a woman who won't.

■———————————————————————————————

aggravating (ag′rə vā′ting) *adj.* annoying; irritating.

Matthew hitched the <u>sorrel</u> into the buggy in due time and Marilla and Anne set off. Matthew opened the yard gate for them, and as they drove slowly through, he said, to nobody in particular as it seemed:

"Little Jerry Buote from the Creek was here this morning, and I told him I guessed I'd hire him for the summer."

Marilla made no reply, but she hit the unlucky sorrel such a vicious clip with the whip that the fat mare, unused to such treatment, whizzed indignantly down the lane at an alarming pace. Marilla looked back once as the buggy bounced along and saw that aggravating Matthew leaning over the gate, looking wistfully after them.

"Do you know," said Anne <u>confidentially</u>, "I've made up my mind to enjoy this drive. It's been my experience that you can nearly always enjoy things if you make up your mind firmly that you will. Of course, you must make it up *firmly*. I am not going to think about going back to the asylum while we're having our drive. I'm just going to think about the drive. Oh, look, there's one little early wild rose out! Isn't it lovely? Don't you think it must be glad to be a rose? Wouldn't it be nice if roses could talk? I'm sure they could tell us such lovely things. And isn't pink the most bewitching color in the world? I love it, but I can't wear it. Redheaded people can't wear pink, not even in imagination. Did you ever know of anybody whose hair was red when she was young, but got to be another color when she grew up?"

"No, I don't know as I ever did," said Marilla mercilessly, "and I shouldn't think it likely to happen in your case, either."

Anne sighed.

"Well, that is another hope gone. My life is a perfect graveyard of buried hopes. That's a sentence I read in a book once, and I say it over to comfort myself whenever I'm disappointed in anything."

"I don't see where the comforting comes in myself," said Marilla.

---

sorrel (sôr′əl) *n.* reddish-brown horse.

confidentially (kon′fi den′shə lē) *adv.* in a trusting tone suggesting something told in private.

"Why, because it sounds so nice and romantic, just as if I were a heroine in a book, you know. I am so fond of romantic things, and a graveyard full of buried hopes is about as romantic a thing as one can imagine, isn't it? I'm rather glad I have one. Are we going across the Lake of Shining Waters today?"

"We're not going over Barry's pond, if that's what you mean by your Lake of Shining Waters. We're going by the shore road."

"Shore road sounds nice," said Anne dreamily. "Is it as nice as it sounds? Just when you said 'shore road' I saw it in a picture in my mind, as quick as that! And White Sands is a pretty name, too; but I don't like it as well as Avonlea. Avonlea is a lovely name. It just sounds like music. How far is it to White Sands?"

"It's five miles; and as you're evidently bent on talking you might as well talk to some purpose by telling me what you know about yourself."

"Oh, what I *know* about myself isn't really worth telling," said Anne eagerly. "If you'll only let me tell you what I *imagine* about myself you'll think it ever so much more interesting."

"No, I don't want any of your imaginings. Just you stick to bald facts. Begin at the beginning. Where were you born and how old are you?"

"I was eleven last March," said Anne, resigning herself to bald facts with a little sigh. "And I was born in Bolingbroke, Nova Scotia. My father's name was Walter Shirley, and he was a teacher in the Bolingbroke High School. My mother's name was Bertha Shirley. Aren't Walter and Bertha lovely names? I'm so glad my parents had nice names. It would be a real disgrace to have a father named—well, say Jedediah, wouldn't it?"

"I guess it doesn't matter what a person's name is as long as he behaves himself," said Marilla, feeling herself called upon to <u>inculcate</u> a good and useful moral.

---

inculcate (in kul′kāt) *v.t.* fix firmly in the mind or memory by teaching or example.

"Well, I don't know." Anne looked thoughtful. "I read in a book once that a rose by any other name would smell as sweet, but I've never been able to believe it. I don't believe a rose *would* be as nice if it was called a thistle or a skunk cabbage. I suppose my father could have been a good man even if he had been called Jedediah; but I'm sure it would have been a cross. Well, my mother was a teacher in the High School, too, but when she married father she gave up teaching, of course. A husband was enough responsibility. Mrs. Thomas said that they were a pair of babies and as poor as church mice. They went to live in a weeny-teeny little yellow house in Bolingbroke. I've never seen that house, but I've imagined it thousands of times. I think it must have had honeysuckle over the parlor window and lilacs in the front yard and lilies of the valley just inside the gate. Yes, and muslin curtains in all the windows. Muslin curtains give a house such an air. I was born in that house. Mrs. Thomas said I was the homeliest baby she ever saw, I was so scrawny and tiny and nothing but eyes, but that mother thought I was perfectly beautiful. I should think a mother would be a better judge than a poor woman who came in to scrub, wouldn't you? I'm glad she was satisfied with me anyhow; I would feel so sad if I thought I was a disappointment to her—because she didn't live very long after that, you see. She died of fever when I was just three months old. I do wish she'd lived long enough for me to remember calling her mother. I think it would be so sweet to say 'mother,' don't you? And father died four days afterwards from fever, too. That left me an orphan and folks were at their wits' end, so Mrs. Thomas said, what to do with me. You see, nobody wanted me even then. It seems to be my fate. Father and mother had both come from places far away and it was well known they hadn't any relatives living. Finally Mrs. Thomas said she'd take me, though she was poor and had a drunken husband. She brought me up by hand. Do you know if there is anything in being brought up by hand that ought to make people who are

brought up that way better than other people? Because whenever I was naughty Mrs. Thomas would ask me how I could be such a bad girl when she had brought me up by hand—reproachful-like.

"Mr. and Mrs. Thomas moved away from Bolingbroke to Marysville, and I lived with them until I was eight years old. I helped look after the Thomas children—there were four of them younger than me—and I can tell you they took a lot of looking after. Then Mr. Thomas was killed falling under a train and his mother offered to take Mrs. Thomas and the children, but she didn't want me. Mrs. Thomas was at *her* wits' end, so she said, what to do with me. Then Mrs. Hammond from up the river came down and said she'd take me, seeing I was handy with children, and I went up the river to live with her in a little clearing among the stumps. It was a very lonesome place. I'm sure I could never have lived there if I hadn't had an imagination. Mr. Hammond worked a little sawmill up there, and Mrs. Hammond had eight children. She had twins three times. I like babies in <u>moderation</u>, but twins three times in succession is *too much*. I told Mrs. Hammond so firmly, when the last pair came. I used to get so dreadfully tired carrying them about.

"I lived up river with Mrs. Hammond over two years, and then Mr. Hammond died and Mrs. Hammond broke up housekeeping. She divided her children among her relatives and went to the States. I had to go to the asylum at Hopeton, because nobody would take me. They didn't want me at the asylum, either; they said they were overcrowded as it was. But they had to take me and I was there four months until Mrs. Spencer came."

Anne finished up with another sigh, of relief this time. Evidently she did not like talking about her experiences in a world that had not wanted her.

"Did you ever go to school?" demanded Marilla, turning the sorrel mare down the shore road.

---

moderation (mod′ə rā′shən) *n.* state of being kept within reasonable limits and not going to extremes.

"Not a great deal. I went a little the last year I stayed with Mrs. Thomas. When I went up river we were so far from a school that I couldn't walk it in winter and there was vacation in summer, so I could only go in the spring and fall. But of course I went while I was at the asylum. I can read pretty well and I know ever so many pieces of poetry off by heart—'The Battle of Hohenlinden' and 'Edinburgh after Flodden,' and 'Bingen on the Rhine,' and lots of the 'Lady of the Lake' and most of 'The Seasons,' by James Thompson. Don't you just love poetry that gives you a crinkly feeling up and down your back? There is a piece in the Fifth Reader—'The Downfall of Poland'— that is just full of thrills. Of course, I wasn't in the Fifth Reader—I was only in the Fourth—but the big girls used to lend me theirs to read."

"Were those women—Mrs. Thomas and Mrs. Hammond— good to you?" asked Marilla, looking at Anne out of the corner of her eye.

"O-o-o-h," faltered Anne. Her sensitive little face suddenly flushed scarlet and embarrassment sat on her brow. "Oh, they *meant* to be—I know they meant to be just as good and kind as possible. And when people mean to be good to you, you don't mind very much when they're not quite—always. They had a good deal to worry them, you know. It's very trying to have a drunken husband, you see; and it must be very trying to have twins three times in succession, don't you think? But I feel sure they meant to be good to me."

Marilla asked no more questions. Anne gave herself up to a silent rapture over the shore road and Marilla guided the sorrel abstractedly while she pondered deeply. Pity was suddenly stirring in her heart for the child. What a starved, unloved life she had had—a life of drudgery and poverty and neglect; for Marilla was shrewd enough to read between the lines of Anne's history and divine the truth. No wonder she had been so delighted at the prospect of a real home. It was a pity she had to be sent back. What if she, Marilla, should

---

drudgery (druj′ə rē) *n.* tiring, boring, or menial work.

indulge Matthew's unaccountable whim and let her stay? He was set on it; and the child seemed a nice, teachable little thing.

"She's got too much to say," thought Marilla, "but she might be trained out of that. And there's nothing rude or slangy in what she does say. She's ladylike. It's likely her people were nice folks."

The shore road was "woodsy and wild and lonesome." On the right hand, scrub firs, their spirits quite unbroken by long years of tussle with the gulf winds, grew thickly. On the left were the steep red sandstone cliffs, so near the track in places that a mare of less steadiness than the sorrel might have tried the nerves of the people behind her. Down at the base of the cliffs were heaps of surf-worn rocks or little sandy coves inlaid with pebbles as with ocean jewels; beyond lay the sea, shimmering and blue, and over it soared the gulls, their pinions flashing silvery in the sunlight.

"Isn't the sea wonderful?" said Anne, rousing from a long, wide-eyed silence. "Once, when I lived in Marysville, Mr. Thomas hired an express wagon and took us all to spend the day at the shore ten miles away. I enjoyed every moment of that day, even if I had to look after the children all the time. I lived it over in happy dreams for years. But this shore is nicer than the Marysville shore. Aren't those gulls splendid? Would you like to be a gull? I think I would—that is, if I couldn't be a human girl. Don't you think it would be nice to wake up at sunrise and swoop down over the water and away out over that lovely blue all day; and then at night to fly back to one's nest? Oh, I can just imagine myself doing it. What big house is that just ahead, please?"

"That's the White Sands Hotel. Mr. Kirke runs it, but the season hasn't begun yet. There are heaps of Americans come there for the summer. They think this shore is just about right."

"I was afraid it might be Mrs. Spencer's place," said Anne mournfully. "I don't want to get there. Somehow, it will seem like the end of everything."

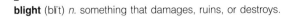

Get there they did, however, in due season. Mrs. Spencer lived in a big yellow house at White Sands Cove, and she came to the door with surprise and welcome mingled on her benevolent face.

"Dear, dear," she exclaimed, "you're the last folks I was looking for today, but I'm real glad to see you. You'll put your horse in? And how are you, Anne?"

"I'm as well as can be expected, thank you," said Anne smilelessly. A <u>blight</u> seemed to have descended on her.

"I suppose we'll stay a little while to rest the mare," said Marilla, "but I promised Matthew I'd be home early. The fact is, Mrs. Spencer, there's been a queer mistake somewhere, and I've come over to see where it is. We sent word, Matthew and I, for you to bring us a boy from the asylum. We told your brother Robert to tell you we wanted a boy ten or eleven years old."

"Marilla Cuthbert, you don't say so!" said Mrs. Spencer in distress. "Why, Robert sent the word down by his daughter Nancy and she said you wanted a girl—didn't she, Flora Jane?" appealing to her daughter who had come out to the steps.

"She certainly did, Miss Cuthbert," corroborated Flora Jane earnestly.

"I'm dreadful sorry," said Mrs. Spencer. "It is too bad; but it certainly wasn't my fault, you see, Miss Cuthbert. I did the best I could and I thought I was following your instructions. Nancy is a terrible flighty thing. I've often had to scold her well for her heedlessness."

"It was our own fault," said Marilla resignedly. "We should have come to you ourselves and not left an important message to be passed along by word of mouth in that fashion. Anyhow, the mistake has been made and the only thing to do now is to set it right. Can we send the child back to the asylum? I suppose they'll take her back, won't they?"

"I suppose so," said Mrs. Spencer thoughtfully, "but I don't think it will be necessary to send her back. Mrs. Peter

---

blight (blīt) *n.* something that damages, ruins, or destroys.

Blewett was up here yesterday, and she was saying to me how much she wished she'd sent by me for a little girl to help her. Mrs. Peter has a large family, you know, and she finds it hard to get help. Anne will be the very girl for her. I call it positively providential."

Marilla did not look as if she thought Providence had much to do with the matter. Here was an unexpectedly good chance to get this unwelcome orphan off her hands, and she did not even feel grateful for it.

She knew Mrs. Peter Blewett only by sight as a small, shrewish-faced woman without an ounce of superfluous flesh on her bones. But she had heard of her. "A terrible worker and driver," Mrs. Peter was said to be; and discharged servant girls told fearsome tales of her temper and stinginess, and her family of pert, quarrelsome children. Marilla felt a qualm of conscience at the thought of handing Anne over to her tender mercies.

"Well, I'll go in and we'll talk the matter over," she said.

"And if there isn't Mrs. Peter coming up the lane this blessed minute!" exclaimed Mrs. Spencer, bustling her guests through the hall into the parlor, where a deadly chill struck on them as if the air had been strained so long through dark green, closely drawn blinds that it had lost every particle of warmth it had ever possessed. "That is real lucky, for we can settle the matter right away. Take the armchair, Miss Cuthbert. Anne, you sit here on the ottoman and don't wriggle. Let me take your hats. Flora Jane, go out to put the kettle on. Good afternoon, Mrs. Blewett. We were just saying how fortunate it was you happened along. Let me introduce you two ladies. Mrs. Blewett, Miss Cuthbert. Please excuse me for just a moment. I forgot to tell Flora Jane to take the buns out of the oven."

Mrs. Spencer whisked away, after pulling up the blinds. Anne, sitting mutely on the ottoman, with her hands clasped tightly in her lap, stared at Mrs. Blewett as one fascinated. Was she to be given into the keeping of this sharp-faced,

---

superfluous (sů pûr′flü əs) *adj.* extra; more than is needed or wanted.
qualm (kwäm) *n.* twinge of conscience; sudden doubt or misgiving.

542

sharp-eyed woman? She felt a lump coming up in her throat and her eyes smarted painfully. She was beginning to be afraid she couldn't keep the tears back when Mrs. Spencer returned, flushed and beaming, quite capable of taking any and every difficulty, physical, mental or spiritual, into consideration and settling it out of hand.

"It seems there's been a mistake about this little girl, Mrs. Blewett," she said. "I was under the impression that Mr. and Miss Cuthbert wanted a little girl to adopt. I was certainly told so. But it seems it was a boy they wanted. So if you're still of the same mind you were yesterday, I think she'll be just the thing for you."

Mrs. Blewett darted her eyes over Anne from head to foot.

"How old are you and what's your name?" she demanded.

"Anne Shirley," faltered the shrinking child, not daring to make any stipulations regarding the spelling thereof, "and I'm eleven years old."

"Humph! You don't look as if there was much to you. But you're wiry. I don't know but the wiry ones are the best after all. Well, if I take you you'll have to be a good girl, you know—good and smart and respectful. I'll expect you to earn your keep, and no mistake about that. Yes, I suppose I might as well take her off your hands, Miss Cuthbert. The baby's awful fractious, and I'm clean worn out attending to him. If you like I can take her right home now."

Marilla looked at Anne and softened at sight of the child's pale face with its look of mute misery—the misery of a helpless little creature who finds itself once more caught in the trap from which it had escaped. Marilla felt an uncomfortable conviction that, if she denied the appeal of that look, it would haunt her to her dying day. Moreover, she did not fancy Mrs. Blewett. To hand a sensitive, "highstrung" child over to such a woman! No, she could not take the responsibility of doing that!

"Well, I don't know," she said slowly. "I didn't say that Matthew and I had absolutely decided that we wouldn't keep her.

In fact, I may say that Matthew is disposed to keep her. I just came over to find out how the mistake had occurred. I think I'd better take her home again and talk it over with Matthew. I feel that I oughtn't to decide on anything without consulting him. If we make up our mind not to keep her we'll bring or send her over to you tomorrow night. If we don't you may know that she is going to stay with us. Will that suit you, Mrs. Blewett?"

"I suppose it'll have to," said Mrs. Blewett ungraciously.

During Marilla's speech a sunrise had been dawning on Anne's face. First the look of despair faded out; then came a faint flush of hope; her eyes grew deep and bright as morning stars. The child was quite transfigured; and, a moment later, when Mrs. Spencer and Mrs. Blewett went out in quest of a recipe the latter had come to borrow she sprang up and flew across the room to Marilla.

"Oh, Miss Cuthbert, did you really say that perhaps you would let me stay at Green Gables?" she said, in a breathless whisper, as if speaking aloud might shatter the glorious possibility. "Did you really say it? Or did I only imagine that you did?"

"I think you'd better learn to control that imagination of yours, Anne, if you can't distinguish between what is real and what isn't," said Marilla crossly. "Yes, you did hear me say just that and no more. It isn't decided yet and perhaps we will conclude to let Mrs. Blewett take you after all. She certainly needs you much more than I do."

"I'd rather go back to the asylum than go to live with her," said Anne passionately. "She looks exactly like a—like a gimlet."

Marilla smothered a smile under the conviction that Anne must be reproved for such a speech.

"A little girl like you should be ashamed of talking so about a lady and a stranger," she said severely. "Go back and sit down quietly and hold your tongue and behave as a good girl should."

"I'll try to do and be anything you want me, if you'll only keep me," said Anne, returning meekly to her ottoman.

When they arrived back at Green Gables that evening Matthew met them in the lane. Marilla from afar had noted him prowling along it and guessed his motive. She was prepared for the relief she read in his face when he saw that she had at least brought Anne back with her. But she said nothing to him, relative to the affair, until they were both out in the yard behind the barn milking the cows. Then she briefly told him Anne's history and the result of the interview with Mrs. Spencer.

"I wouldn't give a dog I liked to that Blewett woman," said Matthew with unusual vim.

"I don't fancy her style myself," admitted Marilla, "but it's that or keeping her ourselves, Matthew. And, since you seem to want her, I suppose I'm willing—or have to be. I've been thinking over the idea until I've got kind of used to it. It seems a sort of duty. I've never brought up a child, especially a girl, and I dare say I'll make a terrible mess of it. But I'll do my best. So far as I'm concerned, Matthew, she may stay."

Matthew's shy face was a glow of delight.

"Well now, I reckoned you'd come to see it in that light, Marilla," he said. "She's such an interesting little thing."

"It'd be more to the point if you could say she was a useful little thing," retorted Marilla, "but I'll make it my business to see she's trained to be that. And mind, Matthew, you're not to go interfering with my methods. Perhaps an old maid doesn't know much about bringing up a child, but I guess she knows more than an old bachelor. So you just leave me to manage her. When I fail it'll be time enough to put your oar in."

"There, there, Marilla, you can have your own way," said Matthew reassuringly. "Only be as good and kind to her as you can be without spoiling her. I kind of think she's one of the sort you can do anything with if you only get her to love you."

Marilla sniffed, to express her <u>contempt</u> for Matthew's opinions concerning anything feminine, and walked off to the dairy with the pails.

"I won't tell her tonight that she can stay," she reflected, as she strained the milk into the creamers. "She'd be so excited that she wouldn't sleep a wink. Marilla Cuthbert, you're fairly in for it. Did you ever suppose you'd see the day when you'd be adopting an orphan girl? It's surprising enough; but not so surprising as that Matthew should be at the bottom of it, him that always seemed to have such a mortal dread of little girls. Anyhow, we've decided on the experiment and goodness only knows what will come of it."

---

contempt (kən tempt′) *n.* scorn; disdain; disrespect.

meet Lucy Maud Montgomery

Growing up on her grandparents' farm on Prince Edward Island, Lucy Maud Montgomery (1874–1942) used her imagination as a "passport to fairyland." Montgomery wrote, "I have no companionship except that of books and solitary rambles in wood and fields. This drove me in on myself and early forced me to construct for myself a world of fantasy and imagination very different indeed from the world in which I had lived." Although she had a family, her childhood and early youth were lonely.

Montgomery drew on memories of those childhood feelings and experiences to write stories for children. The success of her book *Anne of Green Gables* led to five sequels and two more books about its heroine, Anne Shirley. Years after their publication, several of the books were made into movies.

RESPONDING TO *Literature*

THINK • TALK • WRITE

1 Would you like to have Anne for a friend? Explain why or why not in your journal.

2 Briefly describe Anne from Marilla's point of view. Then describe her from Matthew's point of view. Why do you think they have different opinions of Anne?

3 How does Anne feel about Green Gables and Prince Edward Island? How does Marilla feel about them? What do their reactions tell you about each of them?

4 Did you predict that Marilla would allow Anne to stay at Green Gables? Why or why not?

5 The theme of an orphaned or lost child looking for a home is common to many cultures. What cartoons, plays, movies, or books can you think of with this theme? Why do you think this theme is such a popular one?

ACTIVITIES

- **Write About Plot: Complication**
  With classmates, write a dramatic sketch of the scene at Mrs. Spencer's house. The person playing Marilla must act genuinely confused as she looks at Anne and listens to Mrs. Blewett. Add other plot complications. Practice saying your lines with feeling. Then perform your sketch for an audience.

- **Present an Island Ecosystem**
  Green Gables is on Prince Edward Island, off the coast of eastern Canada in the Gulf of St. Lawrence. Find out more about the plants and animals in this area. Then make a model or a chart of the island's ecosystem. Display your project in the classroom.

VOCABULARY PRACTICE

On a separate piece of paper, write whether the following pairs of words are *synonyms* or *antonyms*.

1 ignorance—knowledge

2 affliction—suffering

3 whim—caprice

4 deftly—clumsily

5 blight—damage

6 evidently—obviously

7 abstracted—attentive

8 reverie—daydream

9 confidentially—privately

10 contempt—respect

MY LAND IS FAIR FOR ANY EYES TO SEE

Stone City, Iowa   *1930   Grant Wood   Joslyn Art Museum   Omaha, Nebraska*

My land is fair for any eyes to see—
Now look, my friends—look to the east and west!
You see the purple hills far in the west—
Hills lined with pine and gum and black-oak tree—
Now to the east you see the fertile valley!
This land is mine, I sing of it to you—
My land beneath the skies of white and blue.

This land is mine, for I am part of it.
I am the land, for it is part of me—
We are akin and thus our kinship be!
It would make me a brother to the tree!
And as far as eyes can see this land is mine.
Not for one foot of it I have a deed—
To own this land I do not need a deed—
They all belong to me—gum, oak, and pine.

—Jesse Stuart

A good short story sometimes leaves readers wanting more. Many stories introduce characters, places, and situations that readers might enjoy getting to know at greater length. Paintings, like the one below, often do the same thing.

Traffic Conditions 1949 Norman Rockwell Norman Rockwell Family Trust

Courtesy Curtis Publishing

What is the most important thing happening in this scene? What makes you think so? Would you like to know more about these characters and this situation?

Why do you think Rockwell included so many different people? How are they alike or different? Whom do you like the most?

Think about stories you have read. Can you recall any elements found in those stories that appear in this painting as well?

LIGHT

ELEMENTS OF A SHORT STORY

CHARACTERS are the people or animals in a short story. Characterization is the way a writer presents characters.

- **Direct characterization** takes place when the writer tells you how a character looks, acts, and thinks.
- **Indirect characterization** takes place when the writer lets you draw your own conclusions about a character from how the character speaks or acts or how people react to the character.

SETTING is the time and place in which the story's action occurs.

PLOT is the sequence of events in a short story. The plot is usually built around a conflict, or struggle between opposing forces.

- **External conflicts** take place between a character and an outside force, such as another character or a force of nature.
- **Internal conflicts** take place within a character's mind, such as deciding what to do about a serious problem.

Most plots follow five stages.

- **Exposition** introduces the characters, setting, and conflict.
- **Rising action** builds suspense as the conflict becomes clear.
- **Climax** is the point of greatest interest. The conflict is resolved.
- **Falling action** shows the effects of the climax and tells what happens to the characters next.
- **Resolution** answers any remaining questions related to the plot.

POINT OF VIEW is the standpoint from which a story is told. In *first-person point of view,* the person telling the story is a character in the story. In *third-person point of view,* the person telling the story is someone outside the story.

THEME is the writer's main message. Sometimes it is stated directly. More often a theme is inferred from characters, plot, setting, and point of view.

In the selections that follow, you will learn more about short stories. Your discoveries will help you in writing a short story of your own.

SHORT STORY

· ·

VIVA NEW JERSEY

CONNECT TO LITERATURE

Who is your best friend? How did you meet your best friend? What things do you do together? In your journal, tell how you met your best friend. Then read the selection to find out how Lucinda finds a pet—and a friend—in her new country.

INTRODUCTION TO THE MODEL SHORT STORY

As you read the stories in this unit, you will find that all of them contain certain elements: characters, setting, plot, point of view, and theme. Each author uses these basic elements to weave a story for the reader to enjoy—and perhaps to learn from.

As you read "Viva New Jersey," use the notes in the margin to help you understand the basic elements of a story. You might also note your own thoughts and impressions in your journal.

DID YOU KNOW?

- Cuba is the largest of a group of islands in the West Indies. It is about 90 miles south of Florida. (See the map above.)

- Several different Native American peoples inhabited Cuba when Columbus arrived in 1492. The Spanish used the island as the base for their explorations of the Americas.

- Today, sugar and sugarcane products account for about two-thirds of all exports from Cuba.

- Fidel Castro took control of Cuba's government in 1959 and has ruled ever since. Many Cubans fled because of the hardships of life on their island. Castro has frequently clashed with the United States government because of his hard-line Communist beliefs.

VIVA NEW JERSEY

BY
GLORIA GONZALEZ

As far as dogs go, it wasn't much of a prize—
a hairy <u>mongrel</u> with clumps of bubble gum
wadded on its belly. Pieces of multicolored hard
candies were matted in its fur. The leash around
its neck was fashioned from a cloth belt, the kind
usually seen attached to old bathrobes. The dog's
paws were clogged with mud from yesterday's rain,
and you could see where the animal had gnawed
at the irritated skin around the swollen pads.

The dog was tied to an <u>anemic</u> tree high
above the cliffs overlooking the Hudson River and
the majestic New York City skyline.

---

mongrel (mong′grəl) *n.* animal, especially a dog, of mixed breed.
anemic (ə nē′mik) *adj.* lacking vitality or spirit.

The pronouns *her* and *she* help indicate the point of view from which the story is told. The author is acting as the narrator who stands outside the story and refers to all characters as *he, she,* or *it.* This is called **third-person point of view.**

Lucinda traveled the route each day on her way to the high school, along the New Jersey side of the river. The short walk saddened her, despite its panoramic vista of bridges and skyscrapers, for the river reminded her of the perilous journey six months earlier, when she and her family had escaped from Cuba in a makeshift boat with seven others.

They had spent two freezing nights adrift in the ocean, uncertain of their destination, till a U. S. Coast Guard cutter towed them to the shores of Key West.

From there they wound their way north, staying temporarily with friends in Miami and finally settling in West New York, New Jersey, the most densely populated town in the United States. Barely a square mile, high above the Palisades, the town boasted a population of 85,000. Most of the community was housed in mammoth apartment buildings that seemed to reach into the clouds. The few private homes had cement lawns and paved driveways where there should have been backyards.

Gonzalez compares and contrasts Cuba and New Jersey to show how homesick Lucinda is. **Setting,** the place and time in which the story happens, is an important element in this story.

Lucinda longed for the spacious front porch where she'd sat at night with her friends while her grandmother bustled about the house, humming her Spanish songs. Lucinda would ride her bike to school and sometimes not see a soul for miles, just wild flowers amid a forest of greenery.

Now it was cement and cars and trucks and motorcycles and clanging fire engines that seemed to be in constant motion, shattering the air with their menacing roar.

Lucinda longed painfully for her grandmother. The old woman had refused to leave her house in Cuba, despite the family's pleas, so she

---

panoramic (pan′ə ram′ik) *adj.* of or like a wide or complete view of an area.
perilous (per′ə ləs) *adj.* hazardous; dangerous.
cutter (kut′ər) *n.* small, fast ship used by the Coast Guard.

had remained behind, promising to see them again one day.

The teenager, tall and slight of build with long dark hair that reached down her spine, was uncomfortable among her new classmates, most of whom she towered over. Even though the majority of them spoke Spanish and came from Cuba, Argentina, and Costa Rica, they were not like any of her friends back home. These "American" girls wore heavy makeup to school, dressed in jeans and high heels, and talked about rock singers and TV stars that she knew nothing of. They all seemed to be busy, rushing through the school corridors, huddling in laughing groups, mingling freely with boys, and chatting openly with teachers as if they were personal friends.

It was all too confusing.

Things weren't much better at home. Her parents had found jobs almost immediately and were often away from the tiny, cramped apartment. Her brother quickly made friends and was picked for the school baseball team, traveling to nearby towns to compete.

All Lucinda had were her memories—and now this dog, whom she untied from the tree. The animal was frightened and growled at her when she approached, but she spoke softly and offered a soothing hand, which he tried to attack. Lucinda persisted, and the dog, perhaps grateful to be freed from the mud puddles, allowed her to lead him away.

She didn't know what she was going to do with him now that she had him. Pets were not allowed in her building, and her family could be evicted. She couldn't worry about that now. Her main concern was to get him out of the cold.

Lucinda must figure out what to do with the dog. Her attempts to solve this problem will be central to the plot. A character's struggles are called **conflicts.**

Sunday Afternoon *1953 Ralph Fasanella*

Even though it was April and supposedly spring, the weather had yet to top fifty degrees. At night she slept under two blankets, wearing warm socks over her cold feet. Another night outdoors, and the dog could freeze to death.

Lucinda reached her building and comforted the dog. "I'm not going to hurt you." She took off her jacket and wrapped it quickly around the animal, hoping to disguise it as a bundle under her arm. "Don't make any noise," she begged.

She waited till a woman with a baby stroller exited the building and quickly dashed inside, unseen. She opted not to take the elevator, fearful of running into someone, and instead lugged the dog and her schoolbag up the eight flights of stairs.

Lucinda quickly unlocked the apartment door and plopped the dog on her bed. The animal instantly shook its hair free and ran in circles atop her blanket.

Characterization—the revealing of character—occurs as much through action as through description. Lucinda's decision to take in the dog and feed him shows she's compassionate and caring.

"Don't get too comfortable," Lucinda cautioned. "You can't stay."

She dashed to the kitchen and returned moments later with a bowl of water and a plate of leftover chicken and yellow rice.

The dog bolted from the bed and began attacking the food before she even placed it on the floor. The girl sat on the edge of the bed and watched contentedly as he devoured the meal.

"How long has it been since you've eaten?"

The dog swallowed the food hungrily, not bothering to chew, and quickly lapped up the water.

It was then, with the dog's head lowered to the bowl, that Lucinda spotted the small piece of paper wedged beneath the belt around its neck. She slid it out carefully and saw the word that someone had scrawled with a pencil.

"Chauncey. Is that your name?"

---

opted (op′tid) *v.i.* made a choice; chose.

The dog leaped to her side and nuzzled its nose against her arm.

"It's a crazy name, but I think I like it." She smiled. Outside the window, eight stories below, two fire engines pierced the afternoon with wailing sirens. Lucinda didn't seem to notice as she stroked the animal gently.

Working quickly, before her parents were due to arrive, she filled the bathtub with water and soap detergent and scrubbed the animal clean. The dog didn't enjoy it—he kept trying to jump out—so Lucinda began humming a Spanish song her grandmother used to sing to her when she was little. It didn't work. Chauncey still fought to get free.

Once the animal was bathed, Lucinda attacked the clumps of hair with a scissor and picked out the sticky globs of candy.

"My God, you're white!" Lucinda discovered. While using her brother's hair blower, she ran a quick comb through the fur, which now was silvery and tan with faint traces of black. "You're beautiful." The girl beamed.

The dog seemed to agree. It picked up its head proudly and flicked its long ears with pride.

Lucinda hugged him close, "I'll find you a good home. I promise," she told the animal.

Knowing that her parents would arrive any moment, Lucinda gathered up the dog, covering him with her coat, and carried him down nine flights to the basement. She crept quietly past the superintendent's apartment and deposited the animal in a tiny room behind the bank of washing machines.

The room, the size of a small closet, contained all the electrical levers that supplied power to the apartments and the elevator.

Chauncey looked about, confused. He jumped up as if he knew he was about to be abandoned again. His white hairy paw came dangerously close to hitting the <u>protruding</u>, red master switch near the door.

Lucinda knelt to the animal. "I'll be back. Promise."

She closed the door behind her, praying the dog wouldn't bark, and hurried away. An outline of a plan was taking shape in her mind.

Ashley.

The girl sat in front of her in English and always went out of her way to say hi. She didn't seem to hang out with the other kids, and whenever they passed in the corridor, she was alone. But what really made her even more appealing was that she lived in a real house. Just a block away. Lucinda had seen her once going in. Maybe Ashley would take Chauncey.

Lucinda's parents arrived from work, and she quickly helped her mother prepare the scrumptious fried bananas. Her father had stopped at a restaurant on his way home and brought a *cantina* of food—white rice, black beans, avocado salad, and meat stew. Each food was placed in its own metal container and clipped together like a small pyramid. The local restaurant would have delivered the food to the house each day, if the family desired, but Lucinda's father always liked to stop by and check the menu. The restaurant also made fried bananas, but Lucinda's mother didn't think they were as tasty as her own. One of the nice surprises of moving to New Jersey was discovering that the Latin restaurants supplied *cantina* service.

"How was school today?" her mother asked.

"Okay," Lucinda replied.

The dinner conversation drifted, as it always did, to Mama's problems at work with the

> Lucinda has been lonely. Will her kindness to Chauncey gain her a friend? Wondering what will happen next creates a feeling of **suspense** in a story. Authors often use suspense so you will want to keep reading to discover how things turn out.

---

protruding (prō trüd′ing) *v.i.* sticking out; projecting.

cantina (kän tē′nə) *n. Spanish.* package of food taken out from a restaurant.

559

supervisor and Papa's frustration with his job. Every day he had to ride two buses and a subway to get to work, which he saw as wasted hours.

"You get an education, go to college," Lucinda's father sermonized for the thousandth time, "and you can work anywhere you like—even in your own house, if you want. Like a doctor! And if it is far away, you hire someone like me, with no education, to drive you."

Lucinda had grown up hearing the lecture. Perhaps she would have been a good student anyway, for she certainly took to it with enthusiasm. She had discovered books at a young age. School only heightened her love of reading, for its library supplied her with an endless source of material. She excelled in her studies and won top honors in English class. She was so proficient at learning the English language that she served as a tutor to kids in lower grades.

Despite her father's wishes, Lucinda had no intention of becoming a doctor or lawyer. She wasn't sure what she would do—the future seemed far too distant to address it—but she knew somehow it would involve music and dance and magnificent costumes and glittering shoes and plumes in her hair.

They were talking about her brother's upcoming basketball game when suddenly all the lights in the apartment went out.

"*Qué paso!*" her father exclaimed.

Agitated voices could be heard from the outside hallway. A neighbor banged on the door, shouting, "Call the fire department! Someone's trapped in the elevator!"

Groups of tenants mingled outside their apartments, some carrying candles and flashlights. The building had been pitched into darkness.

---

sermonized (sûr′mə nīzd) *v.i.* spoke at length in a moralizing way.
proficient (prə fish′ənt) *adj.* highly skilled; expert.

"We'll get you out!" someone shouted to the woman caught between floors.

Lucinda cried: "Chauncey!"

He must've hit the master switch. She could hear the distant wail of the fire engines and knew it was only a matter of minutes before they checked the room where the dog was hidden.

"I'll be right back!" Lucinda yelled to her mother as she raced out the door. Groping onto the banister, she felt her way down the flights of steps as people with candles hurried to escape.

The rescuers reached the basement before she did. Two firemen were huddled in the doorway checking the power supply. Lucinda looked frantically for the dog, but he was gone.

She raced out into the nippy night, through the throng of people crowded on the sidewalk, and searched for the dog. She was afraid to look in the street, expecting to see his lifeless body, the victim of a car.

Lucinda looked up at the sound of her name. Her mother was calling to her from the window.

"Come home! What are you doing?"

The girl shouted, "In a minute!" The crowd swelled about her as she quickly darted away.

Lucinda didn't plan it, but she found herself in front of Ashley's house minutes later. She was on the sidewalk, with the rest of her neighbors, gazing up the block at the commotion in front of Lucinda's building.

"Hi," Lucinda stammered.

Ashley took a moment to place the face and then returned the smile. "Hi."

Lucinda looked about nervously, wondering if any of the adults belonged to Ashley's family. She didn't have a moment to waste.

Across the River to the Country *1969 Ralph Fasanella*

"What happens," she blurted out, "when a dog runs away? Do the police catch it?"

The blond, chubby teenager, with light green eyes and glasses with pink frames, shrugged. "Probably. If they do, only take it to the pound."

"What's that?" It sounded bad, whatever it was.

"A shelter. Where they keep animals. If nobody claims 'em, they kill 'em."

Lucinda started to cry. She couldn't help it. It came upon her suddenly. Greatly embarrassed, she turned quickly and hurried away.

"Wait up!" The blonde hurried after her. "Hey!"

Lucinda stopped, too ashamed to meet her eyes.

"Did you lose your dog?" Ashley's voice sounded concerned.

Lucinda nodded.

"Well, let's go find him," Ashley prodded.

They searched the surrounding neighborhood and checked underneath all the cars parked in the area in case he was hiding. They searched basements and rooftops. When all else failed, they walked to the park along the river, where Lucinda pointed out the tree where she had found him.

The girls decided to sit on a nearby bench in case Chauncey reappeared, though they realized there was little hope.

Lucinda knew her mother would be frantically worried.

"She probably has the police looking for me," she told Ashley.

"You've only been gone an hour."

"It's the first time I've left the house, except to go to school, since we moved here," she revealed.

It was a beautiful night, despite the cold tingling breeze that swept up from the river. The New York skyline was ablaze with golden

Lucinda notices the world around her differently now that she is making a friend. The setting hasn't changed—just her attitude.

563

windows <u>silhouetted</u> against dark, boxlike steel structures. You could make out the red traffic lights along the narrow streets. A long, thin barge sailed down the river like a rubbery snake.

Lucinda learned that Ashley's mother was a lawyer, often away from home for long periods, and her father operated a small business in New York's Chinatown, which kept him busy seven days a week. An only child, she spent her time studying and writing letters.

"Who do you write to?" Lucinda asked.

"My grandmother, mostly. She lives in Nevada. I spend the summers with her."

Lucinda told her how lucky she was to be able to see her grandmother. She felt dangerously close to tears again and quickly changed the subject. "I never see you with any friends in school. Why?"

Ashley shrugged. "Guess I'm not the friendly type. Most of the girls are only interested in boys and dates. I intend to be a famous writer one day, so there's a lot of books I have to read. Just so I know what's been done."

It made sense.

"What are you going to be?"

Lucinda admitted she had no ambition. No particular desire. But maybe, if she had her choice, if she could be anything she wanted, it would probably be a dancer.

"My grandmother used to take me to her friend's house who used to be a famous ballerina in Cuba. She'd let me try on her costumes, and she'd play the records and teach me the steps. It hurt my feet something awful. Hers used to bleed when she first started, but she said it got easier after the first year."

silhouetted (sil´ü et´id) *v.t.* made a dark outline on a light background.

Ashley told her, "You have the body for it. I bet you'd make a wonderful dancer."

When it became apparent that Chauncey would never return, the girls walked home together.

Despite all that happened, Lucinda found herself sad to have the evening end. For the first time since leaving her homeland, she felt somewhat at peace with herself. She now had someone to talk to. Someone who understood. Someone who carried her own pain.

"Wanna have lunch tomorrow?" Ashley asked her. "I usually run home and eat in front of the television. I'm a great cook. My first book is going to be filled with exotic recipes of all the countries I plan to visit. And if you want," she gushed excitedly, "after school we can go to the library. You can get out a book on how to be a ballerina."

Lucinda agreed immediately, "That would be wonderful!"

The girls parted on the sidewalk, and Lucinda raced home where her <u>irate</u> father and weeping mother confronted her angrily.

"Where have you been! I was only going to wait five more minutes and then I was calling the police! Where were you?"

Before she could stammer a reply, the lights went out.

"Not again!" her mother shrieked.

Lucinda's heart throbbed with excitement. Chauncey was back!

She ran out of the apartment, unmindful of the darkness, with her mother's screams in the air: "Come back here!"

This time Lucinda made it to the basement before the firemen, and she led her pal safely out the building. She reached Ashley's doorstep just as the first fire engine turned the corner.

Lucinda has solved her two main problems—lack of friends and the dog's need for a home. This is called the **resolution** of the plot.

irate (ī rāt′) *adj.* angry; enraged.

MEET GLORIA GONZALEZ

Gloria Gonzalez was born in New York City in 1940. Before her recent move to Las Vegas, Nevada, she lived for many years in West New York, New Jersey—where this story takes place.

Gonzalez has written three young-adult novels, including *Gaucho,* which was made into a TV movie. Today she devotes herself full-time to the kind of writing she loves the most— writing plays. Her first success came at age 25, when she won a national playwrighting contest with her play "Curtains." Since then, her plays have been produced all over the country.

Gonzalez says she likes the immediate feedback she gets from the people who see her plays. With novels, she has to wait "months, even a year after the book is written," to read reviews. In the theater, she can tell right away how much audiences like her work.

More Short Stories

- *Baseball in April* by Gary Soto (Harcourt Brace Jovanovich, 1990). Based on Soto's own experiences as a Mexican American growing up in California, these stories portray the incidents, large and small, that occur in the daily lives of most young people.

- *The Future-Telling Lady and Other Stories* by James Berry (Harper Trophy, 1991). These six stories will transport you to the magical island of Jamaica in the West Indies, where James Berry grew up and which he knows so well.

- *Within Reach: Ten Stories,* edited by Donald R. Gallo (HarperCollins, 1993). Ten well-known authors of young adult fiction wrote original stories—some funny, some sad—for this collection. All are about growing up in the U. S. today.

RESPONDING TO *Literature*

THINK • TALK • WRITE

1 What was most memorable about this story? Respond in your journal.

2 What are Lucinda's two main problems in this selection? How does she resolve each?

3 Compare Lucinda's feelings about her home at the beginning of the story with her feelings at the end. Why does her attitude change?

4 Do you predict Ashley and Lucinda will be good friends? Explain.

5 Imagine your family moved to a different country where you must learn a new language. What adjustments would be hardest to make? Do Lucinda's experiences in her new land seem unusual? Explain.

ACTIVITY

• **Write About Short Stories** Copy and complete this story chart for "Viva New Jersey."

| Title |
| Setting |
| Characters |
| Problem |
| Events |
| Solution |

VOCABULARY PRACTICE

Choose the vocabulary word that best fits in each blank. Write the words on a separate piece of paper.

mongrel	anemic
panoramic	perilous
opted	protruding
sermonized	proficient
silhouetted	irate

Lucinda was a ___**1**___ student. However, she missed having good friends. One day, she befriended a muddy-pawed ___**2**___, little knowing that this choice meant she had ___**3**___ for an exciting night.

She cleaned and fed Chauncey, who looked sad and ___**4**___. She hid him in a small room with electrical levers ___**5**___ from the walls. The dog hit the red master switch that controlled the building's power supply. He then ran out of the building.

While her father ___**6**___ about life, Lucinda worried about her little dog. Finally, she ran out to look for him. She knew her parents would be ___**7**___ if she stayed out late. At night, the city could be a ___**8**___ place. She asked a girl named Ashley to help her. As the girls searched for the dog, they noticed the ___**9**___ view of New York ___**10**___ against the night sky.

At last, when Lucinda had given up all hope, Chauncey came back.

SHORT STORY

RAIN, RAIN, GO AWAY

CONNECT TO LITERATURE

What is your favorite kind of weather? Suppose you planned a picnic? How would you feel if it rained? In your journal, describe a time when the weather spoiled your plans. Then read "Rain, Rain, Go Away" about a family who just hates rainy days.

THINKING ABOUT FORESHADOWING

A story or novel usually contains hints or clues about what will happen. These clues about events that are yet to come are called *foreshadowing*. Foreshadowing helps to build suspense, which creates a more exciting story. As you read the following short story, watch for clues that give hints about how the story might end.

DID YOU KNOW?

Weather forecasting plays an important role in the plot of "Rain, Rain, Go Away." The first modern attempt to forecast weather based on reports from stations across a large area began in Europe in 1820. However, it wasn't until the invention of the telegraph that rapid collection of weather data became possible.

Today's weather stations use rockets, weather satellites, barometers, radar, and other devices to collect data. They communicate the data at high speeds through telecommunications devices. Large computers use the data to model current weather and to predict future weather. Meteorologists then interpret and modify these predictions based on their knowledge of local conditions in order to make the best possible forecast.

RAIN, RAIN, GO AWAY

BY ISAAC ASIMOV
ILLUSTRATED BY BRUNO PACIULLI

"There she is again," said Lillian Wright as she adjusted the <u>venetian blinds</u> carefully. "There she is, George."

"There who is?" asked her husband, trying to get satisfactory <u>contrast</u> on the TV so that he might settle down to the ball game.

"Mrs. Sakkaro," she said, and then, to <u>forestall</u> her husband's <u>inevitable</u> "Who's that?" added hastily, "The new neighbors, for goodness sake."

"Oh."

"Sunbathing. Always sunbathing. I wonder where her boy is. He's usually out on a nice day like this, standing in that tremendous yard of theirs and throwing the ball against the house. Did you ever see him, George?"

"I've heard him. It's a version of the Chinese water torture. Bang on the wall, biff on the ground, smack in the hand. Bang, biff, smack, bang, biff—"

"He's a *nice* boy, quiet and well-behaved. I wish Tommie would make friends with him. He's the right age, too, just about ten, I should say."

"I didn't know Tommie was backward about making friends."

"Well, it's hard with the Sakkaros. They keep so to themselves. I don't even know what Mr. Sakkaro does."

"Why should you? It's not really anyone's business what he does."

"It's odd that I never see him go to work."

"No one ever sees me go to work."

"You stay home and write. What does *he* do?"

"I dare say Mrs. Sakkaro knows what Mr. Sakkaro does and is all upset because she doesn't know what *I* do."

"Oh, George." Lillian retreated from the window and glanced with distaste at the television. (Schoendienst was at bat.) "I think we should make an effort; the neighborhood should."

"What kind of an effort?" George was comfortable on the couch now, with a king-size coke in his hand, freshly opened and frosted with moisture.

"To get to know them."

"Well, didn't you, when she first moved in? You said you called."

"I said hello but, well, she'd just moved in and the house was still upset, so that's all it could be, just hello. It's been two months now and it's still nothing more than hello, sometimes. —She's so odd."

■————————————————

venetian blinds adjustable shades, especially for windows, made of a series of overlapping horizontal slots that can be opened or closed. The shades can be raised or lowered.

contrast (kon′trast) *n.* difference between light and dark on a television screen.

forestall (fôr stôl′) *v.t.* hinder, prevent, or get ahead of by taking action in advance.

inevitable (in ev′i tə bəl) *adj.* that cannot be avoided; obvious or certain.

"Is she?"

"She's always looking at the sky; I've seen her do it a hundred times and she's never been out when it's the least bit cloudy. Once, when the boy was out playing, she called to him to come in, shouting that it was going to rain. I happened to hear her and I thought, Good Lord, wouldn't you know and me with a wash on the line, so I hurried out and, you know, it was broad sunlight. Oh, there were some clouds, but nothing, really."

"Did it rain, eventually?"

"Of course not. I just had to run out in the yard for nothing."

George was lost amid a couple of base hits and a most embarrassing bobble that meant a run. When the excitement was over and the pitcher was trying to regain his composure, George called out after Lillian, who was vanishing into the kitchen, "Well, since they're from Arizona, I dare say they don't know rainclouds from any other kind."

Lillian came back into the living room with a patter of high heels. "From where?"

"From Arizona, according to Tommie."

"How did Tommie know?"

"He talked to their boy, in between ball chucks, I guess, and he told Tommie they came from Arizona and then the boy was called in. At least, Tommie says it might have been Arizona, or maybe Alabama or some place like that. You know Tommie and his nontotal recall. But if they're that nervous about the weather, I guess it's Arizona and they don't know what to make of a good rainy climate like ours."

"But why didn't you ever tell me?"

"Because Tommie only told me this morning and because I thought he must have told you already and, to tell the absolute truth, because I thought you could just manage to drag out a normal existence even if you never found out. Wow—"

The ball went sailing into the right field stands and that was that for the pitcher.

Lillian went back to the venetian blinds and said, "I'll simply just have to make her acquaintance. She looks *very* nice.—Oh, Lord, look at that, George."

George was looking at nothing but the TV.

Lillian said, "I know she's staring at that cloud. And now she'll be going in. Honestly."

George was out two days later on a reference search in the library and came home with a load of books. Lillian greeted him jubilantly.

She said, "Now, you're not doing anything tomorrow."

"That sounds like a statement, not a question."

"It is a statement. We're going out with the Sakkaros to Murphy's Park."

"With—"

"With the next-door neighbors, George. *How* can you never remember the name?"

"I'm gifted. How did it happen?"

"I just went up to their house this morning and rang the bell."

"That easy?"

"It wasn't easy. It was hard. I stood there, jittering, with my finger on the doorbell, till I thought that ringing

the bell would be easier than having the door open and being caught standing there like a fool."

"And she didn't kick you out?"

"No. She was sweet as she could be. Invited me in, knew who I was, said she was so glad I had come to visit. *You* know."

"And you suggested we go to Murphy's Park."

"Yes. I thought if I suggested something that would let the children have fun, it would be easier for her to go along with it. She wouldn't want to spoil a chance for her boy."

"A mother's psychology."

"But you should see her home."

"Ah. You had a reason for all this. It comes out. You wanted the Cook's tour. But, please, spare me the color-scheme details. I'm not interested in the bedspreads, and the size of the closets is a topic with which I can dispense."

It was the secret of their happy marriage that Lillian paid no attention to George. She went into the color-scheme details, was most meticulous about the bedspreads, and gave him an inch-by-inch description of closet-size.

Cook's tour package sightseeing trip, such as those offered by a British travel company named Cook.

dispense (di spens') *v.t.* get along without; do away with; make unnecessary.

meticulous (mə tik'yə ləs) *adj.* showing extreme or excessive concern about details.

"And *clean?* I have never seen any place so spotless."

"If you get to know her, then, she'll be setting you impossible standards and you'll have to drop her in self-defense."

"Her kitchen," said Lillian, ignoring him, "was so spanking clean you just couldn't believe she ever used it. I asked for a drink of water and she held the glass underneath the tap and poured slowly so that not one drop fell in the sink itself. It wasn't affectation. She did it so casually that I just knew she always did it that way. And when she gave me the glass she held it with a clean napkin. Just hospital-sanitary."

"She must be a lot of trouble to herself. Did she agree to come with us right off?"

"Well—not right off. She called to her husband about what the weather forecast was, and he said that the newspapers all said it would be fair to-morrow but that he was waiting for the latest report on the radio."

"*All* the newspapers said so, eh?"

"Of course, they all just print the official weather forecast, so they would all agree. But I think they do subscribe to all the newspapers. At least I've watched the bundle the newsboy leaves—"

"There isn't much you miss, is there?"

"Anyway," said Lillian severely, "she called up the weather bureau and had them tell her the latest and she called it out to her husband and they said they'd go, except they said they'd phone us if there were any unexpected changes in the weather."

"All right. Then we'll go."

The Sakkaros were young and pleasant, dark and handsome. In fact, as they came down the long walk from their home to where the Wright automobile was parked, George leaned toward his wife and breathed into her ear, "So *he's* the reason."

"I wish he were," said Lillian. "Is that a handbag he's carrying?"

"Pocket-radio. To listen to weather forecasts, I bet."

The Sakkaro boy came running after them, waving something which turned out to be an <u>aneroid barometer</u>, and all three got into the back seat. Conversation was turned on and lasted, with neat give-and-take on impersonal subjects, to Murphy's Park.

The Sakkaro boy was so polite and reasonable that even Tommie Wright, wedged between his parents

---

aneroid barometer instrument, used in weather forecasting, featuring a metal box that expands and contracts according to changes in air pressure and a pointer that shows the change.

in the front seat, was <u>subdued</u> by example into a semblance of civilization. Lillian couldn't recall when she had spent so serenely pleasant a drive.

She was not the least disturbed by the fact that, barely to be heard under the flow of the conversation, Mr. Sakkaro's small radio was on, and she never actually saw him put it occasionally to his ear.

It was a beautiful day at Murphy's Park; hot and dry without being too hot; and with a cheerfully bright sun in a blue, blue sky. Even Mr. Sakkaro, though he inspected every quarter of the heavens with a careful eye and then stared piercingly at the barometer, seemed to have no fault to find.

Lillian ushered the two boys to the amusement section and bought enough tickets to allow one ride for each on every variety of <u>centrifugal</u> thrill that the park offered.

"Please," she had said to a protesting Mrs. Sakkaro, "let this be my treat. I'll let you have your turn next time."

When she returned, George was alone. "Where—" she began.

"Just down there at the refreshment stand. I told them I'd wait here for you and we would join them." He sounded gloomy.

"Anything wrong?"

"No, not really, except that I think he must be independently wealthy."

"What?"

---

subdued (səb düd′) *v.t.* brought under control; overcome.
centrifugal (sen trif′yə gəl) *adj.* moving or directed away from a center.

"I don't know what he does for a living. I hinted—"

"Now who's curious?"

"I was doing it for you. He said he's just a student of human nature."

"How philosophical. That would explain all those newspapers."

"Yes, but with a handsome, wealthy man next door, it looks as though I'll have impossible standards set for me, too."

"Don't be silly."

"And he doesn't come from Arizona."

"He doesn't?"

"I said I heard he was from Arizona. He looked so surprised, it was obvious he didn't. Then he laughed and asked if he had an Arizona accent."

Lillian said thoughtfully, "He has some kind of accent, you know. There are lots of Spanish-ancestry people in the Southwest, so he could still be from Arizona. Sakkaro could be a Spanish name."

"Sounds Japanese to me.—Come on, they're waving. Oh, good Lord, look what they've bought."

The Sakkaros were each holding three sticks of cotton candy, huge swirls of pink foam consisting of threads of sugar dried out of frothy syrup that had been whipped about in a warm vessel. It melted sweetly in the mouth and left one feeling sticky.

The Sakkaros held one out to each Wright, and out of politeness the Wrights accepted.

They went down the midway, tried their hand at darts, at the kind of poker game where balls were rolled into holes, at knocking wooden cylinders off <u>pedestals</u>. They took pictures of themselves and recorded their voices and tested the strength of their handgrips.

Eventually they collected the youngsters, who had been reduced to a satisfactorily breathless state of roiled-up insides, and the Sakkaros ushered theirs off instantly to the refreshment stand. Tommie hinted the extent of his pleasure at the possible purchase of a hot-dog and George tossed him a quarter. He ran off, too.

"Frankly," said George, "I prefer to stay here. If I see them biting away at another cotton candy stick I'll turn green and sicken on the spot. If they haven't had a dozen apiece, I'll eat a dozen myself."

---

pedestals (ped′ə stəlz) *n., pl.* any bases or supporting structures.

"I know, and they're buying a handful for the child now."

"I offered to stand Sakkaro a hamburger and he just looked grim and shook his head. Not that a hamburger's much, but after enough cotton candy, it ought to be a feast."

"I know. I offered her an orange drink and the way she jumped when she said no, you'd think I'd thrown it in her face.—Still, I suppose they've never been to a place like this before and they'll need time to adjust to the novelty. They'll fill up on cotton candy and then never eat it again for ten years."

"Well, maybe." They strolled toward the Sakkaros. "You know, Lil, it's clouding up."

Mr. Sakkaro had the radio to his ear and was looking anxiously toward the west.

"Uh-oh," said George, "he's seen it. One gets you fifty, he'll want to go home."

All three Sakkaros were upon him, polite but insistent. They were sorry, they had had a wonderful time, a marvelous time, the Wrights would have to be their guests as soon as it could be managed, but now, really, they had to go home. It looked stormy. Mrs. Sakkaro wailed that all the forecasts had been for fair weather.

George tried to console them. "It's hard to predict a local thunder-storm, but even if it were to come, and it mightn't, it wouldn't last more than half an hour on the outside."

At which comment, the Sakkaro youngster seemed on the verge of tears, and Mrs. Sakkaro's hand, holding a handkerchief, trembled visibly.

"Let's go home," said George in resignation.

The drive back seemed to stretch interminably. There was no conversation to speak of. Mr. Sakkaro's radio was quite loud now as he switched from station to station, catching a weather report every time. They were mentioning "local thundershowers" now.

The Sakkaro youngster piped up that the barometer was falling, and Mrs. Sakkaro, chin in the palm of her hand, stared dolefully at the sky and asked if George could not drive faster, please.

"It does look rather threatening, doesn't it?" said Lillian in a polite attempt to share their guests' attitude. But then George heard her mutter, "Honestly!" under her breath.

A wind had sprung up, driving the dust of the weeks-dry road before it, when they entered the street on

---

resignation (rez′ig nā′shən) *n.* acceptance of something without protest or complaint; submission.
dolefully (dōl′fə lē) *adv.* sadly; in a manner expressing grief or sorrow.

which they lived, and the leaves rustled ominously. Lightning flickered.

George said, "You'll be indoors in two minutes, friends. We'll make it."

He pulled up at the gate that opened onto the Sakkaros' spacious front yard and got out of the car to open the back door. He thought he felt a drop. They were *just* in time.

The Sakkaros tumbled out, faces drawn with tension, muttering thanks, and started off toward their long front walk at a dead run.

"Honestly," began Lillian, "you would think they were—"

The heavens opened and the rain came down in giant drops as though some celestial dam had suddenly burst. The top of their car was pounded with a hundred drum sticks, and halfway to their front door the Sakkaros stopped and looked despairingly upward.

Their faces blurred as the rain hit; blurred and shrank and ran together. All three shriveled, collapsing within their clothes, which sank down into three sticky-wet heaps.

And while the Wrights sat there, transfixed with horror, Lillian found herself unable to stop the completion of her remark: "—made of sugar and afraid they would melt."

---

ominously (om′ə nəs lē) *adv.* in a manner that foretells trouble or misfortune.

spacious (spā′shəs) *adj.* roomy; having much space.

MEET ISAAC ASIMOV

Karsh of Ottawa

Once called "the human writing machine," Isaac Asimov (1920–1992) was the author of over 470 books. "I must write," the prolific Asimov explained. "I look upon everything but writing as an interruption."

He became perhaps the most widely-known science fiction writer in the world. Among his honors were five Hugo Awards from the World Science Fiction Conventions, including best all-time science fiction series (for his *Foundation* series); best novel, 1973 (for *The Gods Themselves*); and best short story, 1983 (for "The Bicentennial Man"). The Science Fiction Writers of America voted his work "Nightfall" the best all-time science fiction story.

Asimov also wrote dozens of popular nonfiction books and articles about science, math, and other topics.

More Science Fiction Stories

- *Dinosaur Tales* by Ray Bradbury (Bantam Books, 1983). Are dinosaurs gone from the earth forever? Not according to Ray Bradbury. Rediscover them in his collection of science fiction stories devoted entirely to dinosaurs.

- *The Asimov Chronicles: Fifty Years of Isaac Asimov, Volume One,* edited by Martin H. Greenberg (Ace Books, 1989). This book gathers together seven memorable stories by one of the great science fiction writers of our time.

- *2041: Twelve Short Stories About the Future by Top Science Fiction Writers,* selected and edited by Jane Yolen (Delacorte Press, 1991). Thrills are ahead for you as you read this collection of stories guaranteed to keep you completely rooted to your chair.

RESPONDING TO *Literature*

THINK • TALK • WRITE

1 Could you predict the ending of this story? Reply in your journal.

2 From whose point of view is this story told? Why do you think Isaac Asimov chose this point of view?

3 Give at least three details that foreshadow the ending of the story. Did Asimov do a good job of foreshadowing? Why or why not?

4 Asimov never tells exactly where the Sakkaros come from. Where do you think they are from? Provide details from the story to back up your answer.

5 Why do the Wrights assume the Sakkaros are from another state or country? In what ways do the Sakkaros fit into American culture? In what ways do they stand out?

ACTIVITIES

- **Write with Foreshadowing** Write a letter from Mr. or Mrs. Sakkaro to friends back home. Foreshadow what will happen to the Sakkaros.

- **Create Sugar Crystals** Stir sugar into a plastic cup of hot water until you cannot dissolve any more. Tie a short string to a pencil, and lay the pencil across the top of the cup so that the string dips into the sugar water. In a few days, crystals will form on the string and in the cup.

VOCABULARY PRACTICE

On a separate piece of paper, write the vocabulary word that best completes each sentence.

forestall	inevitable
dispense	meticulous
subdued	spacious
pedestals	resignation
dolefully	ominously

1 Why won't the paper-towel holder _____ any more paper towels?

2 The clouds were _____ dark, indicating that a storm was coming.

3 She sighed with _____ and agreed to help him one more time.

4 The mansion had _____ rooms with large, valuable carpets.

5 Kellen supposed it was _____ that someday they would meet again.

6 The cadets had to keep their rooms in _____ order.

7 Sari waved her hand to _____ Misha from saying anything more about the secret.

8 The statues were placed on _____ about three feet high.

9 Brad's enthusiasm was _____ after his team lost the championship.

10 My father stared at me _____ when I said that I had dented the car.

SHORT STORY

....

MY FRIEND FLICKA

CONNECT TO LITERATURE

Did you ever have your heart set on a pet, a goal, or something else that was really important to you? Did you achieve your goal? Write about your experience in your journal. Then read "My Friend Flicka" to find out whether Ken McLaughlin obtains the horse that he wants more than anything in the world.

THINKING ABOUT PLOT: CONFLICT

In "My Friend Flicka," the plot is built around a *conflict,* or struggle between opposing forces. The boy in the story must overcome forces both outside and within himself to win his heart's desire. Conflicts can take many forms. They can occur

- between people

- between people and their surroundings

- within a person (for example, the struggle between doing the right thing and doing something known to be wrong)

DID YOU KNOW?

The coming-of-age theme is common in literature. In mythology, a young hero or heroine may become an adult by completing a difficult quest. In modern literature, such as "My Friend Flicka," the hero or heroine rarely takes an actual journey. Instead, the main character often must struggle to overcome family, social, or inner obstacles. By the end of the story, the hero or heroine has achieved something difficult and has become an adult in the eyes of the world.

My friend FLICKA

by Mary O'Hara

Friends 1995 John Fawcett

Report cards for the second semester were sent out soon after school closed in mid-June.

Kennie's was a shock to the whole family.

"If I could have a colt all for my own," said Kennie, "I might do better."

Rob McLaughlin glared at his son. "Just as a matter of curiosity," he said, "how do you go about it to get a *zero* in an examination? Forty in arithmetic; seventeen in history! But a *zero*? Just as one man to another, what goes on in your head?"

"Yes, tell us how you do it, Ken," chirped Howard.

"Eat your breakfast, Howard," snapped his mother.

Kennie's blond head bent over his plate until his face was almost hidden. His cheeks burned.

McLaughlin finished his coffee and pushed his chair back. "You'll do an hour a day on your lessons all through the summer."

Nell McLaughlin saw Kennie wince as if something had actually hurt him.

Lessons and study in the summertime, when the long winter was just over and there weren't hours enough in the day for all the things he wanted to do!

Kennie took things hard. His eyes turned to the wide-open window with a look almost of despair.

The hill opposite the house, covered with arrow-straight jack pines, was sharply etched in the thin air of the eight-thousand-foot altitude. Where it fell away, vivid green grass ran up to meet it; and over range and upland poured the strong Wyoming sunlight that stung everything into burning color. A big jack rabbit sat under one of the pines, waving his long ears back and forth.

Ken had to look at his plate and blink back tears before he could turn to his father and say carelessly, "Can I help you in the corral with the horses this morning, Dad?"

"You'll do your study every morning before you do anything else." And McLaughlin's scarred boots and heavy spurs clattered across the kitchen floor. "I'm disgusted with you. Come, Howard."

Howard strode after his father, nobly refraining from looking at Kennie.

"Help me with the dishes, Kennie," said Nell McLaughlin as she rose, tied on a big apron, and began to clear the table.

Kennie looked at her in despair. She poured steaming water into the dishpan and sent him for the soap powder.

"If I could have a colt," he muttered again.

---

jack pines slender gray pine trees found in the northern United States.

Arizona Cooler *1994   John Fawcett*

"Now get busy with that dish towel, Ken. It's eight o'clock. You can study till nine and then go up to the corral. They'll still be there."

At supper that night, Kennie said, "But Dad, Howard had a colt all of his own when he was only eight. And he trained it and schooled it all himself; and now he's eleven and Highboy is three, and he's riding him. I'm nine now, and even if you did give me a colt now, I couldn't catch up to Howard because I couldn't ride it till it was a three-year-old and then I'd be twelve."

Nell laughed. "Nothing wrong with that arithmetic."

But Rob said, "Howard never gets less than seventy-five average at school; and hasn't disgraced himself and his family by getting more demerits than any other boy in his class."

Kennie didn't answer. He couldn't figure it out. He tried hard, he spent hours poring over his books. That was supposed to get you good marks, but it never did. Everyone said he was bright; why was it that when he studied he didn't learn? He had a vague feeling that perhaps he looked out the window too much; or looked through the walls to see clouds and sky and hills, and wonder what was happening out there. Sometimes it wasn't even a wonder, but just a pleasant drifting feeling of nothing at all, as if nothing mattered, as if there was always plenty of time, as if the lessons would get

done of themselves. And then the bell would ring and study period was over.

If he had a colt—

When the boys had gone to bed that night Nell McLaughlin sat down with her overflowing mending basket and glanced at her husband.

He was at his desk as usual, working on account books and <u>inventories</u>.

Nell threaded a darning needle and thought, "It's either that whacking big bill from the vet for the mare that died, or the last half of the tax bill."

It didn't seem just the <u>auspicious</u> moment to plead Kennie's cause. But then, these days, there was always a line between Rob's eyes and a harsh note in his voice.

"Rob," she began.

He flung down his pencil and turned around.

"Hang that law!" he exclaimed.

"What law?"

"The state law that puts high taxes on <u>pedigreed stock</u>. I'll have to do as the rest of 'em do—drop the papers."

"Drop the papers! But you'll never get decent prices if you don't have registered horses."

"I don't get decent prices now."

"But you will someday, if you don't drop the papers."

"Maybe." He bent again over the desk.

Rob, thought Nell, was a lot like Kennie himself. He set his heart. Oh, how stubbornly he set his heart on just some one thing he wanted above everything else. He had set his heart on horses and ranching way back when he had been a crack rider at West Point; and he had resigned and thrown away his army career just for the horses. Well, he'd got what he wanted—

She drew a deep breath, snipped her thread, laid down the sock and again looked across at her husband as she unrolled another length of darning cotton.

To get what you want is one thing, she was thinking. The three-thousand-acre ranch and the hundred head of horses. But to make it pay—for a dozen or more years they had been trying to make it pay. People said ranching hadn't paid since the beef barons ran their herds on public land; people said the only <u>prosperous</u> ranchers in Wyoming were the dude ranchers; people said—

But suddenly she gave her head a little rebellious, gallant shake. Rob would always be fighting and struggling against something, like Kennie; perhaps like herself too. Even those first years when there was no water piped into the

---

inventories (in′vən tôr′ēz) *n., pl.* detailed lists of goods in stock or owned at a given time.

auspicious (ô spish′əs) *adj.* showing promise of success; favorable.

pedigreed stock animals whose line of ancestors is on record with an association of breeders.

prosperous (pros′pər əs) *adj.* successful; wealthy.

house, when every day brought a new difficulty or danger, how she had loved it! How she still loved it!

She ran the darning ball into the toe of a sock, Kennie's sock. The length of it gave her a shock. Yes, the boys were growing up fast, and now Kennie—Kennie and the colt—

After a while, she said, "Give Kennie a colt, Rob."

"He doesn't deserve it." The answer was short. Rob pushed away his papers and took out his pipe.

"Howard's too far ahead of him; older and bigger and quicker and his wits about him, and—"

"Ken doesn't half try; doesn't stick at anything."

She put down her sewing. "He's crazy for a colt of his own. He hasn't had another idea in his head since you gave Highboy to Howard."

"I don't believe in bribing children to do their duty."

"Not a bribe." She hesitated.

"No? What would you call it?"

She tried to think it out. "I just have the feeling Ken isn't going to pull anything off, and—" her eyes sought Rob's, "it's time he did. It isn't the school marks alone, but I just don't want things to go on any longer with Ken never coming out at the right end of anything."

"I'm beginning to think he's just dumb."

"He's not dumb. Maybe a little thing like this—if he had a colt of his own, trained him, rode him—"

Rob interrupted. "But it isn't a little thing, nor an easy thing to break and school a colt the way Howard has schooled Highboy. I'm not going to have a good horse spoiled by Ken's careless ways. He goes wool-gathering. He never knows what he's doing."

"But he'd *love* a colt of his own, Rob. If he could do it, it might make a big difference in him."

"*If* he could do it! But that's a big if."

At breakfast next morning Kennie's father said to him, "When you've done your study come out to the barn. I'm going in the car up to section twenty-one this morning to look over the brood mares. You can go with me."

"Can I go too, Dad?" cried Howard.

McLaughlin frowned at Howard. "You turned Highboy out last evening with dirty legs."

Howard wriggled. "I groomed him—"

"Yes, down to his knees."

"He kicks."

"And whose fault is that? You don't get on his back again until I see his legs clean."

The two boys eyed each other, Kennie secretly triumphant and

Howard <u>chagrined</u>. McLaughlin turned at the door. "And, Ken, a week from today I'll give you a colt. Between now and then you can decide what one you want."

Kennie shot out of his chair and stared at his father. "A—a—spring colt, Dad, or a yearling?"

McLaughlin was somewhat taken aback, but his wife concealed a smile. If Kennie got a yearling colt, he would be even up with Howard.

"A yearling colt, your father means, Ken," she said smoothly. "Now hurry with your lessons. Howard will wipe."

Kennie found himself the most important personage on the ranch. Prestige lifted his head, gave him an inch more of height and a bold stare, and made him feel different all the way through. Even Gus and Tim Murphy, the ranch hands, were more interested in Kennie's choice of a colt than anything else.

Howard was fidgety with suspense. "Who'll you pick, Ken? Say—pick Doughboy, why don't you? Then when he grows up he'll be sort of twins with mine, in his name anyway. Doughboy, Highboy, see?"

The boys were sitting on the worn wooden step of the door which led from the tack room into the corral, busy with rags and polish, shining their bridles.

Ken looked at his brother with scorn. Doughboy would never have half of Highboy's speed.

"Lassie, then," suggested Howard. "She's black as ink, like mine. And she'll be fast—"

"Dad says Lassie'll never go over fifteen <u>hands</u>."

Nell McLaughlin saw the change in Kennie and her hopes rose. He went to his books in the morning with determination and really studied. A new alertness took the place of the day-dreaming. Examples in arithmetic were neatly written out and, as she passed his door before breakfast, she often heard the <u>monotonous</u> drone of his voice as he read his American history aloud.

Each night, when he kissed her, he flung his arms around her and held her fiercely for a moment, then, with a winsome and <u>blissful</u> smile into her eyes, turned away to bed.

He spent days inspecting the different bands of horses and colts. He sat for hours on the corral fence, very important, chewing straws. He rode off on one of the ponies for half the day, wandering through the mile square

chagrined (shə grind′) *adj.* distressed or annoyed by failure, disappointment, or embarrassment.
hands *n., pl.* units of measure equaling 4 inches, used in expressing the height of a horse.
monotonous (mə not′ə nəs) *adj.* not changing, as in tone, sound, or beat.
blissful (blis′fəl) *adj.* full of joy.

pastures that ran down toward the Colorado border.

And when the week was up, he announced his decision. "I'll take that yearling filly of Rocket's. The sorrel with the cream tail and mane."

His father looked at him in surprise. "The one that got tangled in the barbed wire? That's never been named?"

In a second all Kennie's new pride was gone. He hung his head defensively. "Yes."

"You've made a bad choice, son. You couldn't have picked a worse."

"She's fast, Dad. And Rocket's fast—"

"It's the worst line of horses I've got. There's never one amongst them with real sense. The mares are hellions and the stallions outlaws; they're untamable."

"I'll tame her."

Rob guffawed. "Not I, nor anyone, has ever been able to really tame any one of them."

Kennie's chest heaved.

"Better change your mind, Ken. You want a horse that'll be a real friend to you, don't you?"

"Yes—" Kennie's voice was unsteady.

"Well, you'll never make a friend of that filly. She's all cut and scarred up already with tearing through barbed wire after that mother of hers. No fence'll hold 'em—"

"I know," said Kennie, still more faintly.

"Change your mind?" asked Howard briskly.

"No."

Rob was grim and put out. He couldn't go back on his word. The boy had to have a reasonable amount of help in breaking and taming the filly, and he could envision precious hours, whole days, wasted in the struggle.

Nell McLaughlin despaired. Once again Ken seemed to have taken the wrong turn and was back where he had begun; stoical, silent, defensive.

But there was a difference that only Ken could know. The way he felt about his colt. The way his heart sang. The pride and joy that filled him so full that sometimes he hung his head so they wouldn't see it shining out of his eyes.

He had known from the very first that he would choose that particular yearling because he was in love with her.

The year before, he had been out working with Gus, the big Swedish ranch hand, on the irrigation ditch, when they had noticed Rocket standing in a gully on the hillside, quiet for once, and eyeing them cautiously.

"Ay bet she got a colt," said Gus, and they walked carefully up the draw. Rocket gave a wild snort, thrust her feet out, shook her head wickedly, then fled away. And as they reached

587

Utah Jingler *1994* *John Fawcett*

the spot, they saw standing there the wavering, pinkish colt, barely able to keep its feet. It gave a little squeak and started after its mother on crooked, wobbling legs.

"Yee whiz! Luk at de little *flicka!*" said Gus.

"What does *flicka* mean, Gus?"

"Swedish for little gurl, Ken—"

Ken announced at supper, "You said she'd never been named. I've named her. Her name is Flicka."

The first thing to do was to get her in. She was running with a band of yearlings on the saddleback, cut with ravines and gullies, on section twenty.

They all went out after her, Ken, as owner, on old Rob Roy, the wisest horse on the ranch.

Ken was entranced to watch Flicka when the wild band of youngsters discovered that they were being pursued and took off across the mountain. Footing made no difference to her. She floated across the ravines, always two lengths ahead of the others. Her pink mane and tail whipped in the wind. Her long delicate legs had only to aim, it seemed, at a particular spot, for her to reach

it and sail on. She seemed to Ken a fairy horse.

He sat motionless, just watching and holding Rob Roy in, when his father thundered past on Sultan and shouted, "Well, what's the matter? Why didn't you turn 'em?"

Kennie woke up and galloped after.

Rob Roy brought in the whole band. The corral gates were closed, and an hour was spent <u>shunting</u> the ponies in and out and through the chutes, until Flicka was left alone in the small round corral in which the baby colts were branded. Gus drove the others away, out the gate, and up the saddleback.

But Flicka did not intend to be left. She hurled herself against the poles which walled the corral. She tried to jump them. They were seven feet high. She caught her front feet over the top rung, clung, scrambled, while Kennie held his breath for fear the slender legs would be caught between the bars and snapped. Her hold broke, she fell over backward, rolled, screamed, tore around the corral. Kennie had a sick feeling in the pit of his stomach and his father looked disgusted.

One of the bars broke. She hurled herself again. Another went. She saw the opening and as neatly as a dog crawls through a fence, inserted her head and forefeet,

scrambled through and fled away, bleeding in a dozen places.

As Gus was coming back, just about to close the gate to the upper range, the sorrel whipped through it, sailed across the road and ditch with her <u>inimitable</u> floating leap, and went up the side of the saddleback like a jack rabbit.

From way up the mountain, Gus heard excited whinnies, as she joined the band he had just driven up, and the last he saw of them they were strung out along the crest running like deer.

"Yee whiz!" said Gus, and stood motionless and staring until the ponies had disappeared over the ridge. Then he closed the gate, remounted Rob Roy, and rode back to the corral.

Rob McLaughlin gave Kennie one more chance to change his mind. "Last chance, son. Better pick a horse that you have some hope of riding one day. I'd have got rid of this whole line of stock if they weren't so fast that I've had the fool idea that someday there might turn out one gentle one in the lot—and I'd have a race horse. But there's never been one so far, and it's not going to be Flicka."

"It's not going to be Flicka," chanted Howard.

---

shunting (shun'ting) *v.t.* moving or turning aside or away.
inimitable (i nim'i tə bəl) *adj.* matchless; impossible to imitate.

"Perhaps she *might* be gentled," said Kennie; and Nell, watching, saw that although his lips quivered, there was fanatical determination in his eye.

"Ken," said Rob, "it's up to you. If you say you want her, we'll get her. But she wouldn't be the first of that line to die rather than give in. They're beautiful and they're fast, but let me tell you this, young man, they're *loco!*"

Kennie flinched under his father's direct glance.

"If I go after her again, I'll not give up whatever comes, understand what I mean by that?"

"Yes."

"What do you say?"

"I want her."

They brought her in again. They had better luck this time. She jumped over the Dutch half door of the stable and crashed inside. The men slammed the upper half of the door shut and she was caught.

The rest of the band were driven away, and Kennie stood outside of the stable, listening to the wild hoofs beating, the screams, the crashes. His Flicka inside there! He was drenched with perspiration.

"We'll leave her to think it over," said Rob, when dinnertime came. "Afterward, we'll go up and feed and water her."

But when they went up afterward, there was no Flicka in the barn. One of the windows, higher than the mangers, was broken.

The window opened into a pasture an eighth of a mile square, fenced in barbed wire six feet high. Near the stable stood a wagon load of hay. When they went around the back of the stable to see where Flicka had hidden herself, they found her between the stable and the hay wagon, eating.

At their approach she leaped away, then headed east across the pasture.

"If she's like her mother," said Rob, "she'll go right through the wire."

"Ay bet she'll go over," said Gus. "She yumps like a deer."

"No horse can jump that," said McLaughlin.

Kennie said nothing because he could not speak. It was, perhaps, the most terrible moment of his life. He watched Flicka racing toward the eastern wire.

A few yards from it, she swerved, turned and raced diagonally south.

"It turned her! It turned her!" cried Kennie, almost sobbing. It was the first sign of hope for Flicka. "Oh, Dad! She has got sense. She has! She has!"

Flicka turned again as she met the southern boundary of the pasture; again at the northern; she avoided the barn. Without abating anything of her

---

abating (ə bāt′ing) *v.t.* making or becoming less in force, intensity, or amount.

whirlwind speed, following a precise, accurate calculation and turning each time on a dime, she investigated every possibility. Then, seeing that there was no hope, she raced south toward the range where she had spent her life, gathered herself, and shot into the air.

Each of the three men watching had the impulse to cover his eyes, and Kennie gave a sort of a howl of despair.

Twenty yards of fence came down with her as she hurled herself through. Caught on the upper strands, she turned a complete somersault, landing on her back, her four legs dragging the wires down on top of her, and tangling herself in them beyond hope of escape.

"That wire!" cried McLaughlin. "If I could afford decent fences—"

Kennie followed the men miserably as they walked to the filly. They stood in a circle watching, while she kicked and fought and thrashed until the wire was tightly wound and knotted about her, cutting, piercing and tearing great three-cornered pieces of flesh and hide. At last she was unconscious, streams of blood running on her golden coat, and pools of crimson widening and spreading on the grass beneath her.

With the wire cutter which Gus always carried in the hip pocket of his overalls, he cut all the wire away, and they drew her into the pasture, repaired the fence, placed hay, a box of oats and a tub of water near her, and called it a day.

"I don't think she'll pull out of it," said McLaughlin.

Next morning Kennie was up at five, doing his lessons. At six he went out to Flicka.

She had not moved. Food and water were untouched. She was no longer bleeding, but the wounds were swollen and caked over.

Kennie got a bucket of fresh water and poured it over her mouth. Then he leaped away, for Flicka came to life, scrambled up, got her balance, and stood swaying.

Kennie went a few feet away and sat down to watch her. When he went in to breakfast, she had drunk deeply of the water and was mouthing the oats.

There began, then, a sort of recovery. She ate, drank, limped about the pasture; stood for hours with hanging head and weakly splayed out legs, under the clump of cottonwood trees. The swollen wounds scabbed and began to heal.

Kennie lived in the pasture, too. He followed her around, he talked to her. He, too, lay snoozing or sat under the cottonwoods; and often, coaxing her with hand outstretched, he walked very quietly toward her. But she would not let him come near her.

Often she stood with her head at the south fence, looking off to the

mountain. It made the tears come to Kennie's eyes to see the way she longed to get away.

Still Rob said she wouldn't pull out of it. There was no use putting a halter on her. She had no strength.

One morning, as Ken came out of the house, Gus met him and said, "De filly's down."

Kennie ran to the pasture, Howard close behind him. The right hind leg which had been badly swollen at the knee joint had opened in a festering wound, and Flicka lay flat and motionless, with staring eyes.

"Don't you wish now you'd chosen Doughboy?" asked Howard.

"Go away!" shouted Ken.

Howard stood watching while Kennie sat down on the ground and took Flicka's head on his lap. Though she was conscious and moved a little, she did not struggle nor seem frightened. Tears rolled down Kennie's cheeks as he talked to her and petted her. After a few moments, Howard walked away.

"Mother, what do you do for an infection when it's a horse?" asked Kennie.

"Just what you'd do if it was a person. Wet dressings. I'll help you, Ken. We mustn't let those wounds close or scab over until they're clean. I'll make a poultice for that hind leg

and help you put it on. Now that she'll let us get close to her, we can help her a lot."

"The thing to do is see that she eats," said Rob. "Keep up her strength."

But he himself would not go near her. "She won't pull out of it," he said. "I don't want to see her or think about her."

Kennie and his mother nursed the filly. The big poultice was bandaged on the hind leg. It drew out much poisoned matter and Flicka felt better and was able to stand again.

She watched for Kennie now, and followed him like a dog, hopping on three legs, holding up the right hind leg with its huge knob of a bandage in comical fashion.

"Dad, Flicka's my friend now; she likes me," said Ken.

His father looked at him. "I'm glad of that, son. It's a fine thing to have a horse for a friend."

Kennie found a nicer place for her. In the lower pasture the brook ran over cool stones. There was a grassy bank, the size of a corral, almost on a level with the water. Here she could lie softly, eat grass, drink fresh running water. From the grass, a twenty-foot hill sloped up, crested with overhanging

---

■

poultice (pōl'tis) *n.* soft, moist mass of a substance, such as a mustard compound, heated and applied to a part of the body as a treatment for soreness.

He placed the box of oats under her nose and she ate while he stood beside her, his hand smoothing the satin-soft skin under her mane. It had a nap as deep as plush. He played with her long, cream-colored tresses; arranged her forelock neatly between her eyes. She was a bit dish-faced, like an <u>Arab</u>, with eyes set far apart. He lightly groomed and brushed her while she stood turning her head to him whichever way he went.

He spoiled her. Soon she would not step to the stream to drink but he must hold a bucket for her. And she would drink, then lift her dripping muzzle, rest it on the shoulder of his blue chambray shirt, her golden eyes dreaming off into the distance; then daintily dip her mouth and drink again.

When she turned her head to the south, and pricked her ears, and

Mountain Grown   1994   *John Fawcett*

trees. She was enclosed, as it were, in a green, open-air nursery.

Kennie carried her oats morning and evening. She would watch for him to come, eyes and ears pointed to the hill. And one evening Ken, still some distance off, came to a stop and a wide grin spread over his face. He had heard her nicker. She had caught sight of him coming and was calling to him!

Arab (ar'əb) *n.* Arabian horse, a breed noted for speed, grace, and intelligence.

stood tense and listening, Ken knew she heard the other colts galloping on the upland.

"You'll go back there someday, Flicka," he whispered. "You'll be three and I'll be eleven. You'll be so strong you won't know I'm on your back, and we'll fly like the wind. We'll stand on the very top where we can look over the whole world, and smell the snow from the Neversummer Range. Maybe we'll see antelope—"

This was the happiest month of Kennie's life.

With the morning, Flicka always had new strength and would hop three-legged up the hill to stand broadside to the early sun, as horses love to do.

The moment Ken woke, he'd go to the window, and see her there; and when he was dressed and at his table studying, he sat so that he could raise his head and see Flicka.

After breakfast, she would be waiting for him and the box of oats at the gate; and for Nell McLaughlin with fresh bandages and buckets of disinfectant; and all three would go together to the brook, Flicka hopping along ahead of them, as if she was leading the way.

But Rob McLaughlin would not look at her.

One day all the wounds were swollen again. Presently they opened, one by one; and Kennie and his mother made more poultices.

Still the little filly climbed the hill in the early morning and ran about on three legs. Then she began to go down in flesh and almost overnight wasted away to nothing. Every rib showed; the glossy hide was dull and brittle, and was pulled over the skeleton as if she was a dead horse.

Gus said, "It's de fever. It burns up her flesh. If you could stop de fever she might get vell."

McLaughlin was standing in his window one morning and saw the little skeleton hopping about three-legged in the sunshine, and he said, "That's the end. I won't have a thing like that on my place."

Kennie had to understand that Flicka had not been getting well all this time; she had been slowly dying.

"She still eats her oats," he said mechanically.

They were all sorry for Ken. Nell McLaughlin stopped disinfecting and dressing the wounds. "It's no use, Ken," she said gently, "you know Flicka's going to die, don't you?"

"Yes, Mother."

Ken stopped eating. Howard said, "Ken doesn't eat anything any more. Don't he have to eat his dinner, Mother?"

But Nell answered, "Leave him alone."

Because the shooting of wounded animals is all in the day's work on the western plains, and sickening to everyone, Rob's voice, when he gave the order to have Flicka shot, was as flat as if he had been telling Gus to kill a chicken for dinner.

"Here's the Marlin, Gus. Pick out a time when Ken's not around and put the filly out of her misery."

Gus took the rifle. "*Ja*, Boss—"

Ever since Ken had known that Flicka was to be shot, he had kept his eye on the rack which held the firearms. His father allowed no firearms in the bunkhouse. The gun rack was in the dining room of the ranch house; and, going through it to the kitchen three times a day for meals, Ken's eye scanned the weapons to make sure that they were all there.

That night they were not all there. The Marlin rifle was missing.

When Kennie saw that, he stopped walking. He felt dizzy. He kept staring at the gun rack, telling himself that it surely was there— he counted again and again—he couldn't see clearly—

Then he felt an arm across his shoulders and heard his father's voice.

"I know, son. Some things are awful hard to take. We just have to take 'em. I have to, too."

Kennie got hold of his father's hand and held on. It helped steady him.

Finally he looked up. Rob looked down and smiled at him and gave him a little shake and squeeze. Ken managed a smile too.

"All right now?"

"All right, Dad."

They walked in to supper together.

Ken even ate a little. But Nell looked thoughtfully at the ashen color of his face and at the little pulse that was beating in the side of his neck.

After supper he carried Flicka her oats, but he had to coax her and she would only eat a little. She stood with her head hanging, but when he stroked it and talked to her, she pressed her face into his chest and was content. He could feel the burning heat of her body. It didn't seem possible that anything so thin could be alive.

Presently Kennie saw Gus come into the pasture carrying the Marlin. When he saw Ken, he changed his direction and <u>sauntered</u> along as if he was out to shoot some cottontails.

Ken ran to him. "When are you going to do it, Gus?"

"Ay was goin' down soon now, before it got dark—"

"Gus, don't do it tonight. Wait till morning. Just one more night, Gus."

■───────────────────────

sauntered (sôn′tərd) *v.i.* walked in a slow, relaxed way; strolled.

595

"Vell, in de morning den, but it got to be done, Ken. Yer fader gives de order."

"I know. I won't say anything more."

An hour after the family had gone to bed, Ken got up and put on his clothes. It was a warm moonlit night. He ran down to the brook, calling softly. "Flicka! Flicka!"

But Flicka did not answer with a little nicker; and she was not in the nursery, nor hopping about the pasture. Ken hunted for an hour.

At last he found her down the creek, lying in the water. Her head had been on the bank, but as she lay there, the current of the stream had sucked and pulled at her, and she had had no strength to resist; and little by little her head had slipped down until when Ken got there only the muzzle was resting on the bank, and the body and legs were swinging in the stream.

Kennie slid into the water, sitting on the bank, and he hauled at her head. But she was heavy and the current dragged like a weight; and he began to sob because he had no strength to draw her out.

Then he found a leverage for his heels against some rocks in the bed of the stream, and he braced himself against these, and pulled with all his might; and her head came up onto his knees, and he held it cradled in his arms.

He was glad that she had died of her own accord, in the cool water, under the moon, instead of being shot by Gus. Then, putting his face close to hers, and looking searchingly into her eyes he saw that she was alive and looking back at him.

And then he burst out crying, and hugged her, and said, "Oh, my little Flicka, my little Flicka."

The long night passed. The moon slid slowly across the heavens.

The water rippled over Kennie's legs, and over Flicka's body. And gradually the heat and fever went out of her. And the cool running water washed and washed her wounds.

When Gus went down in the morning with the rifle, they hadn't moved. There they were, Kennie sitting in water over his thighs and hips, with Flicka's head in his arms.

Gus seized Flicka by the head, and hauled her out on the grassy bank, and then, seeing that Kennie couldn't move, cold and stiff and half-paralyzed as he was, lifted him in his arms and carried him to the house.

"Gus," said Ken through chattering teeth, "don't shoot her, Gus."

"It ain't fur me to say, Ken. You know dat."

"But the fever's left her, Gus."

"Ay wait a little, Ken—"

Rob McLaughlin drove to Laramie to get the doctor, for Ken was in violent chills that would not stop. His mother had him in bed wrapped in hot blankets when they got back.

He looked at his father imploringly as the doctor shook down the thermometer.

"She might get well now, Dad. The fever's left her. It went out of her when the moon went down."

"All right, son. Don't worry. Gus'll feed her, morning and night, as long as she's—"

"As long as I can't do it," finished Kennie happily.

The doctor put the thermometer in his mouth and told him to keep it shut.

All day Gus went about his work, thinking of Flicka. He had not been back to look at her. He had been given no more orders. If she was alive, the order to shoot her was still in effect. But Kennie was ill, McLaughlin making his second trip to town taking the doctor home, and would not be back till long after dark.

After their supper in the bunkhouse, Gus and Tim walked down to the brook. They did not speak as they approached the filly, lying stretched out flat on the grassy bank, but their eyes were straining at her to see if she was dead or alive.

She raised her head as they reached her.

"By the powers!" exclaimed Tim, "there she is!"

She dropped her head, raised it again, and moved her legs and became tense as if struggling to rise. But to do so she must use her right hind leg to brace herself against the earth. That was the damaged leg, and at the first bit of pressure with it, she gave up and fell back.

"We'll swing her on to the other side," said Tim. "Then she can help herself."

"*Ja*—"

Standing behind her, they leaned over, grabbed hold of her left legs, front and back, and gently hauled her over. Flicka was as lax and willing as a puppy. But the moment she found herself lying on her right side, she began to scramble, braced herself with her good left leg and tried to rise.

"Yee whiz!" said Gus. "She got plenty strength yet."

"Hi!" cheered Tim. "She's up!"

But Flicka wavered, slid down again, and lay flat. This time she gave notice that she would not try again by heaving a deep sigh and closing her eyes.

Spottin' Strays on Willow Creek *1994 John Fawcett*

Gus took the pipe out of his mouth and thought it over. Orders or no orders, he would try to save the filly. Ken had gone too far to be let down.

"Ay'm goin' to rig a blanket sling fur her, Tim, and get her on her feet and keep her up."

There was bright moonlight to work by. They brought down the posthole digger and set two aspen poles deep into the ground either side of the filly, then, with ropes attached to the blanket, hoisted her by a pulley.

Not at all <u>disconcerted</u>, she rested comfortably in the blanket under her belly, touched her feet on the ground, and reached for the bucket of water Gus held for her.

Kennie was sick a long time. He nearly died. But Flicka picked up. Every day Gus passed the word to Nell, who carried it to Ken. "She's cleaning up her oats." "She's out of

---

disconcerted (dis'kən sûr'tid) *adj.* marked by a loss of self-possession or composure.

the sling." "She bears a little weight on the bad leg."

Tim declared it was a real miracle. They argued about it, eating their supper.

"Na," said Gus. "It was de cold water, washin' de fever outa her. And more dan dot—it was Ken—you tink it don't count? All night dot boy sits dere, and says, 'Hold on, Flicka. Ay'm here wid you. Ay'm standin' by, two of us togedder'—"

Tim stared at Gus without answering, while he thought it over. In the silence, a coyote yapped far off on the plains; and the wind made a rushing sound high up in the jack pines on the hill.

Gus filled his pipe.

"Sure," said Tim finally. "Sure. That's it."

Then came the day when Rob McLaughlin stood smiling at the foot of Kennie's bed and said, "Listen! Hear your friend?"

Ken listened and heard Flicka's high, eager whinny.

"She don't spend much time by the brook any more. She's up at the gate of the corral half the time, nickering for you."

"For me!"

Rob wrapped a blanket around the boy and carried him out to the corral gate.

Kennie gazed at Flicka. There was a look of marveling in his eyes. He felt as if he had been living in a world where everything was dreadful and hurting but awfully real; and *this* couldn't be real; this was all soft and happy, nothing to struggle over or worry about or fight for any more. Even his father was proud of him! He could feel it in the way Rob's big arms held him. It was all like a dream and far away. He couldn't, yet, get close to anything.

But Flicka—Flicka—alive, well, pressing up to him, recognizing him, nickering—

Kennie put out a hand—weak and white—and laid it on her face. His thin little fingers straightened her forelock the way he used to do, while Rob looked at the two with a strange expression about his mouth, and a glow in his eyes that was not often there.

"She's still poor, Dad, but she's on four legs now."

"She's picking up."

Ken turned his face up, suddenly remembering. "Dad! She did get gentled, didn't she?"

"Gentle—as—a kitten—"

They put a cot down by the brook for Ken, and boy and filly got well together.

Meet Mary O'Hara

Mary O'Hara (1885–1980) was a successful screenwriter when she decided to leave Hollywood to move to a ranch in Wyoming. She wrote the story "My Friend Flicka" after a horse on her ranch got sick and died. O'Hara felt that the horse might have recovered if someone had nursed it and kept it company. "My Friend Flicka" was published in January 1941.

A Hollywood editor told her the story would make "tip-top material for the screen"—provided she could first turn it into a popular full-length novel. Amazingly, O'Hara was able to do just that, though she had never before written a book. The novel of *My Friend Flicka* was published soon after she finished it, became a best-seller, and has never been out of print since. The classic movie adaptation came out in 1943.

More Short Stories

- *Coming and Going Men: Four Tales* by Paul Fleischman (Harper & Row, 1985). Before modern transportation and shopping malls, peddlers went from town to town selling goods. These stories describe the changes that take place in a small Vermont town as peddlers come and go.
- *The Wish Giver* by Bill Brittain (Harper Trophy, 1983). Have you ever wished for something and then regretted it when the wish came true? In this humorous Newbery Honor book, three youngsters learn to think carefully before they wish.
- *Children of the Fox* by Jill Paton Walsh (Farrar, Straus and Giroux, 1978). Set in ancient Greece, these three stories tell of courageous young people who risk their lives to aid their country.

RESPONDING TO *Literature*

THINK • TALK • WRITE

1 What did you like best about this story? Respond in your journal.

2 Where is "My Friend Flicka" set? How is this setting important?

3 How are Kennie and Rob McLaughlin alike? How are they different? In what ways does each person change during the story?

4 What is the main conflict in this story? How is it resolved?

5 In this coming-of-age story, the main character learns to be responsible and earns a reward. All cultures have coming-of-age stories. Think of another example, especially a folk tale or myth. What does the main character learn? What clues does the story contain about the culture it comes from?

ACTIVITIES

- **Write About Conflict** Write a dialog between Rob and Nell McLaughlin about giving Flicka to Ken. Have each explain his or her opinion, and then have them resolve their conflict.

- **Be a Book Illustrator** Choose an important scene in "My Friend Flicka." Illustrate the scene with a drawing, a painting, or a clay sculpture.

VOCABULARY PRACTICE

On a separate piece of paper, write the vocabulary word that best substitutes for each italicized word or phrase.

inventories   auspicious

prosperous   chagrined

monotonous   blissful

inimitable   abating

sauntered   disconcerted

1 The accountant kept *detailed lists* of the three stores' goods.

2 The horse *strolled* along the path.

3 Rob felt it was the most *favorable* time to ask for the favor.

4 We wished the newly married couple a long and *successful* life.

5 The baby gave her a *joyful* smile.

6 The bees' buzzing was a peaceful, *unchanging* drone.

7 Seth was *distressed* that his first try had failed, but he resolved to try again.

8 When we saw that the storm was *growing less forceful,* we decided to make a run for home.

9 He was *startled* by her change of mind.

10 The Olympic gymnast was famous for his *matchless* style and grace.

601

WRITING

Do you belong to a club or team? Most of us want to belong somewhere. Write a story about someone who finds a sense of belonging.

PREWRITE

How will you plan and organize your short story? Before you begin, try jotting down the main elements of your story in a few simple phrases. Write your ideas under headings. A chart for a short story about a camp counselor might look like this:

Characters and Setting	What happens? What's the problem?	How does it end?
• Kevin, new summer camp counselor • Another unhappy counselor	• Kevin is unhappy—camp is hard work • Meets another unhappy person • Sees boy drowning	• Counselors save drowning boy • Counselors win respect, are happy

Now organize your notes. Sketch out your ideas in a chart.

DRAFT

One writer began this first draft. Does the beginning give you a feeling for the main idea? Does it make you want to read more?

This writer sets the tone for his audience right away. Does the tone appeal to you?

Start your draft with the help of your prewriting notes. If other thoughts suddenly come to mind, try including them.

> ### Camp No Fun
>
> Counselors run the camp, they're know-it-alls who don't work very hard. At least that's what Kevin had heard. Too bad that actually being a counselor was different. It looked like the summer's not going to be much fun.

A SHORT STORY

REVISE

After you complete your first draft, wait a while. Then try reading it with a fresh eye. The writer of the sample made a few key changes.

Do these two changes make the meaning of the opening sentence more specific? ----------▶

Does changing the language here improve the tone of the piece? Why? ----------▶

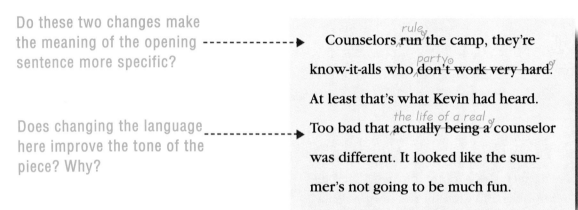

Counselors *rule* run the camp, they're know-it-alls who *party* don't work very hard. At least that's what Kevin had heard. Too bad that *the life of a real* actually being a counselor was different. It looked like the summer's not going to be much fun.

Before you revise your draft, get some opinions from friends. Is the tone appropriate? Does the story involve readers immediately?

PROOFREAD

Review the corrections the writer made. Had you noticed these errors in the previous drafts?

After proofreading, the writer realized that the first sentence was actually two and needed a change in punctuation.

Counselors *rule* run the camp, they're know-it-alls who *party* don't work very hard. At least that's what Kevin had heard. Too bad that *the life of a real* actually being a counselor was different. It looked like the *summer was* summer's not going to be much fun.

PUBLISH

The sample writer decided to read his story aloud to friends. How will you present your story? Will reading it aloud add to its appeal?

WRITING

USING COLORFUL ADJECTIVES AND ADVERBS

ENRICH YOUR WRITING OF **SHORT STORIES.**

Colorful adjectives and adverbs can make the reader feel, taste, touch, hear, or see what's being described. They make your writing come alive.

Which description is easier for you to picture?

Paragraph 1

Maria's legs moved across the court. Her face was set into a frown. The ball left her hands and hit the hoop with a thud. Then the bell ending first quarter rang.

Paragraph 2

Maria's strong legs moved swiftly across the court. Her sweaty face was set into a determined frown. The ball left her hands and hit the hoop with a dull thud. Then the bell ending first quarter rang shrilly.

PRACTICE 1 Respond on a separate piece of paper.

1 Which words in the second paragraph make the basketball game easier to imagine?

2 Replace the adjectives and adverbs in the second paragraph to create a completely different mood.

604

COMPARATIVE AND SUPERLATIVE ADJECTIVES

USE THESE RULES ABOUT ADJECTIVES WHEN WRITING **SHORT STORIES.**

- Use comparative adjectives to compare two things. Many one- and two-syllable adjectives form the comparative by adding *-er.* Use superlative adjectives to compare more than two things. Many one- and two-syllable adjectives form the superlative by adding *-est.*

- Most adjectives of two or more syllables add *more* to form the comparative and *most* to form the superlative. Some adjectives, such as *good* and *bad,* have irregular comparative and superlative forms. *(better, best; worse, worst)*

PRACTICE 2 Change the adjective to its comparative or superlative form.

1 Of all three players, she was the (good).

2 Maria's arms are (long) than Betty's.

3 Jim's playing was bad, but Albert's was (bad).

4 This year's game was (exciting) than last year's.

COMPARATIVE AND SUPERLATIVE ADVERBS

USE THESE RULES ABOUT ADVERBS WHEN YOU ARE WRITING **SHORT STORIES.**

- To form the comparative, add *-er* to most one-syllable adverbs and *more* or *less* to most longer adverbs. To form the superlative, add *-est* to most one-syllable adverbs and *most* or *least* to most longer adverbs.

- Never use *-er* with *more* or *-est* with *most* to form comparative or superlative adverbs.

PRACTICE 3 Change the adverb to its comparative or superlative form.

1 The coach complained (loudly) than anyone about our mistake.

2 Of all the players, Jason is the one who can dribble the (fast).

3 He made it to the hoop (quickly) than the other player.

4 He aims the ball (carefully) than he did last year.

605

WRITING

WRITING A HOW-TO GUIDE

Have you ever thought about the things you know how to do? Some of those things might interest your friends and classmates. One way to share what you know is to write a how-to guide.

PREWRITE

In your journal, list a few things that you do very well. Choose one topic. A flowchart can help you organize your thoughts. If you were writing about how to make shadow puppets, your chart might look like the one at right:

DRAFT Talk about your plans with a partner. Are the steps on your flowchart clear? Add any steps that might help a reader follow your directions. Write your draft.

REVISE Time words, such as *first,* and *next,* can help readers understand the exact order of steps. Include time words when you revise your draft.

PROOFREAD Ask your partner to read your how-to guide. A person who reads something for the first time can often spot errors that the writer overlooked.

PUBLISH Exchange how-to guides with your partner. Following directions, try out one another's projects. With your class, publish a how-to journal that includes everyone's how-to guides.

Get materials (paper, cardboard, glue, fasteners, scissors, rods)

↓

Trace character on paper

↓

Cut character into pieces (for example, arms, legs, body)

↓

Paste pieces on cardboard and recut

↓

Punch holes for fasteners

↓

Attach parts and add rods

▶ *Proofreading Alert!*

Avoid double negatives by removing one of the negative words. Check page 187 in *Spotlight on Success: Writing and Language Handbook.*

PROJECTS

CREATE A POSTER

REMEMBER TO: • PREWRITE • DRAFT • REVISE • PROOFREAD • PUBLISH

Create a poster for your classroom about the connections among living things—plants, insects, people. Brainstorm with classmates before you begin. Then ask yourself the following questions: What's the main idea of my poster? What phrase or sentence expresses that idea? What photo or drawing will grab people's attention? Will every-one understand what I'm saying? You might or-ganize your ideas in a chart like this:

MAIN IDEA:

All living things are connected.

Detail:

Humans depend on plants and animals for food.

Detail:

All organisms coexist in an ecosystem.

Ask classmates what they think of your ideas before you begin.

COMPOSE A SONG

REMEMBER TO: • PREWRITE • DRAFT • REVISE • PROOFREAD • PUBLISH

Create a song about belonging. Begin with the lyrics. They should have a rhythm and rhyme scheme. You might organize your thoughts in an idea cluster like this:

Here are some guidelines for creating your song:

- Use simple, easily sung words.
- Write a melody that goes with your words.
- Perform your song.
- Add percussion instruments or even a piano.

607

PEER PRESSURE: JOINING CLUBS

Have you ever done something just because all your friends did? If your answer is yes, then you gave in to peer pressure. Going along with the group can give you a sense of belonging. That feeling of security is important. But there's a downside: acting like everyone else means not thinking for yourself.

CONSIDER THIS ISSUE: Your school probably has a camera club or a drama club. These are *school* clubs, open to every student. But suppose a group of your classmates start a club. The group does things together, and each week they get together at the home of a member. If you join, you'll be part of the "in" group in your class. But you will also have to do what the other members do, and they won't like you to spend time with classmates who are not in the club. Right now, they want you to join. Think about both sides of the issue before making up your mind.

- Being a club member gives you a chance to do things with friends who are already in the club.
- Going along with the members of the group can mean not thinking for yourself.
- You might think that a club rule or activity is unfair or bad for you.
- Clubs can make people who don't belong feel left out.

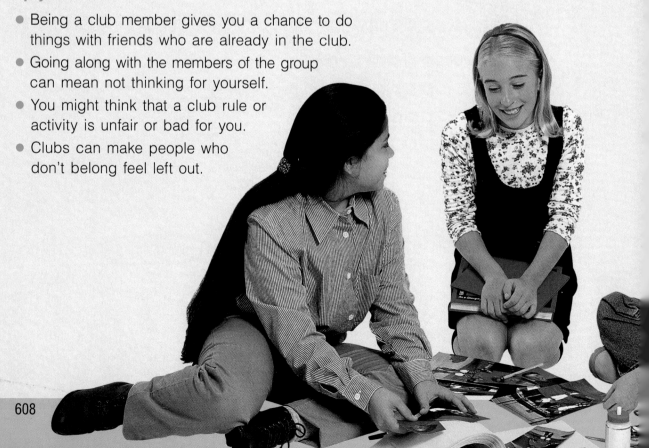

Read the following viewpoints about the issue of joining clubs. Then decide which opinion is closest to your own. Think of more arguments yourself to support the position you choose.

 **VIEWPOINT 1** I think joining a club is a good idea.

- It's fun to have a group of friends to hang out with.
- Everyone I like seems to be a part of the group.
- Club members are loyal to one another.

VIEWPOINT 2 I think it's wrong to join a club.

- Club members can feel pressured to act a certain way, even when they know it's the wrong thing to do.
- Once you join, you might stop being friends with nonmembers.
- If a club doesn't accept everyone, then its members are discriminating against students who aren't allowed to join.

VIEWPOINT 3 I think schools shouldn't allow students to form their own clubs.

- Clubs cause problems because they separate students into groups instead of bringing them together.
- Many students are afraid to speak out against clubs.
- Some clubs are just an excuse for members to keep others out of their groups.

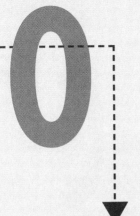

WHAT DO YOU THINK?

Spend a few minutes thinking about the issue of clubs in schools. Do you share one of the viewpoints above, or do you have another? Discuss your feelings with a small group.

real life
CONNECT

HOME • SCHOOL • COMMUNITY

BELONGING: It's knowing that we share a special connection with a person, a group, or a place.

Belonging means we feel connected to others. In addition to our families, we belong to schools, communities, clubs, organizations and to groups of friends.

Often, the sense of belonging exists between two people. Remember how Ken's family feels about him in "My Friend Flicka." When you share similar interests with a group, you form a bond based on experience and friendship.

Some organizations, such as schools or camps, make you fill out an application. Look at this reservation form for a summer camp.

An **application form** includes blank spaces where you write specific information. After reviewing Amanda Morton's reservation form, her summer camp will be able to register her in the camp sessions and activities she has requested.

CAMP MAPAWA
Eagle Ridge, Colorado
RESERVATION FORM

Camp Mapawa offers 12 one-week sessions of exciting camping experience for young people from ages 8 to 16. Located in the magnificent Colorado Rockies, Camp Mapawa is licensed by Certified Camps of America and provides experienced leaders in all fields of outdoor life.

To apply, complete the form below.
PLEASE PRINT

Name <u>Morton Amanda L.</u> AGE <u>12</u> PHONE (000) <u>555-7294</u>
     last   first   middle   years

ADDRESS <u>84 Locust Street   Modena Maine 00000</u>
       number and street   city   state   zip

Please check the sessions you wish to attend. Rates are $250 per week.
- ❑ June 13 - June 20
- ❑ June 20 - June 27
- ❑ June 27 - July 4
- ❑ July 4 - July 11
- ❑ July 11 - July 18
- ☑ July 18 - July 25
- ☑ July 25 - August 1
- ❑ August 1 - August 8
- ❑ August 8 - August 15
- ❑ August 15 - August 22
- ❑ August 22 - August 29
- ❑ August 29 - September 5

Camp Mapawa offers special activities at additional charges.
Check the ones in which you wish to participate.
- ☑ Horseback Riding ($75.00 per week)
- ☑ Sailing ($50.00 per week)
- ☑ Orienteering ($25.00 per week)

A medical certificate completed and signed by a doctor must accompany this application.
☑ Medical certificate enclosed.

number of sessions			amount
2	x $250		$500.00
special activity	number of weeks	dates	
Horseback Riding	2	July 18-August 1	150.00
Sailing	1	July 18-July 25	50.00
Orienteering	1	July 25-August 1	25.00
		Total	$725.00

PAYMENT must accompany this application.
- ❑ Check or money order
- ☑ Credit card (see below)
- ❑ Mastercard ☑ American Express ❑ Visa

CARD NUMBER <u>0000-0000-000-0000</u> EXPIRATION DATE <u>5/95</u>
SIGNATURE OF CARD HOLDER <u>John Morton</u> DATE <u>5/23/93</u>

IONS

Here are three activities that use application forms. Think of other situations in which application forms are important. Then choose an activity below or one of your own and talk or write about it.

PROJECT 1

COMPLETE A FORM Completing a form accurately is an important skill. Choose an organization or group that you'd like to join. Get a membership form and complete it. Be sure to answer all the questions. Then bring the completed form to class.

PROJECT 2

FORM VARIETY You have to fill out application forms for many things. Find an application form in your daily life. It might be a magazine subscription form, a passport application, or a raffle entry form. Make a classroom display of all the forms, and discuss their similarities and differences.

PROJECT 3

MAKE AN APPLICATION Application forms ask you to provide specific information. Think of an interest that you have in common with others in your class. Then design an application form for a school club that focuses on this interest. Before making your form, think about questions that would help the club learn about people who want to join. Bring your form to class, and discuss it in a small group. Ask another student to complete your form.

Dominant Curve (Courbe dominante) April 1936 Vasily Kandinsky
The Solomon R. Guggenheim Museum, New York

A Short Story

The ant climbs up a trunk
carrying a petal on its back;
and if you look closely
that petal is as big as a house
especially compared to the ant that
carries it so olympically.

You ask me: Why couldn't I carry
a petal twice as big as my body and my head?
Ah, but you can, little girl,
but not petals from a dahlia,
rather boxes full of thoughts
and loads of magic hours, and
a wagon of clear dreams, and
a big castle with its fairies:
all the petals that form the soul of
a little girl who speaks and speaks . . . !

—David Escobar Galindo
   translated by Jorge D. Piche

Challenges

UNIT 6

BEFORE READING

....

THE SURVEYOR

CONNECT TO LITERATURE

What can you learn from family stories? In your journal, write down a true story told by or about someone in your family. Does the story help you understand the person better? As you read "The Surveyor," note how the author's attitudes towards Félix Caballero change.

THINKING ABOUT THE FRAME STORY

A *frame* story is a story that introduces and surrounds another story. The first story acts as a "frame" for the second one. Much as a picture frame highlights a painting, the frame story encircles and highlights the story within it.

In "The Surveyor," the author describes how her mother and her aunts would sometimes secretly poke fun at one of her father's friends. Within this frame story, her father recounts his own experience with the man. By sharing her father's story in his own words, the author shows why he admired his friend. The frame story offers contrast for the suspenseful story within.

DID YOU KNOW?

"The Surveyor" comes from *Where the Flame Trees Bloom,* a collection of autobiographical stories by Alma Flor Ada. The author grew up in a large, old house in Cuba. Cuba is a long, narrow island with mountains at both ends and in the middle. Ada's family's home was situated in one of the rich, fertile plains between the mountain ranges. Huge flame trees, twisted with age, formed a path from the house to the river nearby. Many family members lived in the house. Close friends visited often.

THE SURVEYOR

BY ALMA FLOR ADA

My father, named <u>Modesto</u> after my grandfather, was a surveyor. Some of the happiest times of my childhood were spent on horseback, on trips where he would allow me to accompany him as he plotted the boundaries of small farms in the Cuban countryside. Sometimes we slept out under the stars, stringing our hammocks between the trees, and drank fresh water from springs. We always stopped for a warm greeting at the simple huts of the neighboring peasants, and my eyes would drink in the lush green forest crowned by the swaying leaves of the palm trees.

Since many surveying jobs called for dividing up land that a family had <u>inherited</u> from a deceased parent or relative, my father's greatest concern was that justice be achieved. It was not enough just to divide the land into equal portions. He also had to ensure that all parties would have <u>access</u> to roads,

---

Modesto (mō des′to)
inherited (in her′i tid) *v.t.* received from a former owner at his or her death.
access (ak′ses) *n.* ability or right to approach, enter, or use.

Puente cúrvo del ferrocarril mexicano en la Cañada de Metlac   *1881   José María Velasco   Private Collection, Mexico City*

to water sources, to the most fertile soil. While I was able to join him in some trips, other surveying work involved large areas of land. On these jobs, my father was part of a team, and I would stay home, eagerly awaiting to hear the stories from his trip on his return.

Latin American families tend not to limit their family boundaries to those who are born or have married into it. Any good friend who spends time with the family and shares in its daily experiences is welcomed as a member. The following story from one of my father's surveying trips is not about a member of my blood family, but instead concerns a member of our extended family.

Félix Caballero, a man my father always liked to <u>recruit</u> whenever he needed a team, was rather different from the other surveyors. He was somewhat older, unmarried, and he kept his thoughts to himself. He came to visit our house daily. Once there, he would sit silently in one of the living room's four rocking chairs, listening to the lively conversations all around him. An occasional nod or a single word were his only contributions to those conversations. My mother and her sisters sometimes made fun of him behind his back. Even though they never said so, I had the impression that they questioned why my father held him in such high regard.

Then one day my father shared this story.

"We had been working on foot in mountainous country for most of the day. Night was approaching. We still had a long way

---

Félix Caballero (fe′lēks kab ə yâr′ō)
recruit (ri krüt′) *v.t.* hire or get the services of.

to go to return to where we had left the horses, so we decided to cut across to the other side of the mountain, and soon found ourselves facing a deep gorge. The gorge was spanned by a railroad bridge, long and narrow, built for the sugarcane trains. There were no side rails or walkways, only a set of tracks resting on thick, heavy crossties suspended high in the air.

"We were all upset about having to climb down the steep gorge and up the other side, but the simpler solution, walking across the bridge, seemed too dangerous. What if a cane train should appear? There would be nowhere to go. So we all began the long descent . . . all except for Félix. He decided to risk walking across the railroad bridge. We all tried to dissuade him, but to no avail. Using an old method, he put one ear to the tracks to listen for vibrations. Since he heard none, he decided that no train was approaching. So he began to cross the long bridge, stepping from crosstie to crosstie between the rails, balancing his long red-and-white surveyor's poles on his shoulder.

"He was about halfway across the bridge when we heard the ominous sound of a steam engine. All eyes rose to Félix. Unquestionably he had heard it too, because he had stopped in the middle of the bridge and was looking back.

As the train drew closer, and thinking there was no other solution, we all shouted: 'Jump! Jump!', not even sure our voices would carry up to where he stood, so high above us. Félix did look down at the rocky riverbed, which, as it was the dry season, held little water. We tried to encourage him with gestures and

---

dissuade (di swād′) *v.t.* keep (someone) from doing something by persuasion or advice.
avail (ə vāl′) *n.* use; help; advantage.

more shouts, but he had stopped looking down.

We could not imagine what he was doing next, squatting on the tracks, with the engine of the train already visible. And then, we understood. . . .

"Knowing that he could not manage to hold on to the thick wooden crossties, Félix laid his thin but resilient surveyor's poles across the ties, parallel to the rails. Then he let his body slip down between two of the ties, as he held on to the poles. And there he hung, below the bridge, suspended over the gorge but safely out of the train's path.

"The cane train was, as they frequently are, a very long train. To us, it seemed <u>interminable</u>. . . . One of the younger men said he counted two hundred and twenty cars. With the approaching darkness, and the smoke and shadows of the train, it was often difficult to see our friend. We had heard no human sounds, no screams, but would we have heard anything at all, with the racket of the train crossing overhead?

"When the last car began to curve around the mountain, we could just make out Félix's lonely figure still hanging beneath the bridge. We all watched in relief and amazement as he pulled himself up and at last finished walking, slowly and calmly, along the tracks to the other side of the gorge."

After I heard that story, I saw Félix Caballero in a whole new light. He still remained as quiet as ever, prompting a smile from my mother and her sisters as he sat silently in his rocking chair. But in my mind's eye, I saw him crossing that treacherous bridge, stopping to think calmly of what to do to save his life,

---

interminable (in tûr′mə nə bəl) *adj.* endless or seeming to be endless.

emerging all covered with soot and smoke but triumphantly alive—a lonely man, hanging under a railroad bridge at dusk, suspended from his surveyor's poles over a rocky gorge.

If there was so much courage, such an ability to calmly <u>confront</u> danger in the quiet, aging man who sat rocking in our living room, what other wonders might lie hidden in every human soul?

Meet Alma Flor Ada

By the time she reached fourth grade, Alma Flor Ada knew that she would one day be a writer. She says, "I couldn't accept the fact that we had to read such boring textbooks while my wonderful storybooks awaited at home. I made a firm commitment . . . to devote my life to producing schoolbooks that would be fun—and since then I am having a lot of fun doing just that!"

Ada was born in Cuba—where "The Surveyor" takes place—and has also lived in Spain and Peru. She now makes her home in San Francisco, California. Her children, she says, are an inspiration for her writing. They help in other ways, too: "One of my greatest joys is that my daughter collaborates with me and has translated many of my books, some into English and some into Spanish. And she is always an excellent editor of my work." Ada's books include *The Gold Coin* and *Where the Flame Trees Bloom.*

---

confront (kən frunt') *v.t.* face boldly or with defiance.

RESPONDING TO *Literature*

THINK • TALK • WRITE

1 What do you think of Félix Caballero? Why? Share your feelings in your journal.

2 Why does the author enjoy traveling with her father on his surveying trips? Which details suggest that she admires her father?

3 How does Félix solve the problem of avoiding the train on the railroad bridge? Do you think Félix acts bravely? Why or why not?

4 Reread the last sentence of the selection. What do you think the author means? Do you agree with her? Explain.

5 Why is Félix Caballero considered a member of the author's extended family? What benefits can come from having an extended family?

ACTIVITIES

- **Write with a Frame Story** With a small group of classmates, make up a scenario for telling stories. For example, you might pretend to be strangers at a remote inn who pass the evening telling tales. After the group decides on a scenario, each member should write a short story. The group leader should then combine the stories and write an introduction and bridges between the stories, if necessary.

- **Make a Scene** Read the description of the railroad bridge over the mountain gorge. Make a drawing or a diorama of the scene, and paint it. Choose the point in the action that you want to portray in the artwork.

VOCABULARY PRACTICE

On a separate sheet of paper, write the vocabulary word that best answers each question.

inherited   avail
access   confront
recruit

1 You want Wen, an excellent player, to join your softball team. What should you do?

2 Josh hopes to go backstage at a concert. What will he do with any opportunity that arises?

3 Which word describes what happened when Ellen's great-uncle died and left her his collection of kaleidoscopes?

4 You decide to face up to the class bully who has been bothering you at recess. What do you plan to do?

5 The gate to the campsite is locked. If you ask the groundskeeper to open it, what are you seeking?

BEFORE READING

....

NUMBER THE STARS

CONNECT TO LITERATURE

What are some ways that ordinary people can be courageous? Write in your journal about people you know who have met challenges and shown braveness in everyday life. In "Number the Stars," two Danish girls face a frightening challenge. As you read the selection, note how they and other characters find courage.

THINKING ABOUT PROTAGONIST AND ANTAGONIST

The *protagonist* is the most important character—the hero or heroine—in a story or novel. The *antagonist* is the character who opposes the protagonist. Thus, the protagonist and antagonist are often enemies.

Annemarie Johansen is the protagonist in "Number the Stars." Nazi soldiers who come into her home are the antagonists. The Danes and the Germans fought on opposing sides in World War II. This selection describes a confrontation between the antagonists and Annemarie, her parents, and her best friend.

DID YOU KNOW?

This selection is an excerpt from the first half of Lois Lowry's historical novel *Number the Stars.* The novel takes place during World War II. The German army conquered Denmark in 1940. As the Nazis had done in other countries, they planned to arrest the Danish Jews and send them to concentration camps. Resistance fighters, secretly working to overthrow the Nazis, helped almost all the Jewish Danes escape to Sweden. Like the fictional Johansen family, many ordinary Danes helped in the effort to save their Jewish friends and neighbors.

Number the Stars

NUMBER THE STARS
by Lois Lowry

by Lois Lowry

It is 1943 and the Nazis have occupied Denmark. As the German soldiers begin their campaign to "relocate" all the Jews in Denmark, the Johansen family takes in Annemarie Johansen's best friend, Ellen Rosen.

Illustrations by Larry Winborg

Alone in the apartment while Mama was out shopping with Kirsti, Annemarie and Ellen were sprawled on the living room floor playing with paper dolls. They had cut the dolls from Mama's magazines, old ones she had saved from past years. The paper ladies had old-fashioned hair styles and clothes, and the girls had given them names from Mama's very favorite book. Mama had told Annemarie and Ellen the entire story of *Gone With the Wind,* and the girls thought it much more interesting and romantic than the king-and-queen tales that Kirsti loved.

"Come, Melanie," Annemarie said, walking her doll across the edge of the rug. "Let's dress for the ball."

"All right, Scarlett, I'm coming," Ellen replied in a <u>sophisticated</u> voice. She was a talented performer; she often played the leading roles in school dramatics. Games of the imagination were always fun when Ellen played.

The door opened and Kirsti stomped in, her face tear-stained and <u>glowering</u>. Mama followed her with an <u>exasperated</u> look and set a package down on the table.

"I won't!" Kirsti sputtered. "I won't ever, *ever* wear them! Not if you chain me in a prison and beat me with sticks!"

Annemarie giggled and looked questioningly at her mother. Mrs. Johansen sighed. "I bought Kirsti some new shoes," she explained. "She's outgrown her old ones."

"Goodness, Kirsti," Ellen said, "I wish my mother would get *me* some new shoes. I love new things, and it's so hard to find them in the stores."

---

sophisticated (sə fis'ti kā'tid) *adj.* full of worldly knowledge and experience.
glowering (glou'ə ring) *adj.* scowling; showing anger.
exasperated (eg zas'pə rā'tid) *adj.* greatly irritated; provoked to anger.

"Not if you go to a *fish* store!" Kirsti bellowed. "But most mothers wouldn't make their daughters wear ugly *fish* shoes!"

"Kirsten," Mama said soothingly, "you know it wasn't a fish store. And we were lucky to find shoes at all."

Kirsti sniffed. "Show them," she commanded. "Show Annemarie and Ellen how ugly they are."

Mama opened the package and took out a pair of little girl's shoes. She held them up, and Kirsti looked away in disgust.

"You know there's no leather anymore," Mama explained. "But they've found a way to make shoes out of fish skin. I don't think these are too ugly."

Annemarie and Ellen looked at the fish skin shoes. Annemarie took one in her hand and examined it. It was odd-looking; the fish scales were visible. But it was a shoe, and her sister needed shoes.

"It's not so bad, Kirsti," she said, lying a little.

Ellen turned the other one over in her hand. "You know," she said, "it's only the color that's ugly."

"Green!" Kirsti wailed. "I will never, *ever* wear green shoes!"

"In our apartment," Ellen told her, "my father has a jar of black, black ink. Would you like these shoes better if they were black?"

Kirsti frowned. "Maybe I would," she said, finally.

"Well, then," Ellen told her, "tonight, if your mama doesn't mind, I'll take the shoes home and ask my father to make them black for you, with his ink."

Mama laughed. "I think that would be a fine improvement. What do you think, Kirsti?"

Kirsti pondered. "Could he make them shiny?" she asked. "I want them shiny."

Ellen nodded. "I think he could. I think they'll be quite pretty, black and shiny."

Kirsti nodded. "All right, then," she said. "But you mustn't tell anyone that they're *fish*. I don't want anyone to know." She took her new shoes, holding them <u>disdainfully</u>, and put them on a chair. Then she looked with interest at the paper dolls.

"Can I play, too?" Kirsti asked. "Can I have a doll?" She squatted beside Annemarie and Ellen on the floor.

Sometimes, Annemarie thought, Kirsti was such a pest, always butting in. But the apartment was small. There was no other place for Kirsti to play. And if they told her to go away, Mama would scold.

disdainfully (dis dān′fə lē) *adv.* scornfully; with dislike for something thought of as unworthy or beneath one.

"Here," Annemarie said, and handed her sister a cut-out little girl doll. "We're playing *Gone With the Wind.* Melanie and Scarlett are going to a ball. You can be Bonnie. She's Scarlett's daughter."

Kirsti danced her doll up and down happily. "I'm going to the ball!" she announced in a high, pretend voice.

Ellen giggled. "A little girl wouldn't go to a ball. Let's make them go someplace else. Let's make them go to Tivoli!"

"Tivoli!" Annemarie began to laugh. "That's in Copenhagen! *Gone With the Wind* is in America!"

"Tivoli, Tivoli, Tivoli," little Kirsti sang, twirling her doll in a circle.

"It doesn't matter, because it's only a game anyway," Ellen pointed out. "Tivoli can be over there, by that chair. 'Come, Scarlett,'" she said, using her doll voice, "'we shall go to Tivoli to dance and watch the fireworks, and maybe there will be some handsome men there! Bring your silly daughter Bonnie, and she can ride on the carousel.'"

Annemarie grinned and walked her Scarlett toward the chair that Ellen had designated as Tivoli. She loved Tivoli Gardens, in the heart of Copenhagen; her parents had taken her there, often, when she was a little girl. She remembered the music and the brightly colored lights, the carousel and ice cream and especially the magnificent fireworks in the evenings: the huge colored splashes and bursts of lights in the evening sky.

"I remember the fireworks best of all," she commented to Ellen.

"Me too," Kirsti said. "I remember the fireworks."

"Silly," Annemarie scoffed. "You never saw the fireworks." Tivoli Gardens was closed now. The German occupation forces had burned part of it, perhaps as a way of punishing the fun-loving Danes for their lighthearted pleasures.

Kirsti drew herself up, her small shoulders stiff. "I did too," she said belligerently. "It was my birthday. I woke up in the night and I could hear the booms. And there were lights in the sky. Mama said it was fireworks for my birthday!"

---

designated (dez'ig nā'tid) *v.t.* selected for a particular purpose or duty; appointed.
belligerently (bə lij'ər ənt lē) *adv.* with hostility; with eagerness to fight.

Then Annemarie remembered. Kirsti's birthday was late in August. And that night, only a month before, she, too, had been awakened and frightened by the sound of explosions. Kirsti was right—the sky in the southeast had been ablaze, and Mama had comforted her by calling it a birthday celebration. "Imagine, such fireworks for a little girl five years old!" Mama had said, sitting on their bed, holding the dark curtain aside to look through the window at the lighted sky.

The next evening's newspaper had told the sad truth. The Danes had destroyed their own naval fleet, blowing up the vessels one by one, as the Germans approached to take over the ships for their own use.

"How sad the king must be," Annemarie had heard Mama say to Papa when they read the news.

"How proud," Papa had replied.

It had made Annemarie feel sad and proud, too, to picture the tall, aging king, perhaps with tears in his blue eyes, as he looked at the remains of his small navy, which now lay submerged and broken in the harbor.

"I don't want to play anymore, Ellen," she said suddenly, and put her paper doll on the table.

"I have to go home, anyway," Ellen said. "I have to help Mama with the housecleaning. Thursday is our New Year. Did you know that?"

"Why is it yours?" asked Kirsti. "Isn't it our New Year, too?"

"No. It's the Jewish New Year. That's just for us. But if you want, Kirsti, you can come that night and watch Mama light the candles."

Annemarie and Kirsti had often been invited to watch

Mrs. Rosen light the Sabbath candles on Friday evenings. She covered her head with a cloth and said a special prayer in Hebrew as she did so. Annemarie always stood very quietly, awed, to watch; even Kirsti, usually such a chatterbox, was always still at that time. They didn't understand the words or the meaning, but they could feel what a special time it was for the Rosens.

"Yes," Kirsti agreed happily. "I'll come and watch your mama light the candles, and I'll wear my new black shoes."

Sabbath (sab´əth) *n.* day of the week for rest and religious worship.

Hebrew (hē´brü) *n.* religious language of Judaism, originally spoken by the ancient Jews.

*B*ut this time was to be different. Leaving for school on Thursday with her sister, Annemarie saw the Rosens walking to the <u>synagogue</u> early in the morning, dressed in their best clothes. She waved to Ellen, who waved happily back.

"Lucky Ellen," Annemarie said to Kirsti. "She doesn't have to go to school today."

"But she probably has to sit very, very still, like we do in church," Kirsti pointed out. "*That's* no fun."

That afternoon, Mrs. Rosen knocked at their door but didn't come inside. Instead, she spoke for a long time in a hurried, tense voice to Annemarie's mother in the hall. When Mama returned, her face was worried, but her voice was cheerful.

"Girls," she said, "we have a nice surprise. Tonight Ellen will be coming to stay overnight and to be our guest for a few days! It isn't often we have a visitor."

Kirsti clapped her hands in delight.

"But, Mama," Annemarie said, in dismay, "it's their New Year. They were going to have a celebration at home! Ellen told me that her mother managed to get a chicken some-place, and she was going to roast it—their first roast chicken in a year or more!"

"Their plans have changed," Mama said briskly. "Mr. and Mrs. Rosen have been called away to visit some relatives. So Ellen will stay with us. Now, let's get busy and put clean sheets on your bed. Kirsti, you may sleep with Mama and Papa tonight, and we'll let the big girls giggle together by themselves."

Kirsti <u>pouted</u>, and it was clear that she was about to ar-gue. "Mama will tell you a special story tonight," her mother said. "One just for you."

"About a king?" Kirsti asked <u>dubiously</u>.

"About a king, if you wish," Mama replied.

"All right, then. But there must be a queen, too," Kirsti said.

---

synagogue (sin'ə gog') *n.* building used by Jews for religious worship and instruction.
pouted (pou'tid) *v.i.* thrust out the lips, as in displeasure or sullenness.
dubiously (dü'bē əs lē) *adv.* with doubt or uncertainty; skeptically.

632

Though Mrs. Rosen had sent her chicken to the Johansens, and Mama made a lovely dinner large enough for second helpings all around, it was not an evening of laughter and talk. Ellen was silent at dinner. She looked frightened. Mama and Papa tried to speak of cheerful things, but it was clear that they were worried, and it made Annemarie worry, too. Only Kirsti was unaware of the quiet tension in the room. Swinging her feet in their newly blackened and shiny shoes, she chattered and giggled during dinner.

"Early bedtime tonight, little one," Mama announced after the dishes were washed. "We need extra time for the long story I promised, about the king and queen." She disappeared with Kirsti into the bedroom.

"What's happening?" Annemarie asked when she and Ellen were alone with Papa in the living room. "Something's wrong. What is it?"

Papa's face was troubled. "I wish that I could protect you children from this knowledge," he said quietly. "Ellen, you already know. Now we must tell Annemarie."

He turned to her and stroked her hair with his gentle hand. "This morning, at the synagogue, the rabbi told his congregation that the Nazis have taken the synagogue lists of all the Jews. Where they live, what their names are. Of course the Rosens were on that list, along with many others."

"Why? Why did they want those names?"

"They plan to arrest all the Danish Jews. They plan to take them away. And we have been told that they may come tonight."

"I don't understand! Take them where?"

Her father shook his head. "We don't know where, and we don't really know why. They call it 'relocation.' We don't even know what that means. We only know that it is wrong, and it is dangerous, and we must help."

Annemarie was <u>stunned</u>. She looked at Ellen and saw that her best friend was crying silently.

"Where are Ellen's parents? We must help them, too!"

---

stunned (stund) *adj.* dazed; shocked; overwhelmed.

"We couldn't take all three of them. If the Germans came to search our apartment, it would be clear that the Rosens were here. One person we can hide. Not three. So Peter has helped Ellen's parents to go elsewhere. We don't know where. Ellen doesn't know either. But they are safe."

Ellen sobbed aloud, and put her face in her hands. Papa put his arm around her. "They are safe, Ellen. I promise you that. You will see them again quite soon. Can you try hard to believe my promise?"

Ellen hesitated, nodded, and wiped her eyes with her hand.

"But, Papa," Annemarie said, looking around the small apartment, with its few pieces of furniture: the fat stuffed sofa, the table and chairs, the small bookcase against the wall. "You said that we would hide her. How can we do that? Where can she hide?"

Papa smiled. "That part is easy. It will be as your mama said: you two will sleep together in your bed, and you may giggle and talk and tell secrets to each other. And if anyone comes—"

Ellen interrupted him. "Who might come? Will it be soldiers? Like the ones on the corners?" Annemarie remembered how terrified Ellen had looked the day when the soldier had questioned them on the corner.

"I really don't think anyone will. But it never hurts to be prepared. If anyone should come, even soldiers, you two will be sisters. You are together so much, it will be easy for you to pretend that you are sisters."

He rose and walked to the window. He pulled the lace curtain aside and looked down into the street. Outside, it was beginning to grow dark. Soon they would have to draw the black curtains that all Danes had on their windows; the entire city had to be completely darkened at night. In a nearby tree, a bird was singing; otherwise it was quiet. It was the last night of September.

"Go, now, and get into your nightgowns. It will be a long night."

Annemarie and Ellen got to their feet. Papa suddenly crossed the room and put his arms around them both. He kissed the top of each head: Annemarie's blond one, which reached to his shoulder, and Ellen's dark hair, the thick curls braided as always into pigtails.

"Don't be frightened," he said to them softly. "Once I had three daughters. Tonight I am proud to have three daughters again."

o you really think anyone will come?" Ellen asked nervously, turning to Annemarie in the bedroom. "Your father doesn't think so."

"Of course not. They're always threatening stuff. They just like to scare people." Annemarie took her nightgown from a hook in the closet.

"Anyway, if they did, it would give me a chance to practice acting. I'd just pretend to be Lise. I wish I were taller, though." Ellen stood on tiptoe, trying to make herself tall. She laughed at herself, and her voice was more relaxed.

"You were great as the Dark Queen in the school play last year," Annemarie told her. "You should be an actress when you grow up."

"My father wants me to be a teacher. He wants *everyone* to be a teacher, like him. But maybe I could convince him that I should go to acting school." Ellen stood on tiptoe again, and made an <u>imperious</u> gesture with her arm. "I am the Dark Queen," she intoned dramatically. "I have come to command the night!"

"You should try saying, 'I am Lise Johansen!'" Annemarie said, grinning. "If you told the Nazis that you were the Dark Queen, they'd haul you off to a mental institution."

Ellen dropped her actress pose and sat down, with her legs curled under her, on the bed. "They won't really come here, do you think?" she asked again.

Annemarie shook her head. "Not in a million years." She picked up her hairbrush.

The girls found themselves whispering as they got ready for bed. There was no need, really, to whisper; they were, after all, supposed to be normal sisters, and Papa had said they could giggle and talk. The bedroom door was closed.

But the night did seem, somehow, different from a normal night. And so they whispered.

"How did your sister die, Annemarie?" Ellen asked suddenly. "I remember when it happened. And I remember the

---

imperious (im pîr′ē əs) *adj.* haughty; arrogant.

funeral—it was the only time I have ever been in a Lutheran church. But I never knew just what happened."

"I don't know *exactly,*" Annemarie confessed. "She and Peter were out somewhere together, and then there was a telephone call, that there had been an accident. Mama and Papa rushed to the hospital—remember, your mother came and stayed with me and Kirsti? Kirsti was already asleep and she slept right through everything, she was so little then. But I stayed up, and I was with your mother in the living room when my parents came home in the middle of the night. And they told me Lise had died."

"I remember it was raining," Ellen said sadly. "It was still raining the next morning when Mama told me. Mama was crying, and the rain made it seem as if the whole *world* was crying."

Annemarie finished brushing her long hair and handed her hairbrush to her best friend. Ellen undid her braids, lifted her dark hair away from the thin gold chain she wore around her neck—the chain that held the Star of David—and began to brush her thick curls.

"I think it was partly because of the rain. They said she was hit by a car. I suppose the streets were slippery, and it was getting dark, and maybe the driver just couldn't see," Annemarie went on, remembering. "Papa looked so angry. He made one hand into a fist, and he kept pounding it into the other hand. I remember the noise of it: slam, slam, slam."

Together they got into the wide bed and pulled up the covers. Annemarie blew out the candle and drew the dark curtains aside so that the open window near the bed let in some air. "See that blue trunk in the corner?" she said, pointing through the darkness. "Lots of Lise's things are in there. Even her wedding dress. Mama and Papa have never looked at those things, not since the day they packed them away."

Ellen sighed. "She would have looked so beautiful in her wedding dress. She had such a pretty smile. I used to pretend that she was *my* sister, too."

"She would have liked that," Annemarie told her. "She loved you."

"That's the worst thing in the world," Ellen whispered. "To be dead so young. I wouldn't want the Germans to take my family away—to make us live someplace else. But still, it wouldn't be as bad as being dead."

Annemarie leaned over and hugged her. "They won't take you away," she said. "Not your parents, either. Papa promised that they were safe, and he always keeps his promises. And you are quite safe, here with us."

For a while they continued to murmur in the dark, but the murmurs were interrupted by yawns. Then Ellen's voice stopped, she turned over, and in a minute her breathing was quiet and slow.

Annemarie stared at the window where the sky was outlined and a tree branch moved slightly in the breeze. Everything seemed very familiar, very comforting. Dangers were no more than odd imaginings, like ghost stories that children made up to frighten one another: things that couldn't possibly happen. Annemarie felt completely safe here in her own home, with her parents in the next room and her best friend asleep beside her. She yawned contentedly and closed her eyes.

It was hours later, but still dark, when she was awakened abruptly by the pounding on the apartment door.

Annemarie eased the bedroom door open quietly, only a crack, and peeked out. Behind her, Ellen was sitting up, her eyes wide.

She could see Mama and Papa in their nightclothes, moving about. Mama held a lighted candle, but as Annemarie watched, she went to a lamp and switched it on. It was so long a time since they had dared to use the strictly <u>rationed</u> electricity after dark that the light in the room seemed startling to Annemarie, watching through the slightly opened bedroom door. She saw her mother look automatically to the blackout curtains, making certain that they were tightly drawn.

Papa opened the front door to the soldiers.

"This is the Johansen apartment?" A deep voice asked the question loudly, in the terribly accented Danish.

"Our name is on the door, and I see you have a flashlight," Papa answered. "What do you want? Is something wrong?"

"I understand you are a friend of your neighbors the Rosens, Mrs. Johansen," the soldier said angrily.

---

rationed (rash´ənd) *adj.* limited to fixed portions.

"Sophy Rosen is my friend, that is true," Mama said quietly. "Please, could you speak more softly? My children are asleep."

"Then you will be so kind as to tell me where the Rosens are." He made no effort to lower his voice.

"I assume they are at home, sleeping. It is four in the morning, after all," Mama said.

Annemarie heard the soldier stalk across the living room toward the kitchen. From her hiding place in the narrow sliver of open doorway, she could see the heavy uniformed man, a holstered pistol at his waist, in the entrance to the kitchen, peering in toward the sink.

Another German voice said, "The Rosens' apartment is empty. We are wondering if they might be visiting their good friends the Johansens."

"Well," said Papa, moving slightly so that he was standing in front of Annemarie's bedroom door, and she could see nothing except the dark blur of his back, "as you see, you are mistaken. There is no one here but my family."

"You will not object if we look around." The voice was harsh, and it was not a question.

"It seems we have no choice," Papa replied.

"Please don't wake my children," Mama requested again. "There is no need to frighten little ones."

The heavy, booted feet moved across the floor again and into the other bedroom. A closet door opened and closed with a bang.

Annemarie eased her bedroom door closed silently. She stumbled through the darkness to the bed.

"Ellen," she whispered urgently, "take your necklace off!"

Ellen's hands flew to her neck. Desperately she began trying to unhook the tiny clasp. Outside the bedroom door, the harsh voices and heavy footsteps continued.

"I can't get it open!" Ellen said frantically. "I never take it off—I can't even remember how to open it!"

Annemarie heard a voice just outside the door. "What is here?"

"Shhh," her mother replied. "My daughters' bedroom. They are sound asleep."

"Hold still," Annemarie commanded. "This will hurt." She grabbed the little gold chain, yanked with all her strength, and broke it. As the door opened and light flooded into the bedroom, she crumpled it into her hand and closed her fingers tightly.

Terrified, both girls looked up at the three Nazi officers who entered the room.

One of the men aimed a flashlight around the bedroom. He went to the closet and looked inside. Then with a sweep of his gloved hand he pushed to the floor several coats and a bathrobe that hung from pegs on the wall.

There was nothing else in the room except a chest of drawers, the blue decorated trunk in the corner, and a heap of Kirsti's dolls piled in a small rocking chair. The flashlight beam touched each thing in turn. Angrily the officer turned toward the bed.

"Get up!" he ordered. "Come out here!"

Trembling, the two girls rose from the bed and followed him, brushing past the two remaining officers in the doorway, to the living room.

Annemarie looked around. These three uniformed men were different from the ones on the street corners. The street soldiers were often young, sometimes ill at ease, and Annemarie remembered how the Giraffe had, for a moment, let his harsh pose slip and had smiled at Kirsti.

But these men were older and their faces were set with anger.

Her parents were standing beside each other, their faces tense, but Kirsti was nowhere in sight. Thank goodness that Kirsti slept through almost everything. If they had wakened her, she would be wailing—or worse, she would be angry, and her fists would fly.

"Your names?" the officer barked.

"Annemarie Johansen. And this is my sister—"

"Quiet! Let her speak for herself. Your name?" He was glaring at Ellen.

Ellen swallowed. "Lise," she said, and cleared her throat. "Lise Johansen."

The officer stared at them grimly.

"Now," Mama said in a strong voice, "you have seen that we are not hiding anything. May my children go back to bed?"

The officer ignored her. Suddenly he grabbed a handful of Ellen's hair. Ellen winced.

He laughed scornfully. "You have a blond child sleeping in the other room. And you have this blond daughter—" He gestured toward Annemarie with his head. "Where did you get the dark-haired one?" He twisted the lock of Ellen's hair. "From a different father? From the milkman?"

Papa stepped forward. "Don't speak to my wife in such a way. Let go of my daughter or I will report you for such treatment."

"Or maybe you got her someplace else?" the officer continued with a sneer. "From the Rosens?"

For a moment no one spoke. Then Annemarie, watching in panic, saw her father move swiftly to the small bookcase and take out a book. She saw that he was holding the family photograph album. Very quickly he searched through its pages, found what he was looking for, and tore out three pictures from three separate pages.

He handed them to the German officer, who released Ellen's hair.

"You will see each of my daughters, each with her name written on the photograph," Papa said.

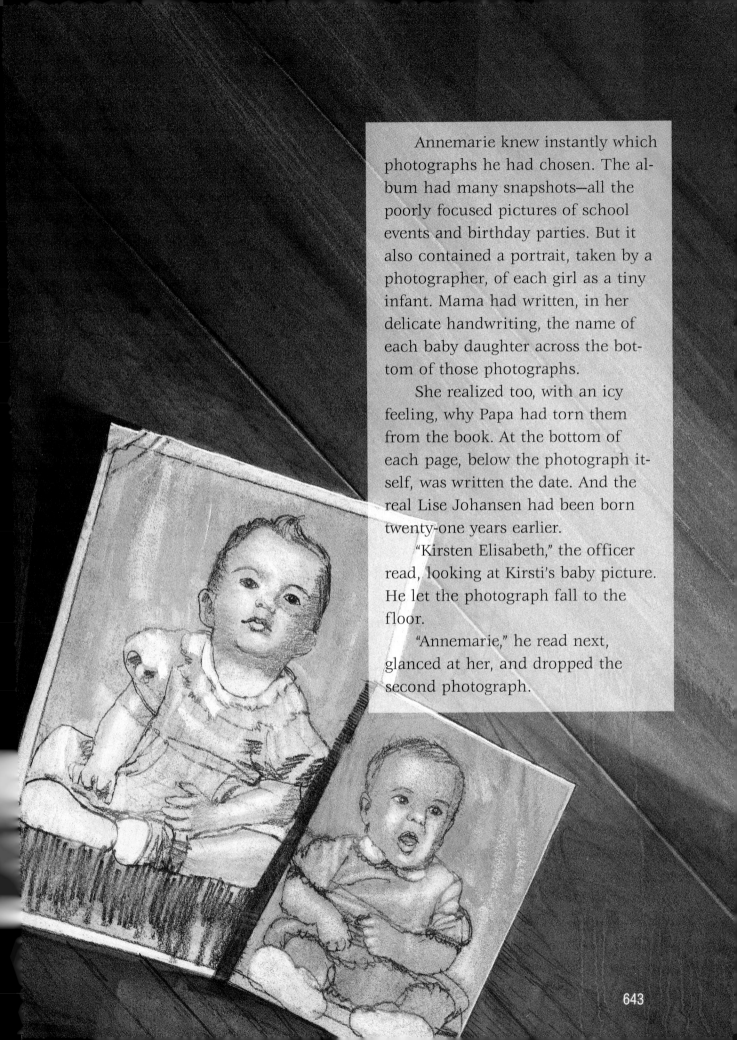

Annemarie knew instantly which photographs he had chosen. The album had many snapshots—all the poorly focused pictures of school events and birthday parties. But it also contained a portrait, taken by a photographer, of each girl as a tiny infant. Mama had written, in her delicate handwriting, the name of each baby daughter across the bottom of those photographs.

She realized too, with an icy feeling, why Papa had torn them from the book. At the bottom of each page, below the photograph itself, was written the date. And the real Lise Johansen had been born twenty-one years earlier.

"Kirsten Elisabeth," the officer read, looking at Kirsti's baby picture. He let the photograph fall to the floor.

"Annemarie," he read next, glanced at her, and dropped the second photograph.

"Lise Margrete," he read finally, and stared at Ellen for a long, unwavering moment. In her mind, Annemarie pictured the photograph that he held: the baby, wide-eyed, propped against a pillow, her tiny hand holding a silver teething ring, her bare feet visible below the hem of an embroidered dress. The wispy curls. Dark.

The officer tore the photograph in half and dropped the pieces on the floor. Then he turned, the heels of his shiny boots grinding into the pictures, and left the apartment. Without a word, the other two officers followed. Papa stepped forward and closed the door behind him.

Annemarie relaxed the clenched fingers of her right hand, which still clutched Ellen's necklace. She looked down, and saw that she had imprinted the Star of David into her palm.

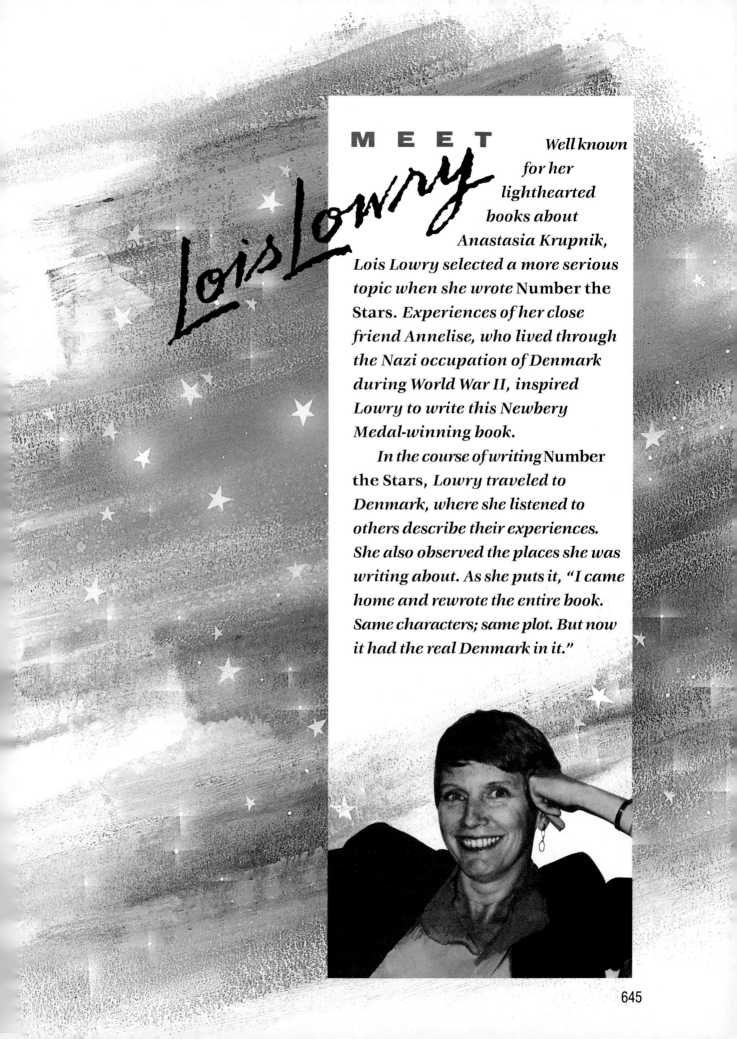

MEET

Lois Lowry

Well known for her lighthearted books about Anastasia Krupnik, Lois Lowry selected a more serious topic when she wrote **Number the Stars.** *Experiences of her close friend Annelise, who lived through the Nazi occupation of Denmark during World War II, inspired Lowry to write this Newbery Medal-winning book.*

In the course of writing **Number the Stars,** *Lowry traveled to Denmark, where she listened to others describe their experiences. She also observed the places she was writing about. As she puts it, "I came home and rewrote the entire book. Same characters; same plot. But now it had the real Denmark in it."*

RESPONDING TO *Literature*

THINK • TALK • WRITE

1 Did you find the last section of this selection suspenseful? Describe your reactions in your journal.

2 What actually happened on the night when Kirsti believes she heard fireworks? What does this incident tell you about what life was like in Denmark at that time?

3 Why does Ellen come to spend the night at the Johansens'? Why do the German soldiers come there in the middle of the night?

4 Why is it so important for Ellen to take off her necklace? How does Annemarie show her courage?

5 Why do you think Annemarie and Kirsti like to watch Mrs. Rosen light the Sabbath candles? Why might a ceremony in any culture have meaning for all people?

ACTIVITIES

- **Write About Protagonists and Antagonists** Imagine that Annemarie is stopped by a German soldier on the street. Write a dialog between the protagonist and antagonist.

- **Record Oral History** Ask an adult who was alive during World War II to share experiences. Record the story and retell it to classmates.

VOCABULARY PRACTICE

On a separate piece of paper, write the vocabulary word that best completes each sentence.

sophisticated	glowering
exasperated	designated
disdainfully	belligerently
pouted	dubiously
stunned	rationed

1 The captain treated Mrs. Johansen _____, as if she were a child.

2 The Rosens were _____ at the shocking news that the Germans planned to "relocate" Danish Jews.

3 The soldiers were _____ at Mr. Johansen and trying to scare him.

4 They spoke angrily and _____ to Mr. Johansen.

5 Ellen pretended her paper doll was a _____ woman going to a ball.

6 The older girls _____ Kirsti to play Bonnie in their make-believe game.

7 Annemarie was _____ with her little sister for being such a pest.

8 Food and other goods are _____ during a war.

9 Kirsti _____ when she had to wear ugly "fish" shoes.

10 At first she reacted _____, but Ellen persuaded her to give it a try.

646

BEFORE READING

···

A BOAT TO NOWHERE

CONNECT TO LITERATURE

In "A Boat to Nowhere," an orphan
gradually becomes part of a family.
What do you think are some important things about belonging to a
family? Write your ideas in your
journal. As you read the selection,
compare your ideas with Kien's
experiences of love and family.

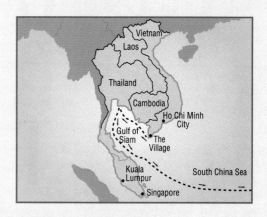

THINKING ABOUT SUSPENSE

Suspense is the growing excitement you feel when a story is
building to a high point. When you find yourself wondering how
a character will escape from danger, the story is suspenseful.

In "A Boat to Nowhere," the uncertainty of the characters' fate
creates suspense. Kien and his "family" face a life-threatening
situation: they are adrift at sea, and no one seems willing to
help them. When Kien must make a decision that could mean
life or death, the suspense builds to a height.

DID YOU KNOW?

This selection is an excerpt from the last chapters of the novel *A
Boat to Nowhere*. The novel takes place at the end of the Vietnam
War. Thay Van Chi, Mai, Loc, and Kien escape from their village
in the southern Vietnam when representatives of the new government arrive. The family sets out in a small fishing boat, the *Sea
Breeze*, traveling in the South China Sea and Gulf of Thailand. The
map above shows their journey. Like other refugees, they are
known as "boat people" and find it hard to get help. Thay Van
Chi, the wise grandfather is sick and getting worse.

a BOAT to nOWHERE

by Maureen
Crane Wartski

illustrated by
Hui Han Liu

mai, her little brother Loc, her grandfather, and Kien, a fourteen-year-old orphan, escaped from their Vietnamese village when it was invaded. They have been refused landing in Thailand and attacked by pirates. They have survived storms at sea and an encounter with other refugees who tried to steal their boat. Their situation grows even more desperate.

Two days out of Outcast Island, Thay Van Chi's cough returned.

"How stupid I was! Why did I throw those pills at Dr. Phan Tri!" Mai mourned.

"It was the only way to make him let go of the *Sea Breeze*. If the others had caught up to us, we'd never have escaped from Bác Thong," Kien comforted her.

But without the medicine, the old man sickened daily. Each day found him weaker, till he could no longer sail the *Sea Breeze*, even for a few minutes at a time.

By stingily dividing and rationing the few fish and coconuts they had brought with them, they managed to make the food last six days, but at the end of that time there was nothing left, not even a bone or a husk of coconut. Fortunately the monsoons had begun and there was plenty of rainwater. This became their only food.

Where was Malaysia? Kien asked himself over and over as he greedily scanned the horizon. The old man insisted that they were still traveling in the right direction, but could Thay Van Chi be relied upon anymore? Kien looked at the old teacher anxiously and saw with some surprise that the old man was watching him.

"You are sailing well, Kien," Thay Van Chi said in his weak whisper of a voice. "You will get the *Sea Breeze* to land. I know it."

"When that day comes you'll be right there with us, Uncle," Kien said, trying to make the Old One laugh. But Thay Van Chi closed his eyes and slid into a weak sleep. If only we hadn't had to leave Outcast Island, Kien thought bitterly. That miserable Bác Thong! Kien tried to get angry, angry enough to kill the pain and hunger and worry in him, but the anger didn't work. It only made things worse.

On the seventh day after leaving Outcast Island, Mai herself began to cough. The cough worsened rapidly, till she could hardly breathe for coughing. Loc was by now too weak and listless to care much, but Kien was terrified.

She needs help, he thought. She needs help, now! Otherwise she might . . .

---

stingily (stin′jə lē) *adv.* ungenerously.

monsoons (mon sünz′) *n., pl.* summer storms characterized by heavy rains.

listless (list′lis) *adj.* lacking energy and a desire to do anything.

He looked at Thay Van Chi and then at Mai. Help. Where could he find help? He desperately searched the horizon for anything that might give him hope, but there was nothing. No shadow, no sign—nothing.

On the eighth day a squall caught the *Sea Breeze,* spinning the boat around with strong winds and drenching everyone with rain. The next day, the ninth day, the sun came out—ferocious and merciless. Mai was so feverish she was <u>delirious</u> and lay talking nonsense in the bottom of the boat. The old man slept more and more, and Loc sat listlessly by Kien, <u>drowsy</u> from weakness.

Once Loc said, "Kien, do you remember the time I saw you in the forest and called you a Monster Man?"

Kien himself was so weak the thought brought tears to his eyes.

"Yes, little brother," he sighed. "I remember."

"You didn't like us very much, then, Kien. You and Mai were enemies back at the Village," Loc said. "You didn't have many friends."

"No," Kien agreed and hoped Loc would be silent, but the little boy went on.

"You did have a friend once. Remember? The one who gave you the watch. You gave Dao the watch to help us escape." Loc sighed and rested his head against Kien's knee. "It seems a long, long time ago . . ."

Yes, it seemed like a long time ago, Kien thought. He tried to remember how it had felt to be free, uncaring, bound to no one and to no loyalty, and he could not remember. He thought of the promise he had made to himself when Jim went away, the promise that never again would

delirious (di lir′ē əs) *adj.* temporarily out of one's mind.
drowsy (drou′zē) *adj.* sleepy; half asleep.

651

he be hurt by caring for anyone as he had cared for Jim. Then Mai began to cough, and all his other thoughts went away.

I have to get some food for her and the old man or they will die, Kien thought.

Without much hope, he dug around in the wooden sides of the boat until he found an old, rusty hook embedded in the wood. Then, tearing some strands from the blanket Mai had taken from Bác Thong's hut, he fashioned a <u>rude</u> fishline. He had no bait, none at all, and very little hope as he dropped the hook and line over the side of the boat, but the hook would not sink. He looked around the boat for something to weight his line, and then saw something small and bright and colorful protruding from the old man's shirt.

Kien reached for this and saw it was the bag of Vietnamese sand that Thay Van Chi had taken from the beach weeks ago. It was heavy enough to weight the fishing line, but . . .

"You can't use that, Kien!" Loc protested as Kien began to tie the bag of sand to the <u>makeshift</u> fishing line. "Grandfather won't like it!"

"He can't enjoy starving, either," Kien grunted. "Maybe sand from Vietnam will bring us good luck."

Perhaps it was the bright color of the bag that tempted the fish, or perhaps the sand did bring them luck. Within a half hour there was a fish! Kien could hardly believe it as he pulled the fish into the boat. He hastily returned the dripping bag of sand to Thay Van Chi, and then woke the old man and Mai. In silence the fish was divided four ways, and they ate it greedily, gulping bones, fins, and <u>entrails</u>.

"Courtesy of the 'sand of Vietnam,'" Kien said, and when he explained, even the old man smiled.

The "sand of Vietnam" plus the head of the first fish attracted two more fish that day, and the crew of the *Sea Breeze* ate them, too. Now, they felt a little stronger. But Mai's cough was worsening, and Thay Van Chi seemed to be sleeping more and more. Kien did not like it. He knew that people who were very sick often slipped into death in just that way.

---

rude (rüd) *adj.* primitive; not developed or advanced.
makeshift (māk'shift') *adj.* used temporarily in place of the proper or usual thing.
entrails (en'trālz) *pl. n.* inner parts of an animal, especially the intestines.

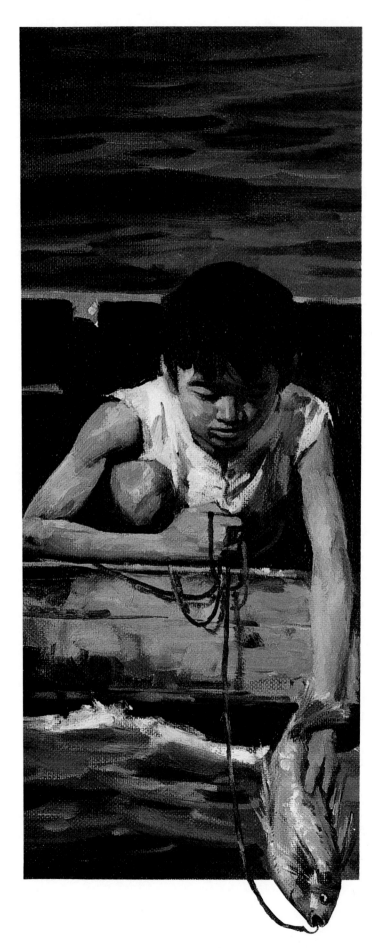

Heaven, he prayed within himself, send us some help. We really need it now.

And on the afternoon of the tenth day a ship came.

At first they thought it was just a trick of light, a cloud sweeping low on the horizon. Then Loc, who had regained some of his strength since eating the fish, cried "Look, Kien! A ship!"

Kien looked up at once, and there it was, painted black and white, with a huge <u>prow</u> that cut through the water like a knife. It really was—

"A ship!" Kien screamed.

Mai sat up and looked around her dazedly.

"Wave your arms! Cry out!" she whimpered, and the old man gasped, "They *must* see us!"

Kien staggered up in the boat and waved his arms wildly. Loc got up and waved too.

"Here we are!" Loc croaked, and Kien shouted, "Come and save us!"

---

prow (prou) *n.* forward part of a boat or ship.

The ship seemed to swing nearer.

"It _sees_ us!" Loc panted. "Grandfather, Mai, they _see_ us!"

The ship was coming nearer still. Kien was filled with such excitement that he couldn't just stand there. With a shout he jumped into the water and began to swim toward the ship.

"I'm here! I'm here!" he gasped, as he made for the ship.

But he had forgotten how weak he was. The spurt of joy could not give him strength, and soon he felt weak all over. Now Kien could see men standing on the deck of the big ship. They were pointing toward him. Any moment now, Kien knew, they would stop.

The ship swept past him in a billowing wash of foaming water that nearly drowned him.

"Don't leave me!" Kien screamed. He began to swim after the ship, but he had no more strength. Water closed over his head. His lungs were bursting. Kicking, he forced himself back to the surface.

One of the men on the deck of the big ship was waving to Kien. He held something in his hand—a round, flat object with a large hole in the middle. A rope was attached to this object, and the man on the deck was making signs to Kien.

"Push your head and shoulders through this opening!" he seemed to say. Kien nodded weakly, and the man on the ship threw the object out into the sea.

It landed near Kien.

"Take hold of that and I'll save you!" the man seemed to be saying.

Desperately, Kien reached for the round object, which was bobbing around some yards away. He pushed himself through the hole in the center of the thing. The man on board nodded in a pleased way and made signs. "Now I am going to pull you on board. You are safe!"

"What about them?" Kien shouted. He jerked his head around, for by now they had passed the *Sea Breeze*. He could see Mai and Loc and the old man, who were all watching him in a <u>bewildered</u> way. "Save them, too!" Kien cried.

The men on the deck all shook their heads. The one who was beginning to haul Kien out of the water shook his head, too. He made a sign to Kien as if to say, "But we are going to save you."

Now Kien understood. The ship was not going to take Loc, Mai, or Thay Van Chi on board. Only he, Kien, would be saved, because he had swum after the boat, and the men on board did not want to see him drown. For a moment, he hung limply from the life saver, staring at the ship. Then he turned back to look at the *Sea Breeze,* already many yards behind him.

If I stay with this ship, Kien thought, I can live!

He wanted to live so much! He wanted to rest, to sleep. Not to worry about food or drink or storms. Mai was sick and the old man was dying. Loc would die soon. They won't blame me if I save myself. I am really not of their family. I don't belong to them.

"I am Kien!" he shouted out loud. "I care for no one! I belong to no one!"

He was being pulled up from the water, foot by foot.

"I want to live!" Kien sobbed. "Don't you understand?"

He turned to look back at the *Sea Breeze* and saw that they were watching him, as if they had heard his cry and understood. And as he looked, Mai waved at him.

Suddenly he saw them all clinging to the mast on the night of the great storm, singing together. He saw Mai feeding the old man that first coconut on Outcast Island, even before she ate

---
bewildered (bi wil′dərd) *adj.* completely confused or puzzled.

anything herself. He felt the gentle touch of the old man's hand.

Without knowing what he did, Kien slid his arms out of the life saver. He felt the water close over his head and kicked himself to the surface. Dazedly he saw that the great ship was moving rapidly away, its deck crowded by watching, pointing men.

"Kien . . . Ki-en!"

The *Sea Breeze* was coming to get him, the old man at the tiller. Kien waited. There were a hundred questions bursting in his mind. Why? he asked himself. Why did I do that?

No one said anything as Kien pulled himself over the side and fell, exhausted, into the bottom of the *Sea Breeze*. As Kien felt again the familiar <u>listing</u> of the boat under him, Loc wailed, "But why didn't they stop for us?"

Mai began to cough.

listing (lis'ting) *v.i.* tilting or leaning to one side.

"No one will stop," she whispered. "We are boat people." She looked hard at Kien. "Why didn't you go with them? They would have saved you."

Why? Kien asked himself again, and then he thought, This is the end. It has to be.

But there was no easy end. Pitifully, they continued to live. A fish caught shortly after the big ship passed them by kept them alive for a little while. And rain, falling almost continuously now, furnished them with water. Then there were no more fish, and only rainwater for food and drink. It <u>distended</u> their bellies and made them all so weak they could do nothing but drift and sleep.

Mai was worse, and Kien worried about her more than he worried about the old man. Mai, Kien felt, could still get well, but for the Old One

■
distended (di stend′id) *adj.*
enlarged by pressure from within; stretched out.

it was only a matter of time. Then, one day, three days after their sighting of the big ship, Thay Van Chi woke from one of his long sleeps and appeared much stronger and very clear in his mind.

"Do you know our position?" he asked Kien.

Kien shook his head. "I've given up on a position," he admitted. "I don't know where we are. We could have sailed in a complete circle and I wouldn't know it." He stopped and looked hard at Thay Van Chi and added happily, "But you are better! Perhaps the crisis has passed and you can guide us again."

"It is said that before the end the lamp burns strongest," the old man said quietly. "It is so for me. I am dying, Kien."

"Don't talk like that!" Kien cried angrily. "What good does it do?"

"The truth must be faced," the old man said calmly. "I am sorry, for you will have to bear the burden, Kien. You are the oldest of this family."

"I am not—" Kien began.

But Thay Van Chi interrupted him to say, "You are also the strongest. You will survive the longest. It will be hardest for you."

"I don't want to listen to you," Kien said savagely, but the old man put his hand into his shirt and drew out the little colorful bag of Vietnamese sand.

"This is yours now," he said. "I give it to you."

"I don't want it. It has nothing to do with me. What good will it do me?"

"If you survive, you must keep my promise to return to Vietnam someday. It is our country, our beloved country, and though you may roam the earth, Kien, you must not forget it. You must someday return to Vietnam and say that Thay Van Chi kept his word."

Kien wanted to cry with frustration. The old man was looking at him. "You must carry out my dying wish," he said sternly.

"Old man," Kien said loudly, "I am not bound to you in any way. You are not my family. I belong to no one! I am here with you because all of us wished to escape from Guyen Thi Lam. Your dying wish does not concern me!"

---

burden (bûr′dən) *n.* heavy load; something very difficult to bear.

frustration (frus trā′shən) *n.* feeling of irritation from disappointment or defeat.

"I have watched you change," Thay Van Chi said to Kien. "At first you were a beggar child who knew only how to survive through his <u>wits</u>, who would hurt and steal and lie to survive. Then that beggar child grew to care for the people of our Village. And when danger came to the Village, you gave up a precious keepsake to buy our safety." The old man closed his eyes, but his voice was strong. "I saw you risk your life to save Loc from the shark, and I have seen you weep when Mai coughs. Why would you have returned to us from that big ship, which would have saved you alone, if you did not care for any of us?"

Kien could say nothing. "I wish I had gone with them!" he finally cried, <u>defiant</u>. "I wish I had left you to die!"

"But you could not. Mai and Loc are your family, now," the old man said. Gently he added, "Kien,

---

wits (wits) *pl. n.* ability to think and reason clearly; good sense.
defiant (di fī′ənt) *adj.* showing bold, open resistance.

659

none of us choose to be born into a family. Heaven wills that. Nor do we choose those we come to love."

Kien bowed his head and thought, It's true. After Jim, I never cared for anyone. I never wanted to care whether you lived or died, old man. I never meant this to happen.

"As my oldest grandson, you must promise to carry out my dying wish," the old man whispered. "Take care of Loc and Mai. You are the strongest."

Kien whispered back, "I will do what you ask."

The old man said nothing. Kien saw that the wise old eyes had become fixed and glazed. Thay Van Chi was dead.

As if the old teacher could still hear him, Kien went on, "I will carry out your promise someday. It is true. I have come to love you, my grandfather. I have come to love you all."

Only then did he begin to weep.

Several days after they buried Thay Van Chi, Mai, Loc, and Kien were rescued by the crew of the freighter Camelot. *When the crew found them, Mai and Loc were both very sick, and even Kien, the strongest, could barely speak and had to be carried to a bed. After being assured that Mai and Loc would be all right, Kien reaffirmed his promise to Thay Van Chi. He had, as the old grandfather had urged, taken care of Mai and Loc.*

Maureen Crane Wartski began her writing career at the age of fourteen, when she sold her first story. Today, with several books to her credit, Wartski acknowledges that a teacher helped her see the importance of writing about people and places that one is familiar with. Living in Bangkok, Thailand, from 1962 to 1966 and visiting Vietnam provided Wartski with the background she needed to write her book *A Boat to Nowhere*.

Wartski believes that the only way to write something of interest to young people is to get to know them and learn what they are interested in. She says, "Young readers react positively to issues that move them or capture their interest." Wartski's own experiences as a high school teacher and as a mother of two sons enabled her to write convincingly about the feelings of the young characters in *A Boat to Nowhere*.

RESPONDING TO Literature

THINK • TALK • WRITE

1 Do you feel you got to know Kien as you read the selection? Can you understand why he risked his life? Respond in your journal.

2 What does Kien use as a weight for his fish hook? Why does he say that the fish is "courtesy of the 'sand of Vietnam'"?

3 Why does Kien jump into the water when the first ship appears? Why does he let go of the life preserver?

4 What does Thay Van Chi tell Kien about belonging to his family? What does he ask Kien to promise to do? Do you think Kien feels like part of that family? Why or why not?

5 Why is it so important to Thay Van Chi that Kien return to his country some day? Do you think most emigrants would feel the same way?

ACTIVITIES

- **Write with Suspense** Write a short story in which the main character faces a serious challenge. Reveal the character's thoughts as he or she decides what to do.

- **Draw a Refugee Map** Today many refugees around the world are seeking safety from war and/or harsh governments. Find out where one such group of refugees come from, and make a map showing their homeland. Attach an index card on which you briefly explain why the refugees fled. Display your map in your classroom.

VOCABULARY PRACTICE

Choose the vocabulary word that best fits in each blank. Write the words on a separate piece of paper.

stingily	listless
drowsy	makeshift
prow	bewildered
burden	frustration
wits	defiant

Kien was sure they were lost in the open sea. He was ____**1**____ at seeing nothing but water all the way to the horizon. But he knew he had to stay calm and keep his ____**2**____ about him. Thay Van Chi was growing more and more ____**3**____ as his illness stole his strength. The grandfather slept weakly in the ____**4**____ of the boat. Mai and Loc were always ____**5**____, or sleepy, too, because of hunger. Kien had ____**6**____ rationed pieces of the last fish he had managed to catch with the ____**7**____ fishing line he had made. Now there was no food. Kien felt too young to face the ____**8**____ of taking care of the other three people; he wanted to cry in ____**9**____. Still, the ____**10**____ boy vowed never to give up.

I Go Forth
to Move About
The Earth

I go forth to move about the earth.

I go forth as the owl, wise and knowing.

I go forth as the eagle, powerful and bold.

I go forth as the dove, peaceful and gentle.

I go forth to move about the earth

in wisdom, courage, and peace.

—Alonzo Lopez

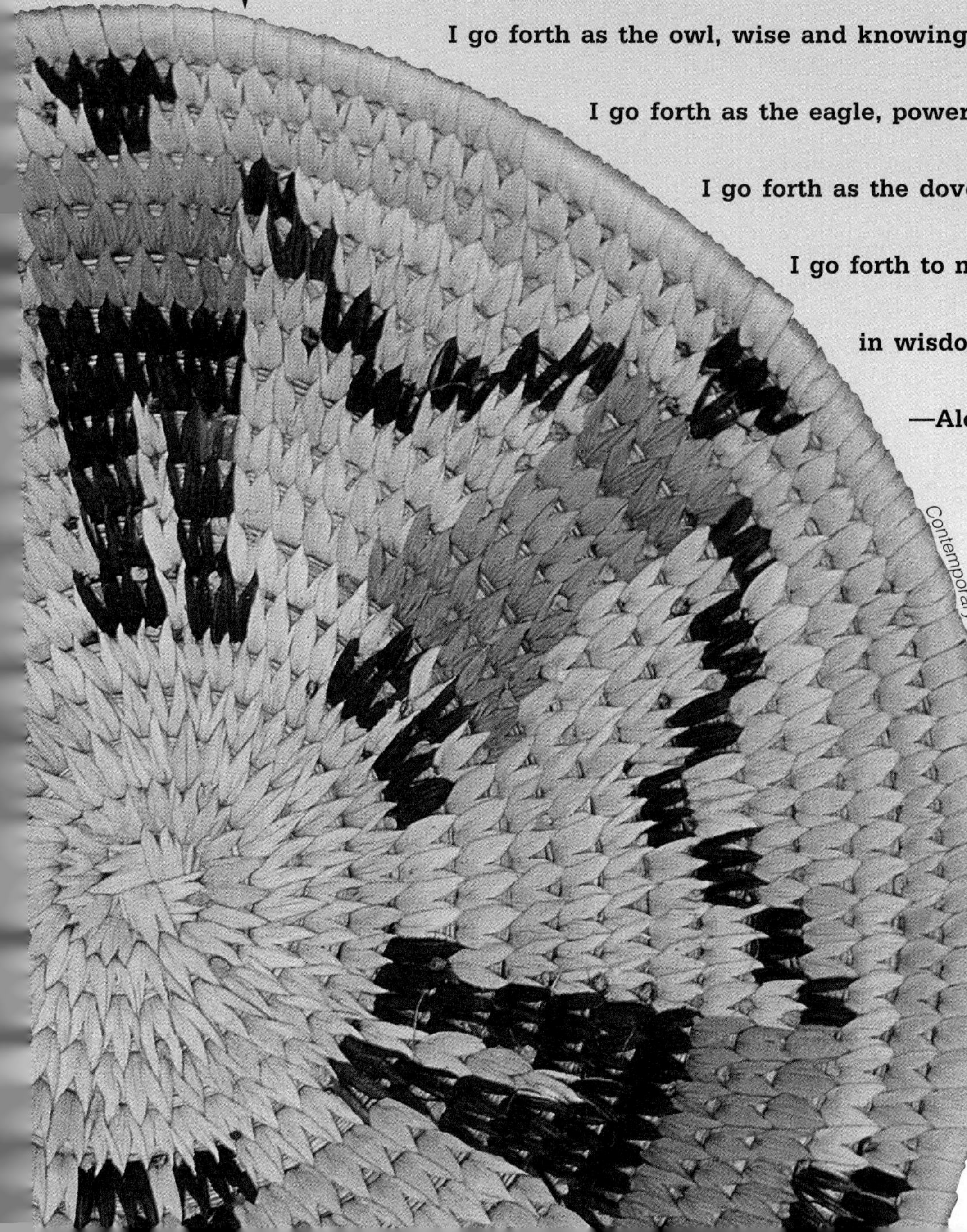

Contemporary Tohono O'odham friendship basket, based on ancestral design

663

the Great

20th century
Inuit sculpture

The great sea
Has sent me adrift
It moves me
As the weed in a great river
Earth and the great weather
Move me
Have carried me away
And move my inward parts with joy.

— *Inuit song
translated by
Knud Rasmussen*

BEFORE READING

....

THE CAY

CONNECT TO LITERATURE

The narrator in "The Cay" is blind, yet he describes the island for the reader. What are some ways you can describe the world around you without mentioning what you see? In your journal, describe a place using your senses of smell, taste, touch, and/or hearing. As you read the selection, note how Phillip describes things.

THINKING ABOUT DIALECT

Dialect is a form of language unique to a particular region. When someone speaks in dialect, he or she doesn't use the standard form of grammar, pronunciation, or vocabulary. In "The Cay," Timothy speaks in a West Indian dialect because he is a native of that area. Sometimes dialect is hard to read. You may need to use context clues to translate his speech into standard English.

As you read the selection, think about why the author wrote Timothy's speech in dialect. Would the story have been as realistic if he spoke in standard English?

DID YOU KNOW?

This selection is an excerpt from Theodore Taylor's novel *The Cay*. The excerpt includes the last five chapters of the book, which takes place in the Caribbean Sea during World War II. Oil refineries on some Caribbean islands helped supply oil and gas products to the United States and its allies. German submarines attacked ships and refineries in this area. These wartime events led to Timothy and Phillip being shipwrecked on a cay, or small island. Because of the confusion of the war and the remoteness of the cay, Timothy and Phillip were stranded without knowing when—or if—they would be rescued.

IT IS 1942 AND THE WORLD IS AT WAR. ELEVEN-YEAR-OLD PHILLIP ENRIGHT AND HIS MOTHER HAVE LEFT THE ISLAND OF CURAÇAO, OFF THE COAST OF VENEZUELA, IN ORDER TO RETURN TO THEIR NATIVE UNITED STATES. BUT WHEN THEIR SHIP IS TORPEDOED, PHILLIP FINDS HIMSELF ALONE ON A RAFT WITH TIMOTHY, A WEST INDIAN. SOON, PHILLIP GOES BLIND FROM A HEAD INJURY HE RECEIVED IN THE SHIPWRECK. THE TWO ARE EVENTUALLY MAROONED ON A CAY—A SMALL ISLAND—IN THE CARIBBEAN. AT FIRST, PHILLIP IS DISTRUSTFUL OF TIMOTHY AND TREATS HIM DISDAINFULLY. GRADUALLY, HOWEVER, TIMOTHY'S KINDNESS WINS PHILLIP OVER, AND THEIR FRIENDSHIP GROWS.

THE CAY

BY THEODORE TAYLOR

ILLUSTRATED BY FLOYD COOPER

*O*ne very hot morning in July, we were down on north beach where Timothy had found a patch of calico scallops not too far offshore. It was the hottest day we'd ever had on the cay. So hot that each breath felt like fire. And for once, the trade wind was not blowing. Nothing on the cay seemed to be moving.

North beach was a very strange beach anyway. The sand on it felt coarser to my feet. Everything about it felt different, but that didn't really make sense since it was only about a mile from south beach.

Timothy explained, "D'nawth is alles d'<u>bleak</u> beach on any islan'," but he couldn't say why.

He had just brought some calico scallops ashore when we heard the rifle shot. He came quickly to my side, saying, "Dat b'trouble."

Trouble? I thought it meant someone had found the cay. That wasn't trouble. Excited, I asked, "Who's shooting?"

"D'sea," he said.

I laughed at him, "The sea can't shoot a rifle."

"A crack like d'rifle," he said, worry in his voice. "It can make d'shot all right, all right. It b'tell us a veree bad starm is comin', Phill-eep. A <u>tempis'</u>."

I couldn't quite believe that. However, there had been, distinctly, a crack like a rifle or pistol shot.

He said anxiously, "D'waves do it. Somewhar far off, out beyond d'Grenadines, or in dat pesky bight off Honduras, a hurrican' is spawnin', young bahss. I feel it. What we heeard was a wave passin' dis lil' hombug point."

I heard him sniffing the air as if he could smell the hurricane coming. Without the wind, there was a breathless

---

bleak (blēk) *adj.* open and exposed to the wind; bare; chilling; gloomy.
tempis' (tempest) (tem′pist) *n.* violent windstorm, usually accompanied by rain, hail, snow, or thunder.

On north beach

silence around our cay. The sea, he told me, was smooth as green jelly. But already, the water was getting cloudy. There were no birds in sight. The sky, he said, had a yellowish cast to it.

"Come along, we 'ave much to do. D'calico scallop can wait dey own self till after d'tempis'."

We went up to our hill.

Now I knew why he had chosen the highest point of land on the cay for our hut. Even so, I thought, the waves might tumble over it.

The first thing Timothy did was to lash our water keg high on a palm trunk. Next he took the remaining rope that we had and tied it securely around the same sturdy tree. "In case d'tempis' reach dis high, lock your arms ovah d'rope an' hang on, Phill-eep."

I realized then why he had used our rope <u>sparingly</u>; why he had made my guideline down to east beach from vines instead of rope. Everyday, I learned of something new that Timothy had done so we could survive.

During the afternoon, he told me this was a <u>freak</u> storm, because most did not come until September or October. August, sometimes. Seldom in July. "But dis year, d'sea be angry wid all d'death upon it. D'wahr."

The storms bred, Timothy said, in the eastern North Atlantic, south of the Cape Verde Islands, in the fall, but sometimes, when they were freaks, and early, they bred much closer, in a triangle way off the northeast tip of South America. Once in a great while, in June or July, they sometimes made up not far from Providencia and San Andrés. Near us. The June ones were only <u>pesky</u>, but the July ones were dangerous.

"Dis be a western starm, I b'guessin'. Dey outrageous strong when dey come," he said.

■

sparingly (spâr'ing lē) *adv.* in small amounts; with care in spending or using.
freak (frēk) *adj.* odd or unusual; bizarre.
pesky (pes'kē) *adj. Informal.* troublesome; annoying.

Even Stew Cat was nervous. He was around my legs whenever I moved. I asked Timothy what we should do to protect him. He laughed. "Stew Cat b'go up d'palm on d'lee side iffen it b'gettin' too terrible. Don' worry 'bout Stew Cat."

Yet I could not help worrying. The thought of losing either of them was unbearable. If something bad happened on the cay, I wanted it to happen to all of us.

Nothing changed during the afternoon, although it seemed to get even hotter. Timothy spent a lot of time down at the raft, stripping off everything usable and carrying it back up the hill. He said we might never see it again, or else it might wash up the hill so that it would be impossible to launch.

Timothy was not purposely trying to frighten me about the violence of the storm; he was just being honest. He had good reason to be frightened himself.

"In '28, I be on d'*Hettie Redd* sout' o' Antigua when d'tempis' hit. D'wind was <u>outrageous</u>, an' d'ol' schooner break up like chips fallin' 'fore d'ax. I wash ashore from d'sea, so wild no mahn believe it. No odder mahn from d'*Hettie Redd* live 'ceptin' me."

I knew that wild sea from long ago was much on Timothy's mind all afternoon.

We had a huge meal late in the day, much bigger than usual, because Timothy said we might not be able to eat for several days. We had fish and coconut meat, and we each drank several cups of coconut milk. Timothy said that the fish might not return to the reef for at least a week. He'd noticed that they'd already gone to deep water.

After we ate, Timothy carefully cleaned his knife and put it into the tin box, which he lashed high on the same tree that held our water keg.

"We ready, Phill-eep," he said.

---

outrageous (out rā′jəs) *adj.* going beyond proper limits; shocking.

*A*t sunset, with the air heavy and hot, Timothy described the sky to me. He said it was flaming red and that there were thin veils of high clouds. It was so still over our cay that we could hear nothing but the rustling of the lizards.

Just before dark, Timothy said, "'Twon't be long now, Phill-eep."

We felt a light breeze that began to ripple the smooth sea. Timothy said he saw an arc of very black clouds to the west. They looked as though they were beginning to join the higher clouds.

I gathered Stew Cat close to me as we waited, feeling the warm breeze against my face. Now and then, there were gusts of wind that rattled the palm <u>fronds</u>, shaking the little hut.

It was well after dark when the first drops of rain spattered the hut, and with them, the wind turned cool. When it gusted, the rain hit the hut like handfuls of gravel.

Then the wind began to blow steadily, and Timothy went out of the hut to look up at the sky. He shouted, "Dey boilin' ovah now, Phill-eep. 'Tis hurrican', to be sure."

We could hear the surf beginning to crash as the wind drove waves before it, and Timothy ducked back inside to stand in the opening of the hut, his big body stretched so that he could hang onto the overhead frame, keeping the hut erect as long as possible.

I felt movement around my legs and feet. Things were slithering. I screamed to Timothy who shouted back, "B'nothin' but d'lil' lizzard, comin' high groun'."

Rain was now slashing into the hut, and the wind was reaching a steady howl. The crash of the surf sounded closer; I wondered if it was already beginning to push up toward our

---

fronds (frondz) *n., pl.* leaves of a palm or fern.

hill. The rain was icy, and I was wet, head to foot. I was shivering, but more from the thought of the sea rolling over us than from the sudden cold.

In a moment, there was a splintering sound, and Timothy dropped down beside me, covering my body with his. Our hut had blown away. He shouted, "Phill-eep, put your 'ead downg." I rolled over on my stomach, my cheek against the wet sand. Stew Cat burrowed down between us.

There was no sound now except the roar of the storm. Even the sound of the wind was being beaten down by the wildness of the sea. The rain was hitting my back like thousands of hard berries blown from air guns.

Once something solid hit us and then rolled on. "Sea grape," Timothy shouted. It was being torn up by the roots.

We stayed flat on the ground for almost two hours, taking the storm's punishment, barely able to breathe in the driving rain. Then Timothy shouted hoarsely, "To d'palm."

The sea was beginning to reach for our hilltop, climbing the forty feet with raging whitecaps. Timothy dragged me toward the palm. I held Stew Cat against my chest.

Standing with his back to the storm, Timothy put my arms through the loops of rope, and then roped himself, behind me, to the tree.

Soon, I felt water around my ankles. Then it washed to my knees. It would go back and then crash against us again. Timothy was taking the full blows of the storm, sheltering me with his body. When the water receded, it would tug at us, and Timothy's strength would fight against it. I could feel the steel in his arms as the water tried to suck us away.

Even in front of him, crushed against the trunk of the palm, I could feel the rain, which was now jabbing into me like the punches of a nail. It was not falling toward earth but being driven straight ahead by the wind.

Hurricane

We must have been against the palm for almost an hour when suddenly the wind died down and the rain became gentle. Timothy panted, "D'eye! We can relax a bit till d'odder side o' d'tempis' hit us."

I remembered that hurricanes, which are great circling storms, have a calm eye in the center.

"Are you all right?" I asked.

He replied hoarsely, "I b'damp, but all right."

Yet I heard him making small noises, as if it were painful to move, as we stood back from the palm trunk. We sat down on the ground beside it, still being pelted with rain, to wait for the eye to pass. Water several inches deep swirled around us, but was not tugging at us.

It was strange and eerie in the eye of the hurricane. I knew we were surrounded on all sides by violent winds, but the little cay was calm and quiet. I reached over for Timothy. He was cradling his head in his arms, still making those small noises, like a hurt animal.

In twenty or thirty minutes, the wind picked up sharply and Timothy said that we must stand against the palm again. Almost within seconds, the full fury of the storm hit the cay once more. Timothy pressed me tightly against the rough bark.

It was even worse this time, but I do not remember everything that happened. We had been there awhile when a wave that must have reached halfway up the palms crashed against us. The water went way over my head. I choked and struggled. Then another giant wave struck us. I lost consciousness then. Timothy did, too, I think.

When I came to, the wind had died down, coming at us only in gusts. The water was still washing around our ankles, but seemed to be going back into the sea now. Timothy was still behind me, but he felt cold and limp. He was sagging, his head down on my shoulder.

"Timothy, wake up," I said.

He did not answer.

Using my shoulders, I tried to shake him, but the massive body did not move. I stood very still to see if he was breathing. I could feel his stomach moving and I reached over my shoulder to his mouth. There was air coming out. I knew that he was not dead.

However, Stew Cat was gone.

I worked for a few minutes to release my arms from the loops of rope around the palm trunk, and then slid out from under Timothy's body. He slumped lifelessly against the palm. I felt along the ropes that bound his forearms to the trunk until I found the knots.

With his weight against them, it was hard to pull them loose, even though they were sailor's knots and had loops in them. The rope was soaked, which made it worse.

I must have worked for half an hour before I had him free from the trunk. He fell backwards into the wet sand, and lay there moaning. I knew there was very little I could do for him except to sit by him in the light rain, holding his hand. In my world of darkness, I had learned that holding a hand could be like medicine.

After a long while, he seemed to recover. His first words, painful and dragged out, were, "Phill-eep . . . you . . . all right . . . be true?"

"I'm okay, Timothy," I said.

He said weakly, "Terrible tempis'."

He must have rolled over on his stomach in the sand, because his hand left mine abruptly. Then he went to sleep, I guess.

I touched his back. It felt warm and sticky. I ran my hand lightly down it, suddenly realizing that I, too, was completely naked. The wind and sea had torn our tatters of clothes from us.

Timothy had been cut to ribbons by the wind, which drove the rain and tiny grains of sand before it. It had <u>flayed</u> his back and his legs until there were very few places that weren't cut. He was bleeding, but there was nothing I could do to stop it. I found his hard, <u>horny</u> hand again, wrapped mine around it, and lay down beside him.

I went to sleep too.

Sometime long after dawn, I awakened. The rain had stopped, and the wind had died down to its usual whisper. But I think the clouds were still covering the sky because I could not feel the sun.

I said, "Timothy," but he did not answer me. His hand was cold and stiff in mine.

Old Timothy, of Charlotte Amalie, was dead.

I stayed there beside him for a long time, very tired, thinking that he should have taken me with him wherever he had gone. I did not cry then. There are times when you are beyond tears.

I went back to sleep, and this time when I awakened, I heard a meow. Then I cried for a long time, holding Stew Cat tight. Aside from him, I was blind and alone on a forgotten cay.

 *I*n the afternoon, I groped west along the hill. Thirty or forty feet from the last palm tree, I began to dig a grave for Timothy. I cleared palm fronds, chunks of sea grape, pieces of wood, dead fish, fan coral, and shells that the sea had thrown up. I marked out a space about seven feet long and four feet wide. Then I dug with my hands.

At first I was angry with Timothy. I said to Stew Cat, "Why did he leave us alone here?" Then as I dug, I had other thoughts.

---

flayed (flād) *v.t.* stripped off the skin of, as by lashing.
horny (hôr′nē) *adj.* hard like horn; calloused.

With his great back to the storm, taking its full punishment, he had made it possible for me to live. When my grandfather died, my father had said, "Phillip, sometimes people die from just being very, very tired." I think that is what happened to Timothy.

I also think that had I been able to see, I might not have been able to accept it all. But strangely, the darkness separated me from everything. It was as if my blindness were protecting me from fear.

I buried Timothy, placing stones at the head of the grave to mark it. I didn't know what to say over the grave. I said, "Thank you, Timothy," and then turned my face to the sky. I said, "Take care of him, God, he was good to me."

There didn't seem to be anything else to say, so I just stood by his grave for a while. Then I felt my way back to the spot where our hut had been. I located wood and piled it around the base of the palm tree that held our water keg and the tin box. Both were to the <u>lee</u> side of the storm.

It took me a long time to get the keg and the tin box to the ground, but I found, on opening the <u>bung</u>, that the water was still sweet and that the matches, wrapped in cellophane inside the tin box, were dry. But the two small bars of chocolate that we had been saving for a "feast," were ruined. I had no taste for them, anyway.

Feeling it everywhere under my feet, I knew that the cay was littered with debris. I started cleaning the camp area, or what was left of it. I piled all the palm fronds, frayed by the wind, in one place; sticks of wet driftwood in another.

With Stew Cat constantly around—I stumbled over him several times—I worked until I felt it was nearing darkness. I'd found one lone coconut in a mass of sea grape and broken sticks. I opened it and ate the meat, offering to share with Stew Cat, who didn't seem interested.

---

lee (lē) *adj.* sheltered from the wind.
bung (bung) *n.* stopper for closing the bunghole in a barrel or cask.

Then I made a bed of palm fronds and sprawled out on it, listening to the still angry sea as it tumbled around the damp cay and thinking: I must feed myself and Stew Cat; I must rebuild the hut and build another signal fire down on east beach; then I must spend each day listening for the sound of aircraft. I knew Timothy had already given up on any schooner entering the dangerous Devil's Mouth.

I was certain that the sea had washed away Timothy's markers atop the coral reef, and I was also sure that my guide vine-rope leading down to the beach had been snapped and tangled by the storm.

But now, for the first time, I fully understood why Timothy had so carefully trained me to move around the island, and the reef . . .

The reef, I thought.

How could I fish without any poles? They must have been washed away. Then I remembered Timothy saying that he would put them in a safe place. The trouble was he'd forgotten to tell me where.

I got up and began to run my hands over each palm trunk. On one of them I touched rope. I followed it around to the lee side with my fingers. And there they were! Not two or three, but at least a dozen, lashed together, each with a barbed hook and bolt sinker. They were one more part of the legacy Timothy had left me.

The sun came out strong in the morning. I could feel it on my face. It began to dry the island, and toward noon, I heard the first cry of a bird. They were returning.

By now, I had taught myself to tell time, very roughly, simply by turning my head toward the direct warmth of the sun. If the angle was almost overhead, I knew it was around noon. If it was low, then of course, it was early morning or late evening.

---

legacy (leg′ə sē) *n.* something handed down from previous generations.

There was so much to do that I hardly knew where to start. Get a campfire going, pile new wood for a signal fire, make another rain catchment for the water keg, weave a mat of palm fibers to sleep on. Then make a shelter of some kind, fish the hole on the reef, inspect the palm trees to see if any coconuts were left—I didn't think any could be up there—and search the whole island to discover what the storm had deposited. It was enough work for weeks, and I said to Stew Cat, "I don't know how we'll get it all done." But something told me I must stay very busy and not think about myself.

I accomplished a lot in three days, even putting a new edge on Timothy's knife by <u>honing</u> it on coral. I jabbed it into the palm nearest my new shelter, so that I would always know where it was if I needed it. Without Timothy's eyes, I was finding that in my world, everything had to be very precise; an exact place for everything.

On the fifth day after the storm, I began to scour the island to find out what had been cast up. It was exciting, and I knew it would take days or weeks to accomplish. I had made another cane, and beginning with east beach, I felt my way back and forth, reaching down to touch everything that my cane struck; sometimes having to spend a long time trying to decide what it was that I held in my hands.

I found several large cans and used one of them to start the "time" can again, dropping five pebbles into it so that the reckoning would begin again from the night of the storm. I discovered an old broom, and a small wooden crate that would make a nice stool. I found a piece of canvas and tried to think of ways to make pants from it, but I had no needle or thread.

Other than that, I found many shells, some bodies of dead birds, pieces of cork, and chunks of sponge, but nothing I could really put to good use.

---

honing (hō′ning) *v.t.* sharpening.

It was on the sixth day after the storm, when I was exploring on south beach, that I heard the birds. Stew Cat was with me, as usual, and he growled when they first screeched. Their cries were angry, and I guessed that seven or eight might be in the air.

I stood listening to them; wondering what they were. Then I felt a beat of wing past my face, and an angry cry as the bird dived at me. I lashed out at it with my cane, wondering why they were attacking me.

Another dived down, screaming at me, and his bill nipped the side of my head. For a moment, I was confused, not knowing whether to run for cover under sea grape, or what was left of it, or try to fight them off with my cane. There seemed to be a lot of birds.

Then one pecked my forehead sharply, near my eyes, and I felt blood run down my face. I started to walk back toward camp, but had taken no more than three or four steps when I tripped over a log. I fell into the sand, and at the same time, felt a sharp pain in the back of my head. I heard a raging screech as the bird soared up again. Then another bird dived at me.

I heard Stew Cat snarling and felt him leap up on my back, his claws digging into my flesh. There was another wild screech, and Stew Cat left my back, leaping into the air.

His snarls and the wounded screams of the bird filled the stillness over the cay. I could hear them battling in the sand. Then I heard the death caw of the bird.

I lay still a moment. Finally, I crawled to where Stew Cat had his victim. I touched him; his body was rigid and his hair was still on edge. He was growling, low and muted.

Then I touched the bird. It had sounded large, but it was actually rather small. I felt the beak; it was very sharp.

Slowly, Stew Cat began to relax.

The attack

Wondering what had caused the birds to attack me, I felt around in the sand. Soon, my hand touched a warm shell. I couldn't blame the birds very much. I'd accidentally walked into their new nesting ground.

They were fighting for survival, after the storm, just as I was. I left Stew Cat to his unexpected meal and made my way slowly back to camp.

*T*en pebbles had gone into my "time" can when I decided to do something Timothy had told me never to do. I was tired of eating fish and sea-grape leaves, and I wanted to save the few green coconuts I'd managed to find on the ground. There were none left in the trees.

I wanted scallops or a <u>langosta</u> to roast over the fire. I didn't dare go out off north beach for scallops because of the sharks. But I thought there might be a langosta clinging to coral at the bottom of the fishing hole.

From what Timothy had told me, the sea entrance to the hole was too narrow for a large fish, a shark, to swim through. Barracuda, he'd said, could go through, but they were not usually dangerous. If there happened to be an octopus down there, it would have to be a very small one. The big ones were always in deep water. So he'd said it was safe for him to dive in the hole.

I sharpened a stick the way Timothy had done, but I knew that if I felt a langosta with my left hand, I would have to be very quick with my right hand, or he would use his tail to push away from me across the sand.

With Stew Cat, I went down to the reef and felt my way along it until I found the familiar edges of the hole. I told

---

langosta (läng gos'tə) *n.* type of spiny lobster.

Stew Cat, "If I'm not out in twenty minutes, you better jump in and get me."

The crazy cat rubbed along my leg and purred.

Holding the sharpened stick in my right hand, I slipped into the warm water, treading for a moment, waiting to see if anything came up. Then I ducked my head underwater, swam down a few feet, and came up again. I was certain that nothing was in the hole aside from the usual small fish I yanked out each morning.

After a few minutes, I had my courage up and dived to the bottom, holding the sharp stick in my left hand now, and using my right hand to feel the coral and rocks. Coming up now and then for air, I slowly felt my way around the bottom of the small pool, touching sea fans that waved back and forth, feeling the organ-pipe coral and the bigger chunks of brain coral.

Several times I was startled when seaweed or sea fans would brush against my face and swam quickly to the surface. It must have taken me nearly thirty minutes to decide that I could hunt langosta in the hole.

This time, I dived in earnest. I went straight down, touched the bottom, and then took a few strokes toward the coral sides of the pool. Timothy had said that langosta were always on the bottom, usually over against the rocks and coral. To my amazement, I touched one on the first sweep and drove the sharp stick into him, swimming quickly to the surface.

Panting, I shouted to Stew Cat, "Lobster tonight!"

I swam to the edge, pushed the langosta off the stick, caught my breath again, and dived.

I dived many times without again touching the hard shell that meant langosta. I began sticking my hands deeper into the shelves and over the ledges near the bottom.

I rested a few minutes, then decided I'd make one more dive. I was happy with the lobster that was now on the reef, but it was quite small, barely a meal for Stew Cat and myself.

I dived again, and this time found what seemed to be an opening into a deep hole. Or at least, the hole went far back. There has to be a big lobster in there, I thought. Up I came again, filled my lungs, and dived immediately.

I ran my hand back into the hole, and something grabbed it.

Terrified, I put my feet against the rocks to pull away. The pain was severe. Whatever had my wrist had the strength of Timothy's arms. I jerked hard and whatever it was came out with my arm, its tail smashing against my chest. I kicked and rose to the surface, the thing still on my wrist, its teeth sunk in deep.

I'm sure I screamed as I broke water, flailing toward the edge of the hole. Then the thing let loose, and I made it up over the side and out of the hole.

Pain shooting up my entire arm, I lay panting on the edge of the pool and gingerly began to feel my wrist. It was bleeding, but not badly. But the teeth had sunk in deep.

It wasn't a fish, because the body felt long and narrow. Some time later, I made an informed guess that it had been a large moray eel. Whatever it was, I never got back into the hole again.

There was no day or night that passed when I didn't listen for sounds from the sky. Both my sense of touch and my sense of hearing were beginning to make up for my lack of sight. I separated the sounds and each became different.

I grew to know the different cries of the birds that flew by the cay, even

The dive

though I had no idea what any of them were. I made up my own names for them according to the sound of their cries. Only the occasional bleat of the gull gave me a picture of that bird, for I had heard and seen them many times around the sea wall in Willemstad.

I knew how the breeze sounded when it crossed the sea grape. It fluttered the small leaves. When it went through the palm fronds the storm hadn't ripped away, it made a flapping noise.

I knew the rustle of the lizards. Some were still on the island after the storm. I could only guess they'd somehow climbed high into the palms. Otherwise, how could they have lived with water lapping over the entire cay?

I even knew when Stew Cat was approaching me. His soft paws on a dried leaf made only a tiny crackle, but I heard it.

One midmorning in early August, I was on the hill, near the camp, when I heard the far-off drone of an airplane. It was up-wind from me, but the sound was very clear. I reached down to feel Stew Cat. He had heard it too. His body was tense; his head pointed toward the sound.

I dropped to my knees by the fire, feeling around the edges until I grasped the end of a stick. I drew it back. Timothy had taught me to lay the fire sticks like a wheel, so that the fire burned slowly in the center, but always had a few unburned ends on the outside. I tended the fire a half dozen times each day.

I spit on the stick until I heard a sizzle. Then I knew there was enough fire or charring on it to light off the base of dried palm fronds beneath the signal fire.

I listened again for the drone. Yes, it was still there. Closer now.

I ran down the hill straight to the signal fire, felt around the palm fronds, and then pushed the stick over them. I blew on it until I heard the crackle of flames. In a few minutes the signal fire was roaring, and I ran to south beach where I would be able to hear the aircraft without hearing the crackling fire.

Standing on south beach, I listened. The plane *was* coming closer!

I yelled toward the sky, "Here! Down here!"

I decided to run back to east beach to stand near the fire and the new arrangement of rocks that spelled out "Help."

Thinking any moment the plane would dive and I would hear the roar of its engines across the cay at low altitude, I stood with Stew Cat a few feet from the sloshing surf. I waited and waited, but there was no thundering sound from the sky. I could hear nothing but the crackling of the fire, the washing sound of the surf.

I ran back to south beach, where I stood very still and listened.

The plane had gone!

Slowly, I returned to east beach and sat down in sea-grape shade. I put my head down on my arms and sobbed, feeling no shame for what I was doing.

There seemed to be no hope of ever leaving the cay, yet I knew I could not always live this way. One day I would become ill or another storm would rage against the island. I could never survive alone.

There had been many bad and lonely days and nights, but none as bad as this.

Stew Cat came up, purring, rubbing along my legs. I held him a long time, wondering why the aircraft had not come down when the pilots saw the smoke.

At last I thought, perhaps they didn't see the smoke. I knew it was going up into the sky, but was it white smoke that might be lost in the blue-white sky, or was it dark and oily smoke that would make a smudge against the blueness? There was no way to tell.

signal fire

If only there were some oily boards! The kind that drifted around the waters of the Schottegat. But I knew that the wood floating up on the beach consisted mostly of branches or stumps that had been in the water for weeks or months. There was nothing in them to make dark smoke.

I began to think of all the things on the island. Green palm fronds might send off dark smoke, but until they were dried, they were too tough to tear off the trees. The vines on north beach might make dark smoke, but the leaves on them were very small.

The sea grape! I snapped some off, feeling it between my fingers. Yes, there was oil in it. I got up and went over to the fire, tossing a piece in. In a moment, I heard it popping the way hot grease pops when it is dropped into water.

I knew how to do it now.

The smoke would rise from the cay in a fat, black column to lead the planes up the Devil's Mouth. If I heard another aircraft, I'd start a fire and then throw bundles of sea grape into it until I was certain a strong signal was going up from the island.

Timothy hadn't thought about black smoke, I was sure. That was it!

Feeling better now, I walked back up the hill to gather the few palm fronds that were left for a new fire base.

I woke up at dawn on the morning of August 20, 1942, to hear thunder and wondered when the first drops of rain would spatter on the roof of the shelter. I heard Stew Cat, down near my feet, let off a low growl.

I said, "It's only thunder, Stew Cat. We need the water."

But as I continued to listen, it did not seem to be thunder. It was a heavy sound, hard and sharp, not rolling. More like an explosion or a series of explosions. It felt as if the cay were shaking. I got up from the mat, moving out from under the shelter.

The air did not feel like rain. It was dry and there was no heavy heat.

"They're explosions, Stew," I said. "Very near us."

Maybe destroyers, I thought. I could not hear any aircraft engines. Maybe destroyers fighting it out with enemy submarines. And those heavy, hard, sharp sounds could be the depth charges that my father said were used by the Navy to sink U-boats.

This time, I didn't bother to take a piece of firewood down to east beach. I dug into the tin box for the cellophane wrapped package of big wooden matches. Four were left. I ran down the hill.

At the signal fire, I searched around for a rock. Finding one, I knelt down by the fire and struck a match against it. Nothing happened. I felt the head of the match. The sulphur had rubbed off. I struck another. It made a small popping noise and then went out.

I had two more matches left, and for a moment, I didn't know whether to use them or run back up the hill to the campfire.

I stopped to listen, feeling sweat trickle down my face. The explosions were still thundering across the sea.

Then I heard the drone of an aircraft. I took a deep breath and struck the next to last match. I heard it flare and ran my left hand over the top of it. There was heat. It was burning.

I reached deep into the fire pile, holding the match there until it began to burn the tips of my fingers. The fire caught and in a moment was roaring.

I ran across the beach to begin pulling sea grape down. I carried the first bundle to the fire and threw it in. Soon, I could smell it burning. It began to pop and crackle as the flames got to the natural oils in the branches.

By the time I had carried ten or fifteen bundles of sea grape to the fire, tumbling them in, I was sure that a column of black smoke was rising into the sky over the cay.

Suddenly, a deafening roar swept overhead. I knew it was an aircraft crossing the cay not much higher than the palms. I could feel the wind from it.

Forgetting for a moment, I yelled, "Timothy, they've come."

The aircraft seemed to be making a sharp turn. It roared across the cay again, seeming even lower this time because the rush of wind from it was hot. I could smell exhaust fumes.

I yelled, "Down here, down here," and waved my arms.

The plane made another tight circle, coming back almost directly over me. Its engine was screaming.

I shouted at Stew Cat, "We'll be rescued!" But I think that he'd gone to hide in the sea grape.

This time, however, the aircraft did not circle back. It did not make another low pass over the island. I heard the sound going away. Soon, it had vanished completely. Then I realized that the explosions had stopped too.

A familiar silence settled over the cay.

All the strength went out of my body. It was the first real chance of rescue, and maybe there would not be another. The pilot had flown away, perhaps thinking I was just another native fisherman waving at an aircraft. I knew that the color of my skin was very dark now.

Worse, I knew that the smoke might have blotted out the lines of rocks that spelled help.

Feeling very ill, I climbed the slope again, throwing myself down on the mat in the hut. I didn't cry. There was no use in doing that.

I wanted to die.

After a while, I looked over toward Timothy's grave. I said, "Why didn't you take us with you?"

*I*t was about noon when I heard the bell.

It sounded like bells I'd heard in St. Anna Bay and in the Schottegat. Small boats and tugs use them to tell the engineer to go slow or fast or put the engines in reverse.

For a moment, I thought I was dreaming.

Then I heard the bell again. And with it, the slow chugging of an engine. And voices! They were coming from east beach.

I ran down there. Yes, a small boat had come into the Devil's Mouth and was approaching our cay.

I yelled, "I'm here! I'm here!"

There was a shout from across the water. A man's voice. "We see you!"

I stood there on east beach, Stew Cat by my feet, looking in the direction of the sounds. I heard the bell again; then the engine went into reverse, the propeller thrashing. Someone yelled, "Jump, Scotty, the water's shallow."

The voice was American, I was certain.

The engine was now idling, and someone was coming toward me. I could hear him padding across the sand. I said, "Hello."

There was no answer from the man. I suppose he was just staring at me.

Then he yelled to someone on the boat, "My Lord, it's a naked boy. And a cat!"

The person on the boat yelled, "Anyone else?"

The rescue

I called out, "No, just us."

I began to move toward the man on the beach.

He gasped. "Are you blind?"

I said, "Yes, sir."

In a funny voice, he asked, "Are you all right?"

"I'm fine now. You're here," I said.

He said, "Here, boy, I'll help you."

I said, "If you'll carry Stew Cat, you can just lead me to the boat."

After I had climbed aboard, I remembered Timothy's knife stuck in the palm tree. It was the only thing I wanted off the cay. The sailor who had carried Stew Cat went up the hill to get it while the other sailor asked me questions. When the first sailor came back from the hill, he said, "You wouldn't believe what's up there." I guess he was talking about our hut and the rain catchment. He should have seen the ones Timothy built.

I don't remember everything that happened in the next few hours but very soon I was helped up the gangway of a destroyer. On deck I was asked so many questions all at once that one man barked, "Stop <u>badgering</u> him. Give him food, medical care, and get him into a bunk."

A voice answered meekly, "Yes, sir, Cap'n."

Down in sick bay, the captain asked, "What's your name, son?"

"Phillip Enright. My father lives in Willemstad. He works for Royal Dutch Shell," I answered.

The captain told someone to get a <u>priority</u> radio message off to the naval commander at Willemstad and then asked, "How did you get on that little island?"

"Timothy and I drifted on to it after the *Hato* was sunk."

"Where's Timothy?" he asked.

I told the captain about Timothy and what had happened to us. I'm not sure the captain believed any of it, because he

---

badgering (baj′ə ring) *v.t.* annoying in a persistent way; pestering.

priority (prī ôr′i tē) *adj.* coming before others in order of importance; deserving special attention.

said quietly, "Son, get some sleep. The *Hato* was sunk way back in April."

I said, "Yes, sir, that's right," and then a doctor came in to check me over.

That night, after the ship had been in communication with Willemstad, the captain visited me again to tell me that his destroyer had been hunting a German submarine when the plane had spotted my black smoke and radioed back to the ship.

There was still disbelief in his voice when he said he'd checked all the charts and publications on the bridge; our cay was so small that the charts wouldn't even dignify it with a name. But Timothy had been right. It was tucked back up in the Devil's Mouth.

The next morning, we docked at the naval base in Cristóbal, Panama, and I was rushed to a hospital, although I really didn't think it was necessary. I was strong and healthy, the doctor on the destroyer had said.

My mother and father flew over from Willemstad in a special plane. It was minutes before they could say anything. They just held me, and I knew my mother was crying. She kept saying, "Phillip, I'm sorry, I'm so sorry."

The Navy had notified them that I was blind, so that it would not be a shock. And I knew I looked different. They'd brought a barber in to cut my hair, which had grown quite long.

We talked for a long time, Stew Cat on my bed, and I tried to tell them all about Timothy and the cay. But it was very difficult. They listened, of course, but I had the feeling that neither of them really understood what had happened on our cay.

Four months later, in a hospital in New York, after many X rays and tests, I had the first of three operations. The piece of timber that had hit me the night the *Hato* went down had damaged some nerves. But after the third operation, when the bandages came off, I could see again. I would always have to wear glasses, but I could see. That was the important thing.

In early April, I returned to Willemstad with my mother, and we took up life where it had been left off the previous April. After I'd been officially reported lost at sea, she'd gone back to Curaçao to be with my father. She had changed in many ways. She had no thoughts of leaving the islands now.

I saw Henrik van Boven occasionally, but it wasn't the same as when we'd played the Dutch or the British. He seemed very young. So I spent a lot of time along St. Anna Bay, and at the Ruyterkade market talking to the black people. I liked the sound of their voices. Some of them had known old Timothy from Charlotte Amalie. I felt close to them.

At war's end, we moved away from Scharloo and Curaçao. My father's work was finished.

Since then, I've spent many hours looking at charts of the Caribbean. I've found Roncador, Rosalind, Quito Sueño, and Serranilla Banks; I've found Beacon Cay and North Cay, and the islands of Providencia and San Andrés. I've also found the Devil's Mouth.

Someday, I'll charter a <u>schooner</u> out of Panama and explore the Devil's Mouth. I hope to find the lonely little island where Timothy is buried.

Maybe I won't know it by sight, but when I go ashore and close my eyes, I'll know this was our own cay. I'll walk along east beach and out to the reef. I'll go up the hill to the row of palm trees and stand by his grave.

I'll say, "Dis b'dat outrageous cay, eh, Timothy?"

---

schooner (skü′nər) *n.* ship that has two or more masts and fore-and-aft sails.

MEET THEODORE TAYLOR

Theodore Taylor says of *The Cay*, "After . . . hearing Dr. Martin Luther King singing spirituals in the lobby of a hotel, I decided to go ahead with the long-brewing story. . . . Three weeks later *The Cay* was completed."

Taylor's interest in writing began at an early age. When he was thirteen, he worked as a cub reporter for the Portsmouth, Virginia, *Evening Star*. Later, experiences in the Naval Reserve gave him the chance to explore firsthand the area of the Caribbean where *The Cay* is set.

The Cay has won many literary awards, including the Lewis Carroll Shelf Award. The book was made into a television movie starring James Earl Jones.

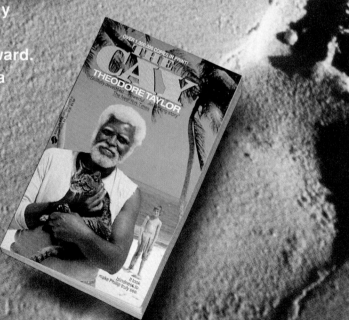

RESPONDING TO *Literature*

THINK • TALK • WRITE

1 What do you think was the most exciting part of this selection? Explain in your journal.

2 How does Timothy know a hurricane is coming? What does he do to prepare for the storm?

3 How does Timothy save Phillip's life? What does Phillip realize at Timothy's death?

4 What things must Phillip do on his own in order to survive? Why are his rescuers so amazed by him?

5 Why do you think Phillip liked to visit the Ruyterkade market in Willemstad? What do you think he learned from his experience?

ACTIVITIES

- **Write About Dialect** Do you and your friends speak standard English when you talk together? Think of expressions you use. Make a glossary of expressions that are popular now. Include pronunciations and definitions.

- **Make a Mural** Phillip survives because he gets food from the sea. Research what kinds of plants and animals live near the islands of the Caribbean in books and magazines. Then, with classmates, make a mural showing the underwater life of the Caribbean.

VOCABULARY PRACTICE

On a separate piece of paper, write the vocabulary word that best completes each sentence.

bleak	sparingly
freak	pesky
outrageous	fronds
legacy	badgering
priority	schooner

1 Something unusual that happened might be called a _____ occurrence.

2 When one thing is more important than something else, it is _____.

3 If your little brother annoys you, you might call him a _____ kid.

4 Someone who keeps asking you the same question is _____ you.

5 The leaves on a palm tree are known as _____.

6 A friend who hands out candy one piece at a time is giving it _____.

7 The beach is so windy and cold that it is called the _____ beach.

8 The bully committed an _____ deed when he stole the kindergartners' lunch money.

9 Money you inherited from your aunt would be her _____ to you.

10 A ship with two or more masts and lengthwise sails is called a _____.

THE HURRICANE

When the hurricane unfolds
Its fierce accordion of winds,
On the tip of its toes,
Agile dancer, it sweeps whirling
Over the carpeted surface of the sea
With the scattered branches of the palm.

—Luis Palés Matos
   translated from the Spanish by Alida Malkus

SP O T on

ESSAY

Do you and your friends ever disagree on issues? If so, you have probably tried to explain your viewpoint and to persuade your friends to agree. How did you do that? If you like to draw, you might have created a cartoon, like the one below.

Drawing by Stevenson; © 1970 The New Yorker Magazine

"So __that's__ where it goes! Well, I'd like to thank you fellows for bringing this to my attention."

What do you think is going on in this scene? Why do you think so? Does the cartoon seem merely humorous, or does it touch on an important issue? What is the main idea of the cartoon?

Think about other cartoons where the artists were clearly trying to make a point. What issues were treated in those? Now think about essays you have read. What were the writers trying to say? What do those cartoons and essays have in common?

LIGHT

ELEMENTS OF AN ESSAY

An essay is a short work of nonfiction that focuses on a single subject. There are two general types of essays.

- **Formal essays** are objective, or impersonal, and serious in tone.
- **Informal essays** are subjective, or personal, and light in tone.

FACTS AND OPINIONS are details about the subject of an essay that are presented by the writer.

- **Facts** are statements that can be proved.
- **Opinions** are statements about a person's beliefs, feelings, or other ideas that cannot be proved.

MAIN IDEA is the most important idea in the essay. The main idea is either stated directly or suggested indirectly by the essay's tone or details.

POINT OF VIEW is the perspective from which an essay is written.

- In the **first-person point of view,** the speaker is a person in the essay and uses the pronouns *I, me*, and *mine*.
- In the **third-person point of view,** the speaker is a person outside the essay and uses the pronouns *he, she*, and *they*.

PURPOSE is the author's reason for writing. An essay can have one or more purposes:
- to persuade
- to entertain
- to explain
- to share feelings and opinions

TONE tells how the essay writer feels toward the subject matter. The tone can reflect any feeling that a writer has about a subject.

In the following essays, you will explore these elements in greater detail. What you discover will help you understand and enjoy essays. It will also help you write an essay of your own.

ESSAY

WHEN SHAPED LIKE A BASKETBALL, THE WORLD IS HER OYSTER

CONNECT TO LITERATURE

In this essay, you'll read about a 12-year-old girl who loves to play basketball. What do you have a passion for? It might be sports, science, dancing, or playing music. In your journal, write about what you love best and why. As you read the selection, compare your feelings with Anna's.

INTRODUCTION TO THE MODEL ESSAY

An essay is a short composition that focuses on one particular topic. When you read the essays in this unit, you will find they have similar elements. For example, each essay has descriptive details, quotations from people, and a tone, or feeling. Each essay has an author's purpose, though the purposes vary.

As you read this essay, look at the notes in the margin. The notes will help you see the structure of the selection and how the basic elements of the essay are connected. While reading, jot down thoughts and impressions in your journal.

DID YOU KNOW?

Basketball was invented in 1891 by James Naismith, who wanted his physical education students to have an indoor sport for winter. At first they attached peach baskets to the balcony at opposites ends of the gym. Since then, the equipment and rules have undergone many changes.

WHEN SHAPED LIKE A
BASKETBALL
THE WORLD IS HER OYSTER
by Elaine Louie

As girls' basketball has changed, so have the girls themselves.

In the 1950's, girls' basketball was like a hand-cranked silent movie. Very slow and very jerky.

A girl dribbled twice, and then stopped, looking around like a frightened deer. If someone ran toward her, she dropped the ball.

No more. Schoolgirl basketball, like the boys' game, is fluid and fast, all galloping legs and whirling, flying elbows. Jump shots. Hooks. Blistering drives downcourt.

This new game has produced girls like my daughter, Anna Sussman, age 12: basketball girls who play ball seven days a week and, if they're New Yorkers, plaster their walls with pictures of John Starks, the Knicks' shooting guard, and wear jerseys with his No. 3 on it.

Two hundred girls ages 10 to 18, Anna among them, went to the Knicks' first sleepaway basketball

The details Louie includes help you "see" the girls and coaches. Details that help you form a mental picture of a person or place are called **descriptive details.**

camp for girls this summer at Manhattan College in the Bronx. The coaches, all college players or coaches on the high school or collegiate level, were tall, slim and rangy. The young girls were a motley crew, tall and short, chunky and wiry. They were black, white, Hispanic, Asian. Most of them wore their hair in ponytails.

What united them was a deep, <u>visceral</u> passion for basketball. For five days in August, they rose at 7 in the morning, played three times a day. And on the last day, when the winners of each division were announced, those who walked <u>languidly</u>, seemingly <u>diffident</u>, to the middle of the gym floor to get their trophies, were yelped at. "Hustle!" yelled the coaches. Hustle was the lesson for life.

Now it is basketball season, time to take to the courts at school or, in Anna's case, at the Carmine Street Recreation Center in Greenwich Village, where she is on two teams, one girls and one boys. By her own description, she is the youngest, shortest, worst player on the girls' traveling team, which will go from borough to borough. She is the only girl on a boys' league team in which she is not as good as most of the boys but is a little better (and taller) than some. Basketball defines her life.

"Carmine Street is my temple," she said. And the hoop is the altar.

Notice how Louie uses her daughter's experiences as an example of her larger **subject**: the changing state of girls' basketball. Essays usually deal with one subject, often in a personal way.

A basketball girl is not born. She works at it—and not in isolation. She has <u>mentors</u>.

Anna picked up her first basketball when she was 5, a kindergarten student at St. Luke's School in Manhattan. Her physical education teacher handed her a regulation-size basketball, asked her to dribble it and later to shoot it.

---

visceral (vis′ər əl) *adj.* arising from or caused by deep emotions or feelings.
languidly (lang′gwid lē) *adv.* in a manner lacking energy or force; sluggishly.
diffident (dif′i dənt) *adj.* lacking confidence in oneself; shy.
mentors (men′tərz) *n., pl.* wise and trusted counselors.

"What do you think we did in gym class," Anna said, seven years later. "Play tag?"

On weekends, her father, Gerry Sussman, a frustrated (5 feet 5 inches tall) basketball player, took her to the Horatio Street playground, across the street from our home, and shot baskets with her, always retrieving the ball, always tossing it, gently, back to her. She thrived on the game—and her father's attention.

In the fourth grade, a year after her father died suddenly, Anna found another basketball mentor, Donna Hartsoe, who worked in the after-school program and would shoot basket after basket with any child she found in the gym, no matter how tiny the child, how small the hands. The joy of making a basket—swish—was <u>contagious</u>.

For two hours each day after school, Anna practiced her shots. Free throws. Jump shots. More free throws. Each afternoon, she made four shots a minute, 400 shots by the end of the day. She wouldn't go home until the last shot went in.

By the fifth grade, she won her first trophy for being the most improved player on the school's junior varsity team. She wasn't the tallest. She wasn't the best. But she practiced, and she hustled.

In the sixth grade, she wanted to quit the team. She hated the coach and was sure the coach hated her. The truth was simpler. Anna hadn't accepted the first rule of sports. The coach rules. We argued, and I had the clichés: You love the sport. You're cutting off your nose to spite your face.

Anna became deaf. But she would listen to Max Gregan, a 24-year-old friend of the family. Max played basketball—and he

---

contagious (kən tā′jəs) *adj.* readily spread.

wasn't her parent. One night, they talked for 20 minutes. And then he said the seven words that spoke to her. "Winners never quit—and quitters never win."

Anna likes to win. In June, she won her second trophy, as the most valuable player on her team. In August, she went to the Knicks' camp. On the first day, the cooks hadn't arrived by lunchtime. Faced with 200 lean, hungry and restless girls, the Knicks made a snap decision. They ordered 50 pizzas.

With the 199 other girls, Anna played ball from 9 in the morning to 8 at night, stopping only to eat. She met Doc Rivers and got Hubert Davis's autograph and the sweat from his brow on her washcloth. Known as the "holy washcloth," it is pinned to her bedroom wall, a tatty red cloth, rigid from dried sweat. By the end of camp, where her team won their division trophy, she was obsessed with the game.

Her school, Hunter, has no team for seventh and eighth graders. But in September, Anna got up at 5:30 in the morning to get to the schoolyard an hour before school started, just to shoot baskets.

Who was on the streets when she emerged from the subway at 7 in the morning at Lexington Avenue and 96th Street? "Rich people walking their dogs," she reported. And who was on the playground with her at 7:10 in the morning? "Me and the security guard," she said.

By October, she stopped getting up at 5:30 in the morning. School was school, and basketball was Carmine Street. Her mentor was her coach, Ray Pagan, the youth director who is known around downtown for teaching values (fairness, honesty, emotional self-control) at the same moment he teaches skills (muffs and stuffs, strips and rips).

His girls don't talk trash. They sweat, but they don't smell. Immaculate personal hygiene is required.

---

personal hygiene cleanliness and grooming; one's own private practices or conditions that aid good health.

So are confidence and aggression. Ray never raises his voice. Neither does he humiliate. When he speaks, the players listen, alert, silent. The girls are so still that even the ponytails don't wag.

On weekdays at 2:30 in the afternoon, the minute school ends, Anna jumps onto the subway, and 40 minutes later, she's in the gym, stuffing her book bag and jeans into the locker. She grabs her Spalding and hits the floor.

Every day, she wears four pairs of pants. Underpants, boxer shorts, basketball shorts and baggy jeans. Why the armature? "Undies because I have to, boxers because the jeans slip down, jeans because it's cold," she said, "and basketball shorts because there's always a game."

Some days, she plays with girls, where she is in awe of Gwyneth Horton for her 3-pointer, Jane Aiello for her speed and jump shot, Folaki Ologunja for her all-around form. Most afternoons, she is the only girl on the floor among a bunch of boys, where she knows her place, which is partly dictated by her height, 5-1. She plays guard.

"I play very aggressive defense, but not so much offense," she said. "I'm small and scrubby and if I try to drive, I usually will run into someone and fall over."

The quotes from Anna add humor and a personal voice to the essay. They help set the overall **tone**, or feeling, of the piece.

Sometimes the boys harass her, but what she hates most is when nobody passes her the ball because she's a girl. Nor is she happy with the backhanded compliment: "You're pretty good for a girl."

On weekends, she is at the gym, having given up birthday parties, Bat Mitzvahs and weekends in the country for basketball. (She has not given up MTV, "Models Inc.," moisturizers, green facial masks or phone calls.)

Last week, Ray asked her if she wanted to play on one of the boys' league teams. She watched her

---

harass (har'əs, hə ras') *v.t.* bother or annoy repeatedly; torment.
Bat Mitzvahs (bät mits'vəz) *n., pl.* ceremonies held for Jewish girls when they are about 13, marking the beginning of adult religious responsibilities.

best friend, Rafe Bartholomew, a boy who towers over her at 5-7 and has a "deadly J," play.

Shaking her head, she said, "They're awfully good." Ray shrugged. "They're just scrubs," he said. On Saturday, she tried out for the team, and at the end of the day, she had made it.

She is the only girl.

She hustles.

Did Louie write this essay to entertain, to persuade, to explain, or to describe? Perhaps she had two or more reasons in mind. An author's reason for writing a piece is called the **author's purpose.**

Meet Elaine Louie

A New York-based writer, Elaine Louie (born 1943) disliked basketball as a child because girls' basketball rules made the game as "slow as a glacier." For her daughter, Anna, though, it's a whole different ball game. "She really does play seven days a week," Louie says.

Anna took time off from basketball to collaborate on Louie's essay. "She interviewed herself," says Louie. "She asked what questions a reader might want to have answered and then wrote down the answers for me." After the *New York Times* published the essay, Anna and her mother received an unexpected reward: A Knicks employee called to offer them courtside tickets to a game.

More Essays

- *A Summer Life* by Gary Soto (University Press of New England, 1990). In this book of short essays, Gary Soto describes the experience of growing up Chicano in Fresno, California.

- *Quiet Strength* by Rosa Parks with Gregory J. Reed (Zondervan, 1994). These essays reflect the passion for justice that has made Rosa Parks a leader in the Civil Rights movement.

RESPONDING TO Literature

THINK • TALK • WRITE

1 How do you feel about Anna? Do you admire her commitment to basketball? Write your feelings in your journal.

2 How is Anna's father her basketball mentor? What do they do together?

3 Why does Anna want to quit basketball in the sixth grade? Who convinces her to continue, and how does she do it?

4 What values does Coach Ray Pagan teach? Why do you think the players respect him?

5 The author describes the New York basketball girls as having different racial and ethnic backgrounds. Why do you think playing sports together may help people connect with each other?

ACTIVITY

● **Write About the Essay** Copy and complete this details chart as you reread the essay. You may need to add detail boxes to the chart.

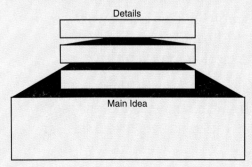

Details

Main Idea

VOCABULARY PRACTICE

Read each book title below. Choose the vocabulary word that best fits the subject of each book. On a separate piece of paper, write the vocabulary word you chose for each title.

languidly	diffident
mentors	contagious
harass	

1 *Overcoming Shyness*

2 *Fighting Tactics in Guerrilla Warfare*

3 *A Handbook for Avoiding Diseases*

4 *Coaches of the Olympic Skaters*

5 *Ted Knowles, the Laziest Man Alive*

ESSAY

THE ABC'S OF COURAGE

CONNECT TO LITERATURE

What is courage? It can mean reacting fearlessly to a dangerous situation. It can also mean bravely facing difficulties in daily life. In your journal, write about times you need courage in everyday life. As you read "The ABC's of Courage," compare your ideas with how the man in the essay shows courage.

THINKING ABOUT PERSUASION

Persuasive writing presents facts in a manner to try to convince the reader of something. A persuasive essay may cause readers to have certain feelings or to adopt certain opinions. As the title of his essay makes clear, Bob Greene believes he knows what courage means. He persuades readers that a man whom many people would consider unsuccessful is actually brave and intelligent. By using descriptive details and quotations, the author reveals both the man's personality and the challenge he faces.

DID YOU KNOW?

According to the Literacy Assistance Center in New York City, over 40 percent of adults in the United States need at least some help in reading and writing. Some of these people are learning English as a second language; others have low literacy abilities and want to improve them. Still others, like the man profiled in this essay, never learned to read as children.

Fortunately, there are also volunteer teachers like Patricia Lord. Literacy Volunteers is one organization that connects the teachers with the people who need their help. The volunteers take a training course in order to learn how to teach others to read and write.

THE ABC's

OF COURAGE

BY BOB GREENE

Premiere 1957 Stuart Davis, United States, 1894–1964 Los Angeles County Museum of Art

It is nearing dusk. The man has finished his day's labor; he is a plumber, and today he was working at a construction site, and his shift has ended.

Now he is sitting in the dining room of Mrs. Patricia Lord, in Cicero, Illinois. Mrs. Lord and the man are bending over a list of words.

"Can you try these now?" Mrs. Lord says.

"Yes," the man says.

He looks at the top word on the list. The word is *is*.

"Is," the man says.

"Yes," Mrs. Lord says.

The next word on the list is *brown*.

The man looks at it for a moment. Then he says: "Brown."

"Yes," Mrs. Lord says.

The next word is *the*.

"The," the man says, touching the word with his hand.

"Yes," Mrs. Lord says.

The next word is *sleep*.

The man hesitates. Seconds pass. He is having trouble with this one.

Finally he says: "Play?"

"No," Mrs. Lord says. "Look at it again."

The man stares. He says nothing. Then he says, "I don't know what it is."

"All right," Mrs. Lord says softly. "Skip it and come back to it later."

The man is fifty-five years old. He is trying to learn how to read. He is a large man, balding and wearing thick glasses; he bears a resemblance to the actor Ernest Borgnine. His plumber's work clothes—denim overalls, a flannel shirt—are still on. Today, as he does twice a week, he has driven straight from work to Mrs. Lord's house. His hands are dirty from his day's labor; as he points to the words on the spelling list you can see that he has not had time to stop and clean up. He has been coming to Mrs. Lord's house for just over a year.

The next word on the list is *down*.

"Down," the man says with confidence in his voice.

"That's right," Mrs. Lord says. "Very good."

The man—we will not name him here, because he has asked us not to—never learned to read as a child. His mother was sick and his father was an alcoholic; the boy did not do well in school, and at the age of twelve he dropped out and began to work. Sometimes his mother would try to teach him something; his father, if he had been drinking, would say, "What are you bothering to teach him for? He don't know nothing."

The man went through most of his life hiding his secret. He learned to be a plumber; he married and started a family. He concealed his inability to read even from his wife and children; his wife did all the paperwork around the house, read all the mail, handled all the <u>correspondence</u>.

A year and a half ago, the man lost a job because he could not read. The company he was working for required each employee to take a written test about safety procedures. The man knew the rules, but could not read the questions. The company allowed him to take the test over, but he didn't have a chance. He couldn't admit the real problem.

Out of work, he felt panic. He heard that a local community college was offering a nighttime course in reading improvement. He <u>enrolled</u>. But as early as the first evening he realized that the course was meant for people who at least knew the basics of reading. After a few sessions he approached the teacher after class.

"I know you can't read," the teacher said to him. "If you'd like to keep coming just to see what you can pick up, it's all right."

Instead, the man went to a dime store and bought a book called *Reading Fun* for ninety-three cents. The book was designed for pre-school-aged children. On the pages of the book were simple, colorful pictures of ambulances and taxis and

---

correspondence (kôr′ə spon′dens) *n.* communication by exchange of letters.

enrolled (en rōld′) *v.i.* signed up (for); registered.

trucks, followed by the proper word for each picture. He looked at the pages and tried to teach himself. He couldn't.

Finally, he sat down with his wife. "You know when I lost my job?" he said. And he told her he couldn't read.

Time went by. On television, he heard a public service announcement about private <u>tutoring</u> offered by the <u>Literacy</u> Volunteers of Chicago. He called up and explained about himself. The person on the other end of the line said that there were no suitable volunteers available at the moment. The man left his name.

Four months later, while he was out of the house, the literacy organization called. When the man arrived back at home, his wife said she had some news for him.

"There's a teacher for you," his wife said. "Her name is Pat."

Patricia Lord, fifty-nine, remembers the first time he showed up at her door.

"He was such a nice man," she said. "At first I didn't realize how deep his problem was. But it soon became clear—he didn't even know the alphabet."

So, twice a week, they started to work together. "He was so grateful," Mrs. Lord said. "I do this for free, but he kept saying that if I ever needed any plumbing done, even if it was an emergency in the middle of the night, he would do it for nothing."

She taught him the alphabet. She taught him how to print letters. She taught him the first words other than his own name that he had ever known how to read or write.

"We work with reading cards," she said. "He picks out words that look interesting to him, and I'll teach him. One of the words he wanted to learn, for instance, was *chocolate.* He was fascinated by it because it was longer than most of the other words on the cards. So we learned it."

There are books scattered all over Mrs. Lord's home— *The Fate of the Earth,* by Jonathan Schell; *Findings,* by

---

tutoring (tü′tər ing) *n.* private instruction given to a student by a teacher or other person.
literacy (lit′ər ə sē) *n.* ability to read and write.

Leonard Bernstein; *Schindler's List,* by Thomas Keneally.

"I tried to explain to him about the pleasures of reading," she said. "It's something he's never known. I've always gotten so much information and so much joy from reading, but when I try to explain that to him, it's almost beyond what he can imagine. When I was young I had a friend, and we'd go sit together in the park and just read for hours, and talk about what we were reading. The idea of something like that seems to intrigue him.

"I tell him that one of these days he'll be able to read a book," Mrs. Lord said. "That's far off in the future, though. I have a second-grade spelling puzzle book, and even that's way too advanced for him right now.

"But he's making progress. There's a list of about forty words that he knows now. When a lesson goes well, he is definitely elated. He'll smile at the end of the session, and he'll get more talkative than usual, and he'll just seem . . . lighter. I can tell that he's feeling good about it."

Detail from **Premiere**

---

talkative (tô′kə tiv) *adj.* tending to talk a great deal.

In the time since he started studying with Mrs. Lord, the man has found a new job. His employers do not know that he cannot read; he is deathly afraid that they will find out and that he will be fired again.

"I never liked to hear anyone called a dummy," he said. "Even when I was a kid, I didn't like it. In fact I once beat up another kid for calling a boy a dummy.

"Let's face it, though, when you work construction, the others would be embarrassed to work with you if they knew you couldn't read—wouldn't they? If they found out about me, I think they'd make it hard on me. Some people get their kicks like that."

He said it was losing the other job that convinced him he had to learn how to read. That, and something else.

"I've got a little granddaughter," he said. "I never want her to come up to me and say, 'Grandpa, read this,' and I can't do it. I already went through life not being able to read to my own children. I want to be able to read to my granddaughter."

He said he was proud of how far he had come in his life without knowing how to read. "I can take a blueprint and figure out how a whole building works," he said. "I built my own house. I think that's a pretty good accomplishment for a man who can't read. That, and going this far in my trade."

Still, he has always known how large the gap in his life was.

"All my life, I've wanted so badly to be able to read something," he said. "I've had to pretend, all my life. When I would go into a restaurant with people from the job, I would hold the menu up and pretend to be reading it. But I didn't understand a word. I'd always ask the waitress what the specials were, and when she'd say them I'd choose one of them. Or I'd order something that I knew every restaurant had.

"It was something I thought about all the time, but who could you go talk to? Many's the time that I wished I could

---

blueprint *n.* photographic print, usually featuring white lines on a blue background, used especially by architects and engineers to show building plans.

read something. But I knew there couldn't be too many people willing to help a person like me, so I just did my best to keep it a secret.

"I've never written a letter in my life. When the holidays came, it was very hard for me to pick out a card for my wife. I'd look at the cards, but I'd have no idea what they said. So I'd buy her a flower instead."

Now that he is studying with Mrs. Lord, he said, he can at least hope that things will change.

"I dream that before long I can really read something," he said. "It doesn't have to be a lot, but just to be able to read something from start to finish would be enough. Mrs. Lord tells me that once you start to read, it comes easier all the time.

"It scares me that there's a possibility I can't do it. I'm fifty-five years old, after all. I get disgusted with myself if I have a bad day here, and I miss a lot of words.

"But when there's been a good day I'll feel great at the end of our lesson. I'll go home and tell my wife, 'I learned this word.' Or I'll say, 'Teacher says I have good handwriting.' And then my wife and I will work on the spelling cards."

He said that, because he is working again, sometimes he will have to skip tutoring sessions. "It kills me when that happens," he said. "But the construction business is pretty good right now, and sometimes in the afternoon the boss will tell me that he needs me to work overtime. I can't tell him why I have to be here. So I'll go off to a pay phone and call Mrs. Lord and give her the bad news.

"I think about reading even when I'm at work, though. I'll be working, but I'll be reciting the alphabet in my head. I keep the spelling cards in my truck, and if it's time for a coffee break I'll go out there and work on my words."

He said that, before he started trying to learn to read, he never picked up a newspaper or a magazine. "Now I like

to pick them up and look at them," he said. "I think to myself that maybe someday I can read them.

"And I'll go into a store now and pick up books. I'll pick up the ones that have covers that look interesting. And then I'll flip through them until I see some words that I know. Most of the pages are filled with words that I don't know. But then I'll see some words that Mrs. Lord taught me—*an* or *is* or *the*—and I'll stare at them. It feels so good to know them."

It is getting darker outside. The man has been up since before dawn. His truck is parked outside Mrs. Lord's house; <u>motorists</u> pass by on their way home.

At the dining room table, Mrs. Lord is helping him to write a sentence. "Let's try 'The cow is brown,' " she says. "First word *the*."

The man checks his list of words. Then, on a clean sheet of paper, he writes: *The*.

"Good," Mrs. Lord says. "Next word, *cow*."

He checks his list and writes the word.

"Very good," Mrs. Lord says. "Now *is*."

That word he knows easily. He writes it.

"Now *brown*," Mrs. Lord says.

He thinks for a second, then writes *brown* at the end of the sentence he has built.

"Right!" Mrs. Lord says. "End of sentence!"

The man looks up. There is something very close to pride in his eyes.

"I can't wait until I can write a letter," he says. "The first letter I write is going to be to my wife. I'm going to tell her how much I love her."

On the cover of *Esquire* every month there is a slogan: "Man At His Best." Once in a while, when you really aren't expecting it, you find out what that means.

■ ———————————————————————————————

motorists (mō′tər ists) *n., pl.* people driving cars.

BOB GREENE

Bob Greene (born 1947) knew he wanted to be a journalist when he was twelve years old. While working on his junior high school newspaper, he beat out adult reporters from local papers and got an exclusive interview with a college basketball star.

Greene has worked as a newspaper columnist since 1971. He has also written regularly for *Esquire* magazine, served as a correspondent on ABC-TV's "Nightline," and published several nonfiction books, including *Hang Time,* about Michael Jordan.

Greene writes about a wide range of people who would never appear in regular news stories. On choosing his subjects, Greene says, "If a story is the first thing I would tell my best friend on the phone at the end of the day, then I know it's good to write a column about."

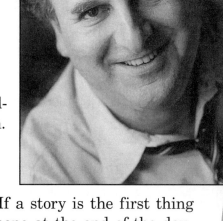

More Essays

- *James Herriot's Treasury for Children* (St. Martin's Press, 1992). Through these essays, follow the author on his rounds as a country vet treating animals from tiny mewing kittens to aging cows.

- *Animals Who Have Won Our Hearts* by Jean Craighead George (HarperCollins, 1994). Read about ten amazing animals who overcame extraordinary challenges in this richly illustrated collection.

RESPONDING TO *Literature*

THINK • TALK • WRITE

1 Do you think the title of the essay is appropriate? Tell why or why not in your journal.

2 Why did the man not learn to read and write when he was a child? What skills did he develop even without being able to read?

3 How did the man keep his illiteracy a secret for so many years? What caused him to finally try to learn to read?

4 What is the man learning from Mrs. Lord? What does he plan to do when he is able to write a letter?

5 Many Americans read and write in a language other than English. Why do you think they may want to be literate in English as well?

ACTIVITIES

- **Write with Persuasion** Is there an issue that you feel strongly about? Choose your topic, research it, and write a persuasive essay. In order to persuade your readers, you may want to include descriptive details and quotations.

- **Role-playing** Imagine that a child or grandchild of the man in the essay wants to help him learn to read and write. With a partner, act out how the child teaches the adult. Present your scenes to the class.

VOCABULARY PRACTICE

On a separate piece of paper, write the letter of the situation that best suggests the meaning of the word in green.

1 correspondence
   a. a couple watching a TV show
   b. a boy and his grandmother writing each other letters
   c. a girl who walks her dog twice a day

2 enrolled
   a. dough being prepared for a pie crust
   b. a ride on a roller coaster
   c. signing up for a computer programming course

3 talkative
   a. a grandfather who loves to tell funny stories
   b. a sleeping dog
   c. a fax machine

4 blueprint
   a. an architect's designs for a new building
   b. a suspect's fingerprints taken by a police officer
   c. an artist illustrating a sad story

5 motorists
   a. mechanics fixing cars at a garage
   b. a family going water-skiing in a motor boat
   c. people driving home from work at the end of the day

ESSAY

A BOY OF UNUSUAL VISION

CONNECT TO LITERATURE

Can you imagine riding a bike or play-ing baseball if you were unable to see? In your journal, write about ways a blind person might learn how to do things in the "seeing" world. As you read "A Boy of Unusual Vision," compare your ideas with the way Calvin—the subject of this essay—has learned to do things.

THINKING ABOUT AUTHOR'S PURPOSE

The reason for writing an essay is called the *author's purpose*. The author may want to entertain, inform, or persuade the reader. You can tell the author's purpose by noticing the tone of the essay, or the attitude the author has toward his or her subject. As in the other essays in this unit, the descriptive details and quotations help the reader "see" the people who are being written about.

As you read "A Boy of Unusual Vision," think about what purpose the author had for writing this essay.

DID YOU KNOW?

Did you know that braille—a system of reading and writing that many blind people use—was invented by a French teenager? Louis Braille devised this system in 1825, when he was only 16 years old. Blinded by an accident as a child, Braille created a scheme of raised dots that could be used for the alphabet, math-ematical symbols, and musical notes. He also designed a stylus and frame that made it possible for blind people to write in braille. In this essay, Calvin Stanley is able to attend public school because he can read his books in braille.

Photos by David Harp, courtesy of the Baltimore Sun

A Boy of Unusual Vision

by Alice Steinbach

First, the eyes: They are large and blue, a light, <u>opaque</u> blue, the color of a robin's egg. And if, on a sunny spring day, you look straight into these eyes—eyes that cannot look back at you—the sharp, April light turns them pale, like the thin blue of a high, cloudless sky.

Ten-year-old Calvin Stanley, the owner of these eyes and a boy who has been blind since birth, likes this description and asks to hear it twice. He listens as only he can listen, then: "Orange used to be my favorite color but now it's blue," he announces. Pause. The eyes flutter between the short, thick lashes. "I know there's light blue and there's dark blue, but what does sky-blue look like?" he wants to know. And if you watch his face as he listens to your description, you get a sense of a picture being clicked firmly into place behind the pale eyes.

He is a boy who has a lot of pictures stored in his head, <u>retrievable</u> images which have been fashioned for him by the people who love him—by family and friends and teachers who have <u>painstakingly</u> and patiently gone about creating a special world for Calvin's inner eye to inhabit.

Picture of a rainbow: "It's a lot of beautiful colors, one next to the other. Shaped like a bow. In the sky. Right across."

Picture of lightning, which frightens Calvin: "My mother says lightning looks like a Christmas tree—the way it blinks on and off across the sky," he says, offering a comforting description that would make a poet proud.

---

opaque (ō pāk´) *adj.* not letting light through; dull.
retrievable (ri trē´və bəl) *adj.* able to be gotten back, recovered, or regained.
painstakingly (pānz´tā king lē) *adv.* in a manner showing close, careful work or attention.

725

"Child," his mother once told him, "one day I won't be here and I won't be around to pick you up when you fall—nobody will be around all the time to pick you up—so you have to try to be something on your own. You have to learn how to deal with this. And to do that, you have to learn how to think."

There was never a moment when Ethel Stanley said to herself, "My son is blind and this is how I'm going to handle it."

Calvin's mother: "When Calvin was little, he was so inquisitive. He wanted to see everything, he wanted to touch everything. I had to show him every little thing there is. A spoon, a fork. I let him play with them, just hold them. The pots, the pans. *Everything.* I showed him the sharp edges of the table. 'You cannot touch this; it will hurt you.' And I showed him what would hurt. He still bumped into it anyway, but he knew what he wasn't supposed to do and what he could do. And he knew that nothing in his room— *nothing*—could hurt him.

"And when he started walking and we went out together—I guess he was about two—I never said anything to him about what to do. When we got to the curbs, Calvin knew that when I stopped, he should step down, and when I stopped again, he should step up. I never said anything, that's just the way we did it. And it became a pattern."

Calvin remembers when he began to realize that something about him was "different": "I just figured it out myself. I think I was about four. I would pick things up and I couldn't see them. Other people would say they could see things and I couldn't."

And his mother remembers the day her son asked her why he was blind and other people weren't.

"He must have been about four or five. I explained to him what happened, that he was born that way and that it was nobody's fault and he didn't have to blame himself. He asked, 'Why me?' And I said, 'I don't know why, Calvin. Maybe there's a special plan for you in your life and there's a reason for this. But this is the way you're going to be and you can deal with it.'"

Then she sat her son down and told him this: "You're *seeing,* Calvin. You're just using your hands instead of your eyes. But you're seeing. And, remember, there is *nothing* you can't do."

It's spring vacation and Calvin is out in the alley behind his house riding his bike, a serious-looking, black and silver two-wheeler. "Stay behind me," he shouts to his friend Kellie Bass, who's furiously pedaling her

---

inquisitive (in kwiz'i tiv) *adj.* eager for knowledge; curious.

726

bike down the one-block stretch of alley where Calvin is allowed to bicycle.

Now: Try to imagine riding a bike without being able to see where you're going. Without even knowing what an "alley" looks like. Try to imagine how you navigate a space that has no <u>visual</u> boundaries, that exists only in your head. And then try to imagine what Calvin is feeling as he pedals his bike in that space, whooping for joy as the air rushes past him on either side.

And although Calvin can't see the signs of spring sprouting all around him in the neighboring backyards—the porch furniture and barbecue equipment being brought out of storage, the grass growing emerald green from the April rains, the forsythia exploding yellow over the fences—still, there are signs of another sort which guide him along his route:

Past the German shepherd who always barks at him, telling Calvin that he's three houses away from his home; then past the purple hyacinths, five gardens away, throwing out their fragrance (later it will be the scent of the lilacs which guides him); past the large diagonal crack which lifts the front wheel of his bike up and then down, telling him he's reached his boundary and should turn back— past all these familiar signs Calvin rides his bike on a warm spring day.

Ethel Stanley: "At six, one of his cousins got a new bike and Calvin said, 'I want to learn how to ride a two-wheeler bike.' So we got him one. His father let him help put it together. You know, whatever Calvin gets he's going to go all over it with those hands and he knows every part of that bike and what it's called. He learned to ride it the first day, but I couldn't watch. His father stayed outside with him."

Calvin: "I just got mad. I got tired of riding a little bike. At first I used to zig-zag, go all over. My cousin would hold onto the bike and then let me go. I fell a lot in the beginning. But a lot of people fall when they first start."

There's a baseball game about to start in Calvin's backyard and Mrs. Stanley is pitching to her son. Nine-year-old Kellie, on first base, has taken off her fake fur coat so she can get a little more steam into her game and the other team member, Monet Clark, six, is catching. It is also Monet's job to alert Calvin, who's at bat, when to swing. "Hit it, Calvin," she yells. "Swing!"

He does and the sound of the ball making solid contact with the bat sends Calvin running off to first base, his hands groping in front of his body. His mother walks over to

---

visual (vizh′ü əl) *adj.* of, relating to, resulting from, or used in sight.

stand next to him at first base and unconsciously her hands go to his head, stroking his hair in a soft, protective movement.

"Remember," the mother had said to her son six years earlier, "there's *nothing* you can't do."

Calvin's father, 37-year-old Calvin Stanley, Jr., a Baltimore city policeman, has taught his son how to ride a bike and how to shift gears in the family's Volkswagen and how to put toys together. They go to the movies together and they tell each other they're handsome.

The father: "You know, there's nothing much I've missed with him. Because he does everything. Except see. He goes swimming out in the pool in the backyard. Some of the other kids are afraid of the water, but he jumps right in, puts his head under. If it were me I wouldn't be as brave as he is. I probably wouldn't go anywhere. If it were me I'd probably stay in this house most of the time. But he's always ready to go, always on the telephone, ready to do something.

■────────────────────────

unconsciously (un kon′shəs lē) *adv.* unknowingly; without being aware.

"But he gets sad, too. You can just look at him sometimes and tell he's real sad."

The son: "You know what makes me sad? *Charlotte's Web.* It's my favorite story. I listen to the record at night. I like Charlotte, the spider. The way she talks. And, you know, she really loved Wilbur, the pig. He was her best friend." Calvin's voice is full of warmth and wonder as he talks about E. B. White's tale of the spider who befriended a pig and later sacrificed herself for him.

"It's a story about friendship. It's telling us how good friends are supposed to be. Like Charlotte and Wilbur," he says, turning away from you suddenly to wipe his eyes. "And when Charlotte dies, it makes me real sad. I always feel like I've lost a friend. That's why I try not to listen to that part. I just move the needle forward."

Something else makes Calvin sad: "I'd like to see what my mother looks like," he says, looking up quickly and swallowing hard. "What does she look like? People tell me she's pretty."

The mother: "One day Calvin wanted me to tell him how I looked. He was about six. They were doing something in school for Mother's Day and the kids were drawing pictures of their mothers. He wanted to know what I looked like and that upset me because I didn't know how to tell him. I thought, 'How am I going to explain this to him so he will really know what I look like?' So I tried to explain to him about facial features, noses, and I just used touch. I took his hand and I tried to explain about skin, let him touch his, and then mine.

"And I think that was the moment when Calvin really *knew* he was blind, because he said, 'I won't ever be able to see your face . . . or Daddy's face,'" she says softly, covering her eyes with her hands, but not in time to stop the tears. "That's the only time I've ever let it bother me that much."

But Mrs. Stanley knew what to tell her only child: "I said, 'Calvin, you *can* see my face. You can see it with your hands and by listening to my voice and you can tell more about me that way than somebody who can use his eyes.'"

Thirty-three-year-old Ethel Stanley, a handsome, strong-looking woman with a radiant smile, is the oldest of seven children and grew up looking after her younger brothers and sisters while her mother worked. "She was a wonderful mother," Mrs. Stanley recalls. "Yes, she had to work, but when she was there, she was with you every minute and those minutes were worth a whole day. She always had time to listen to you."

Somewhere—perhaps from her own childhood experiences—Mrs. Stanley, who has not worked since Calvin was born, acquired the ability to <u>nurture</u> and teach and poured her mothering love into Calvin. And it shows. He moves in the sighted world with trust and faith and the unshakable confidence of a child whose mother has always been there for him. "If you don't understand something, ask," she tells Calvin again and again, in her open, forthright way. "Just ask."

"When he was little he wanted to be Stevie Wonder," says Calvin's father, laughing. "He started playing the piano and he got pretty good at it. Now he wants to be a computer programmer and design programs for the blind."

Calvin's neatly ordered bedroom is outfitted with all the comforts you would find in the room of many ten-year-old, middle-class boys: a television set (black and white, he tells you), an Atari game with a box of cartridges (his favorite is "Phoenix"), a <u>braille</u> Monopoly set, records, tapes, and programmed talking robots. "I watch wrestling on TV every Saturday," he says. "I wrestle with my friends. It's fun."

He moves around his room confidently and easily. "I know this house like a book." Still, some things are

hard for him to remember since, in his case, much of what he remembers has to be imagined visually first. Like the size and color of his room. "I think it's kind of big," he says of the small room. "And it's green," he says of the deep rose-colored walls.

And while Calvin doesn't need to turn the light on in his room he does like to have some kind of sound going constantly. *Loud* sound.

"It's three o'clock," he says, as the theme music from a TV show blares out into his room.

"Turn that TV down," says his mother, evenly. "You're not *deaf,* you know."

---

nurture (nûr′chər) *v.t.* take care of; nourish.
braille (brāl) *n.* system of writing and printing for the blind in which letters are represented by raised dot patterns that may be recognized and read by touch.

Two P.M., Vivian Jackson's class, Room 207.

What Calvin can't see: He can't see the small, pretty girl sitting opposite him, the one who is wearing little rows of red, yellow, and blue barrettes shaped like airplanes in her braided hair. He can't see the line of small, green plants growing in yellow pots all along the sunny window sill. And he can't see Mrs. Jackson in her rose-pink suit and pink enameled earrings shaped like little swans.

("Were they really shaped like little swans?" he will ask later.)

But Calvin can feel the warm spring breeze—invisible to *everyone's* eyes, not just his—blowing in through the window, and he can hear the tapping of a young oak tree's branches against the window. He can hear Mrs. Jackson's pleasant, musical voice and, later, if you ask him what she looks like, he will say, "She's nice."

But best of all, Calvin can read and spell and do fractions and follow the classroom work in his specially prepared braille books. He is smart and he can do everything the rest of his class can do. Except see.

"What's the next word, Calvin?" Mrs. Jackson asks.

"Eleven," he says, reading from his braille textbook.

"Now tell us how to spell it— without looking back at the book!" she says quickly, causing Calvin's fingers to fly away from the forbidden word.

"E-l-e-v-e-n," he spells out easily.

It all seems so simple, the ease with which Calvin follows along, the manner in which his blindness has been <u>accommodated</u>. But it's deceptively simple. The amount of work that has gone into getting Calvin to this point—the number of teachers, vision specialists and mobility instructors, and the array of special equipment—is staggering.

Patience and <u>empathy</u> from his teachers have played a large role, too.

For instance, there's Dorothy Lloyd, the specialist who is teaching Calvin the slow and very difficult method of using an Optacon, a device which allows a blind person to read a printed page by touch by converting printed letters into a <u>tactile</u> representation.

And there's Charleye Dyer, who's teaching Calvin things like "mobility" and "independent travel skills," which includes such tasks as using a cane and getting on and off buses. Of course, what Miss Dyer is really teaching Calvin is freedom; the ability to move about independently and without fear in the larger world.

---

accommodated (ə kom′ə dā′tid) *v.t.* adapted (for); adjusted (for).
empathy (em′pə thē) *n.* sharing of another's feelings without actually going through the same experiences.
tactile (tak′təl, tak′tīl) *adj.* of or relating to touch.

There's also Lois Sivits who, among other things, teaches Calvin braille and is his favorite teacher. And, to add to a list which is endless, there's the music teacher who comes in 30 minutes early each Tuesday to give him a piano lesson, and his home room teacher, Mrs. Jackson, who is as finely tuned to Calvin's cues as a player in a musical duet would be to her partner.

An important part of Calvin's school experience has been his contact with sighted children.

"When he first started school," his mother recalls, "some of the kids would tease him about his eyes. 'Oh, they're so big and you can't see.' But I just told him, 'Not any time in your life will everybody around you like you—whether you can see or not. They're just children and they don't know they're being cruel. And I'm sure it's not the last time someone will be cruel to you. But it's all up to you because you have to go to school and you'll have to deal with it.'"

Calvin's teachers say he's well liked, and watching him on the playground and in class you get the impression that the only thing that singles him out from the other kids is that someone in his class is always there to take his hand if he needs help.

"I'd say he's really well accepted," says his mobility teacher, Miss Dyer, "and that he's got a couple of very special friends."

Eight-year-old Brian Butler is one of these special friends. "My *best* friend," says Calvin proudly, introducing you to a studious-looking boy whose eyes are alert and serious behind his glasses. The two boys are not in the same class, but they ride home together on the bus every day.

Here's Brian explaining why he likes Calvin so much: "He's funny and he makes me laugh. And I like him because he always makes me feel better when I don't feel good." And, he says, his friendship with Calvin is no different from any other good friendship. Except for one thing: "If Calvin's going to bump into a wall or something, I tell him, 'Look out,'" says Brian, sounding as though it were the most natural thing in the world to do when walking with a friend.

"Charlotte would have done it for Wilbur," is the way Calvin sizes up Brian's help, evoking once more that story about "how friendship ought to be."

A certain moment: Calvin is working one-on-one with Lois Sivits, a teacher who is responsible for the braille skills which the four blind

---

evoking (i vō′king) *v.t.* calling forth or bringing out.

children at Cross Country must have in order to do all the work necessary in their regular classes. He is very relaxed with Miss Sivits, who is gentle, patient, smart, and, like Calvin, blind. Unlike Calvin, she was not able to go to public school but was sent away at age six, after many operations on her eyes, to a residential school—the Western Pennsylvania School for the Blind.

And although it was 48 years ago that Lois Sivits was sent away from her family to attend the school for the blind, she remembers—as though it were 48 minutes ago—how that blind, six-year-old girl felt about the experience: "Oh, I was so *very* homesick. I had a very hard time be-

ing separated from my family. It took me three years before I began getting used to it. But I knew I had to stay there. I would have given anything to stay at home and go to a public school like Calvin," says the small, kind-looking woman with very still hands.

Now, the moment: Calvin is standing in front of the window, the light pouring in from behind him. He is listening to a talking clock which tells him, "It's 11:52 A.M." Miss Sivits stands about three feet away from him, also in front of the window, holding a huge braille dictionary in her hands, fingers flying across the page as she silently reads from it. And for a few moments, there they are, as if frozen in a tableau, the two of them standing in darkness against the light, each lost for a moment in a private world that is composed only of sound and touch.

There was another moment, years ago, when Calvin's mother and father knew that the operations had not helped, that their son was probably never going to see. "Well," said the father, trying to comfort the mother, "we'll do what we have to do and Calvin will be fine."

He is. And so are they.

---

tableau (ta blō´) *n.* silent and motionless representation of a scene, painting, or event.

Meet Alice Steinbach

Alice Steinbach came to writing through art. A Baltimore native, she was writing articles about artists when she realized she could apply what she had learned to writing about other kinds of people, too.

Her articles led to a job writing for the *Baltimore Sun.* One day she realized that she didn't know much about children who are blind. After deciding to write about Calvin Stanley, Steinbach spent three weeks interviewing Calvin and his family and observing his daily life. "A Boy of Unusual Vision" won a 1985 Pulitzer Prize and has been reprinted more than 50 times.

Her secret for success? "Observe the world in *your* way: through scientific facts, through art, or through words. Then think about what you observed."

More Essays

• *Boy: Tales of Childhood* by Roald Dahl (Puffin Books, 1984). Roald Dahl is known worldwide as a writer of stories that take weird and often hilarious twists. Find out how Dahl got started in these essays about his youth in Wales.

• *Boys Will Be* by Bruce Brooks (Henry Holt, 1993). Bruce Brooks, an award-winning author of young adult fiction, has written 12 essays expressly for boys—and all those who want to know more about them.

RESPONDING TO *Literature*

THINK • TALK • WRITE

1 Did reading this essay increase your understanding of what it is like to be blind? Explain your answer in your journal.

2 When he plays baseball, how does Calvin know when to swing? Why do his parents encourage him to do things like play baseball and ride bikes?

3 What things make Calvin sad? What does his mother tell him when he says he will never be able to see her face?

4 Who is Calvin's favorite teacher? From what you're read about her, why do you think she teaches braille to children?

5 Why do you think Calvin's parents want him to go to school with children who can see? What might he learn in public school that he would not learn in a school for blind children?

ACTIVITIES

- **Writing About Author's Purpose** Look back at "The Cay," and compare the author's purpose in that piece with the author's purpose in this essay. Write three or more paragraphs to explain your comparison.

- **Test Your Senses** In a small group, choose a part of the school building or grounds to explore. Take turns walking blindfolded to figure out clues for where you are. Describe your findings to the rest of the class.

VOCABULARY PRACTICE

On a separate piece of paper, write whether the following pairs of words are *synonyms* or *antonyms*.

1 opaque—transparent

2 retrievable—lost

3 painstakingly—carefully

4 inquisitive—uninterested

5 accommodated—adjusted

Match the phrases with the words that have the same meaning. Write your answers on a separate piece of paper.

6 visual
7 unconsciously
8 nurture
9 evoking
10 empathy

a ability to share another's feelings

b having to do with sight

c bringing forth

d without being aware

e help grow and develop

WRITING

Many authors find that their favorite place to write about is not an exotic far-off land, but their own neighborhood. Write an essay describing something especially interesting in your neighborhood.

PREWRITE

After you choose your topic, jot down some notes about it in your journal. What is its main idea? What details support that idea? Organize your thoughts into a chart, the way this writer did:

DRAFT

Here's the beginning of the writer's essay about his neighborhood. Discuss it with a partner. How would the two of you improve this paragraph?

MAIN IDEA

The most popular character in my neighborhood is a cat.

Supporting Details

Everyone knows his name and stops to say hello to him. Shopkeepers leave out food for him. When he got sick, people collected money for the vet bills.

This writer tries to engage the reader's attention with a catchy opening statement. See if you can find a catchy opening for your essay.

A Real Cool Cat

The most popular fellow on my street isn't a person at all. He's a cat. His name is Pepper, and he has long black fur, and all the people who no him say that hes the nicest one they have ever met. He's the real cats meow!

It's time to begin your draft.
Go over your notes from your writer's journal. Remember, your essay doesn't have to be perfect right away—the most important thing is to get your ideas on paper.

736

AN ESSAY

REVISE

The writer of this essay revised some details in his first paragraph.

The writer has decided that this detail is not necessary to support the main idea.

The writer has chosen a more informal tone. Contractions such as *they've* can make a sentence sound less formal.

> The most popular fellow on my street isn't a person at all. He's a cat. His name is Pepper, and he has long black fur, and all the people who no him say that hes the nicest one they *they've* have ever met. He's the real cats meow!

Revise your own draft. Have you included unnecessary details?

PROOFREAD

This writer asked a friend to help him proofread his essay. His friend found a few errors that the writer had missed.

Don't forget to use an apostrophe in contractions and possessive nouns.

> The most popular fellow on my street isn't a person at all. He's a cat. His name is Pepper, and he has long black fur, and all the people who no *know* him say that hes the nicest one they *they've* have ever met. He's the real cats meow!

Proofread your essay carefully for errors in spelling, grammar, and punctuation. You might want to ask a friend to double-check it.

PUBLISH

How would you like to present your work? List ideas in your writer's journal.

737

WRITING

BRIGHTENING UP WRITING WITH INTERJECTIONS

ENRICH YOUR WRITING OF **ESSAYS.**

Interjections are words or phrases used to express strong feelings, such as *Wow!, Great!, Oh,* or *Well.* Interjections that stand alone are followed by an exclamation mark. Those that begin a sentence are followed by a comma. If you use them sparingly, interjections can add life and energy to your writing.

Read these sample paragraphs. What is the impact of the interjection used in Paragraph 2?

Paragraph 1

　　Feel like dressing up your city? Start with its parks. A well-kept park can add beauty and pleasure to any city.

Paragraph 2

　　Feel like dressing up your city? Great! Start with its parks. A well-kept park can add beauty and pleasure to any city.

PRACTICE 1 Respond on a separate piece of paper.

1 How does the mood of the first paragraph differ from the mood of the second? Which paragraph seems more formal and distant?

2 Write your own three-sentence paragraph about city parks. Use an interjection to brighten up your writing.

738

PRONOUNS IN PREPOSITIONAL PHRASES

REMEMBER THESE RULES ABOUT PRONOUNS IN PREPOSITIONAL PHRASES WHEN YOU ARE WRITING **ESSAYS.**

- When a pronoun is the object of a preposition, use an object pronoun. Sometimes a preposition has a compound object—an object made up of two or more pronouns joined by a conjunction.

- Don't use a reflexive pronoun as the object of a preposition if the sentence calls for an object pronoun.

PRACTICE 2 Choose the correct pronoun. Then rewrite the sentence on a separate piece of paper.

1 Without the park, summer would be boring for (they, them).

2 Because we worked hard, the garden was dedicated to (we, us).

3 She cleaned up all the litter around (herself, her).

4 The city just won't be the same without (he, him).

SUBJECT-VERB AGREEMENT WITH COMPOUND SUBJECTS

USE THESE RULES ABOUT SUBJECT-VERB AGREEMENT WITH COMPOUND SUBJECTS WHEN YOU ARE WRITING **ESSAYS.**

- In sentences with a compound subject, the conjunctions determine whether the verb will be singular or plural. If the conjunctions are *and* or *both . . . and,* the verb should be plural.

- If the conjunctions are *or, nor, either . . . or,* or *neither . . . nor,* the verb agrees with the subject closest to it.

PRACTICE 3 Choose the correct form of the verb. Then rewrite the sentence on a separate piece of paper.

1 The child and his parents (uses, use) the skating rink.

2 Either gardens or a playground (needs, need) to be built.

3 Both the gym and the track field (is, are) new.

4 Susan or her sisters (come, comes) every day to rake leaves.

PROJECT 1

WRITING A BUSINESS LETTER

Need some challenging experience as a volunteer? Want to write a company to complain about a badly made product? You'll need to write a letter that sounds businesslike and convincing.

PREWRITE

What will you put in your business letter? You've got to keep it short, simple, and to the point. You've got to keep the language formal and polite. To plan your letter, try using a chart like this one:

Message	Reason	Details	Goal
Choose me as summer hospital volunteer	I'm qualified; lots of free time	highly organized; not going to summer camp	experience working in professional setting

DRAFT Remember to whom you are writing as you compose your draft. Keep the language and the tone appropriate.

REVISE Cut out any information that is not necessary to your request. Try the letter out on a partner to see if it is effective.

PROOFREAD Accurate spelling, punctuation, and grammar will contribute to the overall impression you make on the person who gets this letter. Proofread carefully.

PUBLISH Send your letter to the person for whom it was intended and wait for a response.

▶ *Proofreading Alert!*

Use a colon after the salutation in a business letter. Check page 294 in *Spotlight on Success: Writing and Language Handbook.*

PROJECTS

CHALLENGE YOUR COMMUNITY WITH A POSTER

REMEMBER TO: • PREWRITE • DRAFT • REVISE • PROOFREAD • PUBLISH

Challenge the people in your community to face an issue and do something about it. Make a poster that will lead to action. Brainstorm some ideas with a group of friends.

Try filling in a chart like this one as the group comes up with ideas. Then choose one idea to concentrate on. Keep in mind who'll see the posters. How will you get their attention?

Issue	Solution	Poster Ideas
homelessness	cheaper housing	woman in old coat looking into window of comfortable house (Needs text, too.)
drugs	education; determination	"JUST SAY NO!" in giant block letters

MAKE A CARTOON

REMEMBER TO: • PREWRITE • DRAFT • REVISE • PROOFREAD • PUBLISH

People's reactions to life's challenges can sometimes be humorous. Make a cartoon about a challenge that turned out to be funny.

Whether it's the tumble you took the first time you tried skiing or the challenge that turned out to be no challenge at all, you'll want your cartoon to be funny and easy to understand. Plan it out first. Then draw it and add a caption. Use a chart to organize your ideas. Then make a classroom cartoon display.

Characters and Setting	Problem	Caption
me and tennis instructor	I'm holding wrong end of racket, but ball is soaring over net.	"Great! But can you hit it holding the handle?"

V I E W P

WHAT IS A HERO?

Everyone agrees that heroes are special people. We look up to them. Artists, writers, and actors create works based on their lives. Athletes have special talents. We see "heroes" interviewed on television news programs. But what is a hero? Is a hero someone who acts courageously in a dangerous situation or someone who sets an example by daily acts of kindness and compassion? We all have different viewpoints about what makes them special and deserving of our respect.

CONSIDER THIS ISSUE: Your social studies class is planning a special project about community heroes. A group of students is brainstorming a list of community heroes to invite to speak to your class. However, there's a problem: everyone has a different idea about what makes a hero. What do you consider before making your final list?

- Are heroes always people who risk their lives to save others?
- Do heroes have to be famous, or can they be ordinary people?
- Can someone be a hero to one person but not to another?
- Can you be a hero by helping people in small ways?

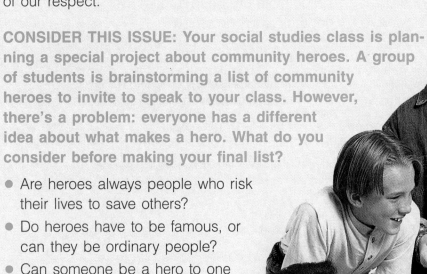

O I N T S

Read the following viewpoints about what it means to be a hero. Then decide which opinion is closest to your own. Think of more arguments yourself to support the position you choose.

VIEWPOINT 1

I think a hero is someone who saves others from danger.

- Heroes risk their lives when necessary.
- Heroes are strong and courageous.
- Heroes are leaders who take charge in emergencies.

VIEWPOINT 2

I think a hero is someone whose good acts set an example for others.

- Heroes can set a good example by their honest, caring behavior in ordinary situations.
- Heroes think of other people first and try to help them.
- It's important for students to look up to people who are kind and who help others.

VIEWPOINT 3

I think heroes are people who work hard and do what they feel they have to do.

- Heroes are people who show great courage in facing the challenges in their lives.
- These heroes are ordinary people who behave decently every day.
- These heroes don't think they are doing anything special.

WHAT DO YOU THINK?

Think about what it means to be a hero. Do you agree with one of the viewpoints above, or do you have another? With a small group, brainstorm your own list of heroic qualities.

real life
CONNECT

CHALLENGES: We reach deep inside ourselves to face an obstacle and to overcome it.

When situations and events challenge us, we're forced to do the best we can, sometimes against impossible odds. For example, ten-year-old Calvin Stanley in "A Boy of Unusual Vision" faces the challenge of learning to see with his hands instead of his eyes. Baseball legend Babe Ruth met many challenges during his career. Read part of an entry about Ruth from a biographical dictionary below.

A **biographical dictionary** is a reference book of articles about the lives of famous people. Each article provides information about the person's life and accomplishments. The entries are arranged in alphabetical order, like entry words in a regular dictionary.

RUTH, GEORGE HERMAN (BABE) *(b. Baltimore, MD., 1895; d. New York, NY., 1948)*, baseball player. Legally committed to St. Mary's Industrial Home for Boys, Baltimore, at age seven, he became the school's star baseball player. In 1914 Ruth joined the Baltimore club of the International League, but because of a financial squeeze, he was sold the same year to the major-league Boston Red Sox. With a brilliant overall record for 1914, his major-league career was launched. Over the next four years, as a regular Red Sox pitcher, Ruth helped Boston win three American League pennants and three World Series titles. Overall, his six years as a Boston pitcher showed eighty-nine victories and forty-six losses, a pace which, if continued, would surely have ranked him as one of baseball's greatest pitchers.

But Ruth's versatility ended his pitching. His exceptional abilities as a hitter prompted Boston manager Ed Barrow in 1918 to place him full-time in the outfield, where he played thereafter. In 1918 he batted .300 and hit eleven homers; a year later he astounded the baseball world by clubbing a record twenty-nine

establishing the department of practical astronomy at Columbia, 1881.

RUTLEDGE, EDWARD *(b. Charleston, S.C., 1749; d. Charleston, 1800)*, lawyer, statesman. Brother of John Rutledge. Member of the First Continental Congress, 1774, and of the Second Continental Congress, 1775–76, he seconded the opinions of his brother. At first opposing independence, he influenced the South Carolina delegation to vote for it and was a signer of the Declaration. Returning home in November 1776 to serve in the defense of the state, he was taken prisoner at the fall of Charleston but was exchanged in time to take his seat in the legislature in January 1782. Although he drew up the bill proposing confiscation of Loyalist property, he was influential in moderating its effect. An active member of the legislature, 1782–98, he was a stiffly conservative Federalist. Elected governor, 1798, he served until his death.

RUTLEDGE, JOHN *(b. Charleston, S.C., 1739; d. 1800)*, statesman, jurist. Brother of Edward Rutledge. After study-

883

I O N S

Here are three activities in which you have to use a biographical dictionary. Think of other situations in which a biographical dictionary would be a useful source of information. Then choose an activity below or one of your own and talk or write about it.

PROJECT 1

USE THE DICTIONARY Biographical dictionaries are a quick source of data about famous people. Work with a partner to research the life of a famous athlete in several biographical dictionaries. Then role-play a news interview with the sports figure. Use the information you found in the biographical dictionaries as the basis for your interview.

PROJECT 2

WRITE AN ENTRY *Current Biography* provides biographical information about living persons. Read several articles in this reference book. Then interview a partner about his or her life and interests. Write an entry about your partner for an edition of *Current Biography.* Your partner should write about you. Evaluate each other's entries.

PROJECT 3

IT TAKES ALL KINDS There are a variety of biographical dictionaries in the reference room of a school or public library. Look through these reference books. On a 3 x 5 card, write the name and publisher of each one and a brief description of the type of biographical information it provides. Share your notes with classmates.

Glossary

This glossary can help you to pronounce and find out the meanings of words in this book that you may not know. The meanings given here are the ones that apply to the words as they are used in the selections in this book.

The words are listed in alphabetical order. Guide words tell you the first and last words on the page. The pronunciation respelling is in parentheses following the word. You can understand the pronunciation respelling by using the key that appears at the bottom of every right-hand page.

When a word has more than one syllable, a dark accent mark (′) shows which syllable is stressed. In some words, a light accent mark (′) shows which syllable has a lighter stress.

The following abbreviations are used in this glossary: *n.* noun, *v.* verb, *v.t.* transitive verb, *v.i.* intransitive verb, *adj.* adjective, *adv.* adverb, *prep.* preposition, *pl.* plural, *interj.* interjection.

The entries in the glossary are based on entries in *The Macmillan/McGraw-Hill School Dictionary 2.*

A

abating (ə bāt′ing) *v.t., v.i.,* making or becoming less in force, intensity, or amount.

abstracted (ab strak′tid) *adj.* lost in thought.

academic (ak′ə dem′ik) *adj.* of or relating to liberal or general education, especially to studies that prepare a student for college.

acceptance (ak sep′təns) *n.* approval; favorable reception.

access (ak′ses) *n.* ability or right to approach, enter, or use.

accommodated (ə kom′ə dā′tid) *v.t.* adapted (for); adjusted (for).

adept (ə dept′) *adj.* highly skilled; expert.

advantage (ad van′tij) *n.* useful or helpful circumstance; benefit; asset.

affliction (ə flik′shən) *n.* misery; suffering; misfortune.

aggravating (ag′rə vā′ting) *adj.* annoying; irritating.

aggrieved (ə grēvd′) *adj.* having hurt feelings or wounded pride.

allotted (ə lo′tid) *v.t.* given out or assigned as a share.

amiss (ə mis′) *adj.* not as it should be; wrong.

anemic (ə nē′mik) *adj.* lacking vitality or spirit.

annoyance (ə noi′əns) *n.* state of being irritated.

apologetically (ə pol′ə jet′ik lē) *adv.* in a regretful way.

apparently (ə par′ənt lē) *adv.* plainly; obviously.

Arab (ar′əb) *n.* Arabian horse, a breed noted for speed, grace, and intelligence.

arcs (ärks) *n., pl.* curved lines between points on a circle.

armory (är′mə rē) *n.* headquarters of a National Guard or other military unit.

assemblage (ə sem′blij) *n.* gathering of persons.

asteroid (as′tə roid′) *n.* any of thousands of small, rocky bodies that revolve around the sun.

atone (ə tōn′) *v.i.* make up, as for a wrong; make amends.

audible (ô′də bəl) *adj.* loud enough to be heard.

auspicious (ô spish′əs) *adj.* showing promise of success; favorable.

automatically (ô′tə mat′ik lē) *adv.* as if acting, moving or operating by itself; as if done without a person′s control.

avail (ə vāl′) *n.* use; help; advantage.

awesome (ô′səm) *adj.* inspiring great wonder combined with fear or reverence.

axis (ak′sis) *n.* imaginary line around which a planet rotates.

B

badgering (baj′ə ring) *v.t.* annoying in a persistent way; pestering.

banished (ban′isht) *v.t.* forced to leave one place, and restricted to another place.

baobab (bā′o bab′) *n.* tropical tree in Africa, having a broad trunk, thick spreading branches, and a fruit resembling a gourd.

barbaric (bär bar′ik) *adj.* savage; brutal.

Bat Mitzvahs (bät mits′vəz) *n., pl.* ceremonies held for Jewish girls when they are about 13, marking the beginning of adult religious responsibilities; parties are often held in celebration.

bazaars (bə zärz′) *n., pl.* marketplaces or streets lined with shops or stalls.

beckoned (bek′ənd) *v.t.* signaled, summoned, or directed (someone) by a sign or gesture.

befuddled (bi fud′əld) *adj.* completely confused or bewildered.

belligerently (bə lij′ər ənt lē) *adv.* with hostility; with eagerness to fight.

berserk (bər sûrk′) *adv.* into a wild or violent rage.

beseechingly (bi sēch′ing lē) *adv.* in an earnest, pleading manner.

bewildered (bi wil′dərd) *adj.* completely confused or puzzled.

biological (bī′ə loj′i kəl) *adj.* having to do with life processes; bodily.

birthright (bûrth′rīt′) *n.* right, privilege, or possession that a person is entitled to by birth.

blackmail (blak′māl′) *n.* attempt to gain money by threatening to reveal damaging information.

bleak (blēk) *adj.* open and exposed to the wind; bare; chilling; gloomy.

blemish (blem′ish) *n.* something that spoils perfection; stain.

blight (blīt) *n.* something that damages, ruins, or destroys.

blissful (blis′fəl) *adj.* full of joy.

blueprint (blü′print′) *n.* photographic print, usually featuring white lines on a blue background, used especially by architects and engineers to show building plans.

blundering (blun′dər ing) *adj.* moving or acting blindly or clumsily.

bolted (bōl′tid) *v.i.* broke away from control; started and ran off.

---

at; **ā**pe; f**ä**r; c**â**re; **e**nd; m**ē**; **i**t; **ī**ce; p**î**erce; h**o**t; **ō**ld; s**ô**ng, f**ô**rk; **oi**l; **ou**t; **u**p; **ū**se; r**ü**le; p**u**ll; t**û**rn; **ch**in; si**ng**; **sh**op; **th**in; **th**is; **hw** in **wh**ite; **zh** in trea**s**ure. The symbol **ə** stands for the unstressed vowel sound heard in **a**bout, tak**e**n, penc**i**l, lem**o**n, and circ**u**s.

botanists (bot′ə nists) *n., pl.* specialists in the science or study of plants.

bouquets (bō kāz′, bü kāz′) *n., pl.* bunches of picked flowers.

braille (brāl) *n.* system of writing and printing for the blind in which letters are represented by raised dot patterns that may be recognized and read by touch.

breeches (brich′iz) *n., pl.* trousers reaching to just below the knees.

bridle (brī′dəl) *n.* part of a horse's harness, including the bit and reins, that fits over the head, used to guide or control the animal.

bung (bung) *n.* stopper for closing the bunghole in a barrel or cask.

burden (bûr′dən) *n.* heavy load; something very difficult to bear.

C

calligraphy (kə lig′rə fē) *n.* art of beautiful or elegant handwriting.

campus (kam′pəs) *n.* grounds, including buildings, of a school, college, or university.

cantina (kan tē′nə) *n. Spanish.* a package of food taken out from a restaurant.

careening (kə rēn′ing) *v.i.* swaying from side to side while moving quickly; lurching.

cavalry (kav′əl rē) *n.* military unit trained to fight on horseback.

centrifugal (sen trif′yə gəl) *adj.* moving or directed away from a center.

chagrined (shə grind′) *adj.* distressed or annoyed by failure, disappointment, or embarrassment.

chariot (char′ē ət) *n.* two-wheeled vehicle drawn by two, three, or four horses and driven from a standing position, used in ancient times in warfare, processions, and races.

chasms (kaz′əmz) *n., pl.* deep cracks or gaps.

choking (chōk′ing) *v.t.* holding back or repressing; stifling.

circulation (sûr′kyə lā′shən) *n.* movement of blood to and from the heart through the blood vessels of the body.

cocky (kok′ē) *adj. Informal.* too confident; self-confident in a swaggering way.

coffin (kô′fin) *n.* box or case into which a dead person is placed for burial.

col (käl) *n.* high, walkable ridge in a mountain range.

coma (kō′mə) *n.* state of deep unconsciousness from which a person cannot easily be aroused.

compensate (kom′pən sāt′) *v.t.* balance out; make up.

concussed (kən kust′) *adj.* injured by a blow to the brain or spinal cord.

confidentially (kon′fi den′shə lē) *adv.* in a trusting tone suggesting something told in private.

conform (kən fôrm′) *v.i.* be the same or similar; correspond.

confront (kən frunt′) *v.t.* face boldly or with defiance.

consideration (kən sid′ə rā′shən) *n.* regard for others and their feelings; respect.

consultation (kon′səl tā′shən) *n.* meeting to get advice, ideas, or opinions.

consumption (kən sump′shən) *n.* amount that is used up.

contagious (kən tā′jəs) *adj.* readily spread.

contempt (kən tempt′) *n.* scorn; disdain; disrespect.

contentment (kən tent′mənt) *n.* state of being happy and content; satisfaction.

contrast (kon'trast) *n.* difference between light and dark on a television screen.

convey (kən vā') *v.t.* express; communicate.

conviction (kən vik'shən) *n.* firm belief or opinion.

coronary (kôr'ə ner'ē) *n. Slang.* heart attack.

correspondence (kôr'ə spon'dəns) *n.* communication by exchange of letters.

counselor (koun'sə lər) *n.* person who gives counsel or advice; adviser.

coveted (kuv'i tid) *v.t.* eagerly desired (someone else's possession).

cowlick (kou'lik') *n.* tuft of hair that grows in a different direction from the rest of the hair and will not lie flat.

crestfallen (krest'fô'lən) *adj.* having had one's feelings or pride hurt.

cringing (krin'jing) *v.i.* shrinking, flinching, or crouching, as in fear, pain, or horror.

crossly (krôs'lē) *adv.* in a bad-tempered, peevish manner.

culvert (kul'vərt) *n.* drain for water under roads, sidewalks, and railroads.

curtly (kûrt'lē) *adv.* abruptly; rudely to the point.

cutter (kut'ər) *n.* small, fast ship used by the Coast Guard.

D

dawdling (dô'dling) *adj.* time-wasting; lingering.

deadweight (ded'wāt') *n.* heavy burden.

debris (də brē') *n.* remains of something broken or destroyed; rubbish.

deemed (dēmd) *v.t.* thought; believed; judged.

defeatist (di fē'tist) *adj.* expecting defeat, or accepting it too readily.

defect (di fekt') *v.i.* desert a group, country, or cause, especially to go to another that is opposed to it.

defiant (di fī'ənt) *adj.* showing bold, open resistance.

deftly (deft'lē) *adv.* skillfully and nimbly.

delirious (di lîr'ē əs) *adj.* temporarily out of one's mind.

deposits (di poz'its) *n., pl.* natural layers, as of minerals.

designated (dez'ig nā'tid) *v.t.* selected for a particular purpose or duty; appointed.

desolate (des'ə lit) *adj.* without people; deserted; cheerless.

desperation (des'pə rā'shən) *n.* recklessness arising from loss of hope.

detours (dē'tùrz) *n., pl.* roundabout or indirect way taken instead of the main road.

devised (di vīzd') *v.t.* invented.

diffident (dif'i dənt) *adj.* lacking confidence in oneself; shy.

diminished (di min'isht) *v.i.* got smaller or less in size or importance.

disarray (dis'ə rā') *n.* condition of disorder or confusion.

disbelief (dis'bi lēf') *n.* refusal to accept the truth or reality of something.

discard (dis'kärd) *n.* useless, worthless, rejected item.

disconcerted (dis'kən sûr'tid) *adj.* marked by a loss of self-possession or composure.

---

at; **ā**pe; **fär**; **câre**; **e**nd; **mē**; **i**t; **ī**ce; **pî**erce; **ho**t; **ō**ld; **sô**ng, **fô**rk; **oi**l; **ou**t; **u**p; **ū**se; **rü**le; **pú**ll; **tû**rn; **ch**in; si**ng**; **sh**op; **th**in; **th**is; **hw** in **wh**ite; **zh** in trea**s**ure. The symbol **ə** stands for the unstressed vowel sound heard in **a**bout, tak**e**n, penc**i**l, lem**o**n, and circ**u**s.

disconsolately (dis kon'sə lit lē) *adv.* with such sadness as to be without cheer, hope, or comfort.

disdainfully (dis dān'fə lē) *adv.* scornfully; with dislike for something thought of as unworthy or beneath one.

disheartened (dis här'tend) *v.t.* discouraged; weakened in hope or will.

disinfectant (dis'in fek'tənt) *n.* substance used to destroy disease-causing germs.

disown (dis ōn') *v.t.* refuse to recognize as one's own; deny responsibility for or connection with.

dispense (di spens') *v.t.* get along without; do away with; make unnecessary.

disrupted (dis rup'tid) *v.t.* broke apart; upset.

dissuade (di swād') *v.t.* keep (someone) from doing something by persuasion or advice.

distended (di stend'id) *adj.* enlarged by pressure from within; stretched out.

distinctive (di stingk'tiv) *adj.* unique; different in kind from others.

distracted (di strak'tid) *v.t.* turned away the mind or attention of; diverted.

dolefully (dōl'fəl lē) *adv.* sadly; in a manner expressing grief or sorrow.

dominant (dom'ə nənt) *adj.* having the main influence, authority, or control; most important.

dorm (dormitory) (dôr'mi tôr'ē) *n.* building designed for group housing, as for students at a college to live and sleep in.

dramatically (drə mat'ik lē) *adv.* strikingly.

dredgers (drej'ərz) *n., pl.* boats equipped for scooping up or removing mud, sand, and other substances from the bottom of a body of water.

drooped (drüpt) *v.i.* hung or sunk down.

drowsy (drou'zē) *adj.* sleepy; half asleep.

drudgery (druj'ə rē) *n.* tiring, boring, or menial work.

dubiously (dü'bē əs lē) *adv.* with doubt or uncertainty; skeptically.

dutifully (dü'tə fəl lē) *adv.* obediently.

dwindled (dwin'dəld) *v.i.* became gradually smaller or less; diminished.

E

eavesdropping (ēvz'drop'ing) *n.* listening to the private conversation of others without their knowing it.

edible (ed'ə bəl) *adj.* fit to eat.

embedded (em bed'id) *adj.* set firmly into something.

embraced (em brāst') *v.t.* hugged.

empathy (em'pə thē) *n.* sharing of another's feelings without actually going through the same experiences.

enchanter (en chant'ər) *n.* one who casts spells.

enrolled (en rōld') *v.i.* signed up (for); registered.

en route (än rüt') *adv.* on the way.

entrails (en'trālz) *pl. n.* inner parts of an animal, especially the intestines.

epidemic (ep'i dem'ik) *n.* rapid spread or sudden, widespread appearance.

epoch (ep'ək) *n.* era; long period of time marked by certain events or conditions.

erstwhile (ûrst'hwīl') *adj.* former.

escort (es'kôrt) *n.* person or persons who accompany another or others as a courtesy, honor, or protection.

ese (ās'ā) *Spanish. Slang.* man.

eternity (i tûr'ni tē) *n.* seemingly endless length of time.

evidently (ev'i dənt lē) *adv.* clearly; obviously.

evoking (i vō'king) *v.t.* calling forth or bringing out.

evolved (i volvd') *v.i.* developed slowly.

exasperated (eg zas′pə rā′tid) *adj.* greatly irritated; provoked to anger.

excretion (ek skrē′shən) *n.* discharge of waste matter from the body.

existence (eg zis′təns) *n.* state of being or life.

explosion (ek splō′zhən) *n.* sudden, loud outburst.

extract (ek strakt′) *v.t.* draw or pull out by effort or force.

F

fantasies (fan′tə sēz) *n., pl.* imaginative hopes and dreams.

fatal (fā′təl) *adj.* causing death, destruction, or ruin.

ferocity (fə ros′i tē) *n.* fierceness.

fertile (fûr′təl) *adj.* able to produce abundant crops.

fidgeted (fij′i tid) *v.i.* made restless movements; was nervous or uneasy.

fineries (fi′nə rēz) *n., pl.* fine or showy clothes or ornaments.

flayed (flād) *v.t.* stripped off the skin of, as by lashing.

flexed (flekst) *v.t.* bent; tightened.

flurry (flûr′ē) *n.* sudden commotion; stir.

forage (fôr′ij) *v.i.* hunt or search for food or supplies.

forebodings (fôr bō′dingz) *n., pl.* feelings that something evil or bad is going to happen.

foremost (fôr′mōst′) *adj.* leading; first in rank or importance.

forestall (fôr stôl′) *v.t.* hinder, prevent, or get ahead of by taking action in advance.

fork (fôrk) *n.* spot where a road splits.

forsaking (fôr sāk′ing) *v.t.* giving up completely.

fractured (frak′chərd) *v.t.* cracked, split, or broken.

frantically (fran′tik lē) *adv.* with wild excitement from worried grief; in great haste.

freak (frēk) *adj.* odd or unusual; bizarre.

frigid (frij′id) *adj.* very cold.

fronds (frondz) *n., pl.* leaves of a palm or fern.

frustration (frus trā′shən) *n.* feeling of irritation from disappointment or defeat.

furtively (fûr′tiv lē) *adv.* slyly; sneakily.

G

gaiety (gā′i tē) *n.* cheerfulness; merry-making; festivity.

gawked (gôkt) *v.i. Informal.* stared stupidly; gaped.

gleeful (glē′fəl) *adj.* merry; joyous.

glowering (glou′ər ing) *adj.* scowling; showing anger.

gnarled (närld) *adj.* having many rough, twisted knots, as a tree trunk or branches.

griped (grīpd) *v.i. Informal.* complained; grumbled.

grove (grōv) *n.* small group of trees without underbrush.

grudged (grujd) *v.t.* allowed unwillingly.

grumpily (grump′ə lē) *adv.* in a bad-tempered, complaining way.

H

hamlet (ham′lit) *n.* cluster of houses in the country; small village.

---

at; **ā**pe; f**ä**r; c**â**re; **e**nd; m**ē**; **i**t; **ī**ce; p**î**erce; h**o**t; **ō**ld; s**ô**ng, f**ô**rk; **oi**l; **ou**t; **u**p; **ū**se; r**ü**le; p**u̇**ll; t**û**rn; **ch**in; si**ng**; **sh**op; **th**in; **th**is; **hw** in **wh**ite; **zh** in trea**s**ure. The symbol **ə** stands for the unstressed vowel sound heard in **a**bout, tak**e**n, penc**i**l, lem**o**n, and circ**u**s.

hands *n., pl.* units of measure equaling 4 inches, used in expressing the height of a horse.

haranguing (hə rang′ing) *v.t.* addressing with a long, noisy, often pompous speech.

harass (har′əs, hə ras′) *v.t.* bother or annoy repeatedly; torment.

hard *n.* firm sheltered beach or stone path sloping down to the water's edge.

hassle (has′əl) *n.* irritation; struggle.

haughtily (hô′tə lē) *adv.* with much pride in oneself and disdain for others.

haven (hā′vən) *n.* place of safety or shelter.

Hebrew (hē′brü) *n.* religious language of Judaism, originally spoken by the ancient Jews.

heed (hēd) *n.* careful attention; notice.

honing (hōn′ing) *v.t.* sharpening.

horny (hôr′nē) *adj.* hard like horn; calloused.

horrifying (hôr′ə fī′ing) *adj.* very dreadful; terrible.

humiliated (hū mil′ē ā′tid) *adj.* feeling or showing shame or extreme embarrassment.

I

idling (īd′ling) *v.i.* parked with the motor running.

ignorance (ig′nər əns) *n.* state of lacking knowledge or education.

illusions (i lü′zhənz) *n., pl.* false or misleading ideas.

imbeciles (im′bə silz) *n., pl.* stupid or foolish people.

imperious (im pîr′ē əs) *adj.* haughty; arrogant.

implied (im plīd′) *v.t.* suggested or expressed indirectly.

implore (im plôr′) *v.t.* ask earnestly.

imprinted (im prin′tid) *v.t.* fixed firmly in the memory.

improvised (im′prə vīzd′) *adj.* made from whatever materials are on hand.

impudence (im′pyə dəns) *n.* act of being rudely bold or forward.

inalienable (in āl′yə nə bəl) *adj.* that cannot be given up or taken away.

incense (in′sens′) *n.* substance that produces a fragrant aroma when burned.

incredulously (in krej′ə ləs lē) *adv.* with disbelief.

inculcate (in kul′kāt) *v.t.* fix firmly in the mind or memory by teaching or example.

inevitable (in ev′i tə bəl) *adj.* that cannot be avoided; obvious or certain.

infantry (in′fən trē) *n.* soldiers trained and equipped to fight on foot.

ingratitude (in grat′i tüd′) *n.* lack of appreciation, as for a kindness or favor.

inherited (in her′i tid) *v.t.* received from a former owner at his or her death.

inimitable (i nim′i tə bəl) *adj.* matchless; impossible to imitate.

inlaid (in′lād′) *adj.* decorated with a material set into the surface.

inquisitive (in kwiz′i tiv) *adj.* eager for knowledge; curious.

inscribed (in skrībd′) *v.t.* written, marked, or engraved on.

instincts (in′stingkts′) *n., pl.* natural tendencies to act a certain way.

intact (in takt′) *adj.* whole; not damaged.

intercepted (in′tər sep′tid) *v.t.* seized or stopped on the way.

interminable (in tûr′mə nə bəl) *adj.* endless or seeming to be endless.

intersections (in′tûr sek′shənz) *n., pl.* places where two roads meet and cross.

intrepid (in trep′id) *adj.* having or showing no fear; courageous; fearless.

inventories (in'vən tôr'ēz) *n., pl.* detailed lists of goods in stock or owned at a given time.

irate (ī rāt') *adj.* angry; enraged.

ironic (ī ron'ik) *adj.* odd, as an outcome of events opposite to what might have been expected.

J

jubilation (jü'bə lā'shən) *n.* feeling of joyful happiness or triumph.

jutted (ju'tid) *v.i.* stuck out; protruded.

K

keener (kē'nər) *adj.* sharper.

kindred (kin'drid) *adj.* similar; alike.

L

labored (lā'bərd) *adj.* forced; done with effort.

laid-back (lād'bak') *adj. Slang.* casual; relaxed; easy-going.

langosta (läng gōs'tə) *n.* type of spiny lobster.

languidly (lang'gwid lē) *adv.* in a manner lacking energy or force; sluggishly.

latitude (lat'i tüd') *n.* distance north or south of the equator, expressed in degrees measured from the earth's center.

lavishly (lav'ish lē) *adv.* grandly; in great amounts.

learned (lûr'nid) *adj.* knowledgeable; well-educated.

lee (lē) *adj.* sheltered from the wind.

legacy (leg'ə sē) *n.* something handed down from previous generations.

lenient (lē'nē ənt, len'yent) *adj.* not harsh; tolerant.

Lent (lent) *n.* period of penitence and prayer observed in Christian churches during the forty days, excepting Sundays, from Ash Wednesday to Easter.

lethargy (leth'ər jē) *n.* state or quality of being without strength, energy, or alertness.

levied (lev'ēd) *v.t.* imposed or collected by force or authority.

listing (lis'ting) *v.i.* tilting or leaning to one side.

listless (list'lis) *adj.* lacking energy and a desire to do anything.

literacy (lit'ər ə sē) *n.* ability to read and write.

logical (loj'i kəl) *adj.* sensible; reasonable.

lurking (lûr'king) *v.i.* moving about in a sneaky manner.

luxury (luk'shə rē) *n.* comfort or pleasure that goes beyond what is really necessary.

M

maize (māz) *n.* corn.

makeshift (māk'shift') *adj.* used temporarily in place of the proper or usual thing.

mammoth (mam'əth) *adj.* huge; gigantic.

maniac (mā'nē ak') *n.* someone who is or seems wildly insane; lunatic.

martyr (mär'tər) *n.* person who suffers or sacrifices greatly for a belief, principle, or cause.

melodramas (mel'ə drä'məz) *n., pl.* sentimental plays acted out with exaggerated emotions.

mentors (men'tərz) *n., pl.* wise and trusted counselors.

---

at; **ā**pe; **fär**; **câr**e; **e**nd; **mē**; **i**t; **ī**ce; **pî**erce; **ho**t; **ō**ld; **sô**ng, **fô**rk; **oi**l; **ou**t; **u**p; **ū**se; **rü**le; **pù**ll; **tû**rn; **ch**in; **si**ng; **sh**op; **th**in; **th**is; **hw** in **wh**ite; **zh** in trea**s**ure. The symbol **ə** stands for the unstressed vowel sound heard in **a**bout, tak**e**n, penc**i**l, lem**o**n, and circ**u**s.

meted (mēt'id) *v.t.* distributed by or as if by measuring.

methane (meth'ān) *n.* gas made of carbon and hydrogen.

meticulous (mə tik'yə ləs) *adj.* showing extreme or excessive concern about details.

midriff (mid'rif) *n.* part of the body below the breast and above the waist.

misbehaved (mis'bi hāvd') *v.t.* conducted oneself badly.

mobility (mō bil'i tē) *n.* quality of being able to move.

moderation (mod'ə rā'shən) *n.* state of being kept within reasonable limits and not going to extremes.

momentarily (mō'mən ter'ə lē) *adv.* briefly; for a short time.

mongrel (mong'grəl) *n.* animal, especially a dog, of mixed breed.

monotonous (mə not'ə nəs) *adj.* not changing, as in tone, sound, or beat.

monsoons (mon sünz') *pl. n.* summer storms characterized by heavy rains.

mortal (môr'təl) *n.* human being; person.

motorists (mō'tər ists) *n., pl.* people driving cars.

mourners (môr'nərz) *n., pl.* people who feel sadness, especially those attending a funeral.

N

nomadic (nō mad'ik) *adj.* wandering from place to place.

nurture (nûr'chər) *v.t.* take care of; nourish.

O

ominously (om'ə nəs lē) *adv.* in a manner that foretells trouble or misfortune.

opaque (ō pāk') *adj.* not letting light through; dull.

opted (opt'id) *v.i.* made a choice.

orator (ôr'ə tər) *n.* skilled public speaker.

ordinance (ôr'də nəns) *n.* regulation or law made by a city or town government.

outrageous (out rā'jəs) *adj.* going beyond proper limits; shocking.

overrun (ō'vər run') *v.t.* swarming or overflowing.

overwrought (ō'vər rôt') *adj.* extremely excited or nervous.

P

pacemaker (pās'māk'ər) *n.* device that controls timing.

painstakingly (pānz'tā'king lē) *adv.* in a manner showing close, careful work or attention.

pall (pôl) *n.* covering of darkness and gloom.

panoramic (pan'ə ram'ik) *adj.* of or like a wide or complete view of an area.

particles (pär'ti kəlz) *n., pl.* very small bits; specks.

pedestals (ped'ə stəlz) *n., pl.* any bases or supporting structures.

pelting (pel'ting) *v.t.* beating against repeatedly.

pendants (pen'dənts) *n., pl.* ornamental objects, such as jewels, that hang from other things.

perilous (per'ə ləs) *adj.* hazardous; dangerous.

persecuted (pûr'si kū'tid) *v.t.* given cruel, harmful, or unjust treatment.

pervading (pər vā'ding) *v.t.* spreading through every part of.

pesky (pes'kē) *adj. Informal.* troublesome; annoying.

physiotherapist (fiz'ē ō ther'ə pist) *n.* person who treats disease or injury by physical methods, such as heat, massage, or exercise.

piazza (pē az'ə) *n.* veranda; porch.

pidgin (pij′ən) *adj.* mixing two or more languages by simplifying grammar and vocabulary, used for communication between people who speak different languages.

pleadingly (plē′ding lē) *adv.* in a begging way.

plundered (plun′dərd) *v.t.* looted or robbed, as during a war.

pointedly (poin′tid lē) *adv.* forcefully; with emphasis.

poultice (pōl′tis) *n.* soft, moist mass of a substance, such as a mustard compound, heated and applied to a part of the body as a treatment for soreness.

pouted (pou′tid) *v.i.* thrust out the lips, as in displeasure or sullenness.

preparatory (pri par′ə tôr′ē) *adj.* serving to prepare, especially for college.

priority (prī ôr′i tē) *adj.* coming before others in order or importance; deserving special attention.

procession (prə sesh′ən) *n.* group of persons or things moving along in a continuous forward movement, especially in a formal or orderly manner.

prodigy (prod′i jē) *n.* extremely gifted or talented person, especially a child.

proficient (prə fish′ənt) *adj.* highly skilled; expert.

proprietor (prə prī′i tər) *n.* owner or operator of a small business establishment.

prosperous (pros′pər əs) *adj.* successful; wealthy.

protruding (prō trüd′ing) *v.i.* sticking out; projecting.

prow (prou) *n.* forward part of a boat or ship.

pummeled (pum′əld) *v.t.* hit again and again with the fists; pounded.

punctual (pungk′chü əl) *adj.* on time; prompt.

Q

qualm (kwäm) *n.* twinge of conscience; sudden doubt or misgiving.

quiver (kwiv′ər) *n.* case for holding arrows.

R

raring (râr′ing) *adj.* very eager.

rascal (ras′kəl) *n.* mischievous or mean, dishonest person.

rash (rash) *adj.* acting with or characterized by too much haste.

rationed (rash′ənd, rā′shənd) *adj.* limited to fixed portions.

rear (rîr) *v.i.* rise on the hind legs.

reasonable (rē′zə nə bəl) *adj.* showing or using good sense; not foolish.

recede (ri sēd′) *v.i.* move back or away.

reception (ri sep′shən) *n.* social gathering, especially one at which guests are formally received.

recoil (ri koil′) *v.i.* draw or shrink back, as in fear, horror, or surprise.

recollecting (rek′ə lekt′ing) *v.t.* calling back to mind; remembering.

recruit (ri krüt′) *v.t.* hire or get the services of.

rejected (ri jek′tid) *adj.* not accepted; turned down or cast aside.

reluctantly (ri luk′tənt lē) *adv.* with hesitation or unwillingness.

repentant (ri pen′tənt) *adj.* feeling, showing, or marked by sorrow or regret.

repetitive (ri pet′i tiv) *adj.* repeating.

---

at; **ā**pe; f**ä**r; c**â**re; **e**nd; m**ē**; **i**t; **ī**ce; p**î**erce; h**o**t; **ō**ld; s**ô**ng, f**ô**rk; **oi**l; **ou**t; **u**p; **ū**se; r**ü**le; p**ù**ll; t**û**rn; **ch**in; si**ng**; **sh**op; **th**in; **th**is; **hw** in **wh**ite; **zh** in trea**s**ure. The symbol **ə** stands for the unstressed vowel sound heard in **a**bout, tak**e**n, penc**i**l, lem**o**n, and circ**u**s.

repulsed (ri pulst') *v.t.* beaten or driven back.

reruns (re'runz') *n., pl.* taped performances shown again after their original showings.

resignation (rez'ig na'shən) *n.* acceptance of something without protest or complaint; submission.

respectively (ri spek'tiv lē) *adv.* with respect to each of two or more in the order presented.

retrievable (ri trē'və bəl) *adj.* able to be gotten back, recovered, or regained.

revenue stamp stamp indicating that the tax due on an item has been paid to the government.

reverie (rev'ə rē) *n.* daydream.

rheumatism (rü'mə tiz'əm) *n.* any of several diseases characterized by inflammation, swelling, and stiffness of the muscles and joints.

rigidity (ri jid'i tē') *n.* state of being fixed, not changing.

roadsters (rōd'stərz) *n., pl.* open automobiles with a single seat for two or more people, often with a rumble seat or luggage compartment in the rear.

roamed (rōmd) *v.t.* wandered over or through a place.

rowdy (rou'dē) *adj.* lively and rough; disorderly.

rubble (rub'əl) *n.* rough, broken pieces of solid material, as stone or rock.

rude (rüd) *adj.* primitive; not developed or advanced.

runt (runt) *n.* weak, undersized person or animal.

S

Sabbath (sab'əth) *n.* day of the week for rest and religious worship.

sapphire (saf'īr) *adj.* having the deep blue color of the precious stone.

satchel (sach'əl) *n.* bag or small suitcase for carrying clothing, instruments, books, or other articles.

satrap (sā'trap) *n.* governor of a province in the ancient Persian empire.

sauntered (sôn'tərd) *v.i.* walked in a slow, relaxed way; strolled.

schooner (skü'nər) *n.* ship that has two or more masts and fore-and-aft sails.

scope (skōp) *n.* opportunity or room for expression or development.

scowling (skou'ling) *adj.* angrily frowning.

scraggly (skrag'lē) *adj.* having a ragged or rough appearance.

senna (sen'ə) *n.* dried leaves of any of several tropical plants, used in making a laxative.

sentimental (sen'tə men'təl) *adj.* characterized by emotion, especially exaggerated or foolish emotion.

serene (sə rēn') *adj.* peaceful; calm.

sermonized (sûr'mə nīzd') *v.i.* spoke at length in a moralizing way.

shift (shift) *n.* scheduled work time.

shiftless (shift'lis) *adj.* lazy; lacking in ambition or energy; good-for-nothing.

shillings (shil'ingz) *n., pl.* former coins of the United Kingdom.

shunting (shun'ting) *v.t.* moving or turning aside or away.

significant (sig nif'i kənt) *adj.* having special value or importance.

silhouetted (sil'ü et'tid) *v.t.* made a dark outline on a light background.

similarities (sim'ə lar'i tēz) *n., pl.* instances or points of likeness.

skirmish (skûr'mish) *n.* brief fight between small groups of persons; any brief or minor conflict.

sledge (slej) *n.* sled or sleigh.

sneered (snîrd) *v.i.* had a facial expression showing hatred or contempt.

solemnly (sol′əm lē) *adv.* in a serious and earnest manner.

somberly (som′bər lē) *adv.* with darkness and gloom.

sophisticated (sə fis′ti kā′tid) *adj.* full of worldly knowledge and experience.

sorrel (sôr′əl) *n.* reddish-brown horse.

spacious (spā′shəs) *adj.* roomy; having much space.

sparingly (spâr′ing lē) *adv.* in small amounts; with care in spending or using.

specifically (spi sif′i klē) *adv.* in particular.

splendor (splen′dər) *n.* great display, as of riches or beautiful objects; magnificence.

stalactites (stə lak′tīts) *n., pl.* mineral formations resembling icicles, which hang from a cave ceiling.

statistics (stə tis′tiks) *n.* information represented in numbers.

stepbrothers (step′bruth′ərz) *n., pl.* sons of one's stepparents by a former marriage.

stingily (stin′jə lē) *adv.* ungenerously.

stunned (stund) *adj.* dazed; shocked; overwhelmed.

subdued (səb düd′) *v.t.* brought under control; overcome.

superfluous (sù pûr′flü əs) *adj.* extra; more than is needed or wanted.

supportive (sə pôr′tiv) *adj.* providing approval, aid, or encouragement.

surveyors (sər vā′ərz) *n., pl.* persons who find shape, area, and boundaries of a region or tract of land by taking measurements.

swanky (swang′kē) *adj. Slang.* very elegant; stylish; luxurious.

synagogue (sin′ə gog′) *n.* building used by Jews for religious worship and instruction.

T

tableau (ta blō′) *n.* silent and motionless representation of a scene, painting, or event.

tactile (tak′təl, tak′tīl) *adj.* of or relating to touch.

talkative (tô′kə tiv) *adj.* tending to talk a great deal.

taut (tôt) *adj.* full of tension or strain; tight.

tempis' (tempest) (tem′pist) *n.* violent windstorm, usually accompanied by rain, hail, snow, or thunder.

tenement (ten′ə mənt) *n.* apartment building or rooming house that is poorly built or maintained and often overcrowded.

terminal (tûr′mə nəl) *n.* station at either end of a railroad, bus, air, or other transportation line.

terrarium (tə râr′ē əm) *n.* small enclosure or container, often of glass, used for growing plants or raising small land animals, such as snakes, turtles, or lizards.

therapist (ther′ə pist) *n.* doctor or other person who treats stress, grief, or mental disorders.

thistledown (this′əl doun′) *n.* soft, silky fuzz on a prickly plant, which has red or purple flowers.

thongs (thôngz) *n., pl.* narrow strips of leather or other material, used especially as fastenings.

tiara (tē är′ə) *n.* ornament resembling a crown, worn on the head.

---

at; āpe; fär; câre; end; mē; it; īce; pîerce; hot; ōld; sông, fôrk; oil; out; up; ūse; rüle; pùll; tûrn; chin; sing; shop; thin; this; hw in white; zh in treasure. The symbol ə stands for the unstressed vowel sound heard in about, taken, pencil, lemon, and circus.

titanic (tī tan'ik) *adj.* huge.

token (tō'kən) *n.* something that serves to indicate or represent some fact, event, object, or feeling; symbol.

trawling (trô'ling) *v.i.* fishing with a strong, usually bag-shaped, net dragged over the ocean bottom.

treachery (trech'ə rē) *n.* betrayal of a trust.

treason (trē'zən) *n.* betrayal of one's country, especially by giving aid to the enemy in wartime.

trek (trek) *n.* journey, especially one that is difficult or slow.

tribute (trib'ūt) *n.* money paid by one ruler or nation to another to show submission or to ensure peace or protection.

truce (trüs) *n.* temporary halt to fighting by mutual agreement.

tutoring (tü'tər ing) *n.* private instruction given to a student by a teacher or other person.

U

ultimate (ul'tə mit) *adj.* greatest possible.

unconsciously (un kon'shəs lē) *adv.* unknowingly; without being aware.

uneasiness (un ē'zē nis) *n.* anxiety; restlessness; tension.

unison (ū'nə sən) *n.* sameness in pitch, as of two or more voices.

V

valiant (val'yənt) *adj.* brave; courageous.

variation (vâr'ē ā'shən) *n.* amount by which something changes.

vertical (vûr'ti kəl) *adj.* upright; straight up and down.

victrolas (vik trō'ləz) *n., pl. Trademark.* early types of record players.

vilest (vīl'est) *adj.* most evil.

vindicate (vin'di kāt') *v.t.* clear (someone) of suspicion or charges of wrongdoing.

violating (vī'ə lā'ting) *v.t.* failing to obey; breaking.

visceral (vis'ər əl) *adj.* arising from or caused by deep emotions or feelings.

visual (vizh'ü əl) *adj.* of, relating to, resulting from, or used in sight.

vitally (vī'tə lē) *adv.* extremely; essentially.

vulnerable (vul'nər ə bəl) *adj.* sensitive; easily hurt.

W

whim (hwim) *n.* sudden or unexpected notion or fanciful idea.

wistfulness (wist'fəl nes) *n.* quality of sad longing or yearning.

withered (with'ərd) *adj.* dried up or shriveled, as from heat or loss of moisture.

wits (wits) *pl. n.* ability to think and reason clearly; good sense.

XYZ

yawning (yôn'ing) *adj.* wide open.

GLOSSARY OF
Literary Terms

A

Acts The main divisions of a play. (See also *Drama, Scenes.*)

Allegory A literary work in which different elements, such as characters or settings, have symbolic meanings.

Alliteration The repetition of consonant sounds, usually at the beginnings of words. For example, in "Ozymandias," page 179, the sands are described as "boundless and bare" and "lone and level." (See also *Poetry.*)

Allusion A reference within a literary work to a character or situation in another literary work or work of art. Page 83 of "Touch System" contains an allusion to Shakespeare's play *The Merchant of Venice.* When Mrs. Gilbreth jokingly compares her husband to the character Shylock, she implies he is being stingy and harsh.

Anecdote A short, often amusing story based on an incident in a person's life. Calvin's mother tells an anecdote about her son learning to "see" with his hands in "A Boy of Unusual Vision," page 724.

Antagonist The character or force that opposes the protagonist, or hero, in a work of literature. The Chimera is the antagonist in "Bellerophon and the Flying Horse," page 199. (See also *Character, Protagonist.*)

Assonance The repetition of a vowel sound in words within a sentence or line of verse. Note the repeated long *i* sound in this line from "Your World," page 270: "But I sighted the distant horizon." (See also *Poetry.*)

Audience The group of people who read a literary work or watch a play, film, or television program.

Author's Point of View The author's point of view is his or her attitude toward the subject of the written work. (See also *Author's Purpose.*)

Author's Purpose The author's purpose is his or her reason for writing a particular work. An author's purpose may be to inform, to persuade, to entertain, to express an opinion, or a combination of those purposes. (See also *Author's Point of View.*)

Autobiography The story of a person's life written by that person. (See also *Anecdote, Biography, Narrative Point of View, Subject, Subjective Details.*)

B

Biography The story of a person's life written by another person. (See also *Autobiography, Subject.*)

C

Character A person, an animal, or a personified object that plays a role in the action of a literary work. A **round character**—such as Rip Van Winkle—is one for whom an author has created a fully developed physical appearance and personality. A **flat character**—such as Brom Dutcher in the same work, page 437—is one who is not fully developed. (See also *Antagonist, Hero/Heroine, Protagonist.*)

Characterization The techniques authors use to present and develop characters. In **direct characterization,** authors comment in a straightforward manner on the nature of a character, as when Olivia Coolidge describes Alexander the Great as "noble and trusting by nature" on page 351. In **indirect characterization,** authors allow readers to draw conclusions about characters based upon the characters' own words and actions as well as upon how other characters react to them. By describing what Pawpaw says and does when Casey changes radio stations, Laurence Yep reveals Pawpaw's insecurities through indirect characterization in "Child of the Owl," page 506. (See also *Character Traits, Character: Motivation.*)

Character: Motivation The reasons fictional characters act, think, or feel certain ways. In "Brother to the Wind," page 272, Emeke's desire to fly is the motivation behind most of his actions. (See also *Character Traits.*)

Character's Point of View A character's perspective on plot events or other characters. Ed Sitrow's point of view about his team's winless season generates humor in "S.O.R. Losers," page 4.

Character Traits The personal qualities that distinguish one literary character from another. For example, in "Anne of Green Gables," page 526, Anne is imaginative and talkative while Marilla is

practical and stern. (See also *Character, Characterization, Character: Motivation.*)

Chronological Order The order in which events happen in time.

Circular Story A story that begins and ends with the same or a similar event. (See also *Short Story.*)

Climax (See *Plot.*)

Colloquialisms Expressions that are used in informal conversation. When the man profiled in "The ABC's of Courage" says he hates for anyone to be called a "dummy" on page 718, he is using a colloquialism. (See also *Dialect.*)

Complications (See *Plot.*)

Conflict The struggle between opposing characters or forces that is central to the action of a literary work. **External conflicts** are those in which a character struggles against another character, society, or force of nature, as when Phillip and Timothy struggle against the tempest in "The Cay," page 666. **Internal conflicts** are those in which a character struggles with an issue or problem within his or her mind, as when Kien struggles to decide whether to abandon the *Sea Breeze* in "A Boat to Nowhere," page 648. (See also *Plot.*)

Connotation The emotional meaning associated with a word and that adds to its literal meaning. (See also *Denotation.*)

D

Denotation The literal dictionary meaning of a word. (See also *Connotation.*)

Descriptive Details Specific instances in a literary work in which an author uses sensory language to create vivid images of characters, events, or places. Note the descriptive details in this passage about the students at Brandermill from "To Live in Two Worlds," page 61: "the hundreds of cool, confident white-skinned girls walking in pairs, sitting on building steps in small groups, laughing and talking." (See also *Figurative Language*.)

Dialect A form of language spoken by a particular group of people or in a specific geographical area. Dialect differs from standard spoken English in its spelling, word use, and pronunciation. Timothy in "The Cay," page 666, speaks a West Indian dialect. (See also *Colloquialisms*.)

Dialog The conversation between characters in a literary work. Usually, dialog is enclosed in quotation marks and tells the exact words a character says. Sometimes, as in drama, quotation marks are not used to enclose dialog. Instead, the words spoken by the actors come after their characters' names. (See also *Drama, Monolog*.)

Direct Address A literary device that enables an author or a literary character to talk directly to an audience. In "This Book Is About Time," page 408, Marilyn Burns uses direct address; she refers to the reader as *you*.

Drama A genre of literature meant to be performed before an audience. In drama the story is told through characters' dialog and actions. (See also *Acts, Dialog, Monolog, Scenes, Stage Directions*.)

E

Episode An event or incident that forms a distinct part of a story and may or may not relate to the plot.

Essay A short work of nonfiction that focuses on a single subject. There are two general types of essays: **formal essays** are objective, or impersonal, and serious in tone; **informal essays** are subjective, or personal, and light in tone. "When Shaped Like a Basketball, the World Is Her Oyster," page 705, is a good example of an informal essay.

Exaggeration The deliberate overstatement of an idea for emphasis or humorous effect. In "Your Three Minutes Are Up," Libby uses exaggeration when she says on page 370 that "the whole eastern seaboard" could hear her mother yell.

Exposition Writing that explains, analyzes, or defines. "Uranus, Neptune, Pluto: Dark Worlds," page 182, is an example of expository writing.

F

Fables Brief stories that teach morals. Most fables tell about animal characters that behave like people. (See also *Folklore, Moral*.)

Facts Statements that can be proved. (See also *Nonfiction, Opinions*.)

Fairy Tales Stories about fanciful characters with unusual abilities. Typical characters in fairy tales include giants, monsters, dragons, gnomes, evil beings, and talking animals. (See also *Folklore*.)

Falling Action (See *Plot*.)

Fantasy A type of literature that takes place in an unreal, imaginary world characterized by magical or supernatural elements. "The Phantom Tollbooth," page 422, belongs to this genre. (See also *Realistic Fiction.*)

Fiction Prose writing that tells an imaginary story in the form of a short story or novel. (See also *Nonfiction, Novel, Short Story.*)

Figurative Language Language that uses imagery and figures of speech to create original and colorful descriptions. Simile, metaphor, and personification are the most commonly used types of figurative language. In "Stars Come Out Within," page 99, Jean Little uses figurative language when she compares Alec's smile to "the sun coming up over the edge of the world and flooding the land with light." (See also *Descriptive Details, Hyperbole, Imagery, Metaphor, Personification, Poetry, Simile, Style.*)

Flashback A scene or an image that interrupts the present action in a story or play to describe an event or events that took place earlier. (See also *Foreshadowing.*)

Folk Hero The major character in a folk tale, whose courageous action and brave deeds are responsible for bringing the story to a happy conclusion. (See also *Folk Tale.*)

Folklore Stories, songs, and poems that have been handed down within a culture from one generation to another. Kinds of folklore include folk tales, fairy tales, tall tales, fables, myths, and legends.

Folk Tale Entertaining story that has been passed along orally from one generation to the next. These stories usually contain a hero or heroine and common folk who often are shown to have better values than their wealthier, more powerful neighbors. "The Jewels of the Sea," page 219, is a Japanese folk tale. (See also *Folk Hero, Folklore.*)

Foreshadowing The literary technique authors use to hint at events that will take place later in a story. Foreshadowing occurs in "Lob's Girl," page 293, when the dog repeatedly overcomes obstacles to be with Sandy. (See also *Flashback.*)

Frame Story A story that contains another story. (See also *Short Story.*)

G

Genre A category of literature having certain characteristics. Examples of genre include: biography, drama, poetry, and short story.

H

Haiku An unrhymed poem of Japanese origin that usually expresses a single thought about nature. A haiku always consists of three lines made up of seventeen syllables: five syllables in the first and third lines, and seven syllables in the second line. (See also *Poetry.*)

Hero/Heroine The central character in a literary work who is often admired for exemplary personal qualities, such as bravery and nobility. Savitri is the heroine of "Savitri and Satyavan," page 208. (See also *Character.*)

Historical Fiction A type of fiction that is based on historical events and characters. "Number the Stars," page 624, which was inspired by actual events during World War II, is an example of this genre. (See also *Fiction*.)

Humor The characteristic of writing that makes it funny or amusing.

Hyperbole A statement that is exaggerated or overstated to emphasize a point or to create a humorous effect. (See also *Exaggeration, Figurative Language*.)

I

Imagery Words and phrases that appeal to the senses and that are used to create vivid descriptions. In "Anne of Green Gables," page 527, lilac trees are "purple with flowers, and their dizzily sweet fragrance drifted up. . . ." (See also *Figurative Language, Sensory Language*.)

Interview A conversation, usually in a question-and-answer format, between a reporter or writer and another person. The person who asks the questions is the **interviewer.** The person who answers the questions is the **subject.** "S.O.R. Losers," page 4, contains a humorous fictional interview.

Irony The effect created when there is a sharp contrast between what is expected to happen and what actually happens or between what is stated and what is meant. The ending of "Petronella," page 242, is full of irony: the sinister-looking enchanter turns out to be much nicer than the handsome prince.

L

Legends Stories handed down through generations that describe the heroic actions of characters. Legends sometimes tell about real historical figures in fictionalized situations. (See also *Folklore*.)

Limerick A humorous verse, or poem, written in one five-line stanza with a regular scheme of rhyme and meter.

Lyric Poem A brief poem that expresses a personal thought or emotion, usually through the use of vivid images and a musical rhythm. "Marie Lucille" (page 433), "Past" (page 469), and "Becoming the Tea" (page 524) are all lyric poems. (See also *Narrative Poem, Poetry*.)

M

Main Idea The main idea is the central idea of a work of nonfiction. The main idea may also refer to the most important idea contained within a paragraph. (See also *Supporting Details*.)

Metaphor Figurative language that suggests a comparison between two things not usually considered to be alike. The statement on page 125 that Rollie Tremaine lived in a "big white birthday cake of a house" is an example of metaphor from "President Cleveland, Where Are You?" (See also *Figurative Language, Poetry*.)

Meter The pattern of rhythm in lines of poetry. (See also *Rhythm*.)

Monolog A long speech delivered by a character in literary work. (See also *Dialog, Drama*.)

Mood The emotional effect or feeling that an author creates in a literary work.

Moral A lesson about life that is taught in a fable. (See also *Fable*.)

Myths Stories set in ancient times that explain important natural events, such as the formation of the earth or the creation of the seasons. Greek and Roman myths describe the actions of gods, goddesses, and mortal heroes and heroines. "Bellerophon and the Flying Horse," page 199, is a Greek myth. (See also *Folklore.*)

N

Narrator The teller of a story. (See also *Narrative Point of View.*)

Narrative Nonfiction A type of writing that tells a story about real people, places, and events.

Narrative Poem A poem that tells a story. (See also *Lyric Poem, Poetry.*)

Narrative Point of View The perspective from which an author tells a story. There are two main types of point of view: first person and third person. In the **first-person point of view**—as in "Opera, Karate, and Bandits," page 324, —the narrator is a character in the story and uses first-person pronouns, such as *I, me,* and *we.* In the **third-person point of view**—as in "Viva New Jersey," page 553—the narrator is an outside observer, rather than a story character, and uses third-person pronouns, such as *he* and *she.* The third-person point of view can be subdivided into two types: limited and omniscient. In the **limited point of view,** the narrator focuses on the thoughts, actions, and feelings of one character. In the **omniscient point of view,** the narrator can reveal the thoughts, actions, and feelings of all the characters. (See also *Narrator.*)

Nonfiction The type of writing that tells about real people, places, and events. Examples of nonfiction include articles, essays, diaries, news stories, letters, biographies, autobiographies, and reviews. (See also *Facts, Fiction, Opinions.*)

Novel A novel is a fictional story of considerable length containing detailed treatments of characters and/or complicated plots. The selection "Last Summer with Maizon," page 18, is an excerpt from the novel of the same name. (See also *Fiction, Short Story.*)

O

Objective Details Small bits of information that can be observed or measured rather than based on an author's thoughts or opinions. For example, the month when *Voyager 2* reached Uranus (January 1986) is an objective detail. (See also *Subjective Details.*)

Onomatopoeia A literary technique involving the use of words in which the sound of a word suggests or imitates its meaning. The word *hissed*—used to describe the sound of the Chimera's snake head in "Bellerophon and the Flying Horse," page 204—is an example. (See also *Poetry.*)

Opinions Statements based on a person's beliefs, feelings, or thoughts about what is true rather than on what can be proved to be true. Douglas expresses an opinion in "Talking About Stepfamilies" when he says, on page 475, "switching homes every week is rotten." (See also *Facts, Nonfiction.*)

P

Parody A humorous imitation of a serious literary work or of an author's writing style. "Petronella," page 242, is a parody of a fairy tale. (See also *Style.*)

Personification Figurative language in which animals or objects are given human characteristics. The description of the storm as an "agile dancer" is an example of personification in the poem "The Hurricane," page 701.

Persuasion A type of writing in which an author tries to convince an audience to believe or accept the ideas being presented. (See also *Propaganda.*)

Play (See *Drama.*)

Plot The series of related events in a literary work. Most plots follow a pattern. The **exposition** introduces the characters and the problems, or **complications,** they face. The part of the story in which the conflict grows is called the **rising action.** The turning point in the story, or the point at which the conflict is resolved and the story outcome is clear, is called the **climax.** The **falling action** describes the events that take place after the climax. The falling action includes the **resolution,** or the outcome of the conflict that is developed in the plot. (See also *Conflict.*)

Poetry A type of literature that expresses ideas and feelings by relying on compact, often musical language that appeals to readers' senses and ignites their emotions. (See also *Alliteration, Assonance, Figurative Language, Haiku, Imagery, Lyric Poem, Metaphor, Narrative Poem, Onomatopoeia, Refrain, Rhyme, Rhythm, Simile, Speaker, Stanza.*)

Propaganda Information and ideas presented to persuade people to do or believe something that may or may not be true. (See also *Persuasion.*)

Prose The kind of everyday writing or speech that does not have the rhyme or rhythm patterns of poetry.

Protagonist The central character in a literary work. Kennie McLaughlin is the protagonist of "My Friend Flicka," page 581. (See also *Antagonist, Character.*)

R

Realistic Fiction A type of fiction that tells an imaginary story about characters and places that could actually exist and events that could actually happen. "A Boat to Nowhere," page 648, is an example. (See *Fantasy.*)

Refrain A repeated line or phrase in a poem that uses recurring rhythms to produce a musical quality. (See also *Poetry.*)

Repetition A literary technique that involves repeating a word or phrase for emphasis or for evoking a rhythm or particular emotional effect. Alonzo Lopez uses repetition by beginning each of the first five lines of "I Go Forth to Move About the Earth," page 663, with the phrase "I go forth."

Resolution (See *Plot.*)

Rhyme A literary technique involving the repetition of the same or similar sounds. When two words rhyme the accented syllables and all the sounds following these syllables sound the same. The most common form of rhyme, **end rhyme,** occurs when words at the ends of several lines of poetry rhyme. The first two lines of the poem "How Many Seconds?" on page 365 feature end rhyme:

How many seconds in a minute?
Sixty, and no more in it.

In **internal rhyme** the rhymes occur within lines of poetry. The last two lines of "I May, I Might, I Must" on page 269 contain both end rhyme and internal rhyme:

will tell you <u>why</u> I think that I
can get across it if I <u>try</u>.

(See also *Poetry.*)

Rhythm A pattern of sounds or beats created by the arrangement of accented and unaccented words or syllables, especially in poetry. Each line in "My Land is Fair for Any Eyes to See," page 549, has five beats with two syllables each. (See also *Poetry.*)

Rising Action (See *Plot.*)

S

Scenes The divisions within acts in a play. The one-act play "Rip Van Winkle," page 437, has three scenes. (See also *Acts, Drama.*)

Science Fiction A type of imaginary story that involves up-to-date or futuristic scientific developments and technology. "Rain, Rain, Go Away," page 569, belongs to this genre.

Sensory Language Descriptive language that appeals to one or more of the five senses: sight, hearing, smell, touch, and taste. Authors use sensory language to create vivid word pictures that heighten an audience's interest. (See *Imagery.*)

Setting Setting is the time and place in which the action of a literary work unfolds. The setting of "Seventh Grade," page 40, is the first day after summer vacation at a Fresno, California, school.

Short Story A brief work of fiction that can usually be read in one sitting. "My Friend Flicka," page 581, is an example. (See also *Circular Story, Fiction, Frame Story, Novel.*)

Simile Figurative language that makes a direct comparison between two apparently unlike things, using the words *like* or *as.* When Robert D. Ballard states on page 150 that the decks of the *Titanic* "had collapsed in on one another like a giant accordion," he is using a simile.

Slang Nonstandard or unconventional speech used by speakers for informal or humorous expression.

Speaker In poetry, the voice that talks to the reader. The speaker is comparable to a narrator in a work of fiction. (See also *Narrator.*)

Stage Directions The means by which actors know where and how to move and speak. Stage directions are set off from dialog by parentheses and/or italics. They often describe scenery, props, and lighting. (See also *Drama.*)

Stanza A group of lines in a poem that has a definite pattern of line-lengths and rhymes that is the same in every stanza of the poem. In free verse a stanza is more like a paragraph in prose writing. (See also *Poetry.*)

Style The distinctive way an author writes. An author's style is shaped by many elements, including word choice, sentence patterns and length, figurative language, and tone. (See also *Figurative Language, Parody, Tone.*)

Subject The person whose life is presented in an autobiography or a biography or who is profiled in an interview or a news article. A subject may be famous or little known, alive or dead, but he or she is always someone who has actually lived. Matthew Henson is the subject of "At Last!," page 311. (See also *Autobiography, Biography, Interview.*)

Subjective Details Small bits of information that are based on personal feelings and opinions rather than on what can be observed and/or proven to be true. (See also *Objective Details.*)

Supporting Details Specific bits of information that directly relate to the main idea in a piece of nonfiction writing. (See also *Main Idea.*)

Surprise Ending The unexpected twist in the ending of any literary work. "Lob's Girl," page 293, features a surprise ending.

Suspense The feeling of uncertainty about what might happen next in a literary work. When the German officers search the Johansens' apartment in "Number the Stars," page 624, the author's use of suspense is highly effective.

Symbolism A literary technique involving the use of an object, event, or character to express an idea more general or broader than itself. In "To James," page 239, Frank Horne uses the race as a symbol for all of life.

T

Tall Tales Humorous stories that exaggerate characters and events beyond belief. (See also *Folklore.*)

Teleplay A drama written for television. (See also *Drama.*)

Theme The underlying idea or message about life or human nature contained in a literary work. A **stated theme** is one the author puts directly into words. An **unstated,** or **implied, theme** is one readers must determine on their own by analyzing other story elements.

Tone An author's attitude toward his or her subject.

Tragedy A dramatic work in which the main character faces a moral struggle and is destroyed because of his or her own actions.

Trickster Tales Stories that describe how clever animals or people play tricks on or otherwise take advantage of animals or people. (See also *Folklore.*)

INDEX OF
Titles by Genre

INDEX OF
Authors and Titles

The page numbers in *italics* refer to biographical information.

INDEX OF
Fine Art

Acknowledgments

The publisher gratefully acknowledges permission to reprint the following copyrighted material:

"The ABC's of Courage" reprinted with the permission of Scribner, an imprint of Simon & Schuster, Inc., from CHEESEBURGERS by Bob Greene. Copyright © 1985 by John Deadline Enterprises, Inc.

"Alexander the Great" from THE GOLDEN DAYS OF GREECE by Olivia Coolidge. Copyright © 1968 by Olivia Coolidge. Used by permission.

Cover permission for ASHANTI TO ZULU: AFRICAN TRADITIONS by Margaret Musgrove, pictures by Leo and Diane Dillon. Copyright © 1976 by Leo and Diane Dillon for pictures. Used by permission of Dial Books for Young Readers, a division of Penguin Books USA Inc.

"At Last!" from MATTHEW HENSON, pp. 89–97, by Michael Gilman. Copyright © 1988 by Chelsea House Publishers. Reprinted by permission of the publisher.

"Banner in the Sky" from BANNER IN THE SKY by James Ramsey Ullman. Copyright 1954 by James Ramsey Ullman (Lippincott). Reprinted by permission of HarperCollins Publishers.

"Becoming the Tea" by Joyce Carol Thomas. Reprinted by permission.

"Bellerophon and the Flying Horse" from TALES FROM ANCIENT GREECE by Pamela Oldfield. Copyright © 1988 by Grisewood and Dempsey, Ltd. Used by permission of Doubleday, a division of Bantam Doubleday Dell Publishing Group, Inc.

"Bicycle Riding" by Sandra Liatsos appeared originally in *Cricket*. Copyright © 1984 by Sandra Liatsos. Reprinted by permission of the author.

"A Boat to Nowhere" is reprinted from A BOAT TO NOWHERE by Maureen Crane Wartski. Reprinted and used by permission of Westminster/John Knox Press.

"A Boy of Unusual Vision" by Alice Steinbach. Copyright © 1984 by *Sun Magazine/The Baltimore Sun*. Used by permission.

"Brother to the Wind" from BROTHER TO THE WIND by Mildred Pitts Walter. Illustrated by Leo & Diane Dillon. Text copyright © 1985 by Mildred Pitts Walter. Illustrations copyright © 1985 by Leo & Diane Dillon. Published by Lothrop, Lee & Shepard Books and reprinted by permission of William Morrow and Company, Inc./Publishers, New York.

"Calender Art" reprinted with the permission of Simon & Schuster Books for Young Readers from CALENDER ART by Leonard Everett Fisher. Text and illustrations copyright © 1987 Leonard Everett Fisher.

"The Cay" from THE CAY by Theodore Taylor. Copyright © 1969 by Theodore Taylor. Used by permission of Doubleday, a division of Bantam Doubleday Dell Publishing Group, Inc.

"Child of the Owl" from CHILD OF THE OWL by Laurence Yep. Copyright © 1977 by Laurence Yep. Reprinted by permission of HarperCollins Publishers.

Cover permission for CHILDREN OF THE MAYA by Brent Ashabranner. Photograph by Paul Conklin. Photographs copyright © by Paul Conklin. Reprinted by permission of Paul Conklin.

"Exploring the *Titanic*" from EXPLORING THE *TITANIC* by Robert D. Ballard. A Scholastic/Madison Press book © 1988. Reprinted by permission of the publisher.

"Grandmother" by Sameeneh Shirazie. Reprinted by permission.

"The Great Sea" Inuit song translated by Knud Rasmussen. Reprinted by permission.

"Hurricane" by Pales Matos, translated by Alida Malkus. Reprinted by permission.

"I am on my way running" Papago song translated by Frances Densmore. Reprinted by permission.

"I Go Forth to Move About the Earth" by Alonzo Lopez from WHISPERING WIND by Terry Allen. Copyright © 1972 by the Institute of American Indian Arts. Used by permission of Doubleday, a division of Bantam Doubleday Dell Publishing Group, Inc.

"I May, I Might, I Must" copyright © 1959 by Marianne Moore, © renewed 1987 by Lawrence E. Brinn and Louise Crane, Executors of the Estate of Marianne Moore from THE COMPLETE POEMS OF MARIANNE MOORE by Marianne Moore. Used by permission of Viking Penguin, a division of Penguin Books USA Inc.

"The Jewels of the Sea" by Yoshiko Uchida. Copyright © 1949 Yoshiko Uchida. Used by courtesy of the Bancroft Library at the University of California, Berkeley.

"Last Summer with Maizon" excerpts from LAST SUMMER WITH MAIZON by Jaqueline Woodson. Copyright © 1990 by Jaqueline Woodson. Used by permission of Bantam Doubleday Dell Books for Young Readers.

"Lob's Girl" from A WHISPER IN THE NIGHT by Joan Aiken. Copyright © 1984 by Joan Aiken. Used by permission of Delacorte Press, a division of Bantam Doubleday Dell Publishing Group, Inc.

"Maniac Magee" from MANIAC MAGEE by Jerry Spinelli. Copyright © 1990 by Jerry Spinelli. By permission of Little, Brown and Company.

"Marie Lucille" by Gwendolyn Brooks. Reprinted by permission.

"Miss Harriet's Room" reprinted with the permission of Simon & Schuster Inc. from THE MOON AND I by Betsy Byars. Copyright © 1991 by Betsy Byars.

"The Mission" by Francisco X. Alarcón, translated by Francisco Aragon. Reprinted by permission.

Cover photograph by Paul S. Conklin reprinted by permission of G. P. Putnam's Sons from MORNING STAR, BLACK SUN by Brent Ashabranner. Illustrations copyright © 1982 by Paul S. Conklin.

"Mummies, Tombs, and Treasure" from MUMMIES, TOMBS, AND TREASURE by Lila Perl. Copyright © 1987 by Lila Perl. Reprinted by permission of Clarion Books, a Houghton Mifflin Company imprint. All rights reserved.

"My Friend Flicka" by Mary O'Hara. Copyright © 1941 by Mary O'Hara. Used by permission.

"My Land Is Fair" by Jesse Stuart. Reprinted by permission.

"Number the Stars" from NUMBER THE STARS by Lois Lowry. Copyright © 1989 by Lois Lowry. Reprinted by permission of Houghton Mifflin Company.

"Opera, Karate and Bandits" from THE LAND I LOST: ADVENTURES OF A BOY IN VIETNAM by Huynh Quang Nhuong. Copyright © 1982 by Huynh Quang Nhuong. Reprinted by permission of HarperCollins Publishers.

"Past" by Arnold Adoff. Reprinted by permission.

"Petronella" from THE PRACTICAL PRINCESS AND OTHER LIBERATING FAIRY TALES by Jay Williams. Copyright © 1978 by Jay Williams. Reprinted by permission of Scholastic Inc.

"The Phantom Tollbooth" from THE PHANTOM TOLLBOOTH by Norton Juster. Copyright © 1961 by Norton Juster. Reprinted by permission of Sterling Lord Literistic, Inc.

Excerpt from "Postscript" from ABOUT THE HOUSE by W. H. Auden. Copyright 1965 by W. H. Auden. Reprinted by permission of Random House, Inc.

"President Cleveland, Where Are You?" from EIGHT PLUS ONE by Robert Cormier. Copyright © 1965 and renewed 1993 by Robert Cormier. Reprinted by permission of Pantheon Books, a division of Random House, Inc.

"Rain, Rain, Go Away" copyright © 1959 by King Size Publications, Inc. from BUY JUPITER AND OTHER STORIES by Isaac Asimov. Used by permission of Doubleday, a division of Bantam Doubleday Dell Publishing Group, Inc.

"Rip Van Winkle" by Washington Irving, dramatized by Adele Thane. Copyright © 1967 by Adele Thane. Used by permission.

"Rip Van Winkle" by Washington Irving, drawings by Gary Kelley. Copyright © 1993 by Gary Kelley. Used by permission.

"S.O.R. Losers" reprinted with the permission of Simon & Schuster Books for Young Readers from S.O.R. LOSERS by Avi. Copyright © 1984 by Avi Wortis.

"Savitri and Satyavan" by Madhur Jaffrey. Copyright © 1985 by Madhur Jaffrey. Used by permission.

"Seventh Grade" from BASEBALL IN APRIL AND OTHER STORIES, copyright © 1990 by Gary Soto, reprinted by permission of Harcourt Brace & Company.

"A Short Story" by David Escobar Galindo, translated by Jorge D. Piche. Reprinted by permission.

"Stars Come Out Within" from STARS COME OUT WITHIN by Jean Little. Copyright © Jean Little, 1990. Reprinted by permission of Penguin Books Canada Limited.

"The Surveyor" from WHERE THE FLAME TREES BLOOM by Alma Flor Ada. Copyright © 1994 by Alma Flor Ada. Used by permission.

"Talking About Stepfamilies" reprinted with the permission of Simon & Schuster Books For Young Readers from TALKING ABOUT STEPFAMILIES by Maxine B. Rosenberg. Copyright © 1990 by Maxine B. Rosenberg

"This Book Is About Time" from THIS BOOK IS ABOUT TIME by Marilyn Burns. Copyright © 1978 by the Yolla Bolly Press. By permission of Little, Brown and Company.

"To James" by Frank Horne. Extensive research has failed to find author/copyright holder of this work.

"To Live in Two Worlds" from TO LIVE IN TWO WORLDS by Brent Ashabranner. Text copyright © 1984 by Brent Ashabranner. Used by permission of the author.

"To You" from COLLECTED POEMS by Langston Hughes. Copyright © 1994 by the Estate of Langston Hughes. Reprinted by permission of Alfred A. Knopf Inc.

"Today I'm Going Yesterday" from SOMETHING BIG HAS BEEN HERE by Jack Prelutsky. Copyright © 1990 by Jack Prelutsky. A Greenwillow Book. Reprinted by permission of William Morrow and Company, Inc./Publishers, New York.

"Touch System" from CHEAPER BY THE DOZEN by Frank B. Gilbreth, Jr. and Ernestine Gilbreth Carey. Copyright © 1948, 1963 by Frank B. Gilbreth, Jr. and Ernestine Gilbreth Carey. Reprinted by permission of HarperCollins Publishers, Inc.

"Travellers" by Arthur St. John Adcock. Reprinted by permission.

"Unfolding Bud" by Naoshi Koriyama. Reprinted by permission.

"Uranus, Pluto, Neptune: Dark Worlds" from JOURNEY TO THE PLANETS by Patricia Lauber. Copyright © 1982, 1990 by Patricia Lauber. Reprinted by permission of Crown Publishers.

"Viva New Jersey" by Gloria Gonzalez. Copyright © 1993 by Gloria Gonzalez from JOIN IN: MULTIETHNIC SHORT STORIES by Donald R. Gallo, ed. Used by permission of Delacorte Press, a division of Bantam Doubleday Dell Publishing Group, Inc.

"When Shaped Like a Basketball, the World Is Her Oyster" by Elaine Louie. Copyright © 1994 by The New York Times. Used by permission.

Cover permission for WHY MOSQUITOS BUZZ IN PEOPLE'S EARS by Verna Aardema, illustrations by Leo and Diane Dillon. Copyright © 1975 by Leo and Diane Dillon, illustrations. Used by permission of Dial Books for Young Readers, a division of Penguin Books USA Inc.

"The World Is Not a Pleasant Place to Be" from MY HOUSE by Nikki Giovanni. Copyright © 1972 by Nikki Giovanni. Reprinted by permission of William Morrow and Company, Inc./Publishers, New York.

"The Year" from THE SONG IN MY HEAD by Felice Holman. Copyright © 1985 by Felice Holman. Reprinted with the permission of Simon & Schuster Books For Young Readers.

"Your Three Minutes Are Up" reprinted with the permission of Simon & Schuster Books for Young Readers from IF THIS IS LOVE, I'LL TAKE SPAGHETTI by Ellen Conford. Copyright © 1983 by Ellen Conford.

"Your World" by Georgia Douglas Johnson appeared originally in HOLD FAST TO DREAMS selected by Arna Bontemps. Extensive research has failed to locate the author and/or copyright holder of this work.

REAL LIFE CONNECTIONS

Dictionary: Excerpt from CONCISE DICTIONARY OF AMERICAN BIOGRAPHY, 2nd edition, Charles Scribner's Sons, 1977. Reprinted by permission of the American Council of Learned Societies.

Directions: Excerpt from FIRST AID: A RANDOM HOUSE PERSONAL MEDICAL HANDBOOK by Paula Dranov, Random House, 1990. Copyright © 1990 by Paula Dranov. Reprinted by permission of Barbara Lowenstein Agency.

Art & Photo Credits

ILLUSTRATIONS

Unit 1: Iskra Johnson (calligraphy), xvi, i; Michelle Laporte (calligraphy), 4, 5, 8, 9, 12, 15; Cornelius Van Wright, 18–22, 27–29, 32, 35; John Ceballos, 40–49; Shonto Begay, 75, 76, 79, 80, 82, 83, 86–89; José Ortega, 69; Mary Newell De Palma, 73, 77. **Unit 2:** Steve Stankiewicz (tech art), 145, 157, 161; Michelle Laporte (calligraphy), 179; Kaji Aso (sumi-e painting), 219. 223, 224, 226; Michelle Laporte (calligraphy), 219, 226; Stephen Schudlich, 233. **Unit 3:** Ed Heins (borders), 242–253; Steven Madson, 257, 258, 260, 262, 264, 267; Diane and Leo Dillon, 272–289; Raphael Montolio, 313, 315, 316, 319, 320; Robert Roth, 324, 325, 327, 329–337. **Unit 4:** Nancy Nimoy, 368–380; Leonard Everett Fisher, 384–403; Michelle Laporte, 405; David Goldin, 422–431; Gary Kelley, 437, 440, 444, 450, 452, 454; Stephen Schudlich, 463. **Unit 5:** David Kampa (calligraphy), 468–469; Oscar Hernandez, 488–493, 497, 501, 502; Winson Trang, 506–521; Michelle Laporte, 523; Roberta Ludlow, 526–547; Bruno Paciulli, 569, 571, 572, 574, 577; Mark Kaplan (background), 581–600. **Unit 6:** Larry Winborg, 624, 625, 627, 628, 630, 631, 634, 638–640, 643, 644; Hui Han Liu, 648, 649, 651, 653, 654, 656, 657, 659, 660; Floyd Cooper, 666–669, 672, 674, 677, 679, 683, 684, 686, 687, 690, 694, 695; Michelle Laporte (calligraphy), 713–721; Stephen Schudlich, 741.

PHOTOGRAPHY CREDITS

All photographs are by the Macmillan/McGraw-Hill School Division (MMSD) except as noted below.

Front Matter: iv–v: *Jungle Tales* (detail), James J. Shannon, 1895. The Metropolitan Museum of Art, Arthur Hoppock Hearn Fund, 1913. (13.143.1). vi–vii: *La Montagna Sainte-Victoire* (detail), Paul Cezanne, The Hermitage Museum. Photo courtesy Scala/Art Resource. viii–ix: *Abstract Speed and Sound (Velocitá astratta y rumore)* (detail), Giacomo Balla, 1913–1914. The Peggy Guggenheim Collection, Venice. Photograph by Miles Aronowitz © The Solomon R. Guggenheim Foundation, New York (FN 76.2553 PG31) x–xi: *The Clock and the Lantern* (detail), Joan Miro, 1915, Private Collection. © 1995 Artists Rights Society, N. Y. /ADAGP, Paris. xii–xiii: *Early Carolina Morning* (detail), Romare Bearden, 1978. Courtesy Estate of Romare Bearden. xiv–xv: *Dominant Curve (Courbe dominante)* (detail), Vasily Kandinsky, April 1936, The Solomon R. Guggenheim Museum. New York. Photograph by David Heald © The Solomon R. Guggenheim Foundation, New York (FN 45.989). **Unit 1:** 4: u. The Metropolitan Museum of Art, Arthur Hoppock. 16: l. The Metropolitan Museum of Art. 35: Hilary Sio. 37: Betsy Bauer. 40: Jayne Scheer. 52–59: Paul Conklin. 62: Michael Freeman/Bruce Coleman, Inc. 63: t. Adam Woofit/Woodfin Camp & Associates; b. Lois Moulton/f Stop Pictures. 67: t. Jennifer Ashabranner; b. Sonlight Images for MMSD. 78: Photo by Edward Byars/Penguin U. S. A. 81: © 1995 Malcolm Varon for MMSD; typewriter courtesy Sutherland Multimedia. 83: Light-Works studio for MMSD; Roller skate courtesy National Museum of Roller Skating. 86: © 1995 Malcolm Varon for MMSD; Victrola courtesy Charles Hummel Collection. 89: Jeff Tinsley for MMSD; Watch courtesy Division of Technology, National Museum of American History, Smithsonian Institution. 90: National Museum of American Art/Art Resource, Inc. 93: © 1995 Malcolm Varon for MMSD; Comptometer courtesy Sutherland Multimedia. 94: UPI/Bettman. 97:–108: courtesy Penguin Books Canada. 112: r. Gerald L. French/FPG. **Unit 2:** 120–121:Photo courtesy Scala/Art Resource 124: Library of Congress; inset: Courtesy Non-Sport Update. 125: Photo MMSD. 125: & 126: Courtesy Non-Sport Update/Photo by MMSD. 127: Library of Congress. 129: Courtesy Non-Sport Update/Photo by MMSD. 131: Library of Congress. 132: Courtesy The Glove Collector/Photo by MMSD. 133: & 134: Courtesy Non-Sport Update/Photo by MMSD. 135: Library of Congress. 135: inset, & 137: Courtesy Non-Sport Update/Photo by MMSD. 139: Bantam Doubleday Dell. 144, 147: Ken Marschall/Madison Press Books Toronto. 152: The Illustrated London News Picture Library. 153: The Mariner's Museum, Newport News, VA. 154–159: Ken Marschall/Madison Press Books Toronto. 161: Terri Corbett. 164: t.l. Julius Fekete/The Stock Market; t.r. Robert Frerck/Odyssey Productions; m. Brian Blake/Photo Researchers, Inc. 164–165: Comstock. 166: t. Egyptian Expedition of the Metropolitan Museum of Art, Rogers Fund 1930 (30.4.144); b. Courtesy of the Egyptian Museum, Cairo. 166–167: Borders by Brian Blake/Photo Researchers, Inc. 168: Luis Villota/The Stock Market. 172–173: Griffith Institute, Ashmolean Museum. 174–175: Griffith Institute, Ashmolean Museum. 177: t. The Granger Collection; m.l. Charles Yerkow; b.r. Richard Chesnut for MMSD; b.r. Robert Frerck/Odyssey Productions.179: Culver Pictures, Inc. 180: Richard Francis/Tony Stone International. 182–191: NASA, color enhanced by publisher. 192: Yerkes Observatory. 193: b.l. Richard Chesnut for MMSD; b.r. NASA, color enhanced by publisher. 195: Stephen Trimble 199: © Erich Lessing/Art Resouce. 202–203: Copyright © Metropolitan Museum of Art. 204: Copyright © The British Museum. 205: Penguin Children's Books, London. 210: & 211: *Lady Feeding a Bird* (detail). 214: *Squirrels in a Plane Tree* (detail) 216: © D. Kirkland/Sygma. Stephen Trimble 218: Westown School/photo courtesy Brandywine River. 226: Deborah Storms/Simon & Schuster. 230: r. Pete Dancs/Tony Stone. **Unit 3:** 238–239: Photo by Miles Aronowitz © The Solomon R. Guggenheim Foundation, New York (FN 76. 2553 PG31). 289: t. Pat Cummings; b. Scott Harvey for MMSD. 291: "Autour d'Elle", by Chagall Art Resource, Inc. 293: Comstock. 294: The Bridgeman Art Library. 299: William Secord Gallery, Inc. 300: The Bridgeman Art Library. 315: Scala/Art Resource (From the Collection of Musee National d'Art Moderne, Paris). 332: Lev T. Mills/Evans Tibbs Collection. 352: 334: The Bettman Archive. 336: The Granger Collection. 352: r. Kathleen O'Donnell/The Image Bank. 341: Brown Brothers. 344: Library of Congress. 360: National Museum, Naples/Scala/Art Resource, Inc. 363: British Museum/Michael Holford 367: t.l. Richard Chesnut for MMSD. 368: The Granger Collection. 373: British Museum/Michael Holford. **Unit 4:** 408–409: Ryuichi Sato/Photonica. 411: l. © Rob Kearney/Photonica; r. H. Bjornson/Photonica. 412: © Pedro Lobo/Photonica. 413: © Rob Kearney/Photonica; r. H. Bjornson/Photonica. 415: © Rob Kearney/Photonica. 415 r.–419: H. Bjornson/Photonica. 422: John Martin. 433: Norton Museum of Art, West Palm Beach. 456: Historic Hudson Valley, Tarrytown, New York. 460: Pete Wilson/Globe. 466: Laurie Platt Winfrey, Inc. **Unit 5** 472: t.C. Marc Weinstein. b. Sonlight Images for MMSD. 505: t. Jerry Spinelli. 521: b.r. Joanne Ryder; b.l., b.m. Sonlight Images for MMSD. 523: F. Jackson/Bruce Coleman. 524: Philadelphia Museum of Art. 541: F. Jackson/Bruce Coleman. 604: David Young Wolff/Photo Edit. 542: Philadelphia Museum of Art. 556: Collection R. Marc Fasanella. 562: Collection R. Marc Fasanella 578: Karsh/Woodfin Camp. 583: John Fawcett. 588: John Fawcett. 591: Joslyn Art Museum, Omaha. 592: N. Rockwell/Curtis Archives. 593: John Fawcett. 598: John Fawcett. 600: Culver Pictures. **Unit 6:** 612–613: Photograph by David Heald © The Solomon R. Guggenheim Foundation, New York (FN 45. 989). 617: photo by Rafael Doniz, Archivo Fotografico Maria Elena Altamirano Piolle. 621: David Maving. 645: Amanda Smith. 661: Maximillan M. Wartski. 664: Take Stock, Inc./Mark Gallup. 699: Bruce Wonder/Image Bank; t. Theodore Taylor. 701: NOAA/Science Photo Library/Photo Researchers 721: Chicago Tribune/Tribune Media Services. 724–733: © Copyright The Baltimore Sun, Photograph by David Harp. 734: The Baltimore Sun. 738: Jeff Spielman/The Image Bank.